The Philippine Island World

—— The Philippine Island World A PHYSICAL, CULTURAL, AND REGIONAL GEOGRAPHY

by *Frederick L. Wernstedt and J. E. Spencer*

UNIVERSITY OF CALIFORNIA PRESS   *1967*

Berkeley and Los Angeles

UNIVERSITY OF CALIFORNIA PRESS
BERKELEY AND LOS ANGELES, CALIFORNIA

CAMBRIDGE UNIVERSITY PRESS
LONDON, ENGLAND

Library of Congress Catalog Card Number: 67–14001

Designed by Betty Binns
PRINTED IN THE UNITED STATES OF AMERICA

TO IRENE AND KATHRYN

The Philippine Island World has been the labor of years of writing, a task complicated by the physical separation of the two authors, at times by the full width of the Pacific and at other times by the North American continent. We have cross-checked for the last time by asking ourselves "What kind of a geography have we produced?" Each of us has independently conceived the hope that our product will not be judged by its lack of unusual organization, or by our reluctance to be innovative either in approach or in techniques of handling data. Our "geography of the Philippines" is a pretty orthodox product, from many points of view. The task of writing about 7,000 islands in a connected and organized manner has so persistently occupied us, and has so insistently perplexed us, that we have had little thought for innovation in methodology. Instead we have tried to describe a sector of the earth in a manner traditional to geography, but with fairly catholic tastes in the selection of subjects and data, and in the overview of the growth of this inhabited island world. Each of us has naturally been more interested in certain topical subjects and in certain islands and groups of territories than has the other, but no chapter has been written entirely by one of us alone. Each of us, furthermore, possesses greater competence in certain areas of geography than in others. There are numerous small islands upon which neither of us has set foot, and a variety of living systems neither of us has shared; however, in most cases we have been able to draw upon firsthand experience, either in depth or in reconnaissance. Between us we have come to know many parts of the island world over a period of more than a score of years. Our respective acquaintances with particular areas have been pooled, but there still are regions wherein our inexperience shows up in the treatment given.

We have shared a concern for the lay of the land and the elements that form the physical environment. We have also shared a liking and a respect for the ways of the Filipinos and for the elements of culture that have led them to shape their occupance and to devise the living systems they have chosen to follow, be they lowlanders or mountaineers, rice or corn farmers, urban merchandisers, town-dwelling, "modernized" professional classes, Roman Catholics, Protestants, Animists, or Moslems. And we have also shared the desire to capture the feeling of those sectors of the island world which have become recognizable as regional units, possessing separate and distinctive personalities. Neither of us has been greatly bothered by the fact that our systematic discussions have not accounted for the shape of every last island, for each particular cultural trait or historical development, or for the last bit of territory left over after outlining the areal units in a manner convenient for the discussion of regions. It has been the normal, the significant, and the descriptive panorama of land and life which we have sought to present. In a world in which people are becoming self-conscious about looking at other places and people through one's own eyes, we have sought to present the geography of the Philippines not as or for Filipinos, but as and for non-Filipinos who live elsewhere but who may, perchance, have wondered, "What is it like there?"

The reader may, and must, judge how successful we have been in using somewhat particularized approaches to certain topics, such as the treatment of Philippine soils, agriculture, cultural history, and population, and whether our regional configurations have significant value. We make little attempt to defend the regional boundaries we have chosen, or the regions themselves, for we are acutely aware of both the issue of convenience and the unevenness in treatment of specific regions. Nevertheless, the analyses of Philippine regions, comprising nearly half the text, take initial steps toward the discussion of regional problems and the greater depth of analyses which may follow from later studies. The maps illustrating this volume are largely originals, and many of the ideas and conclusions presented cannot be documented in the usual manner.

The United States Educational Foundation (Fulbright), the Social Science Research Council, the Geography Branch of the Office of Naval

Research, the National Science Foundation, the Institute of Pacific Relations, the University of California, and The Pennsylvania State University have furnished funds and encouragement to past research projects; these projects all lie behind the present study, but this volume was not originally anticipated and may be considered an unexpected dividend. Several Philippine government offices and agencies supplied significant and material assistance in many places and on numerous occasions.

We have many friends in the Philippines—Filipinos and non-Filipinos alike—to whom we are greatly beholden for the opportunities afforded both of us to travel, to ask questions, and to share in various ways of life. Numerous friends and colleagues in the United States have been helpful on so many occasions that it is impossible to record all their names here. It is difficult to appropriately repay the hospitality accepted, favors presented, and assistance offered, but we are grateful to every one of our friends and colleagues. We must, however, specifically acknowledge Professor Harold Conklin's loan of the aerial ground-survey sketch map presented in figure 50, and we must acknowledge the courtesy of the Geological Society of America and Dr. Philip King for the terrain diagrams, which served as the basic source for the dissected and modified physiographic maps. We both also acknowledge the support and the tolerance of our wives, Irene and Kathryn, which cheerfully persisted to the termination of this volume. To each and every one goes a thank-you for any virtues of this volume; to the authors alone belong the errors and the failures.

The Pennsylvania State University   Frederick L. Wernstedt
University of California, Los Angeles   J. E. Spencer

Contents

Introduction, 1

Part One: The Physical Environment

1. GEOMORPHOLOGY AND PHYSIOGRAPHY   9
2. REGIONAL CLIMATOLOGY   39
3. SOILS, THE PLANT COVER, AND LAND BIOTA   63
    SUMMARY OF PART ONE   109

Part Two: The Cultural and Economic Environments

4. THE CULTURAL HISTORY OF THE FILIPINOS   115
5. POPULATION: GROWTH, SPREAD, AND DISTRIBUTION   136
6. THE SEVERAL AGRICULTURAL ECONOMIES   178
7. RESOURCE EXPLOITATION   229
8. SECONDARY PRODUCTION PATTERNS   258
    SUMMARY OF PART TWO   295

Part Three: The Regional Environments

9. THE NORTH COUNTRY: NORTHERN LUZON AND BEYOND   301
10. THE CORE REGION: CENTRAL AND SOUTHERN LUZON   362

11. THE ISLANDS OF THE SUNDA SHELF   428

12. THE CENTRAL PHILIPPINES: THE VISAYAN ISLANDS   444

13. THE SOUTHERN COUNTRY: MINDANAO AND SULU   502

Statistical Appendix, 599

Notes, 667

Bibliography, 697

Indexes, 707

1. *Philippines and Southeast Asia*   2
2. *Provinces of the Philippines, 1965*   4
3. *Tectonic Provinces of Southeast Asia*   10
4a. *Major Physiographic Features of the Northern Philippines*   14
4b. *Major Physiographic Features of the Southern Philippines*   15
5. *Mean Monthly Temperatures during the Dry Season (May)*   43
6a. *Average Hourly Air Temperatures at Manila during the Dry Season (April)*   44
6b. *Average Hourly Air Temperatures at Manila during the Rainy Season (September)*   44
7a. *Air Mass Source Regions and Prevailing Surface Winds (July)*   47
7b. *Air Mass Source Regions and Prevailing Surface Winds (January)*   47
8. *Major Typhoon Tracks Affecting the Philippines*   51
9. *The Distribution of Mean Annual Precipitation*   54
10a. *Total Annual Precipitation at Manila, 1902–1937*   56
10b. *Total Annual Precipitation at Cebu, 1902–1937*   56
11. *Climates of the Philippines (Köppen)*   59
12. *Climates of the Philippines (Thornthwaite)*   60
13. *Parent Materials for Philippine Soils*   68
14. *Soil Erosion in the Philippines*   79
15. *Soil Erosion on Cebu Island*   80
16. *Philippine Forests*   86
17. *Philippine Grasslands*   100
18. *Centers of Spanish Religious Influence*   124

19. *Distribution of Population on Western Bohol Island*   137
20. *Population of Northern Luzon*   138
21. *Population of Central and Southern Luzon*   139
22. *Population of the Visayan Islands*   140
23. *Population of Mindanao, Palawan, and the Sulus*   141
24a. *Targets of Philippine Internal Migration, 1948–1960*   144
24b. *Sources of Philippine Internal Migration, 1948–1960*   145
25. *Distribution of Selected Ethnolinguistic Groups*   155
26a. *Distribution of Moslems, 1960*   160
26b. *Distribution of Aglipayans, 1960*   161
27. *Irrigated Land in the Philippines, 1960*   186
28. *Lowland Rice in the Philippines, 1960*   196
29. *Upland (Dry) Rice in the Philippines, 1960*   197
30. *Corn (Maize) in the Philippines, 1960*   200
31. *Cassava and Camotes in the Philippines, 1960*   202
32. *Coconuts in the Philippines, 1960*   215
33. *Sugarcane in the Philippines, 1960*   218
34. *Abaca in the Philippines, 1960*   223
35. *Philippine Commercial Fishing Grounds, 1962*   232
36. *Philippine Sawmills, 1960*   243
37. *Philippine Minerals*   249
38. *Salt beds of Manila Bay*   256
39. *Philippine Interisland Core Shipping Fleet, 1956*   262
40. *National and Provincial Roads, 1964*   265
41. *Routes of the Philippine Air Lines, 1965*   268
42. *Philippine Manufacturing Centers, 1963*   275
43. *Regions of the Philippines*   305
44. *Batan-Babuyan Islands*   307
45. *Physiography of the Cagayan Valley*   315
46. *Cagayan Valley Agriculture, 1960*   322
47. *Physiography of the Ilocos Coast*   329
48. *Indicated Migration from the Ilocos Coast*   334
49. *Physiography of the North Luzon Highlands*   343
50. *Rice Terraces and Agriculture in North Luzon (Banaue)*   347
51. *Physiography of the Zambales-Bataan Region*   363
52. *Physiography of the Central Plain*   370
53. *Irrigation on the Central Plain, 1960*   376
54. *Situation of Manila*   383
55. *Districts and Major Streets in Manila*   386
56. *Physiography of Southwestern Luzon*   394
57. *Economic Patterns of Southwestern Luzon*   401
58. *Physiography of Southeastern Luzon*   411
59. *Southeastern Luzon Agriculture, 1960*   417
60. *Physiography of Eastern Luzon*   422
61. *Physiography of Mindoro*   430
62. *Palawan Region*   437
63. *Physiography of the Sibuyan Sea Islands*   448

64. *Physiography of the Eastern Visayas* 456
65. *Eastern Visayan Agriculture, 1960* 464
66. *Physiography of the Central Visayas* 469
67. *Corn (Maize) on the Island of Cebu, 1960* 473
68. *Routes and Frequency of Shipping Services from Cebu, 1956* 481
69. *Physiography of the Western Visayas* 487
70. *Sugarcane in the Western Visayas, 1960* 493
71. *Within the Victorias Sugar District* 494
72. *Physiography of Northern Mindanao* 508
73. *Distribution of Population in Northern Mindanao, 1960* 513
74. *Physiography of Northeastern Mindanao* 518
75. *Physiography of Southeastern Mindanao* 519
76. *Corn Farming in the Davao Gulf Area (Hagonoy-Matanao)* 532
77. *Santo Tomas Settlement Project, Davao* 538
78. *Physiography of Southwestern Mindanao* 543
79a. *Population Distribution in Southwestern Mindanao, 1948* 552
79b. *Population Distribution in Southwestern Mindanao, 1960* 553
80. *Physiography of the Bukidnon-Lanao Highlands* 559
81. *Physiography of the Zamboanga Peninsula* 570
82. *Population and Religion in Zamboanga, 1960* 576
83. *Sulu Archipelago* 583
84. *Peoples of the Sulu Archipelago, 1960* 589

~~~~~~ TEXT TABLES

1. Philippine Vegetation Cover, 1951, 1957   84
2. Area and Stand of Types of Forest in the Philippines, 1951   87
3. Grassland Areas in the Philippine Islands in 1957   103
4. Philippine Regions, by Area and Population   306
5. Population and Area of Metropolitan Manila   389
6. Average Annual Rate of Population Growth for Metropolitan Manila
      and for the Philippines, 1903–1960   390

~~~~~ APPENDIX TABLES

1. *Principal Islands of the Philippines by Area and Population*
2. *Provinces by Area and Population, 1960*
3. *Selected Small Islands by Area and Population, 1960*
4. *Temperature Records for Selected Stations*
5. *Precipitation Records for Selected Stations*
6. *Species of Fish Commonly Caught in Philippine Waters*
7. *Species of Timber Trees Commonly Logged*
8. *Comparative Data on Soil Erosion*
9. *Population by Language Speakers, 1960*
10. *Population by Religious Affiliation by Provinces, 1960*
11. *Population by Educational Achievement by Provinces, 1960*
12. *Comparative Population by Provinces, 1876–1960*
13. *Population Densities by Provinces, 1960*
14. *Chartered Cities, Areas, and Populations, 1960*
15. *Selected Migration Statistics, 1939–1960*
16. *Comparative Crop Areas, 1948 and 1960*
17. *Crop and Animal Frequencies on Farms, 1948 and 1960*
18. *Vegetable Crops Commonly Grown, 1948 and 1960*
19. *Fruit and Nut Crops Commonly Grown, 1948 and 1960*
20. *Beverage Crops Grown, 1948 and 1960*
21. *Minor Crops Grown, 1948 and 1960*
22. *Summary of Crop Areas and Yields, 1960*
23. *Irrigated Land by Provinces, 1960*
24. *Livestock and Poultry Populations, 1939, 1948, and 1960*

xvii

25. *Fisheries Yields, 1939–1963*
26. *Selected Mineral Production Figures*
27. *Road System by Classes and Provinces, 1960*
28. *Highway Densities, 1955*
29. *Selected Transport Data, 1960*
30. *Selected Breakdown on Industrial Establishments, 1960*
31. *Geographical Distribution of Industrial Establishments, 1960*
32. *Selected Manufacturing Data, 1960*
33. *Indexes of Physical Volume of Production, 1949–1963*
34. *Philippine National Income by Industrial Origin, 1949–1962*
35. *Selected Foreign Trade Statistics*
36. *Direction of Foreign Trade*
37. *List of Ports by Classification*

Scattered over a total of about 500,000 square miles of the western Pacific Ocean lies the archipelago of the Philippine Islands. Some 7,100 islands, islets, and rocks make up a land area of 115,600 square miles, roughly equivalent to the state of Arizona or almost twice the size of New England. Large and small gulfs, seas, coral shoals, and areas of deep oceanic water enter into the broad environmental complex. Few archipelagos, and none embracing so many islands and islets, are fortunate enough to form a single political unit. The overall development of a political state based on an archipelago comes to resemble, in international respects, the development of a political state located in a continental situation. The geography of an island world, however, differs markedly from that of a compact land sector of the earth. With a basic geographic position on the oceanic margins of southeastern Asia, 500 miles off the south China coast, the Philippines have shared in three physical and cultural worlds: the Asian world, the Pacific world, and the occidental world (fig. 1). Although basically Malay in ethnic composition, the Philippine cultural world has been enriched by contributions from the Chinese, Japanese, Malaysian, and other mainland Asian worlds. Accessibility from the sea readily permitted early and modern contact with the Occident, chiefly with visitors from Spain and the United States, which served to alter and to add to the Asian base. The Philippines is part of southeastern Asia, and yet it lies somewhat apart from that mainland. It has been stated

with considerable justification that the Philippines is the least oriental country in the Orient. The Philippines celebrated the four hundredth anniversary
of its adoption of Christianity in 1965, and it may be termed the only
Christian country in the Orient. Although the present political system is

Fig. 1. The Philippines in their southeast Asia setting.

basically democratic and of occidental origin, that system has been subtly
modified by oriental influences.

In many physical aspects the Philippines closely resembles the mainland
of southeast Asia. These similarities include some elements of physical
geomorphic history, climatic regimes, vegetative assemblages, and the characteristics of soils. The position of the Philippines, however, on the island arcs

of the Pacific, has given the archipelago a physiographic composition and a topographic form rather unlike most parts of the mainland. Its very surrounding seas, oceanic depths, and coral shoals render to many of the islands a coastal situation quite different from that of mainland regions. The absence of great rivers and river valleys causes orientation of land regions to be differently organized. The Philippine climatic regimes, fundamentally maritime tropical owing to latitude, are conditioned by air masses and atmospheric pressure patterns originating on the adjacent mainland. The rich floral communities are blends of mainland Asian, Indonesian, and Australian realms. Tropical red earths, matured into soils, resemble those of the Asian mainland, but volcanism has altered the regional complex and the quality patterns to a significant extent.

Although occupying a relatively small land area, the Philippines manages to exhibit an exceptionally high degree of regionality. As it is an insular region, most of its internal subregionalism is also insular, although there are a few large islands where regionalisms approximate those found in large landed territories. Some of the regionalism is purely physical and spatial, whereas other regionalisms are cultural in origin. Rainfall and aridity vary a great deal, depending upon exposure, elevation, and situation, from a few subregions that receive less than 40 inches annually to those that experience more than 200 inches per year. Differences in vegetational cover and development of soils yield local landscapes that range from stunted forest and grassland to the heaviest of tropical rain forests. At the same time, regionalism permeates ways of human living; basic differences in language, religion, economy, and domestic dietary result from a long period of human occupation during which patterns of human life have both yielded to environmental regionalisms and exploited these regional variations in significant manner. In economic development the creative elements in Philippine culture have produced wide diversity in land use, transportation, rural settlement patterns, and urbanism. Almost empty regions contrast sharply with densely populated territories, both at the local level and on a national scale. The archipelago has been divided into more than fifty major political units (fig. 2).

It is a common fault among geographers to credit their chosen region with unusual or even unique combinations of physical and cultural development; the present authors admit to suffering this fault. Nevertheless, we assert that seldom does a territory as small as the Philippine Archipelago possess so many varied and unusual characteristics. We feel that different levels of regionalism are basic to an understanding of the land and life of the Philippines, but the sheer variety of physical and cultural environments complicates systematic analysis of the geography of the Philippines and makes

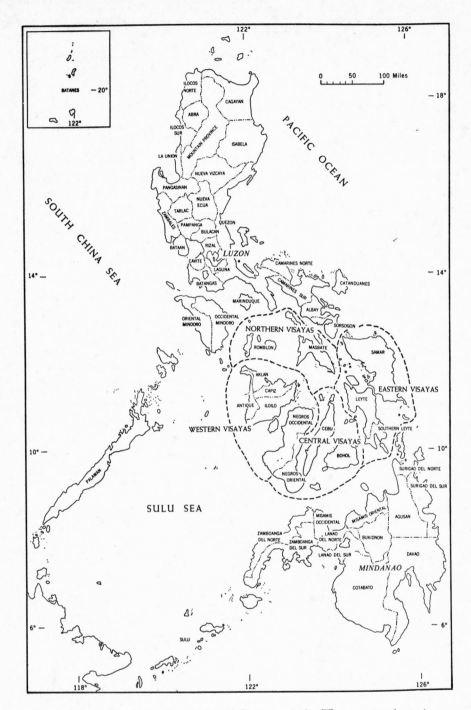

Fig. 2. The political provinces of the Philippines, 1965. There were 56 provinces and the city of Manila as political areas.

difficult the identification of critically meaningful regional entities. The major units selected as the first-order set of regions are arbitrarily delimited for purposes of convenience in attempting to describe the island world. Few geographic studies of the Philippines have attempted in-depth analysis; in a sense, this volume constitutes such an effort. Throughout the entire volume, four basic themes occur and recur. These are: (1) The Philippines is an insular world. (2) This world has its own distinctive combinations of man and land. (3) The Philippines is peripheral to the Asian mainland. (4) The Philippines displays a particular, distinctive, and significant blending of the Orient and the Occident.

PART ONE

The Physical Environment

ONE

~~~~ *Geomorphology and Physiography*

Geomorphology

The Philippine Islands lie in an area of considerable geologic interest and concern, for they form part of the highly interesting and confused picture of island arcs in the western Pacific and circum-Pacific orogenies. In their structures the Philippine Islands appear to share close relationships with the islands of the Indonesian Archipelago with which they have land or submarine ridge connections via the Palawan and Sulu island bridges to Borneo, and via the Talaud and Sarangani ridges, southward across the Celebes Sea to the islands of the Moluccas. Some Philippine structural components and patterns are also encountered in Taiwan, although any direct connections to the north are somewhat tenuous and unclear.[1] The tectonic history of the Philippines appears to be very similar to that of Indonesia; four of the five major tectonic provinces present in Indonesia are also represented in the Philippines (fig. 3).[2]

Active vulcanism, strong seismic activity, and considerable isostatic imbalance characterize the island arc systems of the western Pacific of which the Philippines is a part. Deep oceanic troughs parallel the convex sides of these island arcs; for example, on the Pacific Ocean side of the Philippines is the Philippine Trough, or Emden Deep, which descends to a maximum depth of 34,218 feet within a distance of less than 100 miles from the shores of eastern Mindanao. Broad, deep oceanic basins, such as the South China

Sea and Sulu Sea basins, are present along the concave sides of the Philippine island arcs.

The possible origin of the Philippine Archipelago, and similar island arcs, has been the subject of considerable geologic conjecture and controversy. Willis advanced a "submarine rim and disc" theory according to which igneous materials were forced up in arcuate patterns around the edges of

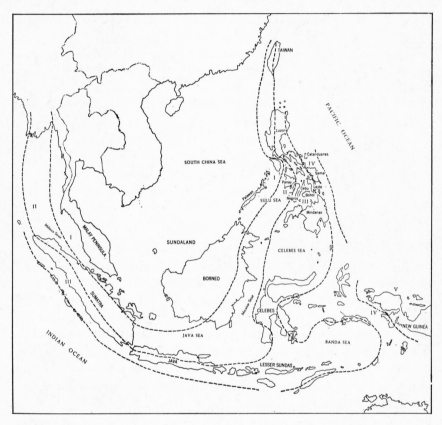

Fig. 3. Major tectonic provinces of southeast Asia (after G. C. Corby), in schematic arrangement.

giant submarine disc platforms.[3] Van Bemmelen proposed a "mounding up" of magmatic materials along structural lines of weakness, possibly along lines of regmatic fracture.[4] More recent investigators tend toward some modification of the Van Bemmelen hypothesis.[5] In essence, these theories assert that the islands of the Philippines are merely the higher portions of submerged mountain masses arranged along lines of structural weakness; that is to say, the islands are the tops of submarine volcanoes, horsts, and anticlinoria.

The islands of Palawan, Balabac, the Calamianes group, and possibly Mindoro also, are part of an ancient continental platform known as Sundaland; therefore, these islands have strong structural affinities with parts of western Borneo, Sumatra, and the Malay Peninsula. These areas can be considered as part of a very old Asian continental shelf. Relative stability, with but shallow subsidence and gentle folding in the Tertiary, characterizes the tectonic history of Sundaland.

The island of Panay and parts of western Luzon (Batangas, Zambales, and the Ilocos coast) belong to a second tectonic province, one that includes the great ocean basins containing the Sulu Sea, Macassar Strait, Java Sea, and the lowlands on the islands of Borneo, Sumatra, and northern Java. Within this second area the principal tectonic activity has been one of large-scale subsidence during and subsequent to the Tertiary. In these latter areas the accumulations of sedimentary materials reached great thickness, and from these Tertiary basins stems much of the petroleum production of Indonesia.

The central longitudinal section of the Philippines, extending from northern Luzon southward through Masbate, Negros, Cebu, Bohol, and Leyte into Mindanao, constitutes a third tectonic province. This region is an area of considerable seismic and volcanic activity; in combination the two processes have created a highly varied topographic landscape characterized by sharp contrasts in local relief. The third tectonic province is quite similar to the volcanic regions of southern and western Java and Sumatra.

The islands of Samar and Catanduanes, and possibly the extreme northeastern corner of Luzon, belong to a fourth tectonic region, one possessing great stability in which only slight tectonic activity has taken place since the Tertiary. This region is very similar to parts of Celebes and western New Guinea. These tectonic provinces do not have exact boundaries, but are shown in figure 3 on the basis of general physiography, geologic history, structure, amount of volcanic activity, and geophysical data.

The relief and physiographic features of the Philippines, at first glance, present a seemingly confused pattern of arrangement. The major topographic features of the islands, however, follow rather easily discernible structural trends. The Luzon Arc, or westernmost structural line, is an early-Tertiary geosyncline that trends generally northeast–southwest and extends from the cordillera lands of northern Luzon (Cordillera Central, Zambales Mountains) through the islands of Lubang, Mindoro, the western Visayas (or Bisayas), Calamianes, Cuyo, Palawan, Balabac, and the Sulu Archipelago into northeastern Borneo. This arc is composed of cuesta-like western and eastern flanks with an intervening median low zone. The flanks of the geosyncline are evident as ridges that appear either topographically as mountain ranges on the larger islands or as chains of small islands in the ocean basins. The western side of the Luzon Arc, which passes along the rim of the South China Sea, is nonvolcanic, whereas the eastern flank, which shows up in the Eastern Cordillera and Bondoc Peninsula of Luzon, and in Burias, Ticao, northwestern Leyte, Zamboanga Peninsula, and the Sulus, exhibits considerable active vulcanism. The intervening Manila Low Zone, located on the crest of the Luzon Arc, is occupied by a series of basins containing seas (Sibuyan, Visayan, and Sulu) through which are projected numerous volcanoes and horsts that have formed many of the central or Visayan islands.

The second Philippine structural arc is the Samar Arc, or eastern structural line, which branches from the Luzon Arc east of Luzon in about 16° North latitude, and passes through the eastern sections of the archipelago (Camarines Peninsula, Catanduanes, Samar, and Dinagat) southward into eastern Mindanao. Although more recent than the Luzon Arc, the Samar Arc has the same topographic expression, that is, a volcanically active inner flank, a nonvolcanic outer flank, and an intervening low zone that is occupied by the Bicol lowland and Leyte Gulf. The two arcs are separated by the Ragay Low Zone, which contains Ragay Gulf and the Mindanao Sea, as well as the Agusan and Cotabato lowlands on Mindanao.

Transverse faulting has played a major tectonic role in the formation of the Philippine Islands, and as the regional plan of the islands suggests, there is a major fault zone present.[6] The Philippine Fault Zone (Philippine Rift) encompasses a wide region of interlacing and branching fractures, but its main axis can be traced for over 700 miles from the southwest-facing escarpment of the Caraballo Mountains on Luzon, northwest of Dingalan Bay, through Polillo Strait, Ragay Gulf, northeastern Masbate, the Central Cordillera of Leyte, to the upper Agusan Valley in Mindanao. The presence of this major fault zone has had an important influence on individual island forms and topography and on the structural alignment of the archipelago. The arcuate structure of the fault zone is convex toward the Pacific and it is paralleled offshore by the deep Philippine Trough. The Philippine Fault Zone is fully as spectacular physiographically and structurally as the better-known San Andreas Fault of California and deserves a place as one of the great regional tectonic features of the earth.

It is probable that archipelagic conditions have existed in the Philippines at least since the beginning of the Tertiary. During and subsequent to the Tertiary there have been several periods of widespread subsidence and subsequent uplift, and deep layers of sediments, which include limestone, conglomerate, carbonaceous silt, and even coal, were laid down over wide areas in the Philippines. These Tertiary sediments were deposited in down-warped or synclinal areas in the presence of relatively quiet waters; the deposits in some instances have accumulated to thicknesses of 15,000–30,000 feet. Tertiary sedimentary rocks underlie approximately 55 percent of the land area of the Philippines.[7] In general, these sediments form foothill and lowland landscapes and frequently appear as cuestas, hogbacks, and interior plateaus. Many of the plains areas, including the Central Plain and Cagayan Valley of Luzon and various smaller coastal and riverine lowlands on Luzon and the other islands, are covered with deep Quaternary depositions. Most of the sedimentation must have taken place in relatively still waters with little wave action, for there is little evidence of any sorting of the materials. The widespread marine transgressions, and associated orogenies, probably occurred at about the same time as similar events in the East Indies.

Basement-complex rocks, mostly exposed in older upland areas, cover approximately 25–30 percent of the archipelago's land surface. These basement-complex rocks consist of a wide assortment of igneous and metamorphic rocks, including peridotites, gabbros, andesites, serpentines, gneisses, and schists. The outstanding feature of these rocks is their basic to ultrabasic composition, and many contain deposits of valuable metallic minerals.

Widespread volcanism also typified much of the Tertiary, but many of the volcanic forms created have been destroyed by erosion. Subsequent volcanic activity in the Quaternary frequently has resulted in the formation of volcanic cones, usually occurring in clusters or chains, and these give a very bold and striking effect to many Philippine landscapes. Approximately 15–20 percent of the Philippines is covered with volcanic materials that occur principally in north central Luzon between the Cagayan Valley and Central Plain, in southwestern Luzon, in the Bicol area, and in Negros, Leyte, and central Mindanao.

Physiography

The physiography of the Philippine Archipelago is quite diverse, owing in part to regional variations in the structural forces, parent-rock materials, and tectonic histories (figs. 4*a*, 4*b*). On the larger islands high mountain masses alternate with narrow structural or alluvial valleys. At the same time there is considerable physiographic diversity from one island to another. Irregular coastlines are normal, and many large islands have strings of small islands along, or off, their coasts. In many instances these small islands are rocky hills, but sometimes they are flat lowlands made into islands by the present level of the sea stand. In the offshore waters between many large islands are

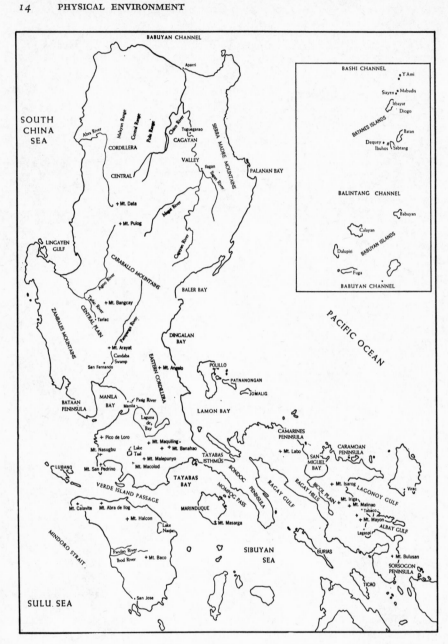

Fig. 4a. Major physiographic elements of the northern Philippines.

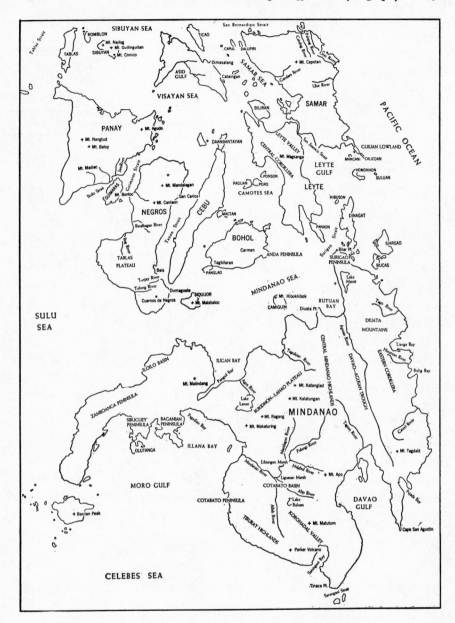

Fig. 4*b*. Major physiographic elements of the southern Philippines.

strings of submerged hills and plains whose crests are now covered with coral reefs.

In general, the heavy rainfall characteristic of most areas in the Philippines has resulted in very rapid and deep weathering of rock materials. As a result, the landform profiles in many areas are somewhat subdued by gentle slopes. Most of the rivers are short, consequent streams with flows that are extremely seasonal; generally they have channels that are much larger than their usual flows warrant. Recent vulcanism and active faulting have contributed an additional degree of sharpness to the topographic landscapes in some regions.

BATAN AND BABUYAN ISLANDS

The northernmost extension of the Philippine Archipelago is formed by two small groups of islands, the Batan and Babuyan islands, numbering nearly forty in all and representing a combined land area of 312 square miles.[8] These islands lie off the northern coast of Luzon and occupy a position between that large island and the large Chinese island of Taiwan farther north. From the far northern island of Y'Ami, in the Batan group, Taiwan lies but 100 miles distant. Both of the two far northern island outliers of the Philippines project from shallow submarine platforms, continuations of the main Philippine platform, but separated from the Taiwan uplift by the 16,000-foot-deep Bashi Channel. Shallower channels separate the two groups from one another (Balintang Channel) and from the island of Luzon (Babuyan Channel).

The islands in both groups exhibit either volcanic or coralline origins. Y'Ami, North Island, Mabudis, Siayan, Diogo, Batan, and Sabtang, in the Batan Islands, and Camiguin, Babuyan, Dalupiri, and Calayan, in the Babuyans, have been formed largely by recent vulcanism. Elevations are relatively high and the topography is rugged, particularly when viewed in proportion to the small areas of the islands. Mount Iraya, an extinct volcano on the tiny, 27-square-mile island of Batan, rises to an elevation of 3,306 feet. Volcanoes on Camiguin and Babuyan rise to between 2,200 and 3,500 feet elevation. There is considerable active vulcanism in the region; as recently as 1952 an active submarine volcano created a new, 500-foot-high island in the area northeast of Camiguin.

On the other hand, the island of Itbayat, the largest of the Batan group, appears to represent an uplifted coral terrace, or possibly even a raised coral atoll, and its rim slopes gently down toward the island interior from the high cliffs that completely encircle it. Ibuhos, Dequey, and Fuga also are probably raised coral terraces. There are numerous examples of karst development in these limestone islands.

LUZON

Luzon is the largest island in the Philippine Archipelago; with an area of 40,420 square miles it contains approximately 35 percent of the land surface of the Philippines. In its overall dimensions the island has a maximum northwest–southeast length of 530 miles and a width that varies from 8 to 138 miles. Approximately 46 percent of the Filipino population lives on Luzon.

Luzon has pronounced areal differences in physiography, owing to its complex physical history. The Central Plain and the Cagayan Valley rank as the two largest contiguous lowland areas in the archipelago, and the Cordillera Central in northern Luzon, although it does not contain the highest peak, certainly is the largest and most important upland area in the Philippines. The island of Luzon can be subdivided into seven major physiographic regions based upon the sharing of common elements of structure, stratigraphy, geology, and relief. These subregions are: the North Luzon Highlands or Cordillera Central, Sierra Madre and Eastern Cordillera, Cagayan Valley, Zambales Mountains, Central Plain, the southwestern volcanic area, and the southeastern peninsulas or Bicol.

The major physiographic components of northern Luzon, that is, the area to the north of approximately 16° North latitude, include the Cordillera Central, with its three parallel-trending subranges, the Sierra Madre and Caraballo Mountains, and the intervening longitudinal valley of the Cagayan and Magat rivers.

The Cagayan Valley occupies an extensive synclinorium that is now floored, for the most part, with deep alluvium deposited by the Cagayan River and its various tributaries, principally the Chico, Ilagan, and Magat rivers. The Cagayan Valley measures approximately 120 miles in north–south length, with an average width of 40 miles, and contains approximately 5,000 square miles of deep Tertiary and Quaternary alluvial fill. Structurally the Cagayan Valley may represent the northern extension of the Central Plain of Luzon which has been cut off from its southern counterpart and displaced to the east by the uplift of the Caraballo Mountains.

A transverse range, the Caraballo Mountains, closes off the southern end of the Cagayan Valley and provides a connecting topographic link between the Cordillera Central and Sierra Madre.

The Caraballo Mountains were formed along the Lingayen Gulf–Dingalan Bay flexure or fault zone in the early Miocene. The formation of these mountains was associated with the initial uplift and marginal faulting of ancestral Cordillera Central. When this general uplift occurred, the Cagayan Valley, as well as the Central Plain, became extensive depositional areas. Sediments of Tertiary and Quaternary origin, mostly limestone sands and clays, blanketed the Cagayan Basin to depths of 10,000–15,000 feet. Only small-scale folding and faulting has taken place in these sediments since their deposition.

The main Cagayan River heads far to the south in the Caraballo Mountains and descends rapidly to the valley floor, reaching it at an elevation of only 300 feet above sea level at a point approximately 140 miles from the river mouth in Babuyan Channel. From this point the river flows northward in broad meanders, acquiring the major tributaries of the Magat and Ilagan rivers near the city of Ilagan, and the Chico River at a point between Tuguegarao and Aparri. Near this latter confluence the river valley is constricted by the gentle Sicalao anticline before it reaches the narrow coastal plain along the north coast. Most of the larger tributaries of the Cagayan enter the valley from the cordilleran lands to the west. The main stream and all its tributaries are subject to extensive flooding during the heavy rainfall of the monsoon or typhoon seasons.

The lofty and massive Cordillera Central is the major structural element of northern Luzon. These highlands interpose between the Cagayan Valley and the South China Sea. The Cordillera Central has an overall width that varies from 36 to 54 miles and an unbroken north–south length of nearly 200 miles. It reaches maximum elevations of 8,000 to 9,000 feet in the south and gradually descends to elevations of approximately 3,000 feet along the northern coast of Luzon. The cordilleran system of northwestern Luzon is composed of three parallel, longitudinal-trending ranges arranged *en echelon*. From west to east these subranges are the Malayan Range, the Central Range, and the Polis Range. The Malayan Range, which reaches maximum elevations of nearly 6,000 feet, fronts above the shores of the South China Sea. Steep slopes are present along the west, and there is little room for the development of coastal plains along the Ilocos coast. The Central Range, with elevations up to 8,800 feet, presents a flat-topped profile, suggesting a previous erosional surface that has been uplifted and exposed to subsequent denudation. Several of the more important rivers of northern Luzon, such as the Chico, Abra, and Agno rivers, have their headwaters on the slopes of Mount Data, within the Central Range. The courses of the latter two rivers, especially, are very much controlled by the parallel longitudinal orientation of the Cordillera Central subranges until they finally manage to break through the intervening Malayan Range and enter the sea. The Polis Range in the east contains Mount Pulog (9,612 feet), the highest point on Luzon and second highest peak in the Philippines. The Polis slopes relatively gently eastward toward the Cagayan Valley. The Cordillera Central is massive, well-watered, deeply dissected, and difficult of access.

Throughout the Cordillera Central basement-complex rocks consisting of gabbros, andesites, serpentines, gneisses, and various other metamorphics are exposed, and upon several of these exposures is concentrated much of the Philippine copper-, gold-, and silver-mining industry.

The Sierra Madre, or Eastern Cordillera, forms the eastern margin of the Cagayan Valley. This mountain range is composed essentially of a large uplifted and tilted block of land with an abrupt slope facing the Pacific Ocean and with a more gentle descent to the Cagayan Valley. Mount Cresta, the highest peak in the Sierra Madre, reaches an elevation of 6,136 feet. The resistant intrusive igneous core of the highlands is overlaid by a mantle of Tertiary sedimentary and basic extrusive igneous rocks. The Sierra Madre is a very rugged, heavily forested, virtually unexplored area, and as yet, no road penetrates it. The cliff-fringed Pacific shores are relieved by only three small lowlands at Palanan, Baler, and Dingalan bays.

The Eastern Cordillera continues along the eastern edge of Luzon, forming the narrow Tayabas Isthmus, which provides the land connection with the southeastern peninsulas of Luzon and, farther southward, forms Bondoc Peninsula. Although the mountains of the Eastern Cordillera actually begin in extreme northeastern Luzon as the Sierra Madre Mountains, they are generally regarded as two highland systems separated by the Lingayen Gulf–Dingalan Bay flexure, or graben, at 16° North latitude. This depression through the eastern cordilleran lands provides the only easy passage from western Luzon to the Pacific coast.

South of the Sierra Madre in central and southern Luzon, the Eastern Cordillera consists of a series of igneous ranges with an overall width of 25–30 miles. In cross section the cordillera has the profile of a low, dissected arch, presenting steep slopes on both sides, but particularly along the shores of the Pacific Ocean. Elevations are moderate, generally no more than 1,000–2,000 feet, except northeast and east of Manila where elevations over 4,000 feet are reached on the summits of Mounts Angelo, Banay, and Caladang. The arch plunges southward, and in the Bondoc Peninsula, elevations descend below 1,000 feet. After plunging beneath the waters of the Sibuyan Sea, the arch reappears as the rugged mountainous islands of Burias and Ticao and eventually, farther south, forms the main cordillera of Leyte. Except in the Tayabas Isthmus, the Eastern Cordillera is not accompanied by an extensive development of coastal lowlands.

The Zambales Mountains, or Western Cordillera, extend from Lingayen Gulf to Bataan Peninsula parallel to the shores of the South China Sea. It may be that the Zambales Mountains are a southern continuation of the Cordillera Central of northern Luzon, offset several tens of miles toward the west along the Lingayen-Dingalan fault. The Zambales highlands appear to be a giant tilted block with a high eastern edge facing the Central Plain, and a more gradual western slope to the coast. They appear as discontinuous ranges of high, rugged peaks with considerable Quaternary vulcanism that is particularly evident in the south on the mountains of Bataan Peninsula. The basement-complex materials, consisting of basic, coarse-grained rocks and volcanics, including andesites, diorites, and gabbros, are exposed throughout the Zambales Mountains. Many short, rapid-flowing, consequent streams drain the western slopes, and each stream builds a small floodplain and delta along the coast. These deltas are connected by a narrow coastal strip of alluvium moved and deposited by coastal currents. The mountain slopes are densely forested and sparsely populated. The Zambales area is highly mineralized.

The Central Plain of Luzon is the largest lowland area and, in an economic sense, the most important physiographic region in the Philippines. The Central Plain is quite similar in structure to the Cagayan Valley. It occupies a large open-ended synclinorium that is oriented in a north–south direction. To the west it is bordered by the Zambales Mountains; to the east lies the Eastern Cordillera. To the north the trough plunges beneath the waters of Lingayen Gulf, and its southern extremity is occupied by the shallow waters of Manila Bay and Laguna de Bay. The Central Plain has an overall length of more than 125 miles and an average width of 40 miles. In only a few places on the plain do elevations rise more than a few feet above sea level. A low, almost imperceptible topographic divide, located between the city of Tarlac and Mount Bangcay, separates the northward drainage of the lowland, dominated by the Tarlac and Agno rivers, from the southward-flowing Rio Grande de Pampanga and its many tributaries. Tertiary and Quaternary sediments, consisting principally of limestones, sands, and shales brought down from the surrounding highlands, or marine sediments deposited during the several periods of sea incursions, cover the lowlands in thicknesses of 10,000–20,000 feet. Several Neocene and Quaternary volcanic masses project up through the deep layers of sediments, forming isolated volcanic cones and peaks. Picturesque Mount Arayat rises abruptly from the plain north of San Fernando, Pampanga, to attain a height of 3,378 feet. In the northern part of the plain there are several gently folded anticlines that give some moderate relief to the topography. Near the mouth, and on the delta, of the Pampanga River there are extensive swamplands that line the northern shores of Manila Bay, and near the confluence of the Angat and Pampanga rivers is the large Candaba Swamp. Throughout most of its length the relief of the Central Plain is that of a broad, essentially level plain.

Southwestern Luzon represents the southward continuation of the Central Plain after its interruption by Manila Bay; but southwestern Luzon shows considerably more evidence of volcanic activity, both past and at present. A narrow wedge of lowlands lying between the Eastern Cordillera and Manila Bay, upon which is situated the city of Manila, forms the land connection between the two segments of the Luzon plain.

Southwestern Luzon can be characterized as an extensive tuff-covered plain from which arise a series of volcanic peaks of different elevations and different ages. Extending south from the entrance to Manila Bay is a string of Miocene volcanic cones which includes Mounts Pico de Loro, Nasugbu, and San Pedrino. These have been lowered in elevation and subdued in relief by deep weathering. A second group of deeply dissected Pliocene cones is found in the area between Laguna de Bay and Lake Taal, and includes Mounts Maquiling, Macolod, and Malepunyo. A third group of volcanoes, the Quaternary volcanoes of Taal and the three-peaked Mount Banahao, is composed of very recent, steep-sided, nearly symmetrical cones. Taal Volcano lies within the caldera occupied by Lake Taal. A period of activity in 1911 was accompanied by considerable destruction to life and property, and in the autumn of 1965 eruptions again covered the core area of the little island volcano with ash and cinders, killing several scores of people and destroying villages and farmlands. Mount Banahao is the highest volcano in southwestern Luzon, reaching an elevation of 7,177 feet. Its subsidiary cones of Mounts San Cristobal and Banahao de Lucban reach to 4,900 feet and 5,983 feet respectively. Elsewhere in the region there are numerous small crater lakes and cinder cones. The tuffaceous rock materials that cover much of southwestern Luzon weather into very fertile agricultural soils.

The large lake named Laguna de Bay separates the volcanic areas in the southwest from the front ranges of the Eastern Cordillera. This large inland water body, which includes a water surface of 356 square miles, probably was a former arm or extension of Manila Bay and was separated from it, on the north, by a slight arching that took place along the eastern shores of the bay. Possibly an earlier southern opening to the sea was cut off by vulcanism and the accumulation of volcanic debris. The Pasig River, which drains Laguna de Bay into Manila Bay, has been able to maintain its course across the northern arch by cutting through the Hagonoy Isthmus.

Southeastern Luzon consists of a large, irregularly shaped peninsula called the Bicol Peninsula. Extending far to the east and south of the main mass of the island, the Bicol Peninsula continues the structural components of Luzon into the eastern Visayan area. The gentle arch of the Eastern Cordillera, appearing as the 8-mile-wide Tayabas Isthmus, forms a narrow land connection with the rest of the island. Actually southeastern Luzon consists of several small peninsulas, including the Camarines, Caramoan, and Sorsogon peninsulas, and numerous offshore islands, the largest of which are the islands of Catanduanes, Batan, and Rapu Rapu. The platform upon which the whole southeastern peninsula rests also underlies the offshore islands of Polillo, Patnanongan, and Jomalig which lie to the north in Lamon Bay. The deep oceanic basins of the Pacific bound the Bicol platform on the east, whereas the Ragay depression, occupied by Ragay Gulf, separates the peninsula from the Eastern Cordillera and Bondoc Peninsula.

The main structural element of the Bicol Peninsula is a long, interior synclinal depression flanked by mountains and hill lands. The Bicol River, the longest waterway in southern Luzon, drains northward through this longitudinal depression, finally emptying into San Miguel Bay. Northeast of the lowland is a row of isolated active and extinct volcanoes, including Mounts Labo, Isarog, Iriga, Malinao, Masarga, and Mayon. Mount Mayon, located northwest of Albay Gulf, is the highest of these cones and consists of a spectacularly symmetrical volcanic cone that rises from the shoreline of Tabaco Bay to an elevation of 7,941 feet. Mayon has been active periodically, but seldom is explosively violent. Sorsogon, the southernmost peninsula of Luzon, is composed entirely of volcanic mountains, dominated in the center by Mount Bulusan (5,110 feet). West of the Bicol Plain, and lying along the shores of Ragay Gulf, is a range of low monoclinal hills called the Ragay Hills. These hills are composed of folded sedimentary materials, mainly limestones and sandstones.

Several large bays indent the coasts of the Bicol Peninsula; among them are San Miguel and Sorsogon bays, and Albay and Lagonoy gulfs. The Bicol Plain, along with the smaller lowland areas around Legaspi, Tabaco, and Lagonoy Gulf, are filled to an indeterminate depth with alluvium, much of which is of volcanic origin.

The compact, 552-square-mile island of Catanduanes is separated from southeastern Luzon by the shallow waters of Maqueda Channel. Catanduanes consists of a rough, hilly interior, which reaches elevations of 1,000–2,500 feet, and small lowlands that are restricted to a few peripheral locations. Volcanic materials occur extensively on the eastern side of the island and deep sediments cover the western side. The largest lowland area is at the town of Virac in the south.

MINDORO-PALAWAN

Mindoro, Palawan, the Calamianes group, Balabac, and the Cuyo Islands make up a geological unit physically separate and in character quite distinct from the rest of the Philippine Archipelago. All of the islands in this geological unit are located on, or close to, the margins of the Sundaland Platform, the ancient and stable block upon which the island of Borneo is also situated.

The island of Mindoro, located southwest of Luzon, is separated from it by the narrow Verde Island Passage. The highland core of Mindoro represents the high point of the western Philippine structural arc; it is the pivotal point where the north–south structural alignment of the areas to the north begins to bend toward the southwest, and after passing through the Calamianes Islands and Palawan, enters northeastern Borneo.

Mindoro has a very regular oval shape without any deep coastal indentations, and without fringing islets. With an area of 3,758 square miles it ranks as the seventh largest island in the Philippines. The island is bordered by the deep, troughlike depressions of the Verde Island Passage, between Mindoro and Luzon, and by Mindoro Strait to the west between Mindoro and the Calamianes Islands. The structural form of Mindoro is that of a great tilted block, falling off in steep slopes on both sides. The interior is rugged, mountainous, dissected, heavily forested, and practically unexplored. Although several high mountains border the north coast, such as Mount Calavite (4,990 feet), which forms the northwestern peninsula of the island, and Mount Abra de Ilog (3,339 feet), the main mountain masses of Mindoro are grouped in two areas: around Mount Halcon (8,481 feet), the highest point on the island, and around Mount Baco (8,160 feet). Most of northern Mindoro has been covered by deep Pliocene volcanic flows emanating from Mounts Halcon and Calavite, whereas central and western sections of the island are underlaid by basement-complex rocks. Thin, moderately folded Tertiary sediments are found in the east and south.

The largest area of lowlands, in places measuring 10 to 12 miles in width, borders the northeastern and eastern coasts of Mindoro; smaller lowlands are found at San Jose, in the southwest, and near the mouths of the Pandan and Ibod rivers, midway along the west coast. Lake Naujan, one of the larger lakes in the Philippines, is situated on the eastern coastal plain. The eastern coast of Mindoro is low-lying, poorly drained, and fringed by marsh and swamp in many sections. Lubang, Golo, Ambil, and Cabra are small islands lying northwest of Mindoro. Granites and various metamorphics underlie these smaller islands. Elevations of 1,500–2,000 feet are encountered on Lubang and Ambil, and a small lowland occupies much of northwestern Lubang.

The divergence of the main western Philippine structural arc, begun in Mindoro, is clearly evident in the northeast–southwest structural alignment of the islands of the Calamianes group, Palawan, and Balabac and Bugsuk. The island of Palawan contains an area of 4,550 square miles and is the fifth largest island of the Philippine Archipelago. Long and narrow, Palawan extends over 270 miles in length, and has a maximum width of only 24 miles. The submarine ridge that forms the island of Palawan rises from the deep waters of the South China Sea and the Sulu Sea, and provides the island with a relatively high and continuously mountainous backbone. Mount Mantalingajan (6,639 feet) in the south is the highest peak on the island, but other mountains, such as Cleopatra Needle and Victoria Peaks, rise well above the 5,000-foot contour. The continuity of the central mountains of Palawan is broken at Honda Bay (10° North latitude) where a narrow lowland crosses the island, connecting with the lowland area around Ulugan Bay on the northwest coast. The areas of lowland on Palawan are very limited for the most part; they are confined to immediate coastal locations, and seldom do they extend more than 5 miles inland. The most important lowlands are in the Ilian, Barbacan, and Caramay river valleys and on the coast in Panacan and Brookes Point municipalities. About a hundred islets and several hundred rocks surround the main island, being most numerous at the northern end.

Very little is known of the structure and stratigraphy of Palawan. Basement-complex rock materials are found at the surface in a few areas near the center of the island behind the city of Puerto Princesa. Elsewhere, sediments appear to cover most of the land surface. Nowhere is there much evidence of recent vulcanism. The long, irregular coastline is coral-fringed for the most part.

The Calamianes (Culion, Busuanga, and Coron) and Balabac (Balabac and Bugsuk) island groups are part of the overall structure of Palawan in that they form the connecting links in the great structural arc that extends from Mindoro to Borneo. Balabac, Bugsuk, Linapacan, and Coron are wholly limestone islands. Busuanga and Culion are quite hilly and composed of highly metamorphosed quartzites. Dozens of coral islets or barely submerged reefs lie offshore.

The hundreds of tiny islands of the Cuyo group are also structurally related to Palawan. These small islands give the impression of being true oceanic islands. Located far out in the northern part of the Sulu Sea, the Cuyo Islands are anchored at the edge of the upturned western flank of the Luzon Arc which also provides the platform for Palawan. The largest island of the group, with an area of 22 square miles, is Cuyo, which is of volcanic structure. Mount Bombon, at the northern end of the island, rises to an elevation of 849 feet. In the north, Quiniluban Island and several adjacent

islands appear to be uplifted coral atolls; however, since elevations on Quiniluban reach to over 1,000 feet, there is also the strong suggestion of recent
volcanic uplift. Most of the other islands of the Cuyo group are of pure coral
origin, and many are completely surrounded by partly submerged coral reefs.
The total land area represented by all of the islands of the group is only 46
square miles.

The important island of Marinduque appears to be closely related to
Luzon Island structurally, and only the relatively shallow waters of Tayabas
Bay and Mompog Pass separate the two islands. Nearly circular in shape,
Marinduque appears as an isolated volcanic mass surrounded by coral reefs.
The interior of the island is mountainous, and reaches elevations around
2,000 feet; however, Mount Marlanga, a dormant volcano on the southern
peninsula, attains a height of 3,795 feet. A central core of crystalline materials, principally diorites and serpentines, is flanked by a series of steeply
dipping volcanics. This core is highly mineralized. A narrow coastal plain,
surfaced largely with recent limestone materials, fringes the coastline in the
northeast. The west-flowing Boac River is the island's major drainage artery,
and at its mouth the river has built a small delta upon which is located the
provincial capital. Marinduque Island has an area of 347 square miles.

VISAYAN ISLANDS

The Visayas are an extensive group of large and small islands that lie between
Luzon and Mindanao, but belong structurally to neither. The Visayan area
consists of a series of raised blocks with intervening grabens, and has experienced considerable recent volcanic activity. Because the term "Visayan" also
has a cultural connotation, often being used to refer to the island inhabitants,
designation of the specific islands that comprise the group varies with
different authorities and different academic disciplines. In consideration of
their lack of structural affinity with other outside areas, and the presence of
deep channels and basins that intervene between them and the outside areas,
the following major islands are herein referred to as the Visayan group:
Panay, Negros, Cebu, Bohol, Leyte, Samar, Masbate, Romblon, Sibuyan,
Tablas, and Siquijor, and the numerous intervening smaller islands.

Samar is the largest of the Visayan Islands and includes an area of 5,050
square miles. Unlike most of the other larger islands of the Philippine
Archipelago, Samar lacks a true mountain range. Instead, the interior of the
island is composed of a broad, maturely dissected upland mass of exposed
basement-complex rocks consisting primarily of andesites, basalts, gabbros,
serpentines, and schists. The whole core has been broadly upwarped and
exposed to weathering. Maximum elevations reach only to 2,789 feet on

Mount Capotan, and most of the rugged interior lies between the 500-and 1,000-foot contours. Lowlands are restricted to narrow strips of coastal plains, particularly in the north, and to small river floodplains and deltas. The eastern littoral is fringed along its entire length by a series of small deltaic lowlands, isolated from one another by intervening mountain spurs. The Ulut, Catubig, Palapag, Gandara, and Oras rivers are the major streams of Samar, and each has built up a small alluvial plain along its lower course. The valley of the Catubig is the largest lowland on the island.

The southeastern extension of Samar, the Guiuan lowland, consists of a long narrow peninsula. Together with the adjacent island of Calicoan, this southeast projection is formed of low-lying coralline deposits. Samar is separated from Luzon by San Bernardino Strait and from the island of Leyte to the south by the very narrow San Juanico Strait, the alignment of which appears to be controlled by an obvious northwest–southeast fault. The islands of Capul and Dalupiri off northwestern Samar, and the numerous islands of the Samar Sea, are insular extensions of mountainous structures originating in the Eastern Cordillera of Luzon. Many of these small islands are the tops of recent submarine volcanoes. Nearly a hundred small islands, islets, mud flats, and rocks surround Samar. Many of the larger inshore islands are separated from the main islands only by tidal channels.

Leyte is a very irregularly shaped island, with deep embayments along the northern, western, and southern sides. The island contains an area of 2,785 square miles. Three mountain ranges, aligned approximately parallel to one another and separated by lowlands, furnish the island's basic physiographic frame. One of the highland systems forms the northwestern peninsula of Leyte. This highland area is composed of limestone marls and shales folded into a geanticlinal structure. The limestones frequently form cuestas to the south and west. Highest elevations in this westernmost cordillera are reached in the south on the summit of Mount Magsanga at 1,937 feet. The northeastern highlands of Leyte and the Central Cordillera, with its extension into the offshore island of Biliran, are of igneous origin. These two highlands consist of exposed basement-complex rocks and associated Tertiary and Quaternary volcanics. The Central Cordillera is continuous throughout the length of Leyte, reappearing in the south as the long, narrow island of Panaon and, eventually, as the Eastern Cordillera of Mindanao. Two peaks within the Central Cordillera exceed 4,000 feet in elevation and several exceed 3,500 feet. The northeastern highlands, bordering along San Juanico Strait, reach above the 1,500-foot contour. The broad, alluvium-filled Leyte Valley lies between the northeastern and central highlands and represents a continuation of the large structural basin occupied by the Samar Sea and

Leyte Gulf. Leyte Valley constitutes one of the largest contiguous lowland areas in the Visayan Islands. The smaller Ormoc Plain intervenes between the central range and the northwestern highlands. Elsewhere, lowland areas are confined to narrow coastal strips. There are very few small islands fringing Leyte.

The broad, well-protected waters of Leyte Gulf occupy the large basin between eastern Leyte and the southern extensions of Samar; the gulf is closed off from the open Pacific by the small islands of Manicani, Calicoan, Homonhon, Suluan, Hibuson, and Dinagat. Surigao Strait, between Leyte and Mindanao, provides access to Leyte Gulf from the southwest. Manicani and Homonhon contain relatively large reserves of iron ore, and Dinagat has large deposits of chromite and nickeliferous ores.

Bohol Island lies in the Camotes Sea midway between southern Leyte and the island of Cebu. Bohol is nearly oval in shape and includes an area of 1,492 square miles. The island possesses a rather unusual structure and physiography when compared to other large islands of the Philippines. Two major anticlinal ridges, oriented parallel to one another, form the eastern and western edges of the island. Both of these folds drop off steeply on their seaward edges. Between the two anticlines lies a broad, elevated, southward-plunging syncline that gives the central part of the island the apparance of an interior plateau undergoing active dissection. A maximum elevation of over 2,800 feet is reached on the eastern anticline near the southeastern coast; elsewhere in the higher sections of the island the elevations range between 1,000 and 2,500 feet.

A sharp distinction may be made between the rock materials characteristic of the northern parts of the island and those of the southern parts. In general, northern Bohol is overlaid by volcanic materials that have been deeply weathered and now present a low, rolling, subdued landscape. The southern half of the island is composed of elevated coralline limestone materials that slope abruptly to the sea along the south. In east central Bohol, near the municipality of Carmen, a striking karst landscape has been developed; it features numerous solution cavities and an unusual occurrence of what appear to be "haycock" hills or *magotes*.[9] These hills occur close together and cover an area of approximately 20 square miles. Large, low-grade deposits of manganese ore are located on Anda Peninsula in the southeast. The island is drained by numerous short streams, and where these streams reach the sea, particularly along the northern coast, numerous small alluvial lowlands have been developed. Local relief in the interior upland is not so great that the land cannot be extensively cultivated. Coral reefs and about seventy-five small islands and islets surround the west, north, and northeast coasts of Bohol, but there are no good natural harbors. Access to the principal port and capital city of Tagbilaran has had to be blasted and dredged through obstructing coral reefs.

The small 35-square-mile island of Panglao, located southwest of Tagbilaran, consists of a raised tableland of low elevation, and is formed entirely of coralline limestone. The interior of the island is perfectly flat except in the northeast, and terminates along the shores in abrupt 5- to 20-foot high cliffs.

The three small islands of the Camotes group lie northeast of Bohol. Pagijan, Poro, and Ponson are anticlinal in structure. Deeply weathered volcanics, primarily basalts and peridotites, are overlaid with limestones and sandstones. Mount Three Peaks on Poro, at 1,200 feet, is the highest point in the group.

Siquijor, another small island situated approximately 10 miles east of the southeastern Negros Island city of Dumaguete, is entirely fringed by coral reefs. The island contains a high and much dissected interior, and near the center reaches an elevation of 2,060 feet on Mount Malabahoc. Deep limestone deposits cover all of the island's surface. Level land is limited to narrow river floodplains and deltas, particularly along the southern and northern coasts. Siquijor contains an area of 130 square miles.

The long, narrow island of Cebu, with an area of 1,707 square miles, occupies a position in the geographical center of the Philippine Archipelago. Cebu lies west of the island of Bohol, with which it shares some structural and topographical elements, whereas narrow, deep Tañon Strait sets it apart from Negros Island, which lies farther to the west. Included with Cebu are the small offshore islands of Mactan and Daanbantayan. The overall length of Cebu is 122 miles, and nowhere does its width exceed 20 miles. It ranks ninth in size among the islands of the Philippines.

Geologically, Cebu is geanticlinal in structure. Giant upfolding has covered the highly metamorphosed basement-complex rock core in the north central section of the island's interior. Elsewhere, deep layers of massive, porous limestone and thin covers of coral materials mask the underlying rock materials. In several places karst topography is well-developed. The interior of Cebu consists of a sharp north–south trending topographic divide. Elevations reach almost to the 3,400-foot contour and gradually decrease to the north and south. Largely deforested, the interior uplands are highly dissected and present a topography of sharp relief. All rivers are short and rapid-flowing. The erosive power of these streams on the denuded upland slopes is very great; there has resulted one of the worst erosion problems in the Philippines. The coastline of Cebu is very regular, without embayments, and consists of a series of alternating valleys and ridges reaching down from the central uplands. There is very little level land. One of the rock formations that outcrops in several areas on the island, the Cebu formation, contains commercial quantities of coal.

The small island of Mactan, lying immediately east of a point midway along the coast of Cebu, provides protection for the harbor of the principal port of Cebu City. Mactan is an old raised-coral reef that now stands 8 to 10 feet above the level of the sea and is completely encircled by coral reefs. The little raised-coral reef island of Daanbantayan lies off the northern end of Cebu and is separated from it by the narrow, tidal Daijagon Canal.

Across the narrow Tañon Strait from Cebu lies Negros Island, the fourth largest island of the Philippines. This island has an area of 4,905 square miles. Shaped like a large boot with the toe pointing toward the southeast, the island of Negros has an extreme length of 118 miles and a width that varies from 22 to 49 miles.

Two separate highland systems are present on Negros, a main central range that runs nearly the length of the island, terminating at the instep of the boot, and a double cluster of uplands at the southern end. The southwest–northeast trending, fault-controlled valleys of the Tolong and Tanjay rivers in the south separate these two upland areas. The main mountain range is located close to the eastern shores and appears to be formed of uplifted sediments. Along the western flanks of this central range are several high volcanic masses, including Mounts Silay (5,037 feet), Mandalagan (6,165 feet), and Canlaon (8,088 feet); the latter is the highest point in the Visayas. The central mountains form an almost unbroken barrier to east–west travel across the island. They have been deeply dissected by erosion and present steep slopes on both sides. The range descends abruptly to the eastern coast; leaving little room for the development of coastal plains except where the infrequent rivers have created small isolated deltas or piedmont plains, such as at San Carlos and Bais.

The southeastern peninsula of Negros is formed by a group of several volcanic peaks, dominated by the 6,200-foot-high Cuernos de Negros. Always cloud-shrouded and deeply eroded, the Cuernos has built up an extensive, steeply sloping, piedmont alluvial plain around its base. Several small crater lakes lie in the mountains of southeastern Negros, including Lakes Danao and Balinsasayan. A large plateau, the Tablas, occupies most of southwestern Negros. Its surface, overlaid with recent volcanic and sedimentary materials, presents a rolling-to-rough landscape with a local relief of from 500 to 1,000 feet.

Western Negros consists of a zone of broad plains. These western plains are among the larger Philippine lowlands. Varying from 5 to 30 miles in width, the combined plains extend for almost 100 miles along the western shores of the island. In its northern and central sections the plain is covered with a thick blanket of volcanic tuffs, ashes, and boulders of basalt and andesite, whereas in the south there are deposits of marine sediments. The recent vulcanism prominent along the western flanks of the central mountains intrudes into the western lowlands in the form of numerous cinder cones, particularly southwest of Mount Canlaon. Several large rivers, including the Ilog, Binalbagan, and Bago, drain across the plain.

Guimaras Island, 223 square miles in area, is situated between the two large islands of Negros and Panay. On the side facing Panay, Guimaras forms the eastern enclosure of the narrow Iloilo Strait; the side facing Negros is the western edge of the shallow Guimaras Strait. Guimaras Island is an extension of the hill lands that appear in northeastern Panay. Along the island's eastern side, basement-complex rocks are exposed, though these are overlaid with thick deposits of limestone in the west. Moderately rough and hilly, Guimaras reaches its greatest height of 826 feet in the center of the island on Mount Bontoc. Numerous coral islets mask the southern and southeastern coastlines, narrowing Guimaras Strait to less than 6 miles in the south.

The island of Panay, the westernmost major Visayan island, ranks sixth in size among the Philippine Islands and includes an area of 4,446 square miles. Panay is roughly triangular in shape, and has a high, rugged mountain system paralleling its long western coastline. Midway along the Western Cordillera, near Mount Baloy, a low range of hills breaks off northeastward from the main mountain mass and terminates in the northeastern corner of the island in the moderately high eastern uplands and in rocky-cored offshore islands. The Western Cordillera is composed of a basic porphyritic basalt and tuff basement-complex core. The peaks Madiac and Nangtud, located in the Western Cordillera, are the highest on Panay with elevations of 7,150 and 6,720 feet, respectively. A narrow strip of alluvial lowlands is wedged between the western highlands and the west coast. The northeastern hill lands divide surface drainage between the large Iloilo Basin, to the south, and the short streams that flow northward into the Sibuyan Sea. In the northeast, where a maximum elevation of 2,735 feet is reached on Mount Agudo, the hilly country is underlaid by rock materials of volcanic origin. Off the northeastern coast of Panay are numerous small islands, some of which are quite rocky, while others present small expanses of good agricultural lowland. Along the north coast there is a narrow alluvial lowland and several low-lying and flat islands barely separated from the main island by stream-distributary and tidal channels.

The largest area of lowlands on Panay lies in the Iloilo Basin. This central plain occupies a large downwarp filled with several thousands of feet of Miocene and younger sediments, principally sands, clays and conglomerates. The drainage system of the Iloilo Basin is oriented southeastward toward Guimaras and Iloilo straits. Each of the rivers and streams of the basin has built up a relatively large delta at its mouth, thereby extending the basin toward the southeast. The principal rivers of the Iloilo lowland are the Jalaud, Jaro, and Sibalum.

The unusual shape of the island of Masbate, located northeast of Panay, is the result of a juncture of two of the major structural trend lines of the Philippines. One arm of the island is formed by the main northwest–southeast structural arc that supplies the alignment for the Eastern Cordillera of Luzon and Bondoc Peninsula. The other arm is formed by the second structural arc that trends northeast–southwest and reappears in the uplands of northeastern Panay. Two transverse troughs, now occupied by the valleys of the Asid and Malbug rivers, cut across the highlands from Asid Gulf to the northeast coast. The low anticlinal ridge that forms the island of Ticao extends into the eastern edge of southeastern Masbate between the towns of Dimasalang and Cataingan. Basement-complex rocks exposed over much of the island consist primarily of metamorphosed Mesozoic sediments, mainly slates, and igneous materials. The southeastern arm of Masbate is overlaid by elevated limestone deposits. Along the northeastern and northern coasts, the mountains descend directly to the sea, and the coasts facing Asid Gulf are bordered by plains. A rolling hill topography occurs over much of the interior. The highest elevations on the island are found in the north at 2,280 feet; however, most of the island's interior lies between the 1,000- and 1,500-foot contours. Masbate contains an area of 1,262 square miles.

The small islands of Tablas, Sibuyan, and Romblon, together with 155 smaller named and unnamed islands and islets that lie adjacent, form a 510-square-mile physiographic unit termed the Romblon group. This group of islands is completely encircled by deep waters. To the west, east, and south are the Sibuyan and Visayan seas and Tablas Strait; to the north the islands are separated from Bondoc Peninsula by 6,000-foot-deep water. The islands of the Romblon group project from a sinuous submarine ridge having structural connections with the Western Cordillera on Panay.

All three of the larger Romblon islands are composed of basement-complex rocks, mainly schists, marbles, and igneous materials. These rocks are exposed along eastern Tablas, southern Romblon, and over all of Sibuyan. Small areas of surface limestone occur in western Tablas and in northern Romblon. A linear mountain range, with elevations ranging between 1,600 and 2,000 feet, lies close to the eastern coast of Tablas. Low hills and plains accompany the western shoreline. All of Romblon is hilly, reaching maximum elevation of 1,456 feet in the south. The island of Sibuyan is extremely mountainous. Mount Guitinguitan, located near the center of 173-square-mile Sibuyan Island, rises to a height of 6,724 feet, whereas Mount Nailog in the northwestern corner and Mount Conico in the southeast reach to 2,066 and 3,706 feet, respectively. There is little lowland on either Sibuyan or Romblon.

MINDANAO

The southern island of Mindanao is the second largest island of the Philippine Archipelago and presents a land area of 36,537 square miles, excluding the many islands lying immediately offshore. The island is of a very irregular shape with deep embayments in the Davao and Moro gulfs and in Iligan Bay, several large peninsulas, such as Zamboanga, Surigao, and Cotabato, and an extremely long coastline. Owing to its large size and diverse structural elements, there is considerable variety in the topographic landscape of Mindanao. Mindanao has at least five major mountain systems. Some of these systems exhibit complex structural origins; others have been formed by simple processes of vulcanism. Mount Apo, the highest peak of the Philippines with an elevation of 9,690 feet, is found in the southern part of the central highlands. An extensive plateau and mountain region occupies much of north central Mindanao. Two large interior lowlands are found on the island. Several relatively large offshore islands, representing a combined area of 1,500 square miles, stand to the northeast, also on the Mindanao Platform. Surrounding this platform on all sides are deep oceanic basins, including the Sulu Sea, Celebes Sea, Mindanao Sea, and the very deep Philippine Trough.

Except in a few of the more important mining areas, the geologic information concerning Mindanao is, at best, only reconnaissance in nature.[10] Mindanao Island can be divided into six major physiographic regions: Eastern or Pacific Cordillera, which includes its drowned northern extension as the large offshore islands of Dinagat and Siargao; Davao-Agusan Trough; Central Mindanao Highlands; Bukidnon-Lanao Plateau; Cotabato Basin–Tiruray Highlands; and Zamboanga Peninsula.

The eastern coast of Mindanao, or the Pacific Cordillera region, is a high and rugged mountain zone paralleled offshore by the deep waters of the Philippine Trough. This Eastern Cordillera, which extends for over 250 miles from Bilar Point in Surigao southward to Cape San Agustin in Davao Province, continues the structures first encountered on the island of Polillo off eastern Luzon and continued through the island of Leyte into Mindanao. This major structural arc is continued south of Mindanao beneath the waters of Celebes Sea into the Indonesian island of Celebes as the Talaud Ridge. The northern part of the Pacific Cordillera, locally referred to as the Diuata Mountains, contains several peaks that reach above 6,000 feet elevation. At the southern end of the cordillera another high mountain knot reaches a maximum elevation of 9,217 feet on Mount Tagdalit. The cordillera then continues south to form the mountainous peninsula that is the eastern rim of Davao Gulf. Between the two major mountain masses the crest descends to low elevations in its middle part, particularly west of Lianga and Bislig bays, where valley-like passes of less than 1,000 feet elevation permit access westward. Higher portions of the partially submerged Pacific Cordillera reappear off the northeastern coast of Mindanao as the islands of Dinagat, Siargao, Bucas Grande, and the numerous surrounding smaller islands.

The Pacific Cordillera of Mindanao has the structure of a giant tilted block. The core is composed of a complex igneous and metamorphic basement complex, consisting mainly of serpentines, peridotites, and gabbros. The crest line of these eastern highlands lies closest to the western edge. The western slopes descend rather abruptly to the Agusan-Davao lowland, suggesting the presence of a fault orientation along the western margins of the highlands, but they are deeply dissected by small streams having steep gradients. The eastern slopes are more gradual. The limited areas of level land in eastern Mindanao are confined to a narrow, discontinuous strip of lowland along the east coast, and small floodplains and deltas, particularly along the Cateel, Hinatuan, and Tago rivers. The highlands are well-watered by heavy, year-round rains that everywhere, except in the extreme south, exceed 100 inches annually. There is repeated evidence of faulting throughout the cordillera, and earthquakes still occur frequently. Lake Mainit, in the north, and Pujada Bay, in the south, appear to occupy longitudinal fault troughs or grabens. Faulting also probably explains the numerous offsets from the various subranges of the eastern cordillera lands.

West of the Pacific Cordillera lies the longitudinal Davao-Agusan Trough. This large structural lowland is bordered along its eastern edge by the foot slopes of the Pacific Cordillera, and along western edges by the equally high Central Mindanao Highlands. The lowland is drained to the north by the Agusan River, and to the south by several short rivers, including the Tagum. The northern end of the trough disappears beneath the waters of Butuan Bay and the Mindanao Sea, and the continuation of the trough in the south forms the depression for Davao Gulf.

The Davao-Agusan Trough is one of the largest lowland areas on Mindanao. It extends for a distance of more than 100 miles north and south; only a low drainage divide lying close to the Davao-Agusan provincial boundary interrupts its longitudinal continuity. The width of the lowland proper varies from 12 to 37 miles. A relatively broad strip of the lowlands extends south along the western shores of Davao Gulf. In its northern sections, particularly along the lower and middle course of the Agusan River, much of the land of the Davao-Agusan is low-lying, and the center of the valley is occupied by series of large freshwater lakes and swamps during the primary rainy season. The Agusan River is one of the largest and longest rivers of the Philippines. It originates in the extreme southeastern corner of the island within a few miles of the Pacific Ocean, and after a 180-mile northward course, empties into Butuan Bay. The southern end of the lowland in Davao Province is slightly more elevated, and as a consequence, is better drained. The entire valley floor is covered to considerable depths by Tertiary and Quaternary sediments that include large amounts of alluvially deposited volcanic materials. Much of the lowland remains heavily forested, and until very recently, much of it was virtually inaccessible and unexplored.

Lying west of the Davao-Agusan Lowland, and extending more than 250 miles from Diuata Point, along the Mindanao Sea, southward to Tinaca Point and the Sarangani Strait, is a series of mountain ranges collectively referred to as the Central Mindanao Highlands or Central Cordillera. In the north the Central Highlands are composed of a series of complex structural mountains formed primarily from serpentines and basic intrusive rocks. The southern parts of the highlands are largely of volcanic origin and appear not as a continuous range of volcanic mountains, but as clusters of volcanic peaks separated by low saddles. Generally maximum elevations in the north approach the 4,000-foot contour, whereas in the south they reach well above 5,000 feet, with several peaks considerably higher. West of Davao City is Mount Apo, an active volcano that reaches an elevation of 9,690 feet, the highest point in the Philippines. Its height is nearly matched by two subsidiary peaks. South of Mount Apo the extinct volcano Mount Matutum attains an elevation of 7,521 feet.

The Central Highlands are a much dissected upland and still heavily forested. The mountains interpose a rather continuous barrier to east–west travel across Mindanao and there are few low passes leading through them. Many of the larger rivers of Mindanao, including the Rio Grande de Mindanao (Cotabato), Pulangi, Maridagao, and Tagoloan, have their sources in these rugged, well-watered central uplands.

North central Mindanao is occupied by the extensive Bukidnon-Lanao Plateau. This undulating plateau surface is situated at an elevation of approximately 2,000 feet. Several large, extinct volcanic cones and smaller cinder cones stand above the plateau surface. The Bukidnon-Lanao region has been built up by successive basaltic lava flows, interbedded with ash, tuff, and sandstone materials. The young Tertiary volcanoes, Mounts Katanglad (9,499 feet) and Kalatungan (9,397 feet), dominate the skyline, and probably have provided the sources for most of the volcanic materials that cover the plateau. There is no active vulcanism, although two volcanoes in the area have erupted within historical times (Mount Makaturing in 1891 and Mount Ragang in 1916).[11] The plateau surface and the slopes of the volcanoes are dissected by deep, narrow canyons and ravines with steep walls. Off the north coast of Mindanao lies 96-square-mile Camiguin Island, which is structurally related to the volcanic plateau. Mount Hibokhibok in northern Camiguin is an active volcano whose frequent eruptions in modern times have repeatedly driven the resident population to the mainland.

In the southwestern corner of the Bukidnon-Lanao Plateau, located at an elevation of 2,296 feet, is the 134-square-mile Lake Lanao, the second largest Philippine lake. This large lake appears to have been created either by the damming action of lava flows that blocked its natural drainage or by the collapse of a large volcano which formed the basin the lake now occupies. The Agus River drains Lake Lanao northward, reaching the sea after passing over the plateau escarpment in a course of only 18 miles. A narrow coastal plain fringes the northern coast of Mindanao, wedged between the plateau escarpment and the shores of the Mindanao Sea. A low, rugged outlier of the Central Highlands extends westward almost to the shores of Illana Bay, separating the Bukidnon-Lanao Plateau from the valley of the Mindanao River. Most of the plateau surface and the lower slopes of the mountains are arable. The basaltic lavas have weathered into fairly fertile clay loam soils.

The Cotabato Basin is a broad, northwest–southeast trending intermontane structural depression in southern Mindanao. This depression was covered by the sea as recently as the Pleistocene. The Cotabato lowland extends for almost 60 miles eastward from the shores of Illana Bay to the southern boundary of Bukidnon Province and southeastward to Sarangani Bay. The basin has a north–south width that varies from 50 to 70 miles. A low drainage divide south of the large, shallow Lake Buluan separates the northward-flowing tributaries of the Rio Grande de Mindanao from the southeast-flowing rivers of the Koronadal Valley.

The Koronadal and Allah valleys, the southern extensions of the Cotabato lowland, consist of two narrow plains or corridors flanked by moderately high mountain ranges. The well-drained valley floors have been covered by deep deposits of marine and river alluvium to which, in the Koronadal, has been added considerable recent volcanics from nearby Mount Matutum. The land of the Koronadal slopes gently southeastward toward Sarangani Bay, whereas Allah Valley is drained to the north.

The larger part of the Cotabato lowland is oriented toward the Rio Grande de Mindanao. The many tributaries of the Rio Grande, including the Pulangi and Maridagao from the north, the Allah from the south, and the Malabul, Dalapuan, and Alip from the east, come together in the extensive freshwater swamplands of the Libungan and Liguasan marshes. From these junctures, the low-gradient Rio Grande flows across a broad level plain and through comparatively narrow, terraced, inner valleys caused by a recent uplift near the river mouth and into Illana Bay. The Rio Grande appears to be aggrading its valley above its constriction with thick deposits of river alluvium.

The moderately high Tiruray Highlands shuts off the Cotabato Basin from Moro Gulf and the Celebes Sea to the southwest. Many of the peaks in this range appear to be extinct volcanoes, and several rise to elevations of 4,000 feet. Parker Volcano, which reaches an elevation of 5,700 feet, is classed as an active volcano. The Tiruray Highlands descend abruptly to the coast leaving little room for the development of coastal lowlands.

The very long and narrow Zamboanga Peninsula extends the island of Mindanao some 170 miles farther toward the southwest. Zamboanga Peninsula is almost a separate island; only the low, 8-mile-wide isthmus between Pagadian and Panguil bays connects it to the rest of the island of Mindanao, and a rise in sea level of only a few hundred feet would separate the peninsula from the primary area of the island. The northern part of the peninsula is volcanic in origin and dominated by a cluster of recent volcanoes; among them is Mount Malindang (7,956 feet). The long, narrow southwestern arm of the peninsula consists of a monoclinal ridge composed of sedimentary and metamorphic serpentines, schists, quartzites, and gneisses that have been dissected into a low, rugged hill land. Southern Zamboanga and Olutanga Island, bordering along Moro Gulf, are composed largely of recent sedimentary rocks that have been very recently uplifted. The southern coast is extremely irregular with the two peninsulas of Sibuguey and Baganian jutting far south from the northern main structure of the peninsula. There are extensive lowlands bordering much of this low-lying southern coast. The major drainage of Zamboanga is oriented toward Moro Gulf; elsewhere only short, consequent streams drain the interior uplands. Except along Moro Gulf, there are few sizable lowland areas, and relatively few islets or rocks fringe the peninsula.

A myriad of small islands extends from the southern tip of the

Zamboanga Peninsula southwestward toward northeastern Borneo. These islands, called the Sulu Archipelago, rise from two parallel submarine ridges. The northernmost ridge, which extends from Zamboanga Peninsula to the shores north of Darvel Bay on Borneo and fronts along the Sulu Sea, furnishes the platform for numerous low coral reef islands, principally the islands of the Pangutaran group. The southern ridge, upon which rest the islands of Basilan, Jolo, Siasi, and the Tawi-Tawi groups, links Sibuguey Peninsula in southern Zamboanga to the peninsulas south of Darvel Bay. This latter structural arc is largely volcanic, although in many cases the volcanic cores of the individual islands and island groups are surrounded by young reef limestones.

Basilan, although politically administered as part of Zamboanga del Sur Province, is the largest of the Sulu Archipelago islands with an area of 495 square miles. The island of Basilan is composed entirely of young, mostly basaltic, volcanics. Basilan Peak, the highest point on the island with an elevation of 3,316 feet, is an extinct volcanic cone. Deeply weathered laterized volcanic materials cover the surrounding narrow peripheral lowlands. The island of Jolo, the second largest island of the Sulu Archipelago, has an area of 345 square miles and, also, is almost entirely composed of young volcanics. Many picturesque extinct volcanic cones, among them Mounts Tumatangas, Bahu, Kangagan, and Matungkup, rise in isolated form above the 2,000-foot level. The surrounding lowlands are blanketed with thick mantles of volcanic ejecta. Tawi-Tawi (228 square miles), the southernmost large island of the Sulu group, has a hard serpentine basement-complex core; much of its surface is limestone-covered, and its surface is dissected into generally hilly country, with a maximum elevation of about 1,900 feet. Tawi-Tawi Lagoon, formed by the southern coasts of Tawi-Tawi and the coralline islands of Ungus, Secubun, Latuan, Mantaban, Bilatan, and Simunul, is a superb natural harbor. (A large part of the Japanese fleet used the Tawi-Tawi anchorage during World War II.) The remaining Sulu islands are quite small, but follow the same structural form of their submarine platforms, and many support large populations. The southern Sulus form one of the least known sectors of the Philippines.

Summary

In spite of its comparatively small area, only slightly larger than that of the state of Arizona, the Philippine Archipelago displays considerable variety in its physiographic landscapes. Not only are there significant variations from one island to another, but within each of the larger islands there is a broad array of mountains, hills, plateaus, and plains. Although uplands occur over approximately 65 percent of the land area of the Philippines, there are, nevertheless, extensive lowlands, particularly on the larger islands of Luzon, Mindanao, Negros, and Panay. Most of the islands of the Philippines include a mountainous core to their insular topography. Volcanic, sedimentary, and metamorphic rock materials have played their roles in landform development in varying situations, and rock weathering and land dissection are very rapid in the rainy tropical climate.

Physiographic diversity supplies one of the important basic ingredients in the development of significant regionalism within the Philippine Islands.

TWO

~~~~ *Regional Climatology*

Weather and climate, and their associated atmospheric circulations, in equatorial areas have been regarded frequently as "constant" and without significant change. Such a view is expressed not only to point to the lack of seasonal variations in the tropics, but also to minimize differences among the various tropical regions of the world. And all too frequently those concerned with the tropical climatic scene have been prone to apply climatic criteria developed in the higher latitudes and neither designed for nor applicable to the tropical latitudes. In recent years, however, stimulated by the works of Byers, Riehl, Thornthwaite, Mohr, and in the Philippines, by Deppermann, Manalo, Estoque, and others, it is becoming increasingly demonstrable that a considerable degree of climatic contrast does exist among the major tropical realms, and even within the individual tropical areas.

Introduction

The statement is often made that "the climate of the Philippine Islands is fundamentally maritime and tropical and is characterized by continuous heat and uniformly high humidity." [1] Although this statement is basically correct, it neglects a multitude of minor and, for some areas, significant exceptions. The high temperatures characteristic of the tropical lowlands are not encountered in the highland areas. Furthermore, precipitation shows considerable variation from place to place, both in quantity and seasonality. In the Philippines these exceptions are sufficient to produce regional variety in sensible climate, to bring about changes in the natural vegetation, and to influence man's selection of his cultivated crops.

Four special conditions inherent to the Philippines have resulted in significant modification of the climatic elements and have contributed to the mosaic of climatic patterns: (1) The peripheral position off the Asiatic mainland places the Philippines within range of the continental air masses, storms, and atmospheric pressure conditions. (2) The archipelagic and oceanic nature of the Philippines insures a considerable maritime modification of the elements of land climate. (3) The Philippines also lies astride the main tracks of the westward-moving violent tropical cyclonic disturbances (typhoons or hurricanes) of the western Pacific and is materially affected by them. (4) Most of the larger islands have relatively high mountainous areas, which themselves play extremely important roles in climatic modification by producing lower temperature regimes, blocking air masses, and forcing orographic lifting and consequent adiabatic cooling. These four major sets of conditions, together with several minor or local situations, have combined to form an intricate pattern of climatic subtypes.

All of the Philippine Islands lie within the humid tropics, extending latitudinally over 1,000 miles of ocean surface. The more than 400 stations reporting meteorological observations, most of them recording precipitation only, are distributed from Basco in the Batan Islands in 20° 28′ North latitude to Lapac in the Sulu Archipelago at 5° 30′ North latitude. (See appendix table 4 for records of selected stations.)

Temperature

Throughout the Philippines, mean annual temperatures approximate 80° in the lowlands.[2] The effect latitude plays in the variation of annual temperatures is negligible. Basco and Aparri, located in the extreme north of the archipelago, record mean annual temperatures within two degrees of those obtained at Jolo and Zamboanga, which are located in the extreme south. The sizes of the individual land masses and the collective effect of their combined insular area produce greater effects upon annual temperatures than does latitude. Through some slight continental modification, for example, annual temperatures are approximately two degrees higher on the Central Plain of Luzon and in sections of interior Mindanao than they are along the coasts. Also, warmer temperatures are encountered on the islands of the Sibuyan Sea, such as Romblon and Masbate, where a position near the center of the archipelago, surrounded by other islands, has contributed a slight "continental" warming effect.

The only significant relief from the lowland tropical temperatures is to be found in the highlands. In general, average annual temperatures in the Philippine highlands decrease at a rate approximating the normal lapse rate, approximately one degree for each 280-foot rise in elevation. Baguio, the 5,000-foot-high city in the highlands of northern Luzon, has an average annual temperature of 64.2°; this is 16 degrees cooler than at neighboring San Fernando, La Union, on the lowlands. The cooler temperatures associated with the uplands are sufficient to bring about significant change in natural vegetation, that is, from tropical forests to coniferous forests. This important vegetation change takes place between the 4,000- and 5,000-foot contours. The tropical highlands have become important sites for middle-latitude vegetable gardening and for vacation, rest, and recuperation centers because of their cooler temperatures. In addition to Baguio, smaller and less formal resort centers have been established in other highland areas in the Philippines: Tagaytay City (2,000 feet) and Silang (1,060 feet) in Cavite Province, Mantalongon (2,950 feet) on Cebu, and in the Lake Lanao region of Mindanao (2,296 feet). Although resort centers have not been established in all highland areas, there are numerous other localities with annual temperature regimes suitable for such centers. It is only in North Luzon that a sizable population lives above the level of 5,000 feet, but small groups do live permanently in other highland areas of lower temperature regimes.

Except for the decreases in temperature brought about by increasing elevation, the differences in average annual temperatures in the Philippines are so slight that they are virtually without major significance to the natural or cultural landscape. In seasonal weather patterns, however, almost all of Luzon occasionally is affected by the occurrence of one or more short "cold waves" during December or January when there is a strong push of cold air out of the Asia which sweeps as far south as southern Luzon.

Seasonal contrasts in temperature, or annual temperature ranges, also are minimized in tropical latitudes; this condition continues regardless of altitude. Nevertheless, in the Philippines there are areal differences in seasonal temperatures, and in certain places this seasonality in temperatures is of sufficient magnitude to affect both the physical and cultural landscape. Several factors may account for greater temperature ranges in certain locales of the Philippines: latitude, variations in the amount of solar radiation received, the amount of cloud cover, continental effects, and the degree of exposure to various air masses.

The lowest average monthly temperatures, and the largest annual ranges of temperature, occur in the far north. The average January temperature at Basco is 72.4°, which is 11 degrees less than the average temperature of the warmest month of June. Zamboanga, at the opposite end of the archipelago, records an average January temperature of 79.5°, only one degree less than the average temperature of its warmest month of May. Generally, average annual temperature ranges increase with increasing latitude, except on the island of Luzon where increased distance from the coast causes them to reach their maxima, nearly ten degrees, in the interior of the Cagayan Valley.

It is evident that the areal patterns of annual temperature ranges, and their inferred degrees of seasonal contrasts, are of such a magnitude that they are not simply a matter of latitudinal control. The proximity of the Philippine Islands to the Asian mainland places the archipelago within reach of air masses of continental origin, particularly during the low-sun period. These air masses can and do cause lower than normal seasonal temperatures to prevail in parts of northern Luzon and on the offshore islands to the north during December and January.

Conversely, the maritime tropical air masses normally present in many parts of the Philippines during much of the year tend to lessen the amount of solar radiation received because of their high moisture contents and associated heavy cloud covers. Areas in southern Mindanao and along the Pacific littoral are examples of regions experiencing only narrow temperature ranges because of the presence of these moist air masses throughout the year.

The months of April, May, and June usually constitute "summer" in the Philippines. Normally, these three months are quite dry with clear skies throughout most of the islands, and the near-vertical rays of the sun can burn down with their full force. Stations in the Cagayan Valley, on the Central Plain of Luzon, and in areas in the Sibuyan Sea record temperatures for these months averaging over 84° (fig. 5). Usually during this hot season the fields lie bare because of the lack of moisture, and great clouds of dust aggravate the high actual and sensible temperatures.

The advent of the rainy season, which usually begins around the end of June in most Philippine locales, is attended by somewhat lower actual temperatures. The enormous quantities of moisture present in the lower atmosphere, however, contribute to a considerable degree of human discomfort. Any clothing not exposed to frequent aeration is quickly attacked by molds and other fungi.

The greatest temperature contrasts in the Philippines are not found in seasonal differences of temperatures, but rather in diurnal temperature variations. The "winter" of the tropics is experienced at night rather than during a particular season. During the dry season at Manila (April) a daily minimum

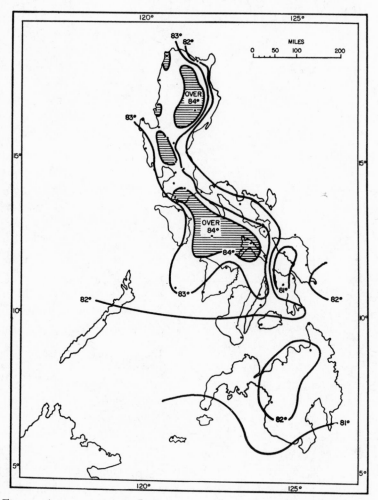

Fig. 5. Average air temperatures for May for 52 selected Philippine weather stations.

of about 75° is reached just before sunrise, followed by a steady increase in temperature until a maximum of 91° is reached between 1:00 P.M. and 3:30 P.M. Following this peak a relatively steady drop in temperature follows until the next morning, with slight departure depending upon current atmospheric conditions such as wind and rain. During the wet season (September) the same regime of diurnal temperatures is followed, except that minima and maxima are not so extreme (76° and 85°–86°), largely because of the moderating effects of the greater cloudiness that accompanies the heavy seasonal precipitation (figs. 6a, 6b).

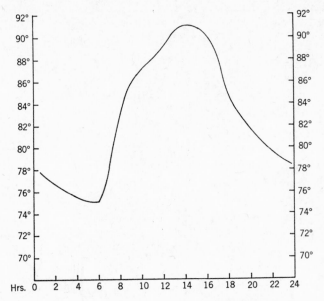

Fig. 6a. Average hourly air temperatures at Manila during the dry season in April.

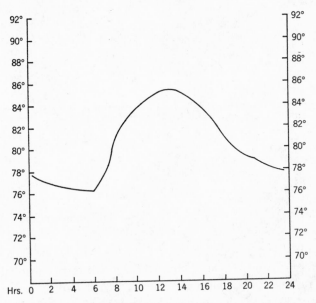

Fig. 6b. Average hourly air temperatures at Manila during the rainy season in September.

Some areal differentiations in diurnal temperatures are caused by latitude, and there is a slight contrast between coastal and interior locations. In general, greater variations in maximum and minimum diurnal sea-level temperatures occur in the higher latitudes in northern Luzon and in certain interior locations. At Aparri, long-term records indicate an average daily minimum temperature in January of 68°, and an absolute minimum of 56.7°. Tuguegarao, lying 40 miles south of Aparri and inland, records its lowest average daily minimum in February at 66°, and the mercury has fallen to a low reading of 54° on two occasions. Daily maxima at Tuguegarao climb to 97.5° during June. In the Visayan area and parts of interior Mindanao mean daily maxima approximate 90°, whereas minima hover close to 72°.

Consideration of Philippine temperatures would be incomplete without mention of the temperature-humidity relationships, or "sensible" temperatures. The air over the Philippines is constantly humid. For Manila, which can be considered representative of much of the Philippines, the average monthly relative humidity varies between a low of 70.7 percent in March and a high of 85.1 percent in September, representing an average absolute moisture content of 7.8 and 10.2 grains of water vapor per cubic foot of air, respectively. The humidity figures of Manila are typical of most west coast stations. The combination of relatively warm temperatures and extremely high relative and absolute humidities makes for uncomfortably high sensible temperatures. Discomfort is especially marked during and immediately prior to the onslaught of the rainy season, April through June, when temperatures attain their maxima while high relative and absolute humidities prevail.

The areal distributions of sensible temperatures follow rather closely the distribution of mean annual precipitation, that is, higher sensible temperatures occur in regions of higher precipitation.

Whereas temperature differences throughout the Philippines are minimal, their variations cannot be ignored completely. The effect of elevation upon temperature is of considerable importance, for marked vegetational changes take place, both in the natural and cultural sectors, from typically tropical plants at lower attitudes to plants more characteristic of the middle latitude at higher altitudes. Certainly the existence of centers such as Baguio and the nearby Trinidad Valley attest to the importance of these elevation-induced cooler temperatures. Although it is difficult to separate the effects of temperature from those of precipitation upon natural vegetation, apparently temperature plays a relatively important role in the distribution of certain commercial forest species, and also influences to some extent the properties of the wood. Generally the woods from the forests of northern Luzon are heavier and frequently harder and stronger than the woods from other parts of the Philippines.[3]

Precipitation

Undoubtedly rainfall is the most important single climatic element in the humid tropics, for it is the most variable in an areal, seasonal, and temporal sense. The quantity and the seasonality of rainfall have had profound effects upon the distributional patterns of the natural vegetation, often determining whether grasslands, jungles, or forests will be present, and affecting to an extent the species composition of each vegetational association. Similarly, tropical soils are greatly affected by differences in the availability of moisture through increases or decreases in run-off, percolation, and leaching. The effects of greater or lesser amounts of rainfall also have strong repercussions in the cultural landscape. Frequently crops are selected on the basis of water availability, for example, rice versus corn, and the crop choice usually determines the cropping systems and associated cultural patterns.

The relative importance of rainfall in the Philippine climatic scene is further substantiated by the large number of precipitation monographs written by earlier students of Philippine climatology such as Coronas, Selga, Algue, Hernandez, and Manalo. Their fundamental climatic work was confined mostly to recognition, based upon precipitation, of the various climatic types found in the Philippines.

The degree of rainfall variation within the Philippines is considerable. Average annual rainfalls for the 459 Philippine rainfall stations vary from a very dry 35 inches at Aggunetan in the Cagayan Valley to an extremely wet 215 inches at Baras on Catanduanes Island. Also, the seasonality of precipitation ranges from stations receiving summer maximums, to those experiencing winter maximums, to those with evenly distributed precipitation. Then there are those stations that experience slight drought conditions, severe drought conditions, or actually have no dry season. (See appendix table 5 for records of selected stations.)

This variety in precipitation has resulted from the interaction of several causes. Philippine precipitation can be the result of orographic lifting; local and frontal convection; or frontal rains associated with the Intertropical Front (ITC), easterly waves, or tropical cyclones. The individual or local occurrence is conditioned largely by exposure, topography, altitude, and prevailing winds and their associated air masses.

Four types of air masses dominate the atmosphere over the Philippine Islands during the course of the year: Indian Ocean, North Pacific, South Pacific, and Northeast Monsoon air masses (figs. 7a, 7b).

Indian Ocean air masses originate over the Indian Ocean in the southern

Fig. 7a. Air mass source regions and prevailing surface winds over the Philippines during July.

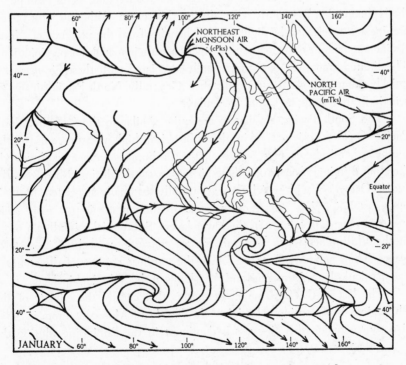

Fig. 7b. Air mass source regions and prevailing surface winds over the Philippines during January.

hemisphere and are drawn northward by the equatorial low pressure trough. As they cross the geographical equator they receive a deflection toward the right upon entering the northern hemisphere (Coriolis force) and arrive in the Philippines from a southwestern direction. These air masses remain dominant over the Philippines from June to September or October, and during this period they are extremely persistent. In their source region the Indian Ocean air masses are warm, very deep and humid throughout, and completely lack subsidence even at the upper levels (mTku). They are convectively unstable air masses and their instability tends to increase over land. The heavy precipitation associated with their presence in the Philippines is usually the result of widespread convection in association with the Intertropical Front. All of the Philippines comes under the dominance of Indian Ocean air, but the effects are especially felt along western exposures.

Toward the end of the period of dominance by Indian Ocean air masses, usually during October, a northeasterly airflow begins to enter the Philippines. Originating within the North Pacific anticyclone, these North Pacific air masses are extremely dry and stable in their source region (mTks). Their trajectories over water to the Philippines impart limited quantities of moisture to the lower layers, whereas they maintain considerable dryness and stability above the 3,000–6,000-foot level. The southward trajectories, however, incite instability, and any convergence triggers violent convection, as for example in the typhoons that frequently occur during this season. Although most of the archipelago receives only slight rainfall benefits from the presence of North Pacific air, many eastern exposures experience their maximum precipitations. The limited amount of moisture usually associated with these air masses is quickly exhausted within a short distance. Generally, North Pacific air masses remain in the Philippines until December.

The South Pacific air masses are quite similar to those of the North Pacific (mTks), originating in the subtropical high pressure area of the southern hemisphere. They approach the Philippines from a southwesterly direction. Limited in moisture, these air masses can be distinguished from the Indian Ocean air, with which they are usually seasonally associated, by their greater stability aloft. The trajectories across the equator impart more moisture and greater instability in the lower layers. Substantial rainfall can occur in the Philippines when these air masses converge or occlude in easterly waves. Their greatest effects are felt in the southern sections of the archipelago, particularly on Mindanao and the islands of the Sulu Archipelago.

The last of the four major air masses that control the climate of the Philippines is of continental origin—the Northeast Monsoon. From its Siberian source region this air mass is dominant in the Philippines during the winter period from December to March. Cold and dry in their source region (cPks), these air masses rapidly absorb heat and moisture over ocean surfaces, causing greater instability. The Northeast Monsoon air masses can approach the Philippines from two directions. Those air masses affecting northern Luzon usually move out from central China, cross the relatively narrow South China Sea, and arrive quite dry and cool in the Philippines. On the other hand, those air masses that strike the central and southern Philippines usually leave the Siberian source region across the Japanese Sea, follow a long trajectory over warm water, and arrive more moist and less cool than their Chinese counterparts. The Japanese Sea air can be associated with limited amounts of precipitation, whereas the central China stream only serves to further intensify the drought.

The occurrence of precipitation in various parts of the Philippine Archipelago, or its nonoccurrence, can be linked rather closely with the presence of particular air masses. These air masses are, in essence, in direct control of this basic element of Philippine climatology. Whether precipitation will actually occur from them, however, is controlled by the various atmospheric conditions that can cause the air masses to rise, cool, and condense.

In the Philippines five kinds of mechanisms operate to produce precipitation: the Intertropical Front, easterly waves, tropical cyclones, local convection cells, and orographic lifting. Most of the Philippine precipitation results from the presence of the Intertropical Front or passage of the tropical cyclones.

The Intertropical Front, commonly referred to as the Intertropical Convergence Zone (ITC), is the zone of convergence of southern and northern hemisphere air. The converging airstreams meet along a variety of frontal slopes and result in heavy convectional rainfall. The passage of the ITC over a particular area is usually accompanied by large amounts of rainfall, particularly where and when the front stagnates. Because of the drawing-in of distant air masses the effects of the ITC can be felt through increased rainfall to considerable distances from the actual location of the front. In January the ITC is situated south of the equator near Java and the Lesser Sundas. In this position south of the Philippines, a northerly or northeasterly flow of air across the Philippines is set in motion, bringing North Pacific and Northeast Monsoon air masses into the area. In July the position of the ITC lies north of the archipelago, actually running through or near Formosa, and southwestern air masses flow across the archipelago (Indian Ocean and South Pacific air masses). In the intervening months the ITC lies between these two extreme positions, and frequently the front actually crosses through the Philippines. Its presence is evidenced by very heavy rainfall, considerable cloudiness, and somewhat lower temperatures. It has been estimated that 65 percent of Manila's rainfall is produced by weather patterns associated with the Intertropical Front.[4]

On occasion, particularly during the winter, the Philippines is affected by weak easterly waves. These shallow troughs apparently are born in the equatorial low-pressure system. They usually occur in association with the presence of North Pacific air masses. Traveling steadily from the east, their trailing ends extend into the Philippines, and they make their presence felt through increased frontal precipitation. A significant, although still quantitatively undetermined, portion of the Philippine precipitation can be attributed to the trailing edges of easterly waves.

Tropical cyclones or typhoons, locally referred to as "baguios," (equivalent to the Caribbean hurricane), are an extremely important feature of the Philippine weather and climate scene. The origin of these typhoons is still debated; various meteorologists theorize a development through continued growth of convection cells over equatorial oceans, whereas others believe frontal shearing and the resultant formation of instability waves along the Intertropical Front to be responsible. Still others ascribe to them origins as complex dynamic instability waves. Be that as it may, these violent tropical storms develop near or slightly east of the Marianas Islands, whip across the western Pacific, and bring very strong winds and extremely heavy rainfalls to the Philippines. Many areas in the Philippines receive as much as one-third of their total annual precipitation from typhoons. A typhoon that stagnated over Baguio on July 14 and 15, 1911, caused 45.99 inches of rain to be deposited in a single 24-hour period from noon on the fourteenth, an amount that still is regarded as the world's 24-hour precipitation record.[5] The direct effects of typhoons are usually confined to those areas that lie within 150 miles of the storm centers; however, air masses are drawn over the Philippines into these whorling vortices from much greater distances. Where these converging air masses meet orographic obstacles, or where local convection cells are present, considerable precipitation can occur. Thus the typhoons can bring about increased precipitation to areas lying at considerable distances from the storm's center.

Not all parts of the archipelago are equally exposed to typhoons, nor are the storms so frequent or so severe in some areas as in others (fig. 8). An average of twenty such storms occur in the western Pacific each year; fifteen usually pass close enough to the Philippines to affect its weather materially, and five or six, on the average, actually touch the Philippines.

Although typhoons can occur during any month, they are quite rare during the period from January to May. They are most frequent in the

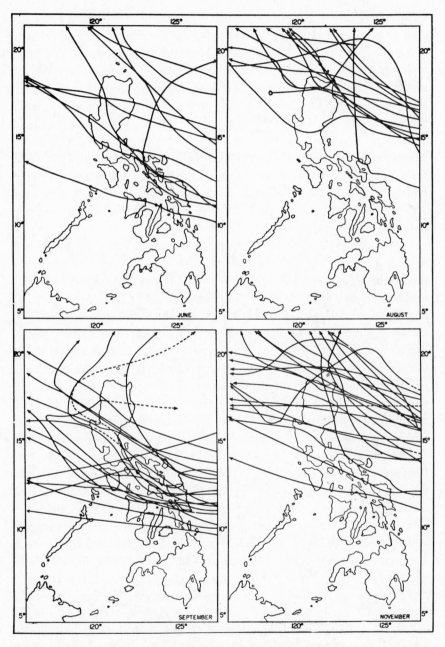

Fig. 8. Tracks of remarkable typhoons affecting the Philippines, 1903–1952, during selected months (after *Philippine Coast Pilot*).

months from July to November. August is the month of maximum frequency with 20 percent of the total. Generally the early-season storms pass through, or north of, the northern Philippines. More than 40 percent of Philippine typhoons are restricted to this area. With the advancing season, however, the storms take more southerly tracks. Typhoons are most frequent in the central Philippines during October, November, and December. The typhoons strike the eastern Visayan islands of Samar and Leyte, and along the coasts of eastern and northern Luzon, with greatest frequency and severity. Southern Mindanao, the southern Visayan Islands, and Palawan are rarely affected by their high winds; however, these latter areas are not completely free from typhoons.[6] The occasional typhoon that goes off the normal track to proceed across the South China Sea may affect the western Visayas and northern Palawan.

The destructive aspects of the baguios should not be minimized; nevertheless, there are frequently overlooked beneficial effects, such as the drought-breaking rains they sometimes bring. The typhoons must be considered an integral part of the Philippine climatic scene.

The mountainous regions of the Philippines contribute significantly to increased precipitation by forcing air masses to ascend. The actual quantitative effects upon increased rainfall by these orographic barriers are not clearly understood. The amount of rainfall produced by forced orographic ascent will vary considerably and will depend upon the height of the barrier, the temperature and water content of the air, and the rate of ascent. Unfortunately, few high-altitude stations in the Philippines have recorded data upon which the quantitative effects of relief on precipitation can be inferred. On the Indonesian island of Java, however, H. J. de Boer, working with data from several hundred highland stations, established a relatively definite relationship between elevation and rainfall.[7] On Java the rainfall increases with increasing elevation until a maximum is reached between 2,500 and 3,500 feet, an amount that remains relatively constant up to the 5,000-foot contour and then sharply decreases. Similar experiments in Hawaii corroborate De Boer's conclusions.[8] These conclusions would appear valid; for, in general, the amount of condensed water during the pseudoadiabatic ascent is greater at higher temperatures than it is at lower temperatures. Furthermore, at the higher elevations there are more gaps in the mountain ridges, so part of the air can pass around the barrier instead of ascending over it. It would be surprising if somewhat similar conditions did not prevail in the Philippines, and it can be assumed that in the Philippines exposed slopes between the 2,000- and 5,000-foot levels receive annual precipitations in excess of 100 inches, and perhaps in excess of 150 inches in most places.

In the Philippines, as elsewhere, the effects of orographic lifting are not confined to the actual mountain slopes. The airstreams begin their ascent several miles in front of the actual slopes, attempting to smooth out their rising trajectories. Thus a belt of greater precipitation extends several miles in front of the mountains. Conversely, the areas lying in the lee of the high mountains rank among the driest regions of the Philippines.

Although the greatest amount of orographic rainfall occurs on the sparsely settled mountain lands, the precipitation so caused is highly significant to man because these highlands are the source regions for most of the major streams and rivers of the Philippines.

PRECIPITATION DISTRIBUTION

In order to understand more fully the significance of precipitation differences in the Philippines four aspects of precipitation must be considered. Each aspect, in turn, brings about its own patterns of areal distribution. The four important precipitation variables are: (1) differences in annual precipitation; (2) differences in the duration, intensity, and adequacy of the rainy season; (3) differences in the length and severity of the drought season, if any; and (4) the consideration of departures from mean precipitation values, or precipitation variability.

Although the average quantities of yearly precipitation represent only one phase of precipitation analysis, in the Philippines their study can be quite rewarding if interpreted within limitations. Generally, an annual precipitation of 60 to 70 inches is considered marginal for the cultivation of lowland rice within the tropics without irrigation, and areas receiving less than 60 inches must irrigate the crop.[9] Conversely, areas receiving annual precipitations in excess of 120 inches, unless these precipitations are strongly seasonal in regime and followed by a dry period, are usually of slight agricultural importance because of the prevalence of poor drainage and the absence of a suitable harvest period. In the Philippines approximately 10 percent of the land receives less than 70 inches annually, whereas 30 percent receives precipitations in excess of 120 inches annually (fig. 9).

The areas that receive excessive precipitation, exceeding 120 inches annually, occur in three types of locations: (1) mountainous west coasts, (2) mountainous east coasts, and (3) in sections of Mindanao Island. The three areas of heaviest precipitation have important differences in seasonal patterns. West coast locations are exposed to the full onslaughts of southwestern air masses, and receive the majority of their annual rainfall, up to as much as 90 percent, during the dominance of this airstream in the summer and early fall months of July through October. Drought conditions prevail during the rest

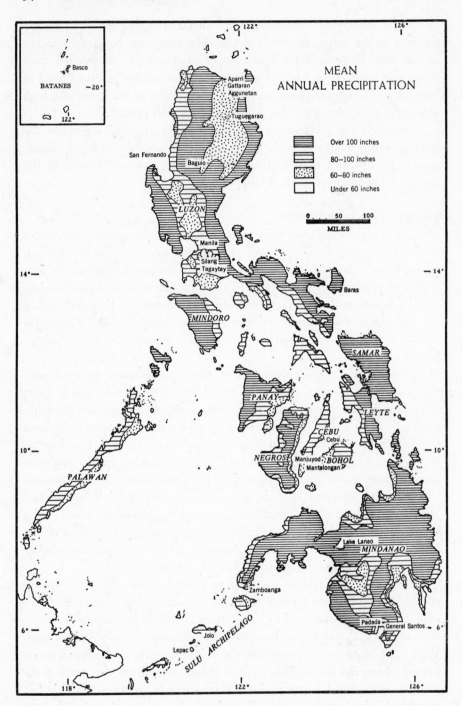

Fig. 9.

of the year, providing an ideal harvest period and thereby encouraging an intensive agricultural occupance. The duration and severity of the drought period at these west coast stations varies from place to place, but usually it is possible to raise at least one crop of rice during the year. Although the eastern littorals experience a definite winter maximum in precipitation because of their exposures to northeastern airstreams, there is no period of real drought. The heavy, year-round rainfall and the presence of typhoons, which are particularly frequent along these coasts, have precluded intensive agricultural occupance. The nearness of the island of Mindanao to the equator, and to the mean position of the Intertropical Convergence Zone, ensures to many parts of that island moderately heavy, year-round rains. The quantity of monthly precipitation, however, is not as great in much of Mindanao as in the other areas of heavy precipitation, and drainage on the southern island is somewhat better organized and more adequate. A much more intensive year-round use of the land is thereby made possible. The upland east coast of Mindanao may be a region of very heavy year-round precipitation, but there is slight use of these uplands so far, and no precipitation data.

The areas of relatively light precipitation, under 70 inches annually, usually are found in somewhat sheltered locations, sheltered from the full effects of the dominant airstreams. The Cagayan Valley and Central Plain of Luzon, much of the central Visayan islands of Cebu, eastern Negros, western Leyte, and northern Mindanao, and various sheltered coastal and intermontane locations in southern and southeastern Mindanao and the Cotabato Valley receive between 50 and 70 inches of rainfall annually. Six Philippine precipitation stations, from a total of 459 stations, record mean annual precipitation under 50 inches, and four of the stations (Aggunetan, Cagayan; Manjuyod, Negros Oriental; General Santos, Cotabato; and Padada, Davao) receive less than 40 inches annually. The lighter rainfall areas, particularly in the Cagayan Valley and in the Visayas and Mindanao, stand out clearly on Philippine crop maps. Normally lowland rice, a crop that demands a great amount of water, is preferred by most Filipinos, but in these dry areas it has been replaced by the less water-demanding maize. (See fig. 30.) Characteristically, the rice-producing lands of the Philippines are found in those areas lying between the 70- and 100-inch isohyets.

Mean annual precipitation figures conceal considerable year-to-year variations, often to a degree not generally associated with the humid tropics. Whereas the average annual precipitation of Cebu City is 61.46 inches over a 36-year period, individual years have shown amounts varying from a low of only 30 inches in 1914 to a high of more than 88 inches in 1910 (figs. 10*a*, 10*b*). Long-term Manila data exhibit even greater precipitation variability

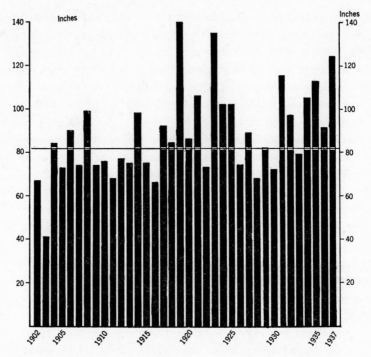

Fig. 10*a*. Total annual precipitation at Manila for the years 1902–1937; the mean is 82.00 inches.

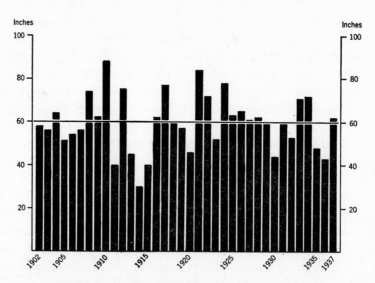

Fig. 10*b*. Total annual precipitation at Cebu City for the years 1902–1937; the mean is 64.01 inches.

than Cebu. Manila's average annual precipitation over an 89-year period is a humid 81.52 inches; during this period extreme values of 154 inches in 1919 and 36 inches in 1885 have occurred. Other stations in the Philippines have similar departures from mean precipitation values. Such a degree of precipitation variability has profound effects upon a Philippine agriculture that, for the most part, does not utilize water-storage and irrigation techniques.

Perhaps the most critical aspect of Philippine precipitation—critical, that is, to the fundamentally agriculturally oriented Filipino population—lies in the duration and severity of the dry season in the various parts of the archipelago. Mohr, working in Indonesia, asserts that a mean monthly rainfall of 4 inches is usually sufficient to create "wet" climatic and edaphic conditions in the tropics.[10] Mohr also agrees with Köppen [11] and DeMartonne [12] that relatively moist tropical conditions prevail, as opposed to "wet" conditions, as long as average monthly rainfall remains above 2.4 inches. On the basis of these criteria, the lengths of the dry periods in the various parts of the Philippines vary from areas experiencing no periods of drought, under either of the above criteria, to those regions experiencing as many as six months with inadequate precipitation. Invariably the longer and more severe dry periods are found along the western sides and in central sections of the archipelago, whereas eastern and southern locations have shorter dry periods or are perennially moist.

The effects of the dry season upon agriculture can be circumvented, however, if adequate precipitation occurs during the remainder of the year. In the Philippines, as elsewhere in southern and eastern Asia, rice is the preferred crop. Some varieties of lowland rice can mature in as few as four months, although those varieties requiring five or six months are more commonly selected because of their higher yields. Thus, if a particular area receives at least four or five months of precipitation adequate for lowland rice, then nonirrigated rice agriculture is not seriously affected by the drought.[13]

In general, the areas within the Philippines that experience the greatest duration and severity of drought are the Ilocos coast and Central Plain of Luzon, where five or six months are virtually rainless. All west coast locations experience a period with at least four months of pronounced dryness. Conversely, the entire eastern coast of the archipelago and most of the island of Mindanao have no drought period. Fortunately, most of the Philippines experiences a sufficient number of months with precipitation adequate for nonirrigated lowland rice culture; however, there are some important exceptions. Among the larger and more important areas lacking adequate precipitation for lowland rice cultivation are sections of the Cagayan Valley of northern Luzon, the central Visayan Islands, and parts of northern, south central, and southeastern Mindanao.

Climates of the Philippines

A method or system by which the various climatic elements of an area are classified into type-groupings should clearly differentiate climatic types based upon categories significant to either the physical or cultural environments, or both. Unfortunately, the more widely employed systems of climatic classification were designed primarily for use in the temperate latitudes and they present definite shortcomings in their applications to the Philippine tropical scene. Figure 11 shows the application of the widely used Köppen system,[14] and figure 12 maps climatic regions according to the Thornthwaite climatic classification system.[15] Whereas the two maps appear to possess considerable similarity, in detail they are quite different, and the two systems differ rather markedly in their conceptual frameworks.

All of the Philippines, with the exception of the areas at elevations exceeding 4,000 to 5,000 feet, fall well within the limits of Köppen's humid tropical climatic category (A). The humid tropical climates receiving adequate rainfall in all seasons (Af) are found in the areas exposed to northeastern air masses, as for example, eastern coastal locations, mountainous locales where normal convective processes are supplemented by orographic lifting, or on Mindanao where the Intertropical Front is active for most of the year. The humid tropical climates with precipitation adequate to support a forest growth, but strongly seasonal in character (Am), are found along western exposures that are fully exposed to southwestern air masses but are sheltered from northeast air movements. In this latter climatic type a pronounced period of drought is experienced from November to May, but sufficient precipitation falls during the rainy season to compensate for, or bridge over, the drought. The third major Köppen climatic type found in the Philippines is that commonly referred to as the tropical savanna climate (Aw). Similar to the Am climate in its precipitation regime, the savanna climate does not have a wet season sufficiently rainy to compensate for the drought period. Tropical grasses are the typical natural vegetation of the savanna climates. Usually the highland areas are encompassed by a climatic type similar to that encountered in the temperate latitudes (Cw or Cf). Although the Köppen system is adequate to differentiate broad climatic zones, its failure to consider two important climatic factors appears to seriously restrict the utility of its application to the Philippines. First, there is no provision for distinguishing the wide ranges of precipitation within the Af and Am climatic types. Thus, such climates as Iba and Olongapo, with over 150 inches of rainfall annually, are grouped together with Cebu and Duma-

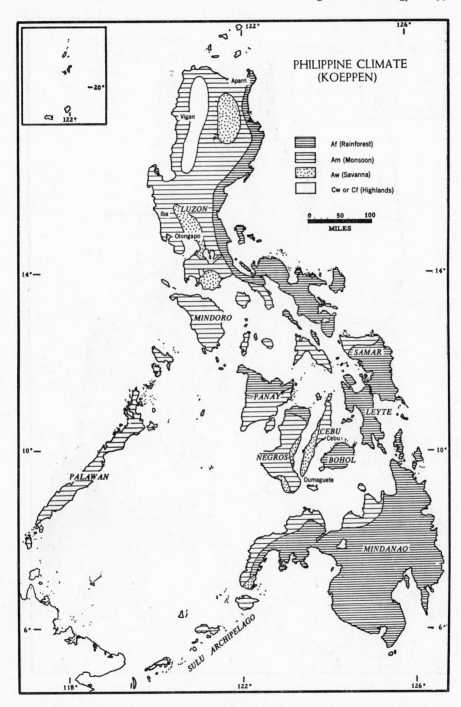

Fig. 11.

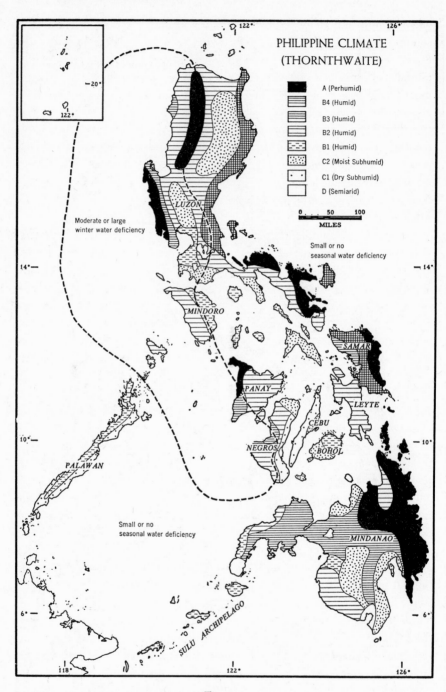

Fig. 12.

guete with 61 and 56 inches, respectively. Second, the Köppen system fails to consider the duration of the drought period, concerning itself only with the *driest one month*. Thus Vigan, with five months of less than one inch of rainfall per month, is climatically equivalent to Aparri, which has only one month with less than two inches. These distinctions represent important climatic differences in the Philippines.

The Thornthwaite classification, because of its more detailed analysis of monthly precipitations and their potential evapotranspiration ratios, presents a more meaningful and definitive climatic zonation of the Philippines. Four major Thornthwaite climatic types, based upon precipitation amounts and their effectiveness, can be distinguished in the Philippines. These in turn are subdivided into eight subtypes.

Type A, perhumid climatic regions generally receiving annual precipitation over 100 inches, occurs along the eastern coast, in northwestern Panay, and in the Zambales Mountains and Cordillera Central of Luzon. Four subgroupings of Thornthwaite's humid climates (B) are based upon diminishing precipitation, and all have wide geographical distribution within the archipelago. Large areas of northern and southeastern Luzon, most of the islands of Panay, western Negros, Leyte, Bohol, and most of Mindanao fall within this climatic grouping. Whereas the perhumid climates are, for the most part, sparsely settled, the humid regions support moderately high agricultural densities. A third climatic type, the subhumid climates (C), is surprisingly well-defined culturally. With few exceptions the subhumid climatic areas, both moist and dry phases, are densely populated. The Cagayan Valley and Central Plain of Luzon, the central Visayas, and northern and southeastern Mindanao are among the more important agricultural and economic sections of the nation. The island of Cebu falls almost entirely within the dry subhumid climates; yet on this island are some of the most densely settled lands of the entire archipelago. All subhumid areas reflect interior positions, and are thus protected from moisture-bearing air masses. Several Philippine stations actually fall into Thornthwaite's semiarid classification (D). These latter stations, all receiving less than 45 inches of rainfall annually, occupy particularly well-sheltered locations.

The Thornthwaite system also distinguishes seasonality of precipitation. Three regimes of precipitation are found in the Philippines. Three areas, the southern tip of Zamboanga Peninsula, southeastern Negros, and Cebu, show small or no seasonal water surpluses. Western exposures throughout the archipelago show a marked winter drought. The remainder of the archipelago is distinguished as having small or no seasonal water deficiencies.

Of the two classifications, the Thornthwaite system appears to present a rather realistic and definitive application to the Philippines. Not only are significant regions clearly differentiated, but the various climatic types show considerable coincidence with land-use patterns.

Summary

Because of its profound effects upon man's natural environment, climate is a factor of utmost importance for any nation fundamentally concerned with primary uses of the land, as is the Philippines. To a very considerable degree climate controls natural vegetation, and together climate and the resulting biotic environment have profound effects upon soil development through weathering, leaching, eluviation, and humus accumulation. Similarly, although lacking an absolute effect, the selection of crops and cropping systems and the resultant crop yields reflect prevailing climatic conditions rather clearly.

Except for limited areas in the highlands, temperature differences in the Philippines are of minor consideration. Any meaningful analysis of Philippine climatology must rest upon a consideration of quantity and effectiveness of precipitation, and must express the adequacy of moisture in terms of particular water needs. As is pointed up, the application of the Thornthwaite system of classification to the Philippines results in a relatively clear portrayal of the very great range of moisture conditions and regimes.

THREE

Soils, the Plant Cover, and Land Biota

Soils and Soil Processes

INTRODUCTION

Soils are the natural media for virtually all plant growth, and as such, they constitute the greatest single resource that any nation possesses. The relative importance of the soil resource is of truly major significance to the economic survival of a nation such as the Philippines, in which approximately 70 percent of the labor force (in the 1960's) is engaged in agricultural activities, and in which fully 40 percent of the gross national income is derived from the agricultural sector. In quantitative terms the maximum total of agriculturally usable land in the Philippines approximates 45 million acres. Some 28 million acres of this total was already in farms in 1957, with the crop-acreage total for that year amounting to about 17 million acres.[1] In the Philippines, agriculture provides the basic staple foods for subsistence, and at the same time, earns the major share of foreign-exchange credits through the export of its products. Thus, the basic economic strength of the nation rests with the proper cultivation and utilization of soil resources. The range of Philippine soils extends from some very rich soils to some quite poor soils. In some instances soil structure, drainage, and inherent soil fertility rather easily determine cropping and cultivation practices, whereas in others the Filipino farmer has not made the most of his soils owing to the neglect of management practices making for maximum productivity. The Filipino farmer usually comes to his modern calling from a historical tradition of simple crop growing, a tradition in which the concept of careful management and maintenance of the soil never became established.

An intelligent program of soil management must be prefaced by a period of basic research and soil inventory. The field of soil science is not well developed in the Philippines, owing in part to budget considerations on the national level, and in part to general public apathy. The first soil survey was undertaken by C. W. Dorsey, an American soil scientist, shortly after the inauguration of the American administration in the province of Batangas; but American leadership neither developed a survey bureau nor stimulated Filipino interest in or concern for soil studies. It was not until the pioneering work of the eminent American tropical soil scientist Dr. Robert W. Pendleton that the classification of Philippine soils was begun.[2] Pendleton, in his position in the College of Agriculture at Los Baños, proceeded to train a whole generation of competent Filipino soil scientists; yet their contributions have been minimized by economic limitations. Systematic soil surveying by a national government agency began in 1934 with the formation of the Soil Survey Committee, and by late 1939 reconnaissance soil surveys had been completed for six of the Philippine provinces.[3] Since 1939 the responsibility for soil surveying has been centralized in the Bureau of Soils of the Department of Agricultural and Natural Resources.

Soil surveys in the Philippines have been in the nature of reconnaissance surveys, with almost no really complete surveys of large areas ever carried out. The unit of survey is the province, and the map scales range from 1:75,000 to 1:250,000. As of 1962, a total of 48 provinces representing 82.6 percent of the area of the Philippines had been covered by preliminary, reconnaissance surveys; however, only 29 of the provincial surveys had been published, owing to limitations of bureau funds. Reconnaissance erosion surveys have been made of a number of provinces. A few detailed studies of small areas have been undertaken, but most of these special reports have received very limited distribution. Numerous articles appear in the current literature on soil research, soil types, soil conservation, fertilizer reactions, and special soil situations.[4] A total of 210 soil series have been identified and described in the Philippines. Soil erosion looms as a constant menace in most areas, and as yet few measures have been adopted to preserve, let alone replenish, Philippine soil fertility.

SOIL GENESIS UNDER HUMID TROPICAL CLIMATES

Soils are complex mixtures, in greatly varying proportions, of fragmented and partly or wholly weathered rocks and minerals, organic materials, water, and air. They are dynamic, that is to say they are constantly undergoing change, but they normally reach a state of near equilibrium with their environment after a long period of exposure to specific and stable sets of conditions. True soils are the product of the action of climate and living organisms upon the parent material, as conditioned by the local relief.[5]

In general, humid tropical soils are less fertile than their mid-latitude counterparts. In addition, humid tropical soils require much skill in their manipulation under conditions of fully cleared fields and are very susceptible to mismanagement. Vigorous and frequent cultivation as practiced in the mid-latitudes is not really required in the tropics, and mismanagement often results from too much cultivation. Humid tropical soils do not need cultivation for "spring warming" in order to hasten the decomposition of organic matter and warm the seed bed. Overcultivation of humid tropical soils produces extra-rapid leaching out of soluble elements and the very rapid disappearance of organic compounds. The development of clean-weeded fields under regular cropping conditions exposes field surfaces to heavy rains, causing a compacting of surface layers. Subsequent rapid drying out under heavy solar insolation tends to hasten the chemical formation of hardened surface layers, thereby making it difficult to cultivate by hand tools or by simple powered-tools such as the one-animal scratch plow. Traditional cropping practices, in both shifting cultivation and in permanent-field agriculture, neither sought nor achieved clean-weeded fields that were exposed to rain, sun, hastened chemical processes, or damaging erosion. The introduction of mid-latitude practices into the Philippines by the Spanish and early Americans produced no compensatory practices either to maintain soil fertility or to guard against erosion. The Filipinos were not predominately permanent-field agriculturists when the Spanish came, and their conversion to cropping the same fields every year was not accompanied by the acquisition of high-level farming skills that could improve the nature and quality of soils.

Humid tropical soils do not represent the "great treasure storehouse of nature" frequently described, and extreme care is needed in their correct use. Furthermore, soil erosion, although a constant menace throughout the world, takes an especially violent form in parts of the humid tropics. To be sure, many different soils and soil types are encountered in the humid tropical lands; yet exceptionally fertile soils are a distinct rarity.

Although it would be naïve to assert that all humid tropical soils fall into the same major soil class because the phenomena of tropical climates make them so, there is, nevertheless, considerable truth to the statement. Mature soils are the product of an interaction of temperature, water movements, air in the soil, time and weathering stages, parent materials, and organic life. All of these elements are variables that assume particular sets of values in different parts of the earth. In the humid tropics, four of these variables assume values compatible with the particular aspect of tropical climate regionally operative. The four are essentially climatic variables: high temperatures in slight ranges, moist warm air, abundant warm water, and organic matter of a tropical variety responsive to conditions of climate.

Analyses of humid tropical soils show that, in general, these soils are quite low in phosphorous and the more assimilable bases. So great is their deficiency in the bases that most of the tropical soils show rather strong acidic reactions.

The leaching processes operate somewhat differently on different kinds of parent rock material, and they operate at different rates; but on all types of rock material they operate in the same direction, the reduction of soluble elements useful to growing plants. Leaching of the basic rocks tends to result in the removal of silica, calcium, magnesium, potassium, and the sodium oxides, plus the various other trace elements, thereby leaving in the soil residues of aluminum trihydrates and limonite. When carried on for a long period of time this process results in a soil so sterile that no amount of mechanical manipulation can make it productive. The leaching of the acidic rocks commonly tends to result in the decomposition of the rock material into kaolins and kaolinitic clays, to which is added a volume of hydrated alumina, formed directly. In both the basic and acidic rocks continuous leaching of the surface layers makes for poor textures, and such soils become of poor tilth, hard to cultivate by hand or by simple mechanical means. Finally, surface bodies of material (no longer true soil) composed of these residual concentrations of hydrated iron and aluminum oxides become quite hard, uncultivable, and form the end product laterite. The essential process of leaching is termed laterization. The new terms *latosol* and *latozation* refer to this same end product and to the process. Though the latter terms have now found fairly wide usage, there are good reasons for the retention of the older terms; we have preferred the older terms and use them here. Heavily laterized soils, and laterite, are useless as cropping surfaces, though laterite is used as a building stone in areas where it occurs.

Not all rock materials lend themselves equally to the formation of tropical laterite soils; nor are lateritic soils necessarily the dominant type of soil in all humid tropical areas. Limestone rocks, for example, seldom develop into lateritic soils; instead they normally reach the intermediate lateritic stage of Terra Rossa soils. Limestones rarely occur in nature as rocks composed of pure calcium carbonate ($CaCO_3$); they usually contain varying quantities of other minerals, principally quartz, feldspar, and hornblende. Sandstone is another rock that does not lend itself to laterization. The prolonged weathering of standstone leads to the formation of deep, almost pure deposits of sand, without developing any layering of materials or a true soil profile. On the other hand, basalt, gabbro, andesite, diorite, serpentine, and other ultramafic igneous rocks, and particularly shales and silts of the sedimentary group, usually develop strong lateritic soils relatively rapidly.

It is in large part because of the prevailing climatic conditions, and what they mean to the soil-forming processes, that humid tropical soils, as a whole, are considered to be quite poor. Furthermore, these soils tend to rapidly become poorer under use. The leaching away of soluble minerals, the rapid decomposition and removal of organic matter, and the mechanical compacting and erosion under torrential rainstorms after the forest cover is cleared away are contributions of the humid tropical climate to soil development.

THE SOILS OF THE PHILIPPINES

Philippine soils are as varied as the parent rock-materials base and the humid tropical climate permit. Parent rock materials were originally of primarily igneous origins, and vulcanism has played, and continues to play, the dominant diastrophic role. It has been generally accepted by geologists that the basic formation of the Philippines was the result of the mounding up of ultrabasic to intermediate igneous materials on the ocean floor. Ultimately in the areas of lower relief or in basins of subsidence, extensive sedimentation of water-worked igneous materials occurred. The subsequent elevation of many of these sediment-filled basins, which took place particularly during the Miocene period, resulted in the present-day occurrence of sedimentary materials at almost every elevation. These elevated occurrences, in turn, continue to supply abundant materials of both volcanic and sedimentary origins for deposition in new areas. Past land subsidences and the prolonged periods of marine transgression have resulted in the widespread deposition of marine sediments consisting mainly of coralline limestone. Metamorphism of Philippine igneous and sedimentary rocks has not been extensive. Figure 13 presents the highly varied and frequently complex distributional patterns of the more important parent rock materials from which the soils of the Philippines have developed. Each parent material develops its own distinctive soil characteristics, depending upon local climate, topography, and stage of development.

The climate of the Philippines is, in general, humid tropical. There are, of course, upland regions on many islands with some tropical highland variation in climate, and there are lowland regions in rain-shadow positions

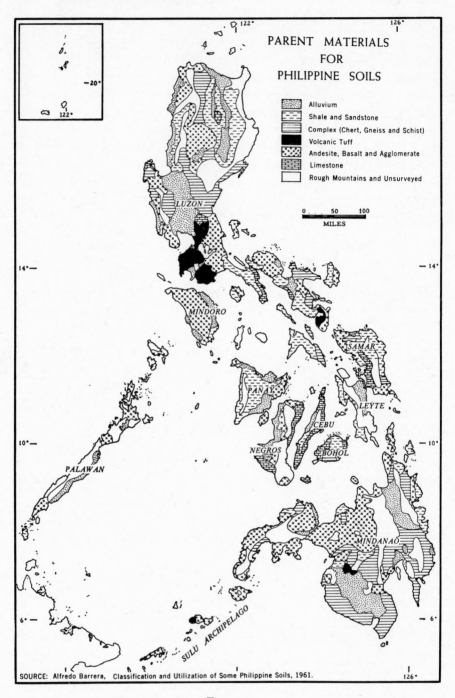

Fig. 13.

which have climatic subtypes of the tropical wet-and-dry variety. There are also lowland and upland subregions of perhumid conditions. All of these subregional variations in the climate produce different subpatterns of soil-forming processes, and it cannot properly be inferred that all of the climatic influences on soil formation operate alike in all parts of the Philippines. However, the existing knowledge of the processes of tropical soil formation is insufficient to distinguish the specific impact of these local variations, and the general knowledge of Philippine soils is insufficient to apply the knowledge of the differential impacts of the local climatic varieties. In the following discussion, therefore, a generalized effect of the humid tropical climatic regime is assumed as normally operative, and the discussion of soils is presented from the viewpoint of the variation in classes of parent materials.

Classes of parent materials and soil types. Soils developed from alluvium constitute the most important agricultural soils in the Philippines, for they support most of the present-day Philippine agricultural activities. Whereas this importance stems in part from inherent characteristics of fertility, the real significance of the alluvial soils lies in the fact that they are found in the principal lowland areas of the archipelago. A wide variety of soil types has developed from the alluvial deposits, although four types of alluvially derived materials constitute the principal parent materials for Philippine soil development: shale, limestone, recent unconsolidated alluvial deposits, and older alluvial deposits, the latter usually occupying the piedmont or terrace lands. In addition, volcanic materials form a significant parent material in the nonalluvial category for several important soil types.

Almost all of the shale found in the Philippines is relatively soft and porous. Some shales are calcareous in composition; others are not. The differential weathering of shale under Philippine climates normally results in landforms exhibiting sloping surfaces, so that patterns of relief range from undulating hills to steep-faced mountains. Whereas the soils developed from these rocks usually exhibit good to excessive surface drainage, their internal drainage is relatively poor, and percolating water is impeded by the high clay content. Nineteen soil series in the Philippines have been identified as shale-derived, and shales underlie approximately 10 percent of the total land area. Since shale is the sedimentary rock most prone to laterization, many of the soils that have developed from these rocks are dark red to reddish brown in color, and have high concentrations of iron and aluminum hydroxides. Where a good supply of humus is present the soil takes on a darker, almost black color in its uppermost horizons. The two types of shale parent materials—calcareous and noncalcareous—occur over extensive areas. The soils derived from calcareous shales, belonging mainly to the Sevilla and Lugo soil series, are relatively productive, whereas those derived from noncalcareous shales, that is, those of the Palompon, Maasin, and Alimondian series, are generally of low fertility. Shale soils frequently are quite deep, with a solum varying from 6 to 24 inches in depth. Usually they are of fine texture, very sticky and plastic when wet, and they harden upon drying. Soils derived from calcareous shales are characteristic of much of the central Visayan area, and are particularly widespread on Cebu, Bohol, western Samar and Leyte, and in eastern Negros. Soils derived from noncalcareous shales occur over extensive areas in northern and southeastern Luzon, over much of the islands of Panay and Leyte, and appear in southern and eastern Mindanao. All of the shale-derived soils are extremely susceptible to mechanical erosion and lend themselves to pronounced gulleying. These soils are unsuited to lowland rice and most other grains, owing in large part to limitations imposed by steep slopes. Generally they are best suited to the cultivation of fruit trees or root crops.

Sandstones occur only in small patches widely distributed throughout the Philippines; they actually underlie less than 5 percent of the land surface of the archipelago. Sandstones are found mainly in the older upland areas in which undulating to rolling local relief has developed. The soils formed from sandstones usually have a compacted layer of clay in the subsoil—a clay that has been removed by leaching from the upper horizons of the soil. The presence of this clay layer obstructs the free movement of water within the soil. The top layers of the soil are composed of almost pure, coarse, granular sands with occasional iron concretions. Philippine soils derived from sandstones are usually brownish gray to gray in color and show a complete absence of organic matter. Soil fertility normally is quite low. The eighteen soil series in the Philippines which have been identified as sandstone-derived have generally been left in their primary or secondary forest growth, or now support permanent pastures. The largest single occurrence of sandstone-derived soils, embracing the Inabanga, Libertad, and Lourdes soil series, is on the island of Bohol, where they comprise 12 percent of the soils. Sandstones underlie smaller areas in the Cagayan Valley and in the Tayabas Isthmus of Luzon, on Masbate, and in northeastern Mindanao.

Beach sands, another source of sandy parent materials, are found along most coastal margins, and result from local accumulation through the action of waves and currents. Beach sands frequently are composed of nearly pure silica, but sometimes they acquire abundant supplies of marine life and then generally become calcareous in nature. No well-defined soil characteristics develop, and such "soils" are azonal in nature, often consisting of a single stratum of water-worked, deposited sand. Soils derived from beach sands are excessively well drained; and since vegetation finds a precarious foothold, they are virtually useless for agriculture. The coconut appears to be the only important economic plant adaptable to cultivation on soils derived from beach sands. Beach sands occupy considerably less than 1 percent of the land area of the Philippines, but since sandy beach coasts are a traditionally preferred settlement site of Filipinos, the area is of far greater importance than its relatively small percentage would indicate. Deposits of nearly pure silica sands can be used in the manufacture of glass, and commercial-grade silica sands (90–95 percent Si) found in northern Mindoro, in parts of Quezon Province, and at Green Island Bay in northeastern Palawan, are used in Manila by the bottling industry.

Limestone offers an extremely important parent material for Philippine soils, both in terms of the relatively large surfaces that it underlies— approximately 13 percent of the land area of the archipelago—and the relatively fertile soils that are developed from it. Most of the limestones encountered in the Philippines are of coralline origin, and seldom appear stratified. Although there are a few areas underlaid by hard limestones, most of the limestone rock is weak and porous. Limestones are distributed widely and at all elevations, and frequently they cover the interior uplands of many islands. The leaching process eventually removes all calcium carbonate from the parent limestone. The resultant mature-to-old soil usually has a very high concentration of alumina and iron.

Two distinctive soil types can develop under similar climatic conditions from limestone parent materials, depending for their differences upon the relative hardness of the parent rocks. Soft porous limestones weather rapidly and deeply under the heavy and warm Philippine rains. The calcium is quickly removed by solution, the other minerals decompose rapidly, and soon a reasonably attractive habitat is offered plants. Within a short time the developing soil is presented with abundant organic matter that is incorporated into the soil. The soils developed from the weaker limestone rocks acquire a deep black color. They are never very deep because of the extreme solubility of their chief rock constituent. Their friable structures and relatively high organic contents make them easily tilled, moderately fertile, and highly prized. These black soils derived from the softer limestone parent materials are called Rendzina soils elsewhere in the world. They cover extensive areas in the Philippines. They are characteristic through much of the Visayan area, and are particularly widespread on the islands of Cebu, Bohol, Negros, and Samar. They also appear frequently in northern Mindanao and in Cotabato Province. Smaller areas of Rendzina soils are scattered from northeastern Luzon into southern Palawan, Balabac, and Bugsuk. The soils developed from soft limestones are not suitable for the cultivation of lowland rice because their porous nature prohibits inundation; however, both corn and coconuts do rather well. Great caution must be exercised in the proper use and care of the upland Rendzina soils, for they are highly susceptible to erosion, a fact to which the stark, gullied interior lands of Cebu attest.

Weathering of the harder, lighter-colored limestone rocks proceeds much more slowly than in the softer limestones. There is seldom an opportunity for more than 4 or 5 inches of soil to accumulate in one place because of the long time required for its development. Hence, vegetation on these thin soils is usually sparse, and very little organic matter is available for incorporation into the soil. Instead of the dark color of the Rendzina soils, a deep-red or reddish-brown color develops. The soils developed from the harder limestone materials approach more nearly the tropical laterite soils, and they are called Terra Rossa soils. The Terra Rossa has a high content of residual clays. The soils are plastic and sticky when wet, becoming friable and tillable only after drying. Still, the soils are relatively fertile, favoring the cultivation of corn, coconuts, bananas, and citrus fruits; but they, too, are distinctly unsuited for lowland rice.

Terra Rossa and Rendzina soils are known by the soil series names Bolinao and Faraon in the Philippines. Both series are widely distributed, each following much the same distributional patterns as the other. Everywhere that limestone rocks appear, either as an outcrop or parent material for soil formation, the availability of soil moisture poses a serious problem to effective agricultural use. The porous structure of limestone promotes rapid percolation of rainwater. Often just a few consecutive rainless days result in rather severe edaphic drought conditions.

Unconsolidated alluvium constitutes the parent materials for the most important and intensively cultivated soils in the Philippines. Alluvium occupies approximately 15 percent of the land surface of the archipelago. The sites for most alluvial deposition have been along the coasts of the various islands, and in the major stream valleys and lowland basins. The combination of relatively deep, fertile alluvial soils and the extensive areas of nearly level topography upon which alluvium usually occurs constitute the principal base for the predominantly agricultural economy of the Philippines.

Two types of alluvium contribute parent materials for soil development: recent alluvial deposits and older fan or terrace alluvial materials. In general, the coarse gravelly and sandy nature of much of the recent alluvium precludes anything but a rather poor parent material for soil development. Most of the soils developed from recent alluvial deposits are of low fertility and difficult to work. At the same time, the location of these deposits in narrow bands along river courses places them within an area of possible inundation by floodwaters. The floods, however, need not be considered only a curse, for although certain field crops may be destroyed in the process, the newly deposited sediments brought by the floodwaters often serve to rejuvenate soils and restore lost soil fertility. Sands, gravels, silts, and clays are the more common recent alluvial materials. Usually the resulting soils are too immature to show well-developed soil profiles. Soil drainage is good to excessive, and water percolation is very rapid. Crops requiring good drainage, such as sugarcane, coconuts, fruit trees, and vegetables, are particularly well suited to these soils. The recent alluvial soils that are excessively sandy or gravelly can be used for little else but the very tolerant coconut palm. Three soils derived from recent alluvium with exceptionally high fertilities are the San Manuel, Quingua, and Umingan series. These latter soils have deep, loose, friable loams. Light brown to brownish in color these three soil series have a slightly acidic reaction and have been developed from noncalcareous alluvial materials. All three soils are relatively widespread in occurrence, highly prized as agricultural soils, and intensively cultivated in lowland rice and corn. Supplementary irrigation is essential for cultivation of the Umingan series, but not for the other two. In addition to rice and corn, peanuts, sweet potatoes, beans, and tobacco do extremely well on soils belonging to these series. Approximately thirty other soil series are derived from recent alluvium. Often sandy and gravelly and generally too porous for crops demanding large amounts of water, most of the other alluvial soils are rated as of relatively low fertility.

Older alluvium, which usually is encountered in flat-lying deposits well back from present stream channels, often appears as older river-terrace lands. Frequently the soils that develop from these older materials are of relatively high fertility; they are usually of very fine texture and, on the whole, composed of clay and sandy loams. Plastic, sticky, and compacted when wet, the soils developed on older alluvium have poor or impeded internal drainage. Lowland rice is the favored crop. Where slightly better natural drainage conditions are present, or where artificial drains have been installed, sugarcane, corn, or coconuts are extensively cultivated. Several dozen soil series have been identified in the Philippines as having been developed from older alluvium, and each province has one or more series indigenous to it. Each of the Santa Rita, Silay, Isabela, Mandawe, Calumpang, and Palo series of soils, although in most cases restricted to a single island or province, cover extensive areas of the Philippines, and each occupies a position of some significance in agricultural production. Soils of the Santa Rita series have a widespread distribution on Panay, underlying most of the better rice-producing areas in the southern part of the Iloilo Basin. Heavy, compacted, and poorly drained, the Santa Rita soils are considered quite fertile and produce rice yields sufficiently high to rank the province of Iloilo second only to the central Luzon provinces. The Palo soil series occupies large areas of Leyte Valley. These are considered to be the best soils for agriculture on the island. Poorly drained and relatively rich in organic matter, the Palo soils are devoted almost exclusively to lowland rice. The deep, sandy loams and clay loams of the Mandawe series also are considered excellent agricultural soils. Developed from water-laid igneous sediments, the Mandawe soils constitute virtually the only major tillable land on Cebu. Rice, corn, and sugarcane are intensively cultivated on these youthful secondary soils. The Calumpang series comprises the most important rice soils of Rizal and Laguna provinces. Developed from water-laid volcanic tuffs, the Calumpang soils produce high yields, and with irrigation, can produce two crops of rice within a single year. On the other hand, the Isabela and Silay series, which are the most important soils of western Negros, are relatively infertile and moderately acidic. Where they are provided with artificial drainage and heavily fertilized, sugarcane may be grown as the principal crop, although resultant yields are relatively low.

Volcanic materials have been an important parent material to Philippine soils. Generally, two basic kinds of volcanic rock can be identified as contributing most to Philippine soil development: (1) volcanic ejecta, which includes mainly tuffs and sands, and (2) harder igneous materials, which include mainly andesites and basalts. As volcanic activity, both past and present, is extremely widespread in the Philippines, a very considerable portion of the soils are developed either directly or indirectly from the products of vulcanism—a portion that represents nearly one-quarter of the total soil cover. Soils derived from volcanic materials may develop from volcanic materials after they have been redeposited elsewhere by water.

Areas of recent volcanic ejecta are confined mainly to the provinces of Laguna, Batangas, Cavite, and Rizal in southwestern Luzon, and more particularly, to the vicinity of Taal Volcano. Similar smaller areas surround Mount Bulusan in Sorsogon and appear in Bukidnon, Lanao del Sur, and the northern parts of Cotabato Province on Mindanao. Generally the ejected materials weather rapidly and to very great depths. Residual soils formed from volcanic ejecta usually have top horizons 12–20 inches in depth, with a loose, coarse, granular structure. Ranging in color from brown through dark brown to nearly black, these soils vary from slightly below to slightly above average fertility. Sugarcane, upland rice, coconuts, and various vegetables and tree fruits do well where the volcanic materials have weathered in place. In areas where these volcanic parent materials have been deposited by water the soils tend to have a much higher clay content. In these areas the internal drainage of the soil is impeded, the ponding of water is facilitated, and lowland rice becomes the most important crop.

Basalt, andesite, gabbro, and other hard igneous materials usually develop soils that show strong lateritic tendencies in maturity or old age. The basalts, in particular, frequently form true lateritic soils. In all instances the igneous rocks are deeply weathered and form reddish to reddish-brown soils with fairly friable structures. Internal drainage is good, water permeability moderate, concentrations of calcium and phosphorous are very low, and the soils are quite acidic. A strong leaching action is facilitated by the rolling to steeply sloping topography that characterizes many of the areas of hard igneous rocks. In the province of Bataan these igneous-derived soils constitute more than 80 percent of the total soil cover, whereas in the provinces of Laguna, Iloilo, Negros Occidental, and Zambales they make up more than 25 percent of the total soil cover. Although the soils are as yet unsurveyed and unclassified, there are extensive areas of igneous-derived soils in eastern, central, and southeastern Luzon, in Mindoro, and in central and western Mindanao.

The Antipolo, Guimbalaon, and Luisiana soil series are the most important and widespread of the nearly sixty recognized Philippine soil series developed from the hard igneous rocks. These three soil series have average soil depths of more than 10 feet unless subsequent erosion, to which they are especially prone, has stripped off some of the top soil layer. Weathering has penetrated so deeply that most of the soils lack the good development of a true profile. The soils are sticky when wet but become quite friable when dry, with a coarse granular structure. As soils for cropping they are heavy in texture but of good tilth. Coconuts, sugarcane, upland rice, and various tree fruits are cultivated extensively with yields at or near the national averages. The soils of the Antipolo series may be considered the most typical of mature zonal tropical soils, and closely resemble the old red earths and near-laterites found elsewhere in southeast Asia. Their reddish tinge is caused by the presence of unhydrated ferric oxides; a deeper red color usually indicates the presence of better drainage conditions. A yellow or yellowish coloration is imparted by hydrated ferric oxides. The Antipolo soil is usually enriched with considerable residual alumina. The friable nature of these soils, and their great porosity, is due to the peculiar structure of the substance making up such soils. In the process of development from hard igneous parent materials, the oxides cohere, forming granules or pellets of various sizes. A few of the larger aggregates are sometimes cemented, giving rise to concretions in the soil. Because of the high permeability of Antipolo and similar soils they are not, as a rule, subjected to erosion so long as the native vegetation is undisturbed; however, once cleared of plant cover they are quickly attacked. The Guimbalaon and Luisiana series differ from the Antipolo only in their lesser degree of laterization.

Metamorphic rocks are not widely distributed in the Philippines. A few small areas underlaid by cherts, jasper, and slate can be found in northern Palawan, on the islands of the Calamianes group, and in parts of southeastern Mindanao along the southern shores of Davao Gulf. The soils that develop from these very hard parent materials are quite shallow; usually a layer of only a few inches of loose soil lies immediately upon bedrock. Run-off is excessive and soil erosion severe. The primary metamorphic rock soils are gray to grayish brown in color, of low fertility, and are especially deficient in phosphorous and potassium. The Malalag and Coron are the only two recognized soil series derived from metamorphic materials. Their agricultural utility is extremely limited and most of these soils are, or should be, in grasses and forests.

Although they are not soils in the normal sense, brief comment should be added concerning the bottom surfaces under the bogs, marshes, and swamps that total about 1.7 million acres in the Philippines (not included in the 45 million acres of usable land). Scattered around the coasts of many of the islands are littoral marshes, shallow bayhead marshes, estuarine river-mouth swamps, and shallow sectors between islands pitched just below present sea level. In a few regions, notably the valleys of the Cotabato River and the Agusan River of Mindanao, there are interior freshwater marshes of variable size dependent upon the volume of seasonal flooding of the two river basins. Some of the coastal localities carry mangrove associations as plant cover, others carry mixed forest-reed-grass associations, and the deepest of the interior freshwater marsh areas carry a plant cover of mixed reeds, grass, and floating plants into which the water hyacinth has become a significant invader. Some of these areas are going through a "normal" geological process of sedimentation at the present time, accumulating annual increments of mineral sediment and organic matter. Others are zones of such heavy accumulation of plant material that they are forming peat bogs. Within the humid tropics, as elsewhere, when anaerobic conditions prevail the annual increment of organic material is only partially decomposed, without final mineralization, so that this increment remains in place and accumulates more and more deeply. Such areas in the Philippines have received little study or detailed mapping. A good many of the littoral and shallow bayhead marshes, however, are being turned into diked and controlled pond units for the raising of various fish. In some areas there has been agricultural penetration of the bog, swamp, and marsh areas for the growing of wet-field rice or, more primitively, for the simple growing of swamp rice. In the Cotabato and Agusan valleys, there is both permanent occupation of the lightly flooded sectors of freshwater marsh, and seasonal occupation of the more heavily flooded sectors. There has been little reclaiming of such wet landscapes, by large-scale diking and draining, for normal agricultural use. Although such areas represent only a small total, significant use could be made of some of the areas through organized projects of diking and drainage.

As a last note on soils we add a brief comment concerning the highly terraced sector of Mountain Province in north Luzon. In the present generation there are only about 75,000 acres of highly terraced farmland in Mountain Province, and many cultivators of such lands also crop nonterraced lands of various sorts. There have been only very minor additions to such areas in recent decades. In general, the soils of Mountain Province highlands must be termed skeletal soils, though small patches of soil materials in all different stages of soil formation can be found on specific sites. In the development of highly terraced fields a rather formal traditional process is followed. The retaining wall is started and the bottom is filled with assorted rubble from nearby sources. Construction of the retaining wall is continued as behind-the-wall fill is accumulated. Toward the desired top of the field, building of a "profiled" soil structure, is begun with the subsoil filling of clays and clayey materials, which are normally compacted as much as possible. Subsoil material grades into topsoil in the final filling. Topsoil is carefully collected from near and far, from valley bottoms, shelves, niches, and catchment pockets, to be carefully spread over the subsoil fill. Such a process results in the construction of a wet-field surface, a level field surface that will retain water and has a topsoil as productive as can be gathered from the weathered mantle of the locality. Such soils "age" and mature in time, if well cared for, and even develop "profiles" somewhat normal to wet-rice fields. Normal denudation, or abnormal erosive removal, must be compensated by periodic filling with additional topsoil, this process serving to rejuvenate or replenish soil productivity. Some terraces, built on sites without water supplies adequate to the growing of wet-field rice, are utilized for production of sweet potatoes or other crops, but the process is essentially the same. Such soils, of course, cannot be discussed under the normal heading of soil types, for each field constitutes a unique and different artificial soil.

SUMMARY

In view of the generally infertile soil base of many tropical areas, Philippine soils certainly rank among the more fertile and more varied. The extensive occurrence of coralline limestone and volcanic materials provides parent materials that are better sources for fertile soil development than are found in most other areas of the tropics. When compared to many areas outside the tropics, the Philippines do not have a highly fertile soil base, but it is not a really poor soil base. The manner in which the Filipino farmer has used this base, however, presents a much more unattractive picture.

Climate, slope, soil type, and vegetation cover are the major controls on extent and severity of soil erosion. With the clearing of virgin lands, whether for permanent agriculture or by shifting cultivation, the forces of erosion are unleashed. Unbridled, the erosive agent of running water has attacked nearly three-fourths of the farmland in the Philippines. In short, approximately 22 million of the 29 million acres of farmland in the Philippines now suffers from slight to severe soil depletion (fig. 14 and appendix table 8). Thirteen provinces, equally divided between Luzon and the Visayan area, have seen over one-half of their total soil cover mistreated. Unconcerned in the past because of the large reserves of arable land still awaiting the plow, the Filipino farmers have paid scant heed to the mounting grim evidence in decreasing crop yields, increasing flooding, and the silting up of rivers and harbors. Today the problem of field erosion in the Philippines is so serious as to menace the very ability of the nation to feed itself adequately, a problem that the future will compound manyfold.

The island of Cebu provides an even grimmer specter of things to come if proper remedial measures of soil conservation are not undertaken immediately. On this island fully 90 percent of the total soil cover now suffers from various degrees of erosion, and nearly 60 percent of the land is classified as severely eroded (fig. 15). On more than one-third of the island's land *all of the topsoil has been removed.* The serious soil erosion problem on Cebu has arisen from a combination of causes, most of them symptomatic of conditions also prevailing in other parts of the archipelago. On Cebu a large proportion of the land under cultivation lies on very steep slopes; many slopes range in steepness up to 45 degrees. The increasingly crowded population of the island has forced the continued occupance of many of the steeply sloping lands in spite of the many obvious hazards. In order to bring these lands under cultivation almost the whole of the natural forest cover has been removed. To further compound the soil erosion problem, corn grown as a row crop is continuously planted on the steeply sloping fields. During the preparation of fields, the Cebuano farmer usually plows up and down the slope, thus creating natural furrows between the rows of corn which are, in essence, miniature gullies or rivulets. The downpours so typical of the tropical climates simply enlarge upon the drainage system thus provided. The parts of

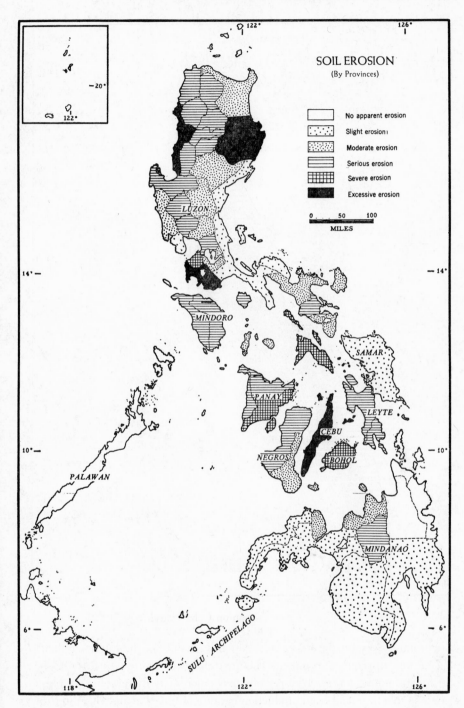

Fig. 14.

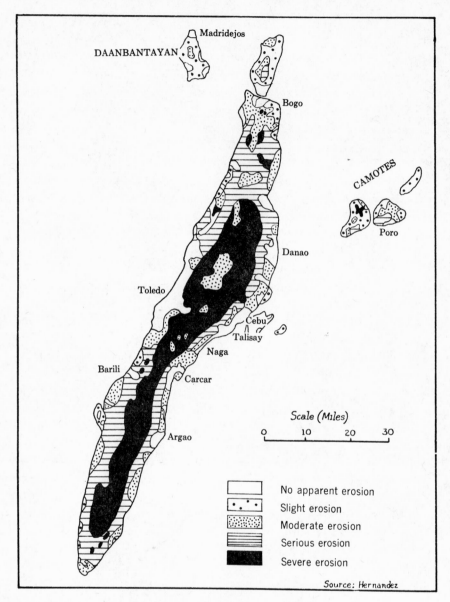

Fig. 15. Soil erosion on Cebu Island.

Cebu most severely affected by soil erosion lie mainly in the interior uplands or on the surrounding piedmonts. The net effects of severe erosion on Cebu include removal of the fertile topsoil from much of the land, elimination of considerable farmland from production because of forced abandonment of the severely eroded fields, and the frequent destruction of fields and crops on the lowlands below. Removal of the more water-retentive topsoil and the natural vegetation cover has led to an increased susceptibility to edaphic drought in the badly eroded areas of Cebu, and it is very apparent that many plants now suffer from even a short dry period.

In varying degrees, Cebu's erosion problems are duplicated in many other parts of the Philippines. Equally severe erosion problems are present in the provinces of Batangas, Ilocos Sur, and La Union, and they are only slightly less evident in the provinces of Abra, Batanes, Bohol, Cavite, Iloilo, and Masbate. Only the relatively undeveloped provinces of Agusan, Surigao, and Palawan appear to have escaped the ravages of accelerated erosion. In general, lowland areas in the Philippines are not as exposed to soil erosion as the sloping lands, although deposition of erosion debris such as gravels and other stream-wash materials from adjacent uplands will frequently ruin lowland fields. Furthermore, one of the more serious forms of erosion in the lowland is that of stream-bank cutting in which streams cut away their banks during periods of heavy rainfall. Considerable good farmland has been destroyed in this way.

Erosion is minimized in the hill and mountain country where the original forest cover has been left intact. The removal of this vegetation, however, will initiate a particularly violent form of erosion because of the presence of steep slopes. The area of greatest erosion in the Philippines has been the intermediate piedmont zone. These gently sloping lands, with slopes ranging between 3 percent and 8 percent and occasionally reaching up to 15 percent, have been occupied mainly by marginal or ephemeral farmers. Particularly in the densely populated areas where fertile lowlands are both limited in area and already intensively utilized, the population has faced the problem of expansion into the adjacent piedmont and foothill lands. Unfamiliar with contour plowing and planting, or unwilling to put these methods into practice, the farmers have usually planted these sloping lands to row crops. In areas where the soil is extremely shallow or contains a hardpan layer, thereby impeding percolation of rainwater, a very rapid run-off often ensues. To cultivate these latter soils properly, deep plowing must be done so that the impervious layer is broken and free movement of soil water restored, an operation that is difficult to accomplish with only the power of a single carabao. Contour plowing, field terracing, cover cropping, proper rotation of crops, and green or compost manuring are possible remedies. The long-range national solution will have to include retiring from cultivation all badly eroded land and replanting it to woodlands or orchards, and careful preservation of the natural vegetation of all potentially dangerous areas.

All Philippine soils are naturally deficient in the very important plant nutrients of nitrogen, phosphorous, and potassium, and the advanced stage of soil erosion in many parts of the farming area has not lessened these deficiencies. Artificial fertilization of virtually all agricultural soils is a necessity except in a few of the newly opened pioneer areas. Prior to World War II, only the sugar farmers availed themselves of commercial fertilizers, largely because of the commercial orientation of this industry and the prospects of an immediate cash return through higher yields after application. Immediately after the war the Fertilizer Administration of the national government was formed, and commercial fertilizers were imported for distribution at an average annual rate of 40,000 tons, in addition to other private-industry imports. This agency also launched an extensive education program among the farmers which has been reasonably successful in creating an awareness of the benefits to be gained from a fertilization program. Lacking any production facilities within the Philippines, most of the fertilizers had to be imported. Only agricultural lime and very small quantities of guano and phosphate rock were produced within the country. Since there would be an ever-increasing demand for commercial fertilizers by Philippine agriculture, and since the purchase of these fertilizers would constitute a constant drain upon the nation's foreign credits, the establishment of a Philippine fertilizer industry was strongly encouraged. The National Power Corporation, in conjunction with the development of the hydroelectric potential of the Agus River at Maria Cristina Falls on Mindanao, was the first to establish production facilities. A 50,000-ton ammonium sulphate fertilizer plant was opened early in 1952. Local copper pyrites and iron pyrites are utilized for the production of these fertilizers. Two private corporations have entered into fertilizer production elsewhere recently. Sulphuric acid, recovered from the large-scale copper-mining operations in western Cebu, is used to process imported phosphate rock into superphosphate fertilizers at Sangi, Cebu, and a smaller superphosphate plant has recently been established near Manila. Several additional fertilizer plants are in the planning stages.

Fertilizer imports remain a major item of financing, however, in spite of the encouraging developments of a Philippine fertilizer industry. The imports of potassium nitrates, ammonium phosphates, potassium sulphates, ammonium sulphates, and mixed fertilizers grew rapidly during the 1950's and continued at a record 140,000 tons as late as 1960. The quantities of fertilizers needed to restore Philippine soil fertility reach astronomical levels. Soil chemists with the Bureau of Soils place the Philippines' total current need of phosphate fertilizer alone at 3,700,000 metric tons.[6]

Neglect of the nation's soil resource by the Filipino farmers has for too long been the general rule. With the remaining virgin farmland rapidly disappearing from the contemporary scene, and with an exploding population facing a very real problem of feeding itself in the not-too-distant future, soil mismanagement is completely intolerable. True knowledge of the soils, their potentials, and limitations, will go far to institute a more effective utilization of this valuable resource. Only careful use and proper care will ensure future generations a sound base to the agricultural economy of the nation.

Finally, it may be pointed out that the above discussion of the plight of Philippine soils pertains to the same country often pictured in one of the most distinctive of the world's photographs, that of the famous rice terraces at Banaue, Mountain Province, north Luzon. Accompanying comment on the photograph frequently infers that Filipinos are among the most accomplished and skillful farmers in the world. The facts are, of course, that the northern Luzon terracing system represents an ancient technique that was part of a distinctive culture complex and was evolved not to prevent soil erosion but to facilitate water control for the production of wet-field rice in mountainous landscapes. True terracing has been used but slightly by the Malay ethnic elements of the Philippine population and is but lightly distributed over the Philippines in faint reproductions of the north Luzon terracing. The Filipinos use only a few of the traditional techniques and skills making for soil preservation, soil improvement, and improved soil productivity known and applied elsewhere in the Orient. The Spanish turned the coastal, strand-dwelling Filipinos, who practiced shifting cultivation in the littoral fringe, into interior, land-dwelling sedentary agriculturists practicing permanent-field cropping systems; but they did not teach them the soil-handling techniques that necessarily must accompany permanent-field agriculture if it is to be productive. Late in the Spanish period, commercial crop-growing systems came into use, and American influence extended many elements of these systems. Although experiment stations, improved cultivation techniques, soil conservation practices, and methods of soil improvement have been imported by the Philippines, and occasionally practiced by a few, the general population has not been motivated to carry out an agricultural revolution of the kind necessary either to increase economic production or to maintain and improve the soil resource base on which such a large share of the Philippine economic system rests.

Forest Types and the Vegetation Cover

All evidence suggests that before man's arrival upon the Philippine scene almost the entire archipelago was clothed by dense and complex tropical rain forests, except possibly for a few rain-shadow positions in which the cover was less heavy and resembled monsoon forests. Since his advent, however, well before the dawn of the Christian era, man has seen to it that a good share of

this primeval forest growth was destroyed and either replaced by his cultivated fields or simply allowed to regenerate in useless jungles, secondary
forests, or the tall tropical grasses locally called *cogon*. Some of this destruction was wrought by the early adoption of the system of shifting agriculture
with fire-clearing techniques, or *caingin* agriculture as it is called in the
Philippines. Much later the wasteful exploitation of the forests for logs
and lumber was to bare extensive forests lands. Not only did the caingin
farmers and timber cutters wreak havoc on the forest itself, but incalculable
damage was done to the rest of the natural environment, as for example the
upsetting of soil-moisture conditions, destruction of domestic supplies of
water, and aiding the depletion of soils. Popenoe found in his research among
the shifting agriculturists of Guatemala that fire-clearing actually brought
about a very significant decrease in the amounts of nitrogen, carbon, calcium,
and magnesium in tropical soils, the very elements in which the soils were
already deficient.[7] Wherever a caingin form of agriculture is practiced too
heavily and too continuously, resulting in the degrading of the original
tropical forest cover, tall tropical grasses and mixed jungle growths succeed.
In modern times the small farmer often follows in the wake of the timber
cutter, preventing the regeneration of the forest cover. So much of the
original mature forest growth in the Philippines has been removed that at
present the Philippines falls far short of the world's average per capita forest
acreage of 4 acres, with scarcely 1½ acres of forest per Filipino. Philippine
forestry experts have estimated that 31 of the 55 Philippine provinces no
longer have the required minimum forest cover, and in each of these provinces less than 10 percent of the original forest cover remains.[8]

In the Philippines at present slightly more than one-third of the total land
surface is classed as cultivated land, and the aggregate area is increasing rapidly
(table 1). Forests cover nearly one-half of the area, and nearly two-thirds of

Table 1   PHILIPPINE VEGETATION COVER, 1951 AND 1957

Ground cover	Acreage in 1951	Percent	Acreage in 1957	Percent
Commercial forest	28,206,000	36.38	23,043,000	31.37
Noncommercial forest	11,020,000	15.00	9,490,000	12.92
Grass and open land	12,536,000	17.06	13,363,000	18.42
Cultivated land	20,213,000	27.50	25,523,000	34.88
Swamp	1,514,000	2.06	1,769,000	2.41

SOURCE: National Economic Council, *Raw Materials Resources Bulletin*, and Bureau of
Forestry.

these forests can be classed as commercial forests (fig. 16). Grasslands, the Philippine cogonales, now occupy more than one-sixth of the Philippine lands, with swamps, and marshes covering the remainder.

The importance of the natural vegetation cover to the Philippines is obvious. The forest trees constitute an important timber resource, both as a source of domestic lumber supplies and as a major item of export. At present nearly 500,000 employees and their families are dependent upon the logging and sawmilling industry, and countless thousands of additional Filipinos are engaged in the gathering of many important minor forest products. Second, the preservation and proper management of the Philippine vegetation cover is of utmost importance to ensure adequate supplies of domestic water and to aid in the prevention of accelerated soil erosion and soil fertility depletion. On the other hand, many of the grasslands, which now stand largely unused, could be developed as bases for an extensive, and much needed, cattle-grazing economy. Even the swamps and marshlands have their uses as sources of thatching and roofing materials.

The continued neglect, abuse, overuse, and exploitation of its natural vegetation base can only mean accumulating grief to the Philippines. Fortunately, most of the lands of the Philippines not under some specific use remain part of the public domain and are still subject to governmental regulation.

The natural vegetation of the Philippines is highly diversified, as is the case with most tropical areas. It is convenient to subdivide Philippine natural vegetation into nine major vegetation associations. The first type encountered upon approaching the island coasts is a narrow strip of beach vegetation, which includes those plants that possess varying degrees of tolerance to saline or brackish water conditions. The second vegetation type, usually encountered farther inland, is the tall dipterocarp forest, the highly complex and very important commercial forests characteristic of the Philippine lowlands, which include the so-called Philippine mahoganies. Actually the term "mahogany" is a misnomer, for the true mahogany genus *Swietenia* is not native to the Philippines.[9] Intermixed with these dipterocarp forests on the lowlands and lower slopes of the hill and mountain land is the dry forest, with or without the molave tree (*Vitex parviflora*). The dry forests occupy the areas of climatic or edaphic drought and contain some of the most valuable and durable Philippine woods. Midway up the mountain slopes above the dipterocarp forest is the dense, medium-height mid-mountain forest with a wealth of undergrowth, including numerous ferns, lianas or climbing vines, and epiphytes. The ever-moist moss or mist forests are found in the higher mountain areas where clouds hang and the air is constantly saturated.

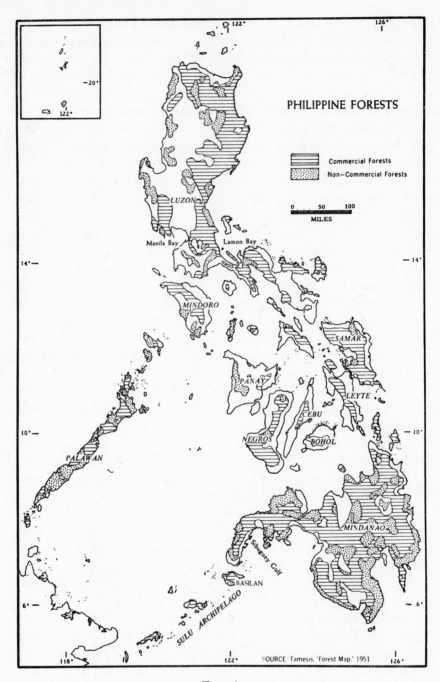

Fig. 16.

Second-growth broadleaf forests have replaced the original forests in cleared or burned-over original forest areas. Dense and jungle-like, this second growth has little economic value in the earlier stages of regrowth and represents a gradual succession back toward the mature dipterocarp forests. In certain plateau areas and mountain country in central and northern Luzon and on Mindoro, located at elevations between 3,000 and 5,000 feet, are the open pine forests. Extensive cogonal or grassland areas occur in forest clearings that have been burned repeatedly, and frequently cover hills and lower mountain slopes that have been denuded of their original forest growth. Finally, there are in the Philippines several areas of extensive freshwater swamp- and marshlands, containing growths of swamp grasses, tall reeds, and various palms. (See table 2 and appendix table 7.)

PHILIPPINE FORESTS

The Philippine forests are the source of so many kinds of woods with so wide a range of color, grain, texture, ease of working, hardness, weight, and strength properties that there is a wood suitable for any use. They range in color from white lanete to jet ebony and kamagong, and from bright yellow bangkal to bloodred narra and tindalo, including most intermediate shades. The lightest and softest dapdap, only slightly heavier than South America balsawood; the varying weights and hardnesses of mayapis, white lauan, almon, red lauan, apitong, narra, guijo, ipil, yakal, kamagong, dangula, and malabayabas; and the heaviest and strongest mancono—all may be found in the Philippine forests. (See table 2 and appendix table 7.)

Table 2   AREA AND STAND OF TYPES OF FOREST IN THE PHILIPPINES, 1951

Forest type	Percent of land area	Area (in sq. mi.)	Volume (in thousands of bd. ft.)
Dipterocarp	30.15	34,614	405,070,769
Dry forest			
Molave	1.01	1,159	13,747,335
No Molave	0.98	1,125	13,242,246
Mid-mountain	6.15	7,055	
Moss forest	1.98	2,273	
Pine forest	1.91	2,192	11,040,300
Second-growth	11.20	12,851	
Mangrove		814	4,425,161

SOURCE: Bureau of Forestry, 1951.

The beach vegetation. The narrow band of vegetation which fronts along the coasts of many of the Philippine Islands is composed of four natural vegetation association subtypes that exhibit various tolerances to brackish water conditions, the presence of sea salt sprays, high winds, and the sandy soils common to most beach areas. The foreshore area is frequently occupied by a tree growth called the mangrove forest. Behind this forest and on the beach itself is a very narrow strip of low creepers, grasses, and a few weeds which occupies the sandy beach and dune area directly back from the waterline. Immediately behind this pioneer vegetation, but still on the beach, is a beach woodland, representing the initial invasion of dryland tree growth. Last, located in river distributaries and estuaries and along tidal streams are the brackish water swamplands, composed mainly of dense growths of the nipa palm (*Nipa fruticans*).

The mangrove forest is found in front of the actual shoreline in sedimentation areas where sediments finer than sand are being deposited, and where the coastal ocean currents are favorable for the plants to grow. These locales are usually near the mouths of the larger rivers, particularly where these rivers empty into protected bays, as narrow strips along tidal streams, and they reach their greatest development on the deltas of the larger rivers. Mangrove forests also are found on shallow coral reefs, where the sea waters are relatively quiet, and on wave-cut terraces off rocky headlands. Mangrove growth will occasionally establish itself along an open coast where some protection from wave action exists.

The mangrove forests occupy approximately 1 percent of the Philippine land area. They are particularly numerous and extensive on the lowlands at the head of Sibuguey Gulf in southwestern Mindanao, on the island of Basilan, along the shores of the islands of Mindoro and Palawan, near the mouth of the Cagayan River of northern Luzon, and along the coasts of the provinces of Camarines Norte, Quezon, and Pangasinan.

Varying from a few feet to several miles in width, these stands of mangrove forest are usually quite dense. Normally the trees are all of medium sizes and even ages. Their dull green leathery leaves are evergreen. Where the mangrove stands are dense, the trees are tall, straight, and clean-boled. Where the stands are more open, the individual trees have low branches, with crooked, gnarled trunks. The mangrove forest, and its associated vegetation types, is quick to establish itself in areas where there is diurnal tidal flooding, for they have the ability to live in these saline environments. On sandbanks, coral reefs, and on river-mouth bars, wherever silt deposits are exposed for only a few days per year, the mangrove can be found flourishing. The seeds are usually waterborne and are germinated on the matured tree before dissemination, although sometimes they are shaped like darts that, falling from the trees, pierce the mud flats and quickly germinate. There are more than thirty species of mangrove growth in the Philippines. The principal differences between species lie in their relative tolerance to inundation and saline conditions. The rhizophora mangrove (*Rhizophora candelaria* and *R. mucronata*) is usually the first to seed. These plants stand on huge piles of roots, called prop roots, which sometimes reach heights of 10 feet or more. Their root networks are widespreading. Fully matured rhizophora mangrove trees will attain diameters of 2 feet and heights up to 80 feet. The bruguiera mangrove (*Bruguiera conjugata, parviflora,* and *sexangula*) occupies those coastal mud flats that are barely inundated by the tides. The bruguiera mangrove has many air-breathing roots, a widespreading lateral root system in which the individual roots bend up in loops called "knees" above the ground. These protruding roots sometimes extend over a 15- to 20-foot radius from the tree. Mature bruguiera trees will range up to 2 feet in diameter and from 40 to 75 feet in height. *Rhizophora* and *Bruguiera* comprise the dominant Philippine mangrove species. The tengel mangrove (*Ceriops tagle* and *C. roxburghiana*) is less frequently encountered and usually occurs in more protected bays as a subdominant species.

Pagatpat (*Sonneratia caseolaria*) and api-api (*Avicennia officinalis*) are occasionally found scattered through the mangrove forest; and in the areas where the forest is poorly developed, they may become dominant. The api-api tree is particularly adaptable to pioneer situations and can establish itself on banks and reefs that are exposed for only a few days per year.

The understory or undergrowth in the mangrove forests is very meager. It usually consists of a scattering of low shrubs and a few herbaceous plants and ferns.

The mangrove forest plays a relatively important role in the encouragement and acceleration of coastal sedimentation. Near the mouths of the larger rivers, particularly at the head of Sibuguey Gulf and in Lamon Bay in southern Quezon Province, there are instances where the presence of mangrove growth has resulted in an annual sediment deposit of 7½ inches. Thus, the mangrove forest is instrumental in building up and out many Philippine coastal areas. Usually the coastal waters shelve gently on the seaward sides of the mangrove, so that even the small interisland boats must keep hundreds of yards from the mangrove barrier at low tide.

The trees of the mangrove forest have great economic utility, and along those coastal areas that lie adjacent to large settlements the forests have been almost totally destroyed. The mangrove is the principal source of firewood in the Philippines, and an excellent charcoal can be prepared from it. Burned, it makes a hot and lasting fire. Mangrove bark, or "cutch," is a source of tannic acid and is used widely as tanning material.

Behind the foreshore mangrove barrier and occupying the sandy beaches immediately above high-tide levels where the sands and sand dunes have become stable is a narrow band of low vegetation, composed principally of low creepers, porcupine grasses, and a few weeds. This dry habitat, which is constantly exposed to salt spray, is only a few yards wide. Short herbs, propagating by means of low runners (*Impmaea pescapae*), and legume herbs (*Canavalia obtusifolia*) are the dominant species. Their presence helps to further stabilize beach conditions, and their adaptability to pioneer sites keeps these plants constantly encroaching upon new beach sands.

Behind this first vegetation on the older beach areas that are still relatively dry-soil habitats is a tangle of low, stunted trees dominated principally by the barringtonia and pandanus or screw pine. The taller coconut palms and casuarinas also are found here. Usually no more than 200 feet wide along the coasts, this beach woodland occasionally will be found occurring in relatively pure stands on the sandy floodplains of the larger rivers. The casuarina (*Equisetifolia*) is the dominant species. This tall, graceful tree has needle leaves and from a distance rather closely resembles the conifers of the middle latitudes. It can establish itself very quickly and often forms pure stands. The casuarina forests supply canoe- and boat-building materials. The leaf fall from the casuarina is so heavy that undergrowth is restricted and is usually confined to a few semiherbaceous vines (*Wedelia biflora*) and thorny bushes called algaroba beans (*Prosopis juliflora*). Coconut palms, either cultivated or self-sown, often are found in this beach zone.

In areas near the mouths of streams and along tidal rivers where brackish, rather than saline, water conditions prevail, is a narrow band of brackish-water swamplands. The nipa palm is the characteristic vegetation. Propagating from subterranean stems or rhizomes that send up short branches, this stout plant represents an erect cluster of up to 20-foot-tall, pinnated leaves. Areas along the northern shores of Manila Bay and along the coasts of Capiz, Surigao, and Quezon provinces are large nipa-palm swamplands. In areas close to dense settlements, the nipa palm, unless under cultivation, is usually absent because of indiscriminate harvesting. Its sap is an important source of alcohol and vinegar, and its long fronds are a prized thatching and roofing material throughout the Philippines.

Since the beach vegetation occupies the coastal areas that man also occupies in large numbers, this vegetation association has suffered most from his depredations. In many areas he has actually had to replant and cultivate the nipa-palm swamps so as to provide himself with a source of thatching materials.

Dipterocarp forests. The Philippine forests represent a very considerable source of national wealth. Although official forestry estimates are perhaps overenthusiastic (see timber volumes in table 2), these forests can be estimated to contain commercial timber conservatively valued at about $20 billion.

The forests, generally, are composed of a great variety of species, although in some ecologic situations particular associations will be dominated by almost pure stands of one or a very few species. There are more than 3,000 arborescent species in the Philippine forests that attain a diameter of 12 inches or more; however, 30 percent of the total land surface of the archipelago, and 57 percent of the total forest area, is covered by members of the lauan, or Dipterocarpacae family. These dipterocarp forests represent nearly 70 percent of the volume of the standing merchantable timber. All major species of the dipterocarp forests are large trees, ranging in height from 125 to 200 feet or more when mature, with diameters of 3 to 6 feet or more. Approximately 51 species, belonging to eight genera, compose the family Dipterocarpaceae. The more common dipterocarp species include: apitong (*Dipterocarpus grandiflorus*), tangile (*Shorea polysperma*), red lauan (*S. negrensis*), white lauan (*Pentacme contorta*), almon (*S. almon*), bagtikan (*S. plicata*), mayapis (*S. squamata*), palosapis (*Anisoptera thurifera*), guijo (*S. guijo*), manggachapui (*Hopea acuminata*), yakal (*Shorea* spp.), narra (*Pterocarpus indicus*), and ipil (*Intsia bijuga*). The present old-age and overmature stands of dipterocarp represent ages of 125 to 300 years.

All members of the Dipterocarpaceae family are tall tropical hardwoods and occur in relatively dense stands. They have a full canopy of broad leaves that are usually evergreen. The dipterocarp trees are found as the dominant tree species on all types of topography, but they prefer the well-watered plains of the Philippines, and similar sites throughout much of southeast Asia. These forests also can be found well-developed on the gentler slopes of mountain masses and on low plateaus with slopes up to 20 degrees; however, the dipterocarps seldom occur in pure, mature stands above 3,000 feet in elevation, and generally they reach their fullest size below the 1,000-foot contour. Dipterocarp trees usually prefer well-drained areas, preferably on deep sandy loams of volcanic origin, and are intolerant of brackish or standing water and sandy beaches or muddy flats.

The term "dipterocarp" means "winged seed," the means by which the mature trees propagate themselves. The seeding process is repeated every few years, but not carried to any great distance from the seed tree. The principal characteristic of the dipterocarp forests is the tiered or storied arrangement of tree heights. Usually the lowland dipterocarp forest is composed of a three-storied arrangement of the species. The uppermost, or first story, is composed entirely of dipterocarps. These tall trees, ranging up to 210 feet in height, and with diameters of from 3 to 6 feet or more, have very straight, clean trunks with only slight taper. Branches and leaves occur only near the tops of the trees, and the canopy of foliage that is formed then is quite closed. The intermediate, or second story, is also composed of lauan trees with average heights up to 125–150 feet. The foliage canopy of this second story occurs immediately below that of the first tier. The lowest, or third tier, is composed of smaller tree growth, 30 to 40 feet in height and up to 6 inches in diameter. Most of the larger dipterocarp trees have a pronounced buttressing of their lower trunks, occasionally extending up to 10 feet above the ground. Lacking tap roots, these tree buttresses afford greater stability to the tree and appear to be larger when branches are more widespreading.

Undergrowth on the floor of the dipterocarp forest is restricted by the lack of sunlight on the forest floor. The quantity of undergrowth will vary within individual forests depending upon the openness of the forest. It is generally composed of several climbing palms (rattans), climbing bamboos and other lianas, several scattered erect palms and bamboos, and numerous epiphytes, including various tree ferns, orchids, and strangling figs.

Although the general term "dipterocarp forest" refers to the climax monsoonal forests of the Philippines, the composition of these forests shows considerable variation, depending upon local site factors. In gross terms, many of the larger islands show regional variation in climate, as discussed earlier. On both the larger and the smaller islands, however, there are many microclimatic variations in precipitation and groundwater conditions within short vertical and horizontal distances which create divergence in ecologic-edaphic environments. These microenvironmental variations become significant to the composition of particular types and subtypes within the broad grouping of dipterocarp forests. The dipterocarp forest subtype most characteristic of the Philippine lowlands is the true lauan forest. In areas where soil drainage is somewhat impaired, such as along long stream courses and on river floodplains, the hagachac-lauan forest association is found. The yakal-lauan forest is found in coastal areas where a short dry season can be expected. The apitong-lauan forest subtype is found in lowland areas within the true lauan association where drier climatic or edaphic conditions prevail. At elevations between 1,300 and 3,000 feet, where a mixing of dipterocarp species and tree species found higher on the mountain slopes occurs, is the homeland of the tangile-oak-lauan forest subtype.

The true lauan forest is the most successful commercial forest found in the Philippines. It occupies the lowland areas near the bases of the mountains and also occurs on the lower slopes of the mountains up to elevations of approximately 1,000 feet. The true lauan forest is extremely widespread throughout the Philippines and is found in scattered distributions on favorable ecologic sites on all of the larger islands. However, it does not tolerate even a short dry season, so that in some ecologic situations having dry periods the true lauan forest changes toward one of the other subtypes. Nearly all of the species in the mature lauan forest are members of the dipterocarp family. White lauan, red lauan, kalunti (*Shorea kalunti*), almon, bagtikan, malaa-nonang (*S. polita*), manggasinoro (*S. philippinensis*), tiaong (*S. toysmanniana*), mayapis, and tangile are the more common trees. The interlacing of the leaf canopies is quite complete and almost all sunlight is excluded from the forest floor. The mature stands of true lauan forest are relatively free from jungle growth. Climbing rattans are numerous, and a few erect palms are found scattered through the forest. The timber volume of the true lauan forest is high, averaging 15,000–25,000 board feet per acre. The once-magnificent lauan forests of northern Negros contained mature stands with as much as 75,000–85,000 board feet of timber per acre in certain favorable locales.

The hagachac-lauan forest occurs in the areas of abundant rainfall on sites near sea level where a very shallow water table is present. Thus, it is most frequently encountered as a narrow strip of forest growth along river courses within the true lauan forests, or it can occur in relatively pure stands on river bottomlands and on raised delta surfaces where there is a deep alluvial soil present. The hagachac-lauan forest subtype is composed of a large number of different species and codominants, a greater variety than in most dipterocarp forests because of the unstable nature of the habitat, one in which the depth of the water table may show extreme seasonal fluctuations and on which river floods are an ever-present hazard. The tree age-structure is very mixed within the hagachac-lauan forest. The leaf canopy tends to remain more open than in the true lauan forest and more sunlight can penetrate to the forest floor. Thus, jungle growth is quite abundant and there are numerous rattans and various lianas. The timber volume of the hagachac-lauan forest is considerably less than in the true lauan forest.

The third subtype of dipterocarp forest, the yakal-lauan forest, is confined to those areas that experience a short dry season. The dominant yakal tree has the ability to live close to the coastlines, and will frequently be found occupying the hill lands and rocky headlands that jut out into the sea. The yakal prefers soils derived from basal volcanic materials. These forests occur as narrow bands of forest growth along most shorelines immediately behind the beach woodlands and are particularly extensive in southern and eastern Luzon, Leyte, and Mindanao. Several of the tree species, because of the presence of drought, are relatively deciduous, although they are never completely bare. Forest growth is relatively open and timber volume thereby reduced to a rather low figure. The lack of volume, however, is partially compensated by the relatively high value of the hard and durable wood of the yakal.

The apitong-lauan forest subtype, or mountain lauan type, occupies the mountain slopes between the well-developed stands of lauans below and the mid-mountain forests above. The tropical oak (*Quercus* spp.) in these forests does not resemble its temperate-latitude relative, and except for the presence of acorns on the ground, it is scarcely recognizable. Generally the tangile-oak association is found in areas where the rainfall is evenly distributed through the year. The forest composition is quite mixed and undergrowth prolific. Rattans, palms, bamboos, and epiphytes are numerous. The trees are somewhat lower in stature, and timber volume is much lower than in the true lauan forests.

The chief commercial value of some of the subtypes of the dipterocarp forests lies not in the durability of their woods, but in the relatively dense pure stands of merchantable timber consisting of trees of similar physical form belonging to relatively few species. The softer members of the dipterocarp family, or Philippine mahoganies, are subdivided commercially into red lauans and white lauans. The red lauans, including tangile, tiaong, and true red lauan, constitute the darker-red mahoganies; whereas the white lauans, including almon, bagtikan, manggasinoro, kalunti, and true white lauan, belong to the lighter-colored group of woods. Red and white lauans are moderately heavy and durable, but are not suitable for any structures exposed to the weather. Apitong, on the other hand, is the most abundant of the heavier and stronger structural timbers of the dipterocarp family, and it can last exposed to the weather for a long time. The wood of the guijo is strong, relatively easy to work, and has good wearing qualities. The hardest and strongest member of the lauan family is yakal. This wood is highly resistant to decay, which makes it particularly suitable for structures exposed to the weather. Yakal is recommended whenever great strength and durability are required.

The present major commercial stands of dipterocarp forests are found in

Mindanao, Negros, Samar, Mindoro, and in eastern and northern Luzon. In these areas the virgin timber stands will contain between 20,000 and 35,000 board feet of timber or more per acre. Nearly 95 percent of the commercial timber volume of the Philippines is contained in the dipterocarp forests, although not all tree species included in these forests belong to the dipterocarp family. No representatives of the dipterocarp family of trees are found in the forests of Palawan.

The so-called dry forest, or molave formation, of the Philippines usually occupies the areas immediately behind the beach woodland or mangrove forest where climatic conditions are too dry for the dipterocarps. Molave also can be found on the steeply sloping hill and mountain lands up to elevations of approximately 2,000 feet, although the forest will attain its best development between sea level and the 500-foot contour. Its occurrence usually is associated with the presence of excessively drained, limestone-derived soils. In essence, the dry forest is found wherever dry climatic or edaphic conditions prevail in distinctive ecologic situations. A climatic condition in which there is a drought period lasting several months prohibits the development of the dipterocarp forest, and only this hardier dry forest can exist. Even so, during the height of the drought the trees of the dry forest will stand bare, for most of the leaves will have fallen.

The dry-forest association contains relatively few large trees, and these are widely scattered. The ground between trees is covered with a growth of low trees, brush, and jungle. The large trees are light-loving, and the forest is quite open. Life is difficult, however, in these dry tropical lowlands, and tree growth is very slow. Short, gnarled, and short-fluted trunks and widespreading branches and crowns are characteristic of tree growth. Tree heights of 30–100 feet, with diameters of 4 feet, are maximum.

Most of the trees in the dry forests are members of the Leguminosae family, although a few scattered representatives of Sapotaceae, Anacardiaceae, Sterculiaceae, Meliaceae, and Verbenaceae may be present. The molave tree is the dominant tree from which the whole forest association commonly takes its name. The molave is a member of the teak family and is found widely distributed through the Philippines, although the stands seldom are heavy and do not provide large volumes of merchantable timber. The wood from the molave tree is highly prized for its great strength and hardness, and the extremely limited supply of the wood often means that even branches and roots are gathered and used. Other large tree species occurring within certain of the dry forests include the narra, the Philippine national tree; tindalo (*Pahudia rhomboidea*); dao (*Dracontemelum dao*); ipil; akle (*Albizzia acle*); and numerous other strong durable and heavy woods. Although many of these less numerous species are widely distributed, the large commercial supplies of narra, akle, and banuyo come from northern Luzon; dao, supa, dungon, and kalantas from Mindoro; and ipil, dao, and kalantas from Palawan.

The woods of the dry-forest trees are noted for their natural beauty and great durability. These are highly sought-after cabinet and furniture woods. Unfortunately, timber volume is very low, averaging no more than 5,000 board feet per acre. And the combination of their very desirable properties and accessible coastal locations has resulted in almost complete destruction of the molave forest from many characteristic areas.

During the past two millenniums of man's occupance of the Philippines, he has succeeded in tearing great gaps in the dipterocarp forests by his practice of shifting agriculture, by the spread of the permanently cultivated landscape, and more recently, by the destructive logging techniques he has pursued in many areas. His period of occupance has resulted in the cutting or burning off of all the larger forest trees over nearly one-half of the lands of the Philippine Archipelago. The falling of the larger timber trees frequently has resulted in the breaking or the killing of much of the younger and smaller tree growth. The clearings thus created have markedly increased the amount of insolation received on the forest floor, which in turn, has resulted in the killing of many of the shade-loving dipterocarp seedlings. Thus an almost completely new plant environment has been created, one in which there are much drier edaphic conditions. Under the circumstances, the dipterocarp forest is not able to regenerate itself immediately. Seeds fail to germinate or young seedlings are burned out by increased sunlight on the forest floor. Instead, in the moister climatic regions of the islands, a broadleafed secondary-growth forest quickly establishes itself. In the drier areas, or in those areas more frequently burned, a grassland is the natural successor.

The secondary forest growth contains a considerable mixture of varieties and species of plant growth which varies widely from site to site. Generally a jungle-like growth of small, soft-wooded, and rapid-growing tree species first take over the forest clearings. This jungle growth usually consists of a dense tangle of undergrowth, and contains numerous vines, several climbing and erect bamboos, and many palms. Most of the undergrowth is composed of small-tree and bush growth. The vines that appear initially in the clearings usually belong to the Convolvulaceae family. Several wild fruit trees quickly enter the clearings, including the papaya, jackfruit, and banana. Ideally, this jungle growth, by providing shade for the forest floor, gradually reestablishes the preclearing edaphic environment; and once this occurs there is a gradual return of the dipterocarp species. The first dipterocarp arrivals usually are representatives of the apitong, tangile, and white lauans.

In the drier areas, grasses first invade the forest clearings; and where nature or man permits these grasslands to be burned over repeatedly the grasses are able to establish themselves permanently. These grasses, which include *Imperata cylindrica* and *Saccharum spontaneum,* have root systems that are relatively fire-resistant, and the repeated burnings in the grass clearings usually succeed only in killing all of the tree seedlings. Where the burnings can be controlled, a few trees, scattered individually or in clumps, manage to establish themselves. In the Philippines these woodland-grassland areas are referred to as parangs. Usually the more fire-resistant tree species are the first to invade the grass clearings. The pioneer trees are the binayuyu (*Antidesma ghaesembilla*) and alibang-bang (*Bauhinia malabarica*). Within a few years these fast-growing pioneer trees begin to shade out the grasses, creating moister and cooler soil environments. Only then do the main dipterocarp species begin to return.

Another early arrival in the forest clearings is the buho, or wild bamboo. This rank-growing grass is quick to take over cutover areas throughout the Philippines, except on the island of Mindanao. It usually favors the areas that possess a short dry season, for the wild bamboo is somewhat deciduous. More than 30 species of bamboo are found in the Philippines, 17 of which are erect-growing. This tallest variety of all grass plants includes the kawayan (*Bambusa spinosa*), which sometimes reaches a diameter of 8 inches and a height of 80 feet. The kawayan-kiling (*Bambusa vulgaris*) and buho (*Schizostachyum lumampao*) range between 15 and 55 feet in height. Bikal (*Schizostachyum diffusum*) is the most important climbing bamboo species. Young or old, the "forests" of bamboo are extremely dense and very difficult of access.

The second-growth forests and the grasslands of the Philippines have little commercial significance, although they supply some firewood and local construction and tool wood.

The dipterocarp and molave forests are not always able to regenerate themselves after cutting because the soil environments may have been changed permanently by the forest-clearing and repeated burning operations. Actually the individual light or shade conditions of a specific site, and the moisture supplies in these particular soils, will favor the survival or the elimination of the various tree species. Under normal circumstances, however, the dipterocarp will reestablish itself and once more appear as the climax vegetation.

Proceeding toward the interior highlands of the various islands, on the intermediate slopes of these uplands between the 2,000- and 3,000-foot-contours, is a variable vegetation association referred to as the mid-mountain forest. This forest association is widely distributed in the archipelago, and is particularly common on exposed windward slopes of the uplands where moisture supplies are abundant and evenly distributed throughout the year. The mid-mountain forest growth has an open character because of the more open nature of the site on sloping land, and because the very tall first, or upper, story of vegetation found in the lowland dipterocarp forests is absent. The mid-mountain forests are of very mixed composition and are shorter in height than the lowland forests. The second-story dipterocarp species of the lowland forest here become the top story, and the dipterocarps are still dominant in the association. Individual trees in this upper story reach heights up to 65 or 70 feet with tree diameters in the neighborhood of 2 feet.

Beneath the top story is an understory, which is composed of short, slender, 25-foot-high trees. There is a fairly great variety of plant species within the mid-mountain forest association. Along the lower limits of the forest there are many rattans, whereas near the upper limits the tree ferns are more characteristic. Ferns, herbaceous plants, and assorted mixed undergrowth frequently form complete carpets on the forest floor. Most of the trees support considerable epiphytic plant growth. Because the large trees of the dipterocarp forests are absent, the mid-mountain forests are not significant as suppliers of commercial timbers.

Immediately above the mid-mountain forests, and extending up onto the high and very rough summits of the mountains is the mossy mist forest. Here, near the tops of the mountain ranges where clouds often shroud the land, is a region of high winds and continually saturated air. The first two stories of trees found in the lowland dipterocarp forests have disappeared, and the tallest trees in the mist forest are dwarfed, crooked-branched, third-story trees. Each plant contains numerous aerial roots, and the branches and trunks of the trees and the floor of the forest often are overlaid with a thick blanket of mosses, leafy liverworts, filmy ferns, and myriads of orchids and vines. The moss carpet may be as thick as 8 inches and is seldom under 2 inches thick. This single story of trees, in some instances ranging up to heights of 65 feet but usually only reaching 20 feet or less, is evergreen. The principal species are the iguem (*Podocarpus*), oak, balakbak (*Sumplocos*), malabayabas (*Tristania*), makaasim (*Eugenia*), *Dacrydium*, and *Myrica*. The timber supplies of the mist forest are of no importance commercially; however, the presence of these forests lends a great deal of protection to watersheds. All the Philippine mist forests still remain part of the public domain and are administered as "protection forests" by the Bureau of Forestry.

The mist forest does not occur everywhere at higher elevations in the Philippines. The pine forest intrudes regions in which distinct wet and dry seasons are present at elevations between 3,000 and 5,000 feet, and in some instances occurs up to nearly 9,000 feet. This pine forest thrusts itself between the mixed oak forests below and the mist forests above, and it occurs above the upper limits of the dipterocarps. The two species of pine indigenous to the Philippines are the Benguet pine (*Pinus insularis*) and tapulau pine (*Pinus merkusii*). These pines are of medium size, with diameters up to 4 and 5 feet and heights ranging up to 120 feet. Their clear, straight, cylindrical trunks closely resemble the southern yellow pines of the United States. They are evergreen and form open stands in which it is fairly easy to move about. Grasslands are an integral part of the pine forests, and most stands of pine occur as groves on broad grasslands. There are no palms, bamboos, or lianas. Benguet pines are widely distributed in the mountains of northern and central Luzon and occur as far south as the provinces of Nueva Ecija and Pangasinan. Benguet pine and tapulau pine are found on the higher slopes of the Zambales Mountains. Tapulau pine is more limited in distribution and its largest occurrence is at the higher elevations in southwestern Mindoro. The Benguet pines are used mainly as mining timbers and for general construction purposes in Mountain Province; however, their supply is very limited and pine lumber is not available on the lowlands nor in the Manila lumberyards. Planted stands of both pines are doing well at higher elevations in parts of northeastern Mindanao.

PHILIPPINE GRASSLANDS

The tall tropical wild grasslands, or cogonales, cover 17 percent of the Philippine land area (fig. 17). They occur on every type of relief, from mountain summits and ridge tops to rolling hill country, plateau lands and flat lowlands. And invariably, wherever these grasslands are encountered, population densities are at their lowest. The Filipino has found it almost impossible to convert the well-established cogonales to agricultural lands, or to any other economic asset.

These wild grasslands are composed of tall, rank-growing, sod-forming, coarse grasses that occur in dense stands. The Philippine cogon (*Imperata cylindrica* and *I. exaltata*) is the first grass to appear in the drier areas after the forests have been removed. Its seeds are disseminated very quickly. Mature cogon grasses stand 5 to 7 feet tall, with ½-inch wide serrated blades. It is the most tolerant of drought of the species of wild grass growing in the Philippines. Talahib (*Saccharum spontaneum*) is the natural successor to *Imperata* after a favorable habitat has been formed. Talahib requires a moister edaphic environment than cogon, but when fully matured it will stand 10 feet in height. It does not form a sod, but occurs in grass clumps or

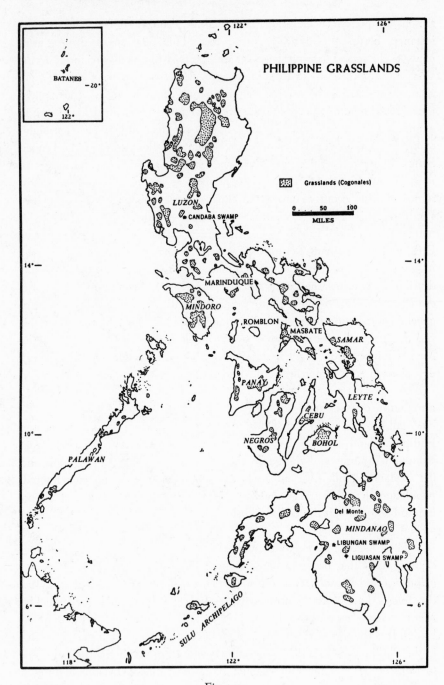

Fig. 17.

bunches. Cogon and talahib are the main grass species; however, the composition of the Philippine cogonales includes more than sixty species of grasses and weeds. Grasses, sedges, wild legumes, composites, spurges, and rubiaceous herbs are found intermixed with the three dominant species of grasses.

The origins of Philippine grasslands is a subject open to reasonable doubt, but we take the position that the largest grassland areas are man-made. Most of the Philippine grasslands are the product of repeated burning. Both lightning and volcanic eruptions do start fires, and vulcanism both burns out vegetation and creates surface covers of coarse and porous materials conducive to rather dry edaphic conditions in which forest replacement may be difficult and slow. Particularly in the latter areas, grasslands may be a first stage in the vegetative recovering of an area rendered barren. There are some regions of open forest, namely the climatically drier regions, in which tree cover is not continuous and in which trees, shrubs, scrub growth, and grasses form the association. These regions however, are not the dominant grassland tracts of the Philippines. Man has been the principal instrument in the creation, propagation, and maintenance of the Philippine grasslands; man has set fires steadily for several different purposes, and the careless handling of fires has extended the areas of burning.

One of the earliest practices in burning was the opening up of forest clearings for cropping, the caingin practice of cutting the vegetation and burning it during a short dry spell. The initial firing of a caingin by a shifting cultivator is normally insufficient to affect the plant succession as grassland. The pre-Spanish Philippines already had a few grassland areas in which repeated burning at short intervals had thoroughly reduced most of the tree growth. It was, however, the continuation of caingin burning at short intervals in the regions of population concentration under Spanish influence which formed one source of consistent expansion of the grasslands. The burning of grasslands as a game-hunting device has also been a contributory cause to the perpetuation and expansion of grasslands; such fire-hunting was practiced at times by both native and Spanish populations in particular areas. A contributory cause introduced by the Spanish is the burning of grasslands, open forest, and second-growth jungle tracts no longer cropped, for the creation and development of cattle pasturage. Such burning began at a very early date in the Spanish period, and has continued right into the present era. Whereas burning as a hunting device and burning for pasture improvement normally allowed fires to burn to their own natural limits, acting to expand the grassland areas, the shifting cultivator seldom burned beyond the clearing in which plant growth had been cut and dried out. However, the cumulative impact of burning at short intervals, and annually, has been to greatly expand regions of grassland plant cover, which have relatively little value.

The natural history of vegetative regeneration in the Philippines has clearly shown that single burnings of cut-and-dried vegetation in crop clearings does not produce a grassland. Particularly when such clearings lie within a zone of forest, the old clearings rapidly become reseeded by many kinds of "weeds," shrubby plants, and tree seedlings. Such clearings are taken over by quick-growing trees within very short intervals unless they lie in quite dry climatic situations or in edaphically droughty situations. The more gradual succession by slow-growing trees eventually returns the old clearing to a cover of heavy forest. In situations, however, where burning is repeated at such close intervals that the slow-growing trees do not get an adequate start, and in situations where much of the forest cover is being burned at close intervals, the replacement process inhibits colonization by the slow growers, permitting only the rapid growers to colonize the burned clearings. If continued for a long enough period, such burning may reduce a large area to rhizomic grasses, bamboos, certain of the palms, and root-sprouting tree forms that are essentially pyrophytes. Such pyrophytes withstand relatively easily quick burning of their above-ground portions, even in annual burns, because they grow rapidly from underground stems, root systems, and rhizomes. Once seed stock over a large area is effectively wiped out, such areas deteriorate into grasslands in which only a few tree forms will remain. The prevention of burning for significant periods, however, will find the marginal colonization of tree forms producing sufficient shade to crowd out the grasses, and once started, the reduction of a grassland to forest cover may proceed steadily and with increasing rapidity. Quick-growing shrubs and trees are the first colonizers, followed more slowly by the slow growers; in the Philippines this successional trend is back toward some form of dipterocarp forest in the course of time. Unfortunately, there are not many areas within which effective control of firing has been practiced; the trend, countrywide, still is to the expansion of the poor grassland cover at the expense of more valuable forest cover.

Grasslands today are extensive and widespread in the Philippines, and all islands contain sizable areas (fig. 17 and table 3). These savanna areas are particularly numerous and extensive in the Cagayan Valley of Luzon, in foothill sections of western Mindoro, in much of northern Panay, in the foothill zones of Negros, over a majority of the interior hill lands of Masbate, and on the extensive plateaus of north central Mindanao in Bukidnon Province.

Where used, the Philippine cogonales are a minor source of thatching materials. Their main utility is for grazing purposes, but unfortunately this use is not as extensive as it should be. The Philippine wild grasslands, however, are of relatively low economic productivity and furnish only a very poor pastureland. The young green grasses can be used for cattle pasturage, but the mature growth is useless. The *Imperata* strains can be browsed to a height of about 12 inches, whereas the *Saccharum* grasses are useful as pasturage up to a height of about 3 feet. At the same time, Philippine grasslands present an extremely difficult environment for agriculture, for with

Table 3   GRASSLAND AREAS IN THE PHILIPPINE ISLANDS IN 1957

Island	Percent of area	Acreage (000 omitted)
Luzon	20.8	5,380.6
Mindanao	12.9	3,021.8
Panay	27.1	770.7
Negros	18.9	593.3
Cebu	47.1	513.2
Bohol	29.0	276.8
Marinduque	8.8	20.8
Palawan	10.3	300.7
Samar	7.3	234.5
Leyte	3.7	66.2
Mindoro	24.0	577.2
Masbate	74.2	599.7
Sulu	13.9	96.9
Philippines	17.1	12,536.1

SOURCE: P. San Buenaventura, "Reforestation of Imperata Waste Lands in the Philippines," *Proceedings of the Ninth Pacific Science Congress, 1957*, II (1958), 54–66

the primitive tools available to most Filipino farmers the grasses cannot be cleared and farmed profitably. Whereas the soils of the freshly cleared and burned-over forest land are relatively soft, readily planted, fertilized by the soluble constituents of the ashes, and initially almost free from pernicious weeds, the grasslands, on the contrary, have a deep sod of intricately interwoven, tough rhizomes and roots which cannot be turned over except by the expenditure of considerable labor with hand tools.

There is a great need to convert the Philippine grasslands into good grazing lands, for many more proteins are needed in the Filipino diet. It is possible that a program of persistent mowing could produce this desired result. In areas where *Imperata* grasses have been mowed regularly, a soft nutritious grass has been encouraged to establish itself. Systematic mowing at the right time, while the grass is still soft, might make it possible to kill the cogon grasses and replace them with grasses of much greater forage value. An encouraging development in utilization of the cogonales areas of the Philippines can be seen at the large Del Monte plantation in Bukidnon in northern Mindanao. Here the former brush and cogon-grass wastelands have been converted to an extremely productive pineapple plantation. With power-plowing and the use of as much as 300–400 pounds of mineral fertilizers per acre annually, it has been possible to produce an annual $10,000,000 crop of pineapple from approximately 15,000 to 20,000 acres of former wastelands.

Conklin, in his study of the Hanunóo of Mindoro, pointed out an interesting relationship between the relatively simple culture and the grass-land environment.[10] When the grasses appear in the caingins they are exterminated as weeds; when they appear in other areas they are either protected, consumed in subsistence activities such as thatching, or used in economically profitable endeavors such as grazing. Although in most respects the Philippine cogonales are viewed as wastelands, there is a strong hope that with proper planning these grasslands can be made once again economically productive.

PHILIPPINE SWAMPS AND MARSHES

The discussion of Philippine vegetation would be incomplete without reference to swamp and marsh areas. Freshwater swamp and marshlands are not extensive in the Philippines; at most, they cover something less than 1 percent of the total land surface of the archipelago. These swamp and marsh areas are in addition to the extensive mangrove and nipa swamplands that accompany many coastal areas and tidal estuaries and have been discussed previously. In the Philippines there are at least three extensive areas of freshwater swamplands located well inland, and there are numerous small swamp areas located in many low-gradient valleys and along slow-flowing streams. A large freshwater swamp area is located along the middle course of the Agusan River in east central Mindanao which, in times of flood, covers an area of several hundred square miles. A second large swamp area on Mindanao accompanies Rio Grande de Mindanao (formerly the Cotabato) and Pulangi River in Cotabato Province. These swamp areas, the Libungan and Liguason marshes, cover a combined area of nearly 200 square miles in times of high water. The largest swamp in the Philippines is the Candaba Swamp of central Luzon which accompanies the lower course of the Rio Grande de Pampanga. Located at the southern end of the Central Plain of Luzon and extending over 20 miles in length, the Candaba Swamp covers more than 200 square miles when flooded. Many of the freshwater swamps of the Philippines are ephemeral, or seasonal in character, and during the dry season present extensive mud flats. In general they are created by the flooding of the large rivers.

The vegetation that occupies most of the Philippine freshwater swamps is composed of low-growing marsh plants; lotus plants; tall, reedlike grasses; floating clumps of water hyacinths; and a heather-like wild rice plant that occurs in large floating islands in Mindanao. In the southern part of the archipelago the sago palm, with its 20- to 30-foot-long pinnate leaves, is found in many swamp areas and furnishes a very poor, starchy famine food.

The freshwater swamp areas of the Philippines are problem areas for most purposes of human occupance. Whereas they frequently serve as routes of water transportation, the lush vegetation often chokes the shipping channels and must be cut regularly to afford passage. Crocodiles are also very common, particularly along the Rio Grande de Mindanao. Fishing is important in most areas. The residents of many swamplands live in high-stilt houses.

SUMMARY

The Philippines, as a part of the southeast Asia floral world, supports one of the world's richest floral communities. There are some 8,500 species of flowering plants, 1,000 species of ferns, and 800 species of orchids in the Philippines. Although of considerable botanical interest, the varied nature of Philippine flora actually constitutes an economic hindrance because useful species are widely scattered throughout the forests. The greatest exception are some of the dipterocarp forests with their nearly pure stands of lauans. In many ways the vegetation cover of the Philippines is one of the country's greatest resources, for under proper management, it can be constantly replenished. Timbers for export grades of lumber can be matured in less than 100 years, and for domestic purposes only 50–75 years are required. In order to benefit from this tremendous potential resource, however, it is vital that the Filipinos regard the present forest cover as something *finite*, and immediately undertake the protective conservation measures necessary for the continuance of this valuable national resource.

The Land Biota

The Philippines belongs within the Oriental Life Region in respect to its wild animal and bird populations, but it is a marginal sector into which only a portion of the life forms of the main region managed to migrate rather late in geologic time. In general, the numerous forms of life widely distributed in Borneo have spread into Palawan, Sulu, and Mindanao, whereas fewer life forms are to be found in the Visayan region, and still fewer forms are distributed throughout Luzon and associated islands.[11] It would appear that the greater part of the land-animal and nonmigratory bird populations reached the Philippines via Borneo only during Pleistocene time, and for many of the forms, their recent distributions represent the early patterns of natural colonization. A few varieties of birds found only in the northernmost sector are obviously related to the Formosan and eastern Asian region, thus indicating a second avenue of entry for the avian forms. A certain number of eastern Asian migratory birds visit the Philippines seasonally. Certainly man has been an agent in the further northward penetration of many of the rodents, and perhaps man has also been involved in northward distributions of other life forms. Among the birds of the archipelago, there are now numerous endemics, ecologically developed within local regional environments. The total Philippine biotic assemblage may be described as a moderate one only. It contains numerous life forms of economic value to man in the past and at present, but the assemblage never provided the rich resource available in the mainland regions of southeastern Asia.

There are nearly 500 species of birds represented in the Philippines, about a fourth of which are seasonally migratory visitors to the islands. The jungle fowl, pheasants, parrots, pigeons, doves, quails, and cuckoos are among the most common regionally resident birds that have provided food resources to the hunter, although some of the ducks and other aquatic birds have also served as lesser food sources. Filipinos have not commonly made much use of feathers and other parts of birds, either for decorative or utilitarian purposes, and such items never became significant products in the Philippine export trade.

The land animals of the Philippine Islands form a distinctive subdivision of the Malayan Subregion of the Oriental Life Region, although Palawan and parts of the Sulu group of islands are commonly classed with Borneo and the other islands properly forming the main Malayan Subregion. Significantly, most of the Philippines possesses a rather restricted variety and population of ordinary land animals. The sambar deer (*Cervus alfredi, philippinus,* and spp.), the pig (*Sus cristatus* chiefly), some of the civets (*Viverra* spp.), palm civets (*Paradoxurus* spp.), cats (*Felix* spp.), and one of the monkeys (*Macaca irus*) were once to be found almost everywhere throughout the archipelago. Other animals were of more restricted territories north of the Visayan island group. Thus, various of the squirrels, tree shrews, lemurs, and the lorises are variably restricted to the southern sectors of the Philippines.

The crocodile (*Crocodylus porosus*) once was fairly widely distributed throughout the Philippines, but it has recently become restricted to Mindanao. The Philippine member of the wild water buffalo, the tamarau (*Bubalus mindorensis*), is confined to Mindoro Island, and all other "wild buffalo" are actually domestic stock gone feral. We do not here extend our discussion to the full breadth of zoogeography to include comment on the bats, all of the rodents, the lesser life forms, and the species regionalization patterns.

To the very early human population of the Philippine Archipelago the assemblage of bird and animal life formed an adequate, if not richly varied, source of food supply to be had for the hunting and the trapping. Such sources complemented the aquatic resources available in fresh and salt waters around the shores of the many inhabited islands. Ecological zoning was well established for many of the forms, with lowland, upland, and particular island regionalisms occurring. Probably the upland interior of Luzon was always a zone of relative scarcity, as the distributional patterns for many of the birds and animals did not include northern Luzon. The Negrito and the proto-Malay inhabitants of the early Philippines could have found those ecological subregions possessing significant populations of land animals and birds. It is likely that by the time the Spanish arrived the hunting resources had not been reduced significantly by the relatively light population of the islands. After about 1700, however, there was a gradual lessening of the populations of birds and animals that formed basic food complements derived from hunting. Contributing to this reduction of game were such factors as the steady increase in human population, the continued expansion of an agricultural landscape, the restriction of the zones of continuous forest on the lowlands and coastal fringes, the competitive restriction of the Negrito to certain island sectors, and the development of the Christian-pagan frontiers and regionalism. All the shifting-cultivator populations, both Christian and pagan, relied both on the gathering of plant products and upon the hunting of birds and animals to some degree to round out their annual economic patterns. In zones of significant buildup of regional human populations, the pressures of hunting increasingly restricted the populations of various birds and animals. Well before the end of the Spanish period in the islands the hunting of deer, some of the doves, pigeons, parrots, jungle fowl, and pheasants had decreased markedly because the useful game had almost disappeared in many local regions. In the contemporary era, hunting has ceased to be an economic pursuit in large areas of the islands.

The case of the wild pig, however, was somewhat different. The wild pig adapted well to the changes in ecological environments, and wild pigs became raiders of the crop fields of both shifting cultivators and sedentary farmers in those areas in which tracts of forest and jungle remained scattered throughout the occupied territory. In the regions of scattered settlement, and in some lightly occupied islands, deer also have adapted well to the changes of environment and have become raiders of the crop fields. In such localities, therefore, hunting of deer and wild pig is still common and serves two purposes. First, the game has food and economic value in its own right. Second, hunting helps to restrict the deer and pig populations so that raiding of crop fields does not become ruinous. Fencing crop fields, protecting them with animal traps, and harvest-season crop watching all are part of the seasonal routine among both Christian and pagan sedentary and shifting-cultivator populations on those agricultural margins, and in those islands still flanked by zones, tracts, or patches of forest, jungle, or unoccupied hill country that can serve as refuge and breeding grounds for deer and pigs.[12] Such hunting patterns, of course, do not occur in the well-settled zones or regions from which forest and jungle have been excluded for decades.

On some of the smaller islands with small human populations, and in some zones of light occupance that remain on the larger islands, sport hunting of wild pigs (termed wild boar hunts) continues at the present time; to a lesser extent the sport hunting of deer also continues. Occasionally sport hunting occurs for tamarau on Mindoro. The sport hunting for particular birds and animals is occasionally widely practiced in the Philippines, but in general, the wild population of game birds and animals is no longer large. The sport hunting of crocodile still occurs occasionally in Mindanao, both in the Agusan and the Rio Grande de Mindanao valleys. Economic hunting of crocodile within the last century has so greatly reduced the crocodile population that such hunting is seldom a highly remunerative occupation at the present time, and it represents only a minor economic activity.

Within the changing patterns of ecological environments, there remains in the Philippines a significant bird and animal population that constitutes destructive pests as far as the crop grower is concerned. On the agricultural frontiers, flanked by forests and jungle tracts, the rat problem can be very severe, and many a rice crop is harvested by rats owing to the scarcity of human harvest labor at the right season. Similarly, on such agricultural frontiers the raiding of crop fields, particularly rice fields, by bird populations normally resident around the fringes of the agricultural frontiers can be disastrous to the grower if labor shortages develop at harvest time. Also, in old-settled zones the large increases in populations of seed-eating birds, particularly the sparrows, constitutes a constant threat to the rice farmer.

The more than 7,000 islands of the Philippines form a separate island realm set beyond the outer fringe of a large continent. Both this marginal position and the multiple-unit aspect are significant elements in a distinctive physical environment. The situation of the Philippines as a very large group of islands some distance from the continent contributes to the climatic character of the country, but it also places the region in a position quite unlike that of mainland countries, and gives it unique space relationships among the world's geographical regions.

The basic form of the archipelago is established by the great structural arcs that curve along the margins between the Pacific Basin and the continent of Asia. As major components in the physical build, these arcs appear as the faulted and folded crests of great ridges created by the tectonic action of the basin against the continent. The visible landmasses that make up the islands at the present stand of sea level are but the very tops of the ridges and volcanoes. Vulcanism along the arcs throughout geologic time has both intruded igneous material into the upper portions of the arcs and extruded material above sea level; the latter activity has created numerous volcanoes, lava flow-beds, and deposits of ashes, cinders, and tuffs that are superimposed upon the basic structural forms of the ridge crests. The basic alignment is north–south, so that the Philippines stretches out over several degrees of latitude but extends less widely in longitude. The convergence and divergence of trends among the primary arcs, however, sets many islands in positions of varied angular relationships to other islands, and also produces the same kind of converging and diverging patterns of angular relationship in mountains and lowlands within individual islands. Structural actions during one geologic era cut across actions during other eras, so that there are ridge lines, fault scarp lines, fold trends, horst and graben trends, and submerged-basin trends that complicate the simple linear arrangements of those surfaces appearing as islands at the present tectonic juncture.

As most of the islands are essentially ridge crests, or groups of ridge crests, most of the islands have hilly to mountainous interiors, large extents of sloping surfaces, and narrow coastal fringes bordered by irregular shorelines set with protruding spurs and reentrant embayments. There are many offshore islands around many coasts which are hills or mountains resting upon submerged spurs; however, there are also numerous very shallow bodies of water above which rounded or flattened hills appear as low and flat islands. Submerged basins between islands sometimes have deep bottoms, and structural deeps lie both within and adjacent to the islands, since such deeps are sectional elements in the basic structure. The larger islands often are compound structures, made up of several sets of ridges situated on divergent lines. Within these larger islands there are downwarped or submerged basins that appear as sediment-filled plains or near–sea level wet lowlands. With a tremendously long coastline, coastal land-shaping processes have had much more to do with minor landforms of the Philippines than is normally true for other of the earth's land areas of comparable size.

The general placement of the Philippine Archipelago, offshore from the continent and in relatively low latitude, produces a near-tropical, humid climatic regime for the whole archipelago. The specific situation of the island realm places it at an angle against, but not quite athwart, the general trends of both the Pacific Trade Wind system and the Asian Monsoon Wind system; the northern half of the archipelago, in addition, lies within the arclike zone of movement of the northern Pacific Typhoon system. As its mountain ridge lines form seasonal rain shadows, and as many smaller islands lie in seasonal lee of larger islands, the archipelago displays a very complex map of local climates. The lowlands are on the hot side the year around; the mountainous cores of many islands project sufficiently high to create temperature regimes akin to those of the tropical highlands, but there are only a few large areas at such elevations. In general, exposed upland island fronts receive heavy falls of rain during one seasonal portion of the year; these same areas may be in rain-shadow position during the rest of the year. Broadly speaking, the eastern fronts of islands lying on the eastern side of the archipelago are rainy the year around, and the zones of seasonal drought lie in the western sector and along west coasts. The Trade Wind–Winter Monsoon combination produces more continuous distribution of rainfall than does the Summer Monsoon, although some exposed west coasts have heavy annual totals of precipitation. Areas having weather patterns punctuated by typhoon passage often experience short spells during which huge amounts of precipitation inundate lowlands and destructive winds often create havoc.

During the time interval in which the tectonic building processes have been at work in primary operations, secondary operations have also occurred. Metamorphism has been widely distributed, creating large units of altered country-rock; and metamorphism and secondary intrusion have further contributed toward a complex distribution of significant economic minerals. During the time interval in which denudational forces have been very active on the mountaintop landscapes—for local slope-gradients often have been steep—continued upbuilding has occurred, and a large volume of precipitation runoff has been available. In some locally subsiding basins, thousands of feet of sediment have been deposited to create alluvial lowlands. Many areas of upland have been very deeply etched by stream erosion, whereas in other areas the denudational process has been hindered by the deposition of massive amounts of volcanic ejecta and the building of volcanoes. In general, the landforms of the archipelago are not extremely bold, for many of the mountaintops, ridge lines, and block units have been softened by denudation to create landscapes of moderate to rounded relief. Although extensive alluvial plains do not surround islands, zones of shallow water surround many of them; in this island world these shallow waters have until very recently formed the main lines and zones of human movement.

The Philippine Archipelago presents a relatively youthful landscape; there are no ancient massifs that have been worn down to the basic cores and weathered into extreme senility. In a few places weathering processes have reduced mantle material to iron ores and other basic types of rock cover. In general, however, the landscape surfaces of the Philippines are young surfaces on which basic weathering processes have not reached maturity. This has produced a complex mosaic of weathered surface materials which, as soils, reflects both the physical diversity and the general youth of the landscape. Philippine soils are generally good, extremely varied in distribution, and locally varied in texture, quality, workability, and productivity.

During the time interval of major upbuilding and denudation, vigorous biogeographic activities have been carried on. Corals have built fringing and capping reefs on surfaces rendered submerged by shallow waters at different stands of sea level or at different stands of particular sectors of structural ridges. Fossil coral reef materials are exposed today at varying elevations above sea level, and living coral reefs are widespread in the shallow waters of today's sea stand. On the land, heavy covers of plant life have clothed surfaces, according to local ecological situations, in heavy and varied growths of forest; these forests have represented one of the strong economic assets of the Philippine environment. Whereas upland forest growth has retarded denudation, some lowland vegetation has abetted sedimentation; fringing mangrove, swamp-plant associations, and strandline associations have affected lowland physical processes to enlarge coastal lowlands.

Within the Philippine Archipelago there is great diversity in local environments, despite the general broad pattern of uniformity. The variation has produced strong differences in character, and in quality, among local environments. Some local environments, as those along the northeast coast of Luzon, have a character, pattern, and quality with which man always finds it difficult to cope, even today. This coast is too rough, too rainy, too windy, too wet, and too far from an easily usable high-quality local environment. Other environments have been attractive, highly usable, with few problem situations, and enjoying circumstances very inviting to man; Manila Bay, Laguna de Bay, and the surrounding lowlands are this type of environment. Some local environments yielded easily to human utilization, whereas others presented characters and qualities that only modern technology and modern aims have found valuable. A significant share of the environmental diversity derives from comparative general location and situation within the whole archipelago, but an even larger share derives from the simple fact that there are more than 7,000 islands, no two of which are identical. In sum, although it is possible to generalize the physical environment as that of an attractive tropical island world, the diversity within the pattern of local environments presents an extremely wide range of conditions; diversity within broad limits is an outstanding characteristic of the Philippine physical environment.

PART TWO

The Cultural and Economic Environments

FOUR

〰〰〰 *The Cultural History of the Filipinos*

"The least oriental country in the Orient" is a phrase sometimes used to describe the Philippines, and with true justification. The Filipinos are proud of their occidental outlook, for this is the only country in the Orient where the language of instruction in all schools is English, where the population is predominantly Christian, and where the "national dress" is essentially derived from European models. Each of the above claims is subject to qualification, but the statement points up the critical fact that the Philippines possesses a pattern of culture that is to be described neither as typically oriental nor as a regional variant of the two chief Asian cultural orientations, Indian and Chinese. Closer analysis of Philippine culture, both material culture manifesting itself in the landscape and nonmaterial culture, reveals a wide range of elements derived from pre-European island sources, from mainland Asian sources, from historical occidental sources, and from contemporary worldwide sources. Basic agriculture ranges from pre-European garden cropping to modern commercial monocrop patterns; manufacturing comprises both native handicraft and contemporary industrialization; transportation has become chiefly modern occidental; the basic dietary is a worldwide combination adapted to the southeast Asian crop-and-habit matrix; sociopolitical structure is a mixture of pre-European and modern; Filipino mores form an intricately compounded system, and much of daily living is a fascinating blend of very old and modern motifs subtly altered to Filipino tastes. Thus it is necessary to review the historical patterns by which these various blends have been produced in order to understand life in the contemporary Philippine Islands.

Pre-Spanish Patterns and Culture Sources

Near the end of the last glacial era, as the now-familiar physical map of the earth's land, sea, mountains, valleys, plains, and islands began to take its present-day shape, the Philippines emerged as one of the world's great island archipelagoes. As the archaeologist can attest, man had been here before that final shaping of the map. As an early wanderer he probably walked across parts of the broad lowland known as Sundaland to the historical geologist and as the South China Sea in today's atlases. The few thousand Negrito still living in small groups scattered throughout the Philippine Islands may well be the remnants of such early wanderers, though not entirely typical of all of them. Later arrivals, of varied ethnic stocks, were water-navigating peoples, crossing the by-then flooded lower sectors of Sundaland by boats. As seagoing peoples they were more mobile than the foot travelers, and they lived differently, arranged their sociopolitical structures differently, and created a different kind of world from that of the earlier land travelers.

Negrito, Proto-Malay, Malay, Indonesian-Malay, Sinitic, Chinese, and possibly other ethnic stocks arrived in the Philippines over the last few thousand years, not in single migrations, but each group in repeated movement patterns and in variable numbers. Some of them were frequenters of the coastal fringes only, but others may have been refugees from mainland zones of conflict, or they may have been adventurous migrators. Still others may have been sea traders who wandered the coasts and seas, establishing short-term bases at selected harbors from which to conduct their trade, piracy, shipping, looting, fisheries, slaving, and casual exploitation of useful land products from the hinterlands of their frequented coasts. The record of prehistoric movement, regional occupance, ethnic relationships, territorial control, and local settlement history for the Philippines is still vague and incomplete.

It is clear, however, that man has lived almost everywhere in the Philippines in recent time, and that many of the later arrivals brought settled living patterns, fairly complex technologies, and mixed patterns of culture into the islands, thus establishing several different typologies of living systems long before the Spanish arrived. Just before the Christian era the mountain country of central and northern Luzon became the home of village-dwelling agricultural peoples who first grew millet and later grew rice on carefully terraced fields in the hilly landscapes where development of permanent water-control systems enabled them to escape both the rigors of the dry seasons and the serious flooding of the lowlands during the wet seasons and typhoon periods. These peoples slowly migrated uphill into what is today Mountain Province; but though they may have originally established themselves in a few other places, they did not occupy a large sector of the Philippines, nor did their manner of handling the agricultural landscape become the general model for all early residents of the Philippines.

In the far southern sector of the archipelago a very different living pattern characterized the Sulu Islanders. Marshy islands, islets set on coral reefs, and rocky volcanic landscapes set in a tropical sea between major islands became the meeting ground of sea traders, shell and coral producers, fishermen, pirates, and slave traders. Boats, pile-built villages and "ports," fishing and the products of the sea, and extensive interregional contacts were fashioned into a way of life that had little to do with the elaboration of a sedentary land-developing living system.

Between these extremes were elaborated different varieties of human living systems. One of the commoner varieties centered on the coastal village located in a protected bay fronting a sandy beach. Offshore was the mobility potential of boat travel and the products of the sea for a share of the living pattern. Inland from the beach lay forested lowlands from which a huge variety of useful plant and animal products could be extracted. Patches of ground in these forests could also be cleared, burned, and cropped for a year or two each. The agricultural system employed was shifting cultivation, caingin, involving group territorial control, a communal concept of usage rights only in land being cropped, simple tools, and relatively simple cropping technology. Shifting cultivation did not make for large surpluses but it was an adaptable agricultural system permitting considerable mobility and movement to new residential sites, for it did not involve costly land-development procedures such as those normal to the mountain folk of northern Luzon.

Variants of the coastal-village living pattern matured in time. Riverine variants penetrated the interiors of the larger valleys on the larger islands. Marsh and swamp versions matured in some of the deeply flooded valleys or coastal marshes, and hill-land variants developed in the interiors of many of the larger islands. Many items were shared in common, or developed in local variety, ranging from varieties of boats, tools, and houses, to social structures, plant complexes, dietary patterns, and ritual systems. Gross similarities were offset by the local variation in detailed island patterns, by the cohesion of a specific system among a particular ethnic stock, by the arrival of a new immigrant stock, or by the splitting off from a parent stock of a nuclear element of increasing population.

For century upon century the elaboration of a Philippine series of living systems continued. A multiple-island group with a long coastline, with varied island interiors, with considerable basic environmental variety between the southern Sulus and the northern Batan Islands, and between sea level and the high mountain ranges of Luzon, Leyte, Mindoro, Palawan, and Mindanao, permitted the living systems to become highly varied, localized, and differentiated within a broad common pattern. The exploration of the rich plant world permitted the domestication of such plants as abaca, cala-mondin, and lanzon that are native only to the Philippines, and the local domestication of some of the yams, taros, bamboos, and fruits common to most of southeastern Asia. The repeated import of other crop plants, such as the millets, rices, bamboos, bananas, citrus, and others native to mainland south-east Asia permitted localization of regional varieties within sectors of the Philippines. The same thing happened, to lesser degree, in the animal world, and in the utilization of fish and other aquatic resources. The import and local development of specific technologies using wood, shell, stone, minerals, gums, and resins gradually brought the Philippines within the common area of Asian mainland systems.

As a general series of economic systems developed, a series of sociopoliti-cal systems also evolved within a common pattern. In the pre-Spanish period no political system matured to the level of a political state in the proper sense of the term, though the Moslem immigrants were bringing in notions of the king (as rajah or sultan), of political stratification of the major and minor tribal chief (as the *datu*), and initiating the very beginnings of the territorial state. Among pre-Moslem peoples the concept of territoriality affixed to a particular area appeared significantly developed only in northern Luzon where the wet, permanent-field, terraced landscape was the basis for cropping systems. Elsewhere only loose concepts of territoriality held sway. Political structuring everywhere was immature and essentially a projection of social, kinship groups normally rather small in total numbers. The *barangay,* as the basic unit of structure, was essentially a kinship group; but it included economic dependents, and its leader also functioned as a political leader for the group resident in a specific locality. The absence of a stable inter-barangay structure made impossible a united reaction to the Spanish take-over of the islands north of the zone of primary Moslem influence. Social structur-ing generally followed a three-level pattern best expressed as nobility, free-man, and dependents, with varying subdivisions of each category.[1] Social structure carried integrated economic implications, labor service, and commodity delivery, particularly from the dependent classes to the nobility and to the barangay chief. Thus, social and political structures were interlocking, with economic functions integrated, among any one people or one locality-residence community. The physical geography of the archipelago, and this low level of sociopolitical institutionalism made for regional separatism, local autonomy, and interregional hostility.

The earliest interregional relationships with southern and eastern parts of the Asian mainland were chiefly those of the common content of ethnic stock, loose patterns of culture, and reactions of peoples to similar environments. In the early centuries of the Christian era interregional trade contacts between Sulu and other parts of island and mainland southeastern Asia undoubtedly extended the contacts and increased the zonal community of relationships, with Hindu traders, Indonesians, and possibly even Arabs participating in the economic trade and exchange of cultural influences. By the eighth century, however, the Philippines had been drawn into a closer relationship with a larger Indonesian regional context by the expansion of politico-economic systems derived originally from mainland political states. Although the Philippines never formed an entity within or marginal to the first such political state, Sri Vijaya, the patterns of sea navigation, peaceful trade, militant piracy, forceful tribute levying, and probably refugeeism certainly brought the southern and western Philippines within a zone of firm contact and significant cultural imprint.

Tenth-century Chinese trade established regular contact with the Sulu interregional center and, later, with more northerly Philippine islands, as the wide distribution of finds of Sung dynasty porcelains clearly attests. Chinese traders became resident in a few chief centers, and abaca, coconut, shell products, coral, cottons, kapok, aromatic woods, varied kinds of mattings, and several forest extracts flowed out of the Philippines into the China trade. Fifteenth-century Japanese trade contacts were significant at least with Luzon, again including a resident Japanese community around Manila Bay.

Indonesian refugees from the militant growth of the Indonesian sea empire of Madjapahit began filtering into Palawan, Sulu, and other southern Philippine islands in the thirteenth century, and early in the fourteenth century the southern half of the Philippines came within the trade and tribute limits of Madjapahit itself. Close behind the ships of Madjapahit came more refugees from Indonesia, fleeing the militant expansion of Islam into the Indies during the fourteenth century. Madjapahit declined as rapidly as it arose, and the spreading force of Islam soon washed the shores of the southern Philippine islands with even more emphatic impact. By 1500, Islam had a foothold in Sulu, from which point it spread into Mindanao, and by 1565 Moslems had leapfrogged as far north as Manila Bay.

By the early sixteenth century, when Spain made her discovery of the Philippines for the western world, the ports of Sulu and northwestern Luzon, at least, had for centuries been the meeting ground for ships, products, and peoples of eastern and southern Asia. Although no political state had matured in the Philippines, though only a few hundred islands were permanently populated by approximately a half-million people from all parts of southern and eastern Asia, primary mainland cultural patterns were broadly distributed. These cultural patterns were still somewhat amorphous and not as yet institutionalized into highly specific forms and modes. Variety of people and culture actually characterized the islands at this point, and the base for economic, demographic, and cultural development had been initiated. It fell to the Spanish to formally shape, institutionalize, and cement the regional and national patterns of culture that basically characterize the Philippines. Coming at such a critical point in regional development, the Spanish impact could begin the process of turning the Filipinos toward the Occident in their development of a regional culture.

Hispanization and Philippinization

Occasionally the Spanish are still described as military conquerors of the Philippines who exploited the islands in the worst tradition of occidental imperialism, and who forcefully planted their political, social, and economic systems upon the Philippines to replace the whole of native culture. Actually, Spain used but little military force within the Philippines to attain control, though she had to militarily defend her control of the Philippines against the Dutch, the British, the Moslems of the far south, and against numerous pirates of the China seas. Actually it is better stated as a case of the Filipinos accepting Spanish culture, with its numerous faults, burdens, and inequities, and of adapting Spanish culture to their own ends despite the Spanish political control and the Spanish overlords who brought the culture. After some three centuries of political controls and overlords, the Filipinos rebelled in the late nineteenth century, but never was an effort made to overthrow Spanish cultural traditions. The Hispanization of the Philippines took place as a cultural process, but part and parcel of this process was the Philippinization of Spanish culture, the two processes becoming essentially one in the creation of a native culture like that of no other part of the world.[2]

By the time Spain came to the Philippines in force, after 1565, some changes had taken place in the Spanish colonial system first elaborated in the Americas. The absence of great volumes of gold and silver in the islands eliminated one of the worst aspects of New World Spanish exploitation; the absence of the eagerly sought spices of the Indies, which were neither grown nor significantly consumed within the Philippines, excluded a primary cause for heavy agricultural exploitation. The only primary objective of the Spanish which could be carried out was the Christianization of the native population. This program was accepted with considerable enthusiasm by the main lowland Malay population north of the Moslem territories, and many elements of Catholic belief, ritual, social procedure, and "national custom" were gradually equated to corresponding elements in native culture. The religious unity did much to establish a new cultural continuity throughout the lowland, coastal, and valley sectors of the Philippines. The Negrito, the proto-Malay inhabitants of the hill country, and the southern Moslems remained outside this growing cultural continuity, finding Christianity and its associated traits one more cause for continued enmity toward the Malay Filipinos.

Spain came upon the Philippine scene just prior to the point at which the Moslem expansion from the south could have swept the whole archipelago into an Islam-oriented cultural tradition. As it was, the Moslem cultural tradition was thoroughly planted in Sulu, southern Mindanao, and associated small islands. The Christian Spanish never could root out the hated Islamic culture they had fought in Spain, but the Moslem envelopment of the Philippines was stayed, and the two traditions of religiously oriented culture have lasted right down to the present. In respect to both new cultural traditions the Philippine situation was permissive, circumstances were conducive, the time was ripe, and each tradition was accepted in its own sector of the Philippine Archipelago.

For the small body of Catholic clergy to get at the widely disseminated population, and for Spanish civil and military bureaucracy to function at all, it was necessary to reorganize the residential distribution of population. The native residential habit involved a variety of small-unit patterns, single houses, clusters of houses, hamlets, elongated villages, or clustered villages. Lacking formalized morphology, these normally were built of perishable materials, and contained almost no buildings, shrines, temples, castles, shops, or factories of the sort that made for truly permanent settlements. The Spanish introduced their own settlement form, the skeleton grid-planned town centered on a plaza, around which the church, the headquarters of the civil bureaucracy, the garrison house, the treasury, and the homes of the principal local citizenry were grouped. This settlement became the center of religious, social, civil, and military administration for a regional territory.[3] The settlement itself was termed the *poblacion*, the political administrative area was the *municipio*, and a collection of municipios territorially contiguous became the *provincia*. These units and terms survive today as *poblacion*, municipality, and province.[4]

The Filipino population passively resisted this system of controlled and centralized residence, for it did not fit their social systems, nor did it fit their commodity exchange and self-subsistent economy. The Spanish, in the end, accepted the housing cluster and the hamlet as the rural *sitio*, and the village (the native *barangay*, the smallest recognizable "political" area before the conquest) as the *barrio*, both of which residential patterns still obtain throughout the Philippines. The sitio and the barrio remained variable in size and amorphous in shape; until late Spanish times neither settlement type contained nonresidential buildings except for the simple chapel used by visiting clergy. The nobility, some of the freemen, and many of the more fully Catholicized families, however, tended to gather around the poblacion because it was to their political, economic, and cultural advantage to do so.

In administration of these political units the Spanish introduced a semielective procedure for staffing positions at and below the level of the municipio. Inevitably the political and social structuring indigenous to the Philippines allowed the hereditary native nobility to capitalize upon the Spanish institutionalization of civil government, and the growth of the *principalia* class perpetuated the native system. Enough elective procedure entered Spanish practice so that the upper classes of Filipinos had become enthusiastically adept at local politics long before the American introduction of more formally elective procedures and party politics. In effect, the Spanish system became rather thoroughly Philippinized, and many of the complaints over Spanish maladministration reflected the oligarchic dominance of upper-class Filipinos over the lesser ranks of the population throughout Spanish time, and down to the present.

Gradually the number of sitios, barrios, municipios, poblaciones, and provincias increased in number as the population grew and Spanish rule became territorially more extensive. The 12 early provinces and about 200 municipios expanded in number to about 40 provinces and military *commandancias* and about 1,100 municipios by the end of Spanish rule. The cultural impact upon the growing population was more complete with the passage of time, and upon the landscape the continued development of poblaciones surrounded by cultivated lands expanded a cultural landscape blending native and Spanish influences.

In the sixteenth century the small Philippine population utilized but a small proportion of the total cultivable landscape, so that there was ample land for agricultural development. The small Spanish population that became resident in the Islands was too small to undertake extensive agricultural development on its own in this tropical environment of alien cropping systems. There were never more than four hundred Spanish clergy resident on the islands at any one time (fig. 18), seldom more than a thousand Spanish military personnel on active duty, and rarely more than a few hundred Spanish civil administrators and private civilians. A high death rate among Spaniards in the Islands was normal, and very few Spanish women came to the Philippines.[5] Pensioned soldiery and some bureaucrats early sought crown grants of land, termed *encomiendas,* which carried the right to levy commodity tribute and labor service from the resident population. Upper-class Filipinos also sought encomiendas. By 1621, the peak period of the encomienda, there were just under 100,000 such grants, chiefly situated in Luzon. The encomienda was not literally a land grant as such, but a grant of the right to collect a tribute from the produce of the land, and to exact labor service from the occupants of the land. Such grantees thus were enabled to live as did the native nobility, without themselves engaging in arduous cultivation. Early Spanish practice recognized native rights to ownership of such lands as were actually cropped and occupied, but all the unoccupied lands of the Philippines became crown land, disposable by the Crown in perpetuity. The Spanish thus brought in the concept of private landowner-ship, completely unknown to the Filipinos at that time, as well as the formalized concept of the encomienda, which, in essence, was already being practiced in the Philippines by Filipinos themselves. The Spanish apparently did not understand the system of communal ownership and rights of usufruct traditional to shifting cultivation; in any case, they disregarded it, just as did Europeans elsewhere in southeastern Asia.

The Spanish encomienda system may be considered an iniquitous one that placed a burden upon the native populace, but it was not essentially different from the preconquest socioeconomic system by which the dependent classes had to deliver shares of their commodity production to the barangay chief, and also were required to perform labor service for the chief and the nobility. The encomienda began to decline as a formal system early in the seventeenth century; fewer grants were made, and by the official rule, grants reverted to the Crown after the death of the second or third successive heir. The Spanish concept of land control, however, involved private owner-ship of land itself, in fee simple, in contrast to the preconquest concept of rights of usufruct, with ownership of the land remaining common to the ethnic group claiming local territoriality.

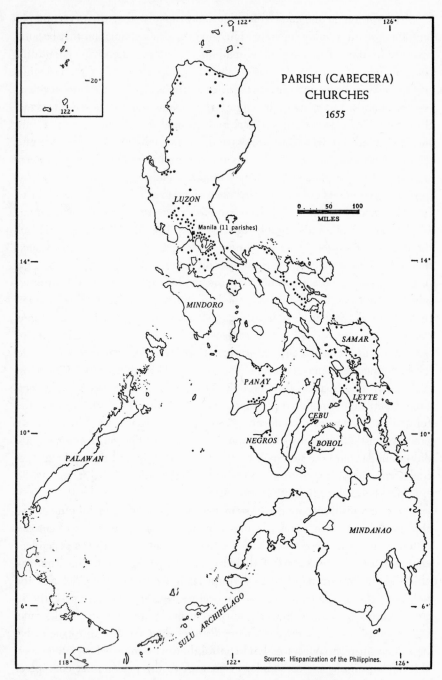

Fig. 18. Centers of religious influence in early Spanish time.

The encomienda right, in the hands of the educated Spanish and the church, eventually became translated, in a great many cases, into fee-simple ownership in de facto terms. Since the educated Spanish and the clergy could in due course procure documents of title in accord with Spanish legal principles, the de jure control over lands passed from ethnic communities to individuals, blood families, or the church. Only when they were settling Filipinos in and around the new poblaciones did the Spanish do much in the way of providing the Filipinos with titles to land, and in the countryside the procurement of title was left to individual initiative. The Philippine nobility, comprising the working bureaucracy, became initiated into the new concepts of land control and themselves acquired fee-simple title to lands, thereby legalizing their preconquest positions of societal control over the dependent classes, who in the new pattern became tenant farmers. Although much has been made of the Spanish encomienda system as the source of modern tenancy in the Philippines, it was probably this process of substitution of one land system for another that permitted a legal landlord class, chiefly Filipino rather than Spanish, Chinese, or ecclesiastical, to come into being during the nineteenth century.[6] Here, too, is a Philippinization of a Hispanic culture complex, effected by the Filipino upper classes to perpetuate their traditional preconquest positions. It is probably fair to suggest that descendants of many of the former rural freeman today make up part of the group of Filipino small landowners who pay taxes on land to which they still do not hold full legal title. Many of the former dependent classes continue as a tenant class, still affected by patterns of reciprocity and obligational mores as these operate today. Some of the former dependent classes and their descendants, by migrating to the frontiers of settlement and taking up new lands, enjoy the same status as now held by the former freemen.

The Spanish never carried out effective land surveys, did little to initiate the provision of title to formerly claimed lands, and made no real effort to put into operation for the Filipinos the systematic control over land in the terms of their own land system. In a sense, the Spanish never were able to cope with the system of communal ownership and rights of usufruct that was the backbone of the preconquest land system; and the Filipino nobility did little to clarify the problem, so that it was the lower social classes of the native population who paid the price in the long run. The Spanish government in the Philippines never paid its own way, constantly ran a deficit, steadily depended upon a subsidy from Mexico, and frequently handed out generous IOU's for commodities and services which seldom could be redeemed. Accumulated volumes of these useless financial obligations periodically gave incentive to rebellion, particularly in periods during which the Spanish were hard pressed to defend the islands, as against the Dutch in the early seventeenth century.

The Spanish did make some effort to alter native Philippine agriculture in terms of its crops and animals. The attempts to introduce Mediterranean crop plants and animals were, for the most part, failures in this tropical environment, but many crop plants from the more tropical parts of the Americas were successfully introduced. Maize, the sweet potato, manioc, peanuts, the pineapple, some of the agaves, and such fruits as the avocado, the guavas, many of the sapotas, cacao, and tobacco were the more important of these. Maize only slowly became accepted as a crop plant by peoples who were essentially growers of millet, rice, yam, and taro, and in the early period maize was of very slight importance. Tobacco's acceptance was more rapid and it was also pushed by the Spanish, a government monopoly in the eighteenth century controlling its production and trade. Cattle and horses from China succeeded where those from Spain did not. In crop growing the Spanish did little to improve the systems and technology, though where they could they turned mobile shifting cultivators into sedentary permanent-field farmers, the better to Christianize them, tax them, and secure the desired labor services. This resulted in a Philippine permanent-field rice culture without the requisite water control to permit first-class wet-field rice growing, so that a low level of rice yields early became a Philippine tradition. Only late in Spanish times did water supplies begin to be developed significantly. Here the north Luzon mountain example of wet-field culture went unheeded.

North of Sulu, in the fifteenth century, Philippine economy was chiefly one of commodity exchange, with local areas of self-subsistence. Manila Bay and the Ilocos coast of northwest Luzon were perhaps the focus of interregional exchange, for here Japanese and Chinese traders were active. The Spanish, finding no significant spice marts in the Philippines, were frustrated in one of their chief objectives, for there was then little enthusiasm for native agricultural products. The upper-class Spanish, therefore, turned to the China trade, and Manila became a center of the Manila Galleon China-Mexico trade. The Manila Spanish became almost totally dependent upon the Chinese traders who brought a steady volume of oriental goods and took away some Philippine domestic commodities and the silver bullion and minted dollars that came as payment from Mexico. A few favored Filipino nobility were admitted to this profitable commerce. The trade program centered on Manila and early turned the city into the chief Philippine port, the chief urban center, the headquarters of the Chinese, the residence of such upper-class Spanish and Filipino principalia as could avoid living in the provinces, the primary center of the Catholic church, and the residential center of such Filipino dependent classes as were needed to facilitate the trade and urban-living patterns.

The region around Manila Bay became the entering wedge for the Chinese element in Philippine culture. Far more intermarriages occurred between Chinese and Filipinos than between Spanish and Filipinos, so that gradually the Chinese ethnic element became significant in this region. Tools, handicraft technology, market-gardening technology and crop plants, and significant portions of the urban domestic dietary were modified by Chinese influence. The Chinese became the skilled craftsmen, providing a large share of secondary production. Perhaps most significant of all was the Chinese role as the commercial trader and trade financier who operated in both the wholesale and the retail trade, rather quickly filling the vacuum created by the appearance of urban commercial activity. Historically, the Filipino outside Sulu had never properly engaged in true commercial trading, had no education from the Spanish in this line, and did not spontaneously respond to the appearance of the commercial opportunity. Late in the Spanish era the Chinese trader began widening his territorial zone of operations into the provincial hinterlands.

A popular illusion has been that Spanish became the language of the Philippines. Probably no more than 10 percent of the Filipino population ever spoke Spanish fluently at any date, though a great many Spanish words infiltrated the many native languages.[7] From the beginning, some clergy learned the native languages and performed their rituals, ceremonies, and services in the native tongue, although many performed services in Latin. Neither government nor the church pushed Spanish as the common or primary language, and a formal system of education appeared only late in the Spanish era. Most of the civil and military bureaucracy was native, and it received only a smattering of nonnative linguistic education. Until very late in Spanish times few papers or periodicals were published, and no extensive written literature was ever available to the native population. The upper-class Filipinos and some of the Chinese learned Spanish, but there never developed a large Spanish-Filipino mestizo population that could have popularized Spanish as a language. The mass of the growing Filipino population remained rural and nonliterate. Most Filipinos had relatively little contact with the Spanish except for the clergy, and the preference of the Spanish for living in the larger poblaciones or in the few urban centers deprived the Filipinos of significant exposure to the Spanish language.

The absence of a militant conquest, the lack of primary reasons for destructively exploiting Filipino labor, and the fact that the Spanish brought few diseases new to the Philippines resulted in a less disastrous drop in the

Filipino population than marked Spanish colonial times in the Americas. At certain periods local rebellions slowed the expansion of, or actually reduced, the native population, and such periods as the war with the Dutch reduced the male population temporarily in the areas from which military personnel could be commandeered. The reduction of preconquest interisland and interregional hostility operated as a stimulus to population growth. The Spanish labor service and forced sale of commodities were burdensome, but not heavy, economic depressants. Therefore, with temporary lulls, the population of the Spanish-controlled sections of the Philippines increased steadily during the entire Spanish era. Starting at not far from a half million in the late sixteenth century, it increased to about 7,000,000 in 1899.

By the end of the Spanish era the inept administration of the Islands, and its almost steady financial bankruptcy, had thoroughly disillusioned and alienated the Filipinos from Spain politically. During this era the Filipinos had adopted large sectors of Spanish culture, and had learned to operate many of the institutionalisms that pertain to the large, advanced society politically organized as a nation-state. The failure of the Spanish to complete a thorough installation of Spanish culture led the Filipinos to adapt what they received to their own cultural choices. The growing Filipino population proved thoroughly able to adjust Spanish institutions to Filipino values, while retaining large sectors of its own basic body of culture.

Modernization and Americanization

It is commonly recognized that the purpose of the United States in assuming its somewhat accidently achieved control over the Philippines was the preparation of the Filipinos for complete independence, and numerous items can be cited to prove this, concluded by the voluntary granting of independence in 1946. That the United States institutionalized a number of powerful instruments of independence and freedom is very true, but unfortunately not all of them were applied equally fully or effectively. The long-run effect of American action, however, did much to both modernize and Americanize a Filipino society already occidentalized to a very considerable degree. Probably the most effective procedures were the installation of an efficient system of secularized, representative government administration, and the installation of a system of free national education.[8] Gradually the first gave domestic self-rule, and the second produced an educated society with, finally, a working countrywide language among what had been a group of societies speaking many different languages and dialects. The American schoolteacher was the agent of cultural change reaching far beyond the language instruction thus provided.[9]

Significant subordinate elements within the governmental administrative system were such features as the establishment of a professional civil service with recruitment based upon ability rather than hereditary social structure; the growth of a judicial system, various legal institutions, and a body of law; the setting up of bureaus that formalized patterns of control over land, forests, and public health, and bureaus that worked with elements of the economy, such as agriculture, forests, minerals, trade, and industry. Many of these were new creations, which evolved slowly, and were accomplishments of the whole American period rather than of the first few years. They carried the organized pattern of development widely throughout the archipelago and to many aspects of Filipino life, whereas Spanish administrative activity had been both restricted in scope and severely limited in volume.

A modern public health program brought control over epidemic diseases, which continued to be a scourge on the Asiatic mainland, whereas Spanish efforts never achieved such control. Road building and port development programs initiated a new era in transport and communications, both on and between islands.[10] Agricultural experiment stations and some rural extension work made possible the improvement of agriculture, and facilitating of internal and foreign trade enabled all Filipinos to participate in both production and consumption programs. Mineral and timber surveys facilitated the growth of mining and lumbering industries.

The secularization of Philippine governmental administration loosened the hand of the church on Christian Philippine society, but more than that, it served gradually to remove the great volume of hostility between the Christian and non-Christian peoples of the islands, and permitted more peaceable integration of all territorial sections of the archipelago into one regional entity. Within island interiors the largest of these problems lay in north Luzon with its large population of pagan peoples. Although the integration of Mountain Province and its non-Christians is not complete in every sense of the term even today, secular governmental policy started the process. Secularity of administration reduced the historical animosity between Catholic and Moslem, ended the Moro raids on the Visayan Islands, and initiated a program of development on the island of Mindanao. Here too, even today, problems remain, but they are not primarily theological problems.

Many of the above measures of government gave tremendous new impetus to the growth of Philippine economy. The initiation of free trade between the United States and the Philippines provided large markets for island products and gave the Filipinos access to the products of an industrial society. Sources of developmental capital, technologic skill, and teaching-participation extending widely throughout the islands and the economy were provided to start the Philippines off on an era of economic development. And yet, not all American efforts were carried to their logical ends, as programs, and many things that should have been done were left undone.[11]

Filipinos are vocal in their charge that American action regarding free-trade arrangements turned the islands into an American colonial holding and unduly stimulated the primary production of export agricultural products. It is not that this export agriculture dominates Philippine economy directly, but that it drew into the agricultural-processing industries handling these export products an overly large fraction of the developmental capital funds available to Filipinos. Further, it is true that the free-trade program acutely tied the Philippines to the American market and the American financial field. Now that the islands are politically independent, Filipinos find profitable non-American economic relationships difficult to develop.

A phenomenon rather more critical than the orientation of the economy revolves around the issue of land control in what was essentially an agrarian society. The upper classes, however, remained quiet on this issue, as they profited from the American failure. A basic governmental decision was one designed to prevent the accumulation of very large landholdings which could thereby allow a pattern of colonial plantation agriculture. The Torrens title system, which makes government the responsible agent in declaring and guaranteeing title to land, was introduced. A beginning attempt to cope with land survey (by which property can be described for issue of title) got hopelessly deluged early in the century by demands for title and surveys, and the cadastral survey of the islands, even today, is far from complete.[12] Even at present far too many small farmers in the Philippines do not hold title to the land they claim, occupy, cultivate, or on which they pay taxes. Unwealthy settlers moving to the frontiers have few resources with which to develop their raw lands; hence they can seldom establish a high level of agriculture or a high standard of living. The numerous government land-settlement schemes have facilitated the establishment of only a very few families in comparison to the demand or in comparison to the number of families who have moved on their own. Wealthy families, in contrast, when acquiring holdings along the settlement frontier have been able to establish larger holdings, secure titles, and generally operate at a higher and more productive level from the start.

At the outset of American supervision the poor distribution of land among the agricultural population was recognized as a result of Spanish governmental inadequacy, and land reform was initiated by the purchase of a few hundred thousand acres of land owned by Catholic religious orders, which was then sold to smallholders. The program of land reform, however, was never extended to the very large holdings of land to which title had been secured in mid-to-late Spanish time by the educated principalia classes who formed the bureaucracy and the upper-class elements of the Filipino population. This failure further institutionalized the inequalities between the Filipino principalia and the dependent classes of the tenant population and led to the agrarian unrest manifested in the immediate post-World War II movement known as the Hukbalahap. Among the non-Christian peoples, who continued to preserve most of the system of communal control and right of usufruct over land, the problem is still partially unresolved, as the tribal *datus* still exercise some degree of control and power over land, its use, and its legal disposition. Here Americanization failed to modernize completely the old Malay traditional systems, yielding instead a Philippinization of the American pattern similar to that which obtained during Spanish times.

Still another zone of difficulty for the Filipino was that the new Americanized representative government never became truly democratic. In instituting new patterns of government, early American administrators necessarily relied on existing Filipino leadership, and the old Malay concept of the tribal datus continued to operate, as it does today to a considerable degree.[13] Although masked by a veneer of organized Spanish political form, the concept personified political leadership that was at once the social superior and the chief wielder of economic wealth. The modernization of political structuring has increased the Philippine influence until the new pattern has become a blend of traditional paternalistic Malay, priest-to-parishioner Spanish, and American political boss to obedient party member. Americanization of the political system, therefore, is also only a veneer in which modernization has preserved the vital element of the traditional Malay system. Philippine election procedures since independence in 1946 have maintained much stronger personal relationships, and considerably more "corruption" in the operations of legal democracy, than in theory should be the ideal.

The statistics of transport at the granting of independence in 1946 indicated a strong advance over conditions of transport in 1898, but American action had developed neither roads nor ports on a countrywide basis that would have permitted the Filipino dependent classes to help themselves economically.[14] Until late in the American period, programs of both road building and port development were effected only in areas of heavy population and strong politico-economic demand, and little was done in the frontier areas to develop facilities that would have permitted the opening up of idle lands by settlers from the overpopulated sections of Luzon, Cebu, Bohol, or

Leyte. On Mindoro, Samar, Palawan, and Mindanao, as well as on other small islands, little was done to integrate the island world into one regional system or to make transport available between the coasts and the interiors.

One other oversight of American supervision lay in the realm of education. The free national system of education instituted by American supervision expanded in terms of the demand of the Filipinos, and the end product was an overconcentration upon liberal arts and white-collar professional segments of secondary and collegiate training. There was too little insistence upon trade school, mechanic arts, and the type of middle-level technological training that produces artisans, mechanics, basic engineers, foresters, agriculturists, and others at the semiprofessional level. The Filipino preference for the legal, medical, and clerical professions, and for general liberal arts produced an educated population insufficiently trained in the practical, operative skills needed to develop the productive resources of the country on a level commensurate with the rapidly increasing standard of living.

Other smaller shortcomings of American supervision could be itemized, but these, as well as those listed above, are discernible in hindsight; the accomplishments of the American period were far greater and more significant than the failures. Although American influence was exerted at many points, the facts are that the framework of the Philippine state, the methods of operation of Philippine society, the general orientation of society and shape of Philippine culture are essentially what the Filipinos have made them. American supervision seldom evoked rebelliousness, for it did not apply its alien judgment in an authoritarian manner without recourse. If anything, American supervision yielded too often to the expressed desires and demands of Filipino leadership, permitting the continuation of a society in which leadership, wealth, and control of the basic structure of that society remained in the hands of traditional elements of leadership. This is the essence of Philippinization, as it operated both under the Spanish and under the American patterns of control.

The Philippine landscape reflects many elements in which the time factor contrasts strongly, in that Americanized Filipinos are creating settlement forms quite alien to the forms produced in the Spanish period. Whereas Spanish efforts sought to concentrate settlement around municipios when possible, American action has been to stimulate the free location of settlement. On the one hand this has produced a notable dispersal of settlement into those rural countrysides served by highways and secondary roads, whereas on the other hand an increase in modern urbanization also is evident. Highways and secondary roads have become lined for miles with loose strings of homesteads, and where formal transport lines have not been built the rural dispersal of homesteads throughout the landscape has occurred. Many sparsely occupied sitios have become sprawling rural clusters of homesteads, and many new sites of settlement have been established. At the same time, many rural barrios have been turned into populous market centers, and villages, small towns, and urban centers have appeared. The formalism of the Spanish town plan has been abandoned, and the new settlements spontaneously develop individuality of shape and structure in which wide streets provide for movement of vehicular traffic, and functional decentralization often is marked.

The combined patterns of stimulation accruing to Filipino society continued the upward spiral of population growth that began late in the Spanish period. From a population of about 7,000,000 in 1898 the total rose to 27,087,000 in 1960, distributed among more than 1,200 towns and cities and about 26,000 barrios. The Central Plain of Luzon and the shores of Manila Bay, continuing a Spanish trend, held a significant share of the total, about 20 percent, with the population of the metropolitan region of Manila totaling close to two million. More than a thousand of the seven thousand islands were permanently inhabited, and the Filipinos had spread out very widely, though there still were regions with but slight population totals.

Tremendous numbers of Filipinos now travel, locally, regionally, and nationally. The old dominance of foot, horse, or small boat travel has all but disappeared from many parts of the Islands, to be replaced by automobile bus, truck, taxi, and private-car traffic. Numerous launches, ferries, and powered craft facilitate interisland movement, and the modern network of airfields places all sectors of the country within short-term contact of each other, but particularly within such contact of Manila. Although commercial rail lines have appeared on the islands of Luzon, Panay, and Cebu, the development of a rail transport network has not been practical in a multi-island world, thus the highway and the air terminal become relatively more significant.[15] The automobile, particularly, has been Philippinized, in that the buses, trucks, jeepneys, and taxis operate in a manner somewhat different from the highly controlled and formal systems of the current American scene.[16]

Filipinos have taken to many of the American consumer goods with enthusiasm, both in the category of "hard goods" and "soft goods." Refrigerators, electric kitchen ranges, electric fans, air conditioners, radios, and other electrically powered utensils, tools, and equipment find a ready acceptance in all those areas served by electricity. Gasoline engines and battery-powered or transistorized equipment have recently increased the distribution of several such items. Wrist watches have spread countrywide. Comic books, newspapers, magazines, literary books, and technical manuals carry a pervasive

"American" impact throughout the Islands which the educational system significantly facilitates. The ice-cream confection, the breakfast roll, the hot dog, and the coffee-break snack spread in widening ripples of consumer indulgence. Bottled soft drinks, chocolate candy bars, soda crackers, Vick's cough drops, and American-type cigarettes can be found in the smallest store in the smallest barrio in the islands. California grapes or oranges, bubble gum, and toothpaste have replaced traditional commodities. Many of these consumer items are, in a sense, but a cultural flourish that indicates a keeping up with the modern world. Others are geographically significant changes in cultural consumer trends. Virginia-leaf tobacco, chocolate candy, coffee, cosmetics, and soft drinks can be, and are, manufactured from locally derived products, and as such, stimulate local industrialization in the consumer-goods ranges. But the steady increase in the consumption of wheat products, particularly prepared cereals and breadstuffs, in a traditional rice-growing and rice-eating culture requires international trade to support it, as the Philippines can grow wheat only with great difficulty and no longer attempts to do so.[17]

It is conventional to suggest that the so-called underdeveloped sectors of the world must be sold the culture complex of industrialization in order to improve their lot. Filipinos have acquired a passion for industrialization that amounts to an overacceptance of the complex as the answer to most of their problems. The Americanization of their culture has outrun the native resource development, economic structure, and technological education of the population. This is a relatively recent form of Americanization and modernization which has not yet matured in the Philippines and which is still in a state of growth and flux; its Philippinization is in the early transitional stage. Political nationalism with regard to industrialization, private enterprise with regard to controls and entrepreneurship, and somewhat irregular development of natural resources characterize the present patterns of the trend toward industrialism.

Summary

Although distinctive Philippinization has been an outstanding reaction of the Filipinos to both Spanish and American supervision of their island world, and though there has been steady reaction against overly Asian orientation in any single direction, there has been a practicality about the Filipino reaction to alien culture which can only be admired. Although there was no unified pattern of culture in any of the varied manifestations during the pre-European era, there was a general correspondence in many basic patterns.

Group leadership and decision-making capacities operated in terms of compromise toward each new pattern of alien culture that came into the Philippines, selecting certain elements from each culture complex. These gradually were modified and fitted into existing complexes in such a way that the essential culture matrix was extended rather than being destroyed. At no point did a resist-to-the-death conservatism possess Filipino leadership or its following, nor were many new elements of culture accepted in complete replacement of prior elements. Whether these selections and modifications of new cultural elements have always been the best is a matter that can be argued, but the Filipinos have been able to make their own collective decisions.

The practicality of the whole cultural process is excellently illustrated by a current phenomenon. The Philippines has a national language today, Pilipino developed from Tagalog (Ta-GAH'-log, not Tag'-a-log), of which they are proud, though it is not yet spoken by even a majority of Filipinos, and though the Philippine Congress usually debates in English. Pilipino is being taught in the schools as the future national language, and it may someday become fully that. But the Filipinos are well aware that their only common language is English, which they matter-of-factly recognize as far more useful than the present Tagalog language in the industrial, technologically complex modern world. In 1962 they had the sense of balance to request that the 3,000 United States Peace Corps volunteers slated to come to the Philippines as language teachers not only refurbish and extend the knowledge of English among Filipinos, but also that these teachers have at least a basic familiarity with the specific language of the area to which they were assigned.

The Filipino population, small as it was between the tenth and sixteenth centuries, was a population capable of cultural growth as well as an increase in numbers under the impact of alien peoples and cultures. Indonesian, Chinese, Japanese, Spanish, and American blood has been added to the already well-compounded Malay bloodstream of the Filipinos until they are today a composite people. By the end of the Spanish era of control the population had grown large enough to be able to express maturely a regional pattern of culture. In sheer numbers, of course, Philippine society has grown more significantly during the period of Americanization, so that this growth is a major element in the orientation of the Philippines toward the American Occident. Oriental and occidental patterns of culture have been compounded to the end that the Philippines is a unique country, of the ancient Orient, but more wholly integrated into the world of the Occident than is any other Asian country.

FIVE

~~~~~ *Population: Growth, Spread, and Distribution*

From an estimated half-million people occupying the Philippines in the late sixteenth century, the total population grew to a total of 27,087,685 on February 15, 1960.[1] In simple gross terms these figures indicate a steady expansion in the numbers of people—people who occupy the landscape in terms of settlement sites, cultivated landscapes, and lines of movement; people who interrupt natural cycles of denudation, plant growth, soil formation, and the circulation of water; people who erect monuments, build roads, build dams, cut channels, remove forests, and otherwise add to, or tamper with, the natural patterns of the earth's surface. Although in 1500 the population was widely scattered and thinly distributed in gross terms, and though the marks of the population on the landscape were then relatively light ones, this is no longer true. Three notable aspects of the population growth pattern are the quickening tempo of population increase, the necessity for Filipinos to move inland away from the coastal littorals of increasingly high density, and the equal need to move away from other regional centers of high density. Examination of the patterns of distribution, of density, and of regional emigration and immigration reveals points of over concentration, marked regional variety, and local scarcity of population. The regional distribution discussed is that of the present, in light of its patterns of growth and change. Patterns of density and movement are presented in the maps (figs.

19–24*b*); and populations by provinces and by islands, listed according to dates, are to be found in the statistical appendix (tables 1–3 and 9–15).

Distribution, Density, and Internal Migration

The 1960 census provides data sufficient for examining certain aspects of the regional characteristics of the Philippine population, as of 1960.

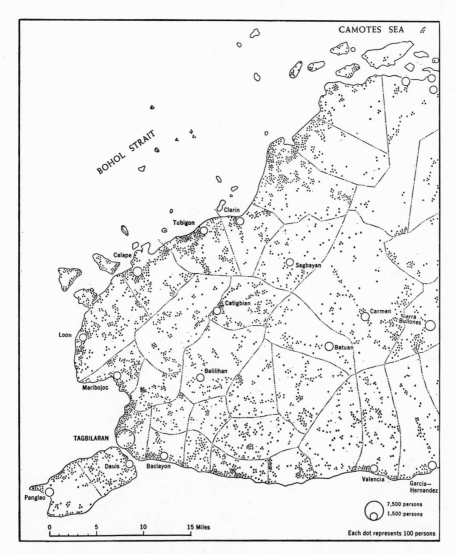

Fig. 19. The distribution of population on western Bohol Island, 1960. The boundaries shown are those of municipalities, as of 1960.

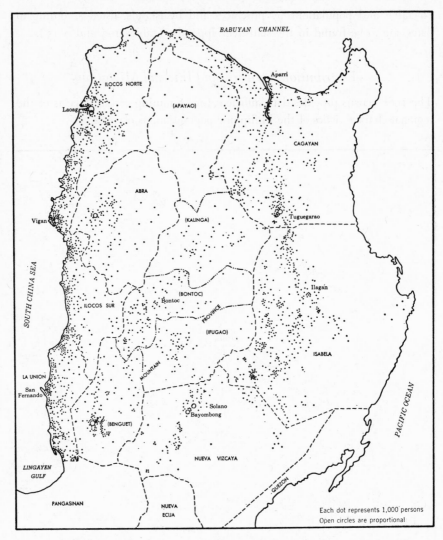

Fig. 20. The distribution of population in northern Luzon, 1960. The boundaries shown are those of provinces, as of 1960.

DISTRIBUTION

In an island realm partially divided into political units there are several approaches to examination of the gross distribution of population: by zones, by political units, by island units, and by geographic regions. Using the traditional subdivision of the Philippines into three zones—Luzon, the Visayas, and Mindanao—an overview yields the following generalizations. Somewhat less than half the total 1960 population (46 percent) was resident

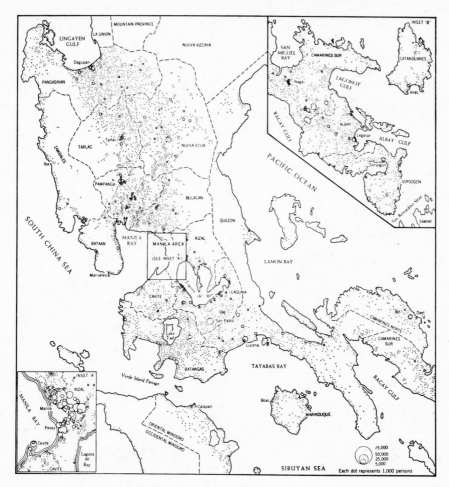

Fig. 21. The distribution of population in central and southern Luzon, 1960. The boundaries shown are those of provinces, as of 1960.

on and near Luzon on about one-third (35 percent) of the total area; about a third (30 percent) lived in the Visayan group of islands on about a fifth (19 percent) of the area; and slightly under a fifth (19 percent) lived on or near Mindanao on almost a third (31 percent) of the total area. In earlier decades Mindanao held an even smaller percentage of the total. Looking somewhat more closely at the simple issue of regional distribution, a bit less than a third of the total population (29 percent) was resident in central Luzon, in and around the Central Plain, Manila Bay, and Laguna de Bay, in an area comprising about a tenth (10.6 percent) of the total area. Within the Visayas about 5 percent of the total population lived on or near Cebu on 1.6 percent

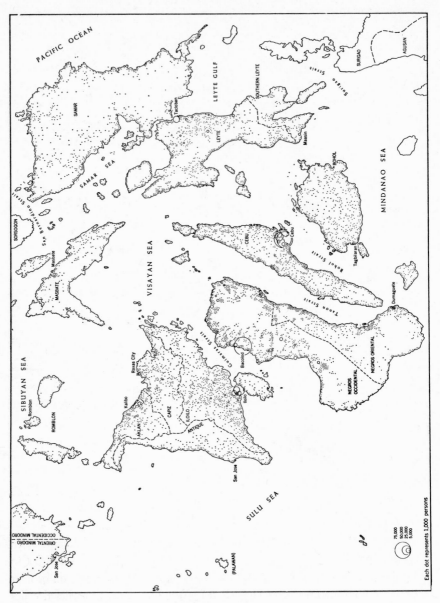

Fig. 22. The distribution of population in the central Philippines, 1960. The boundaries shown are those of provinces, as of 1960.

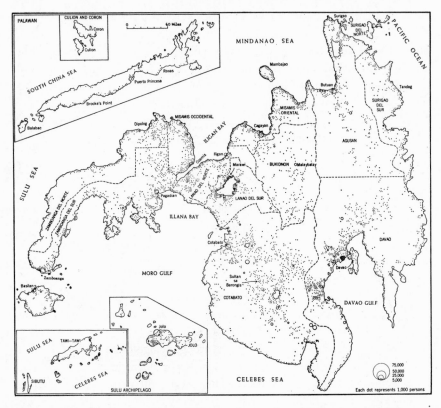

Fig. 23. The distribution of population in the southern Philippines and Palawan, 1960. The boundaries shown are those of provinces, as of 1960.

of the total area. In Mindanao there are fewer zones of overconcentration, although parts of the north coast suffer pressure in this respect.

The most populous province is Rizal, in central Luzon adjoining the political district of Manila. Here 1,463,500 people (5.3 percent of the total) occupied 899 square miles (1.77 percent of the total area) in 1960 in what has become largely an urban landscape forming a sector of the Manila metropolitan region. The small political district of Manila, of course, shows an even higher concentration. The least populous province is Batanes, a group of islands north of Luzon having 10,300 people occupying 74 square miles. Of the larger provinces Palawan (4.8 percent of the area) had only 162,900 people (0.59 percent of the total) in 1960. After Rizal the more populous provinces, in order, are Cebu, Negros Occidental, Leyte, Pangasinan, and Cotabato, each having over a million people in 1960.

The provincial statistics for many of the provinces long carrying a heavy rural population all have shown increases at every census interval, but the rates of increase are lessening. Batanes is the only province showing a 1960 decrease over 1948. Reaching saturation points, in terms of rural settlement, are the three coastal provinces of northwest Luzon, the five provinces forming the heart of the Central Plain of Luzon, and most of the Visayan provinces, but particularly Cebu and Bohol as the old points of migration into northern Mindanao. In many of these cases a considerable share of the increases has been absorbed by the cities and towns as the trend toward urbanization increases.

By 1960 the bulk of the Philippine population had accumulated on those better parts of Luzon and a few of those Visayan islands having a long history of Spanish and American stimulation of agricultural development. The southern groups of islands, Mindanao and Sulu, with less Spanish influence and stimulation were, in broad terms, more lightly populated. Hinterland zones off the main lines of movement on large islands, and medium-to-small islands located at a distance from the central island groups, still showed lighter populations totals in 1960. Both of these, however, have been zones of rapid population gain since the 1948 census date, and as rural regions, will exhibit rapid population growth in the coming years.

As cities all over the Philippines are growing, there was in 1960 a significantly larger share of the total population resident in towns and cities. This trend will continue in the coming years and perhaps will increase disproportionately. The metropolitan region of Manila stands out as the focal center of urbanism within the Philippines. The urban region includes the political district of Manila and the nearer parts of the four provinces that surround the political district. The population of the metropolitan region in 1960 was approaching 2,200,000, of which about one-half resided in the city of Manila itself. Three other formally chartered cities—Pasay City, Quezon City, and Caloocan—lie within the metropolitan region, the other sections of the urban area retaining barrio organizational structures within their provinces. The properly urban population of the rest of the Philippines in 1960 totaled about 3,400,000. A total urban population of about 5,600,000 was resident in thirty-nine chartered cities and numerous urbanized settlements lacking formal political structure as cities.[2]

Table 1 in the appendix lists the population by islands; the political grouping has been eliminated. Seven of the larger islands—Luzon, Mindanao, Samar, Negros, Panay, Cebu, and Bohol—representing 81 percent of the total area, contained roughly 84 percent of the total population in 1960. There are about 1,200 permanently inhabited islands among the 7,100 islands of the archipelago. Table 1 lists the 153 islands that are over 5 square miles in area, with their 1903 and 1960 populations, and there are some surprising totals to be found among the smaller islands. This point is brought out even more plainly, however, in appendix table 3, which gives a representative listing of some of the smallest permanently inhabited Philippine islands. In contrast to the densely inhabited small islands, some islands of both large and small size have small populations permanently resident upon them. Although Palawan and Mindoro are obvious cases of lightly distributed population, Tawi Tawi, Dumaran, and Balabac in the southern zone, and Calayan and Camiguin in the north, carry small populations also (see appendix table 1).

More than 2,500 islands are but small rocks or bare reefs and thus not truly permanently inhabitable. Nearly 2,000 islands are either so mountainous, rough, steep-sloped, and rocky, or so flat, wet, and marshy that they are not permanently inhabited. Such islands often are occupied seasonally or intermittently for various exploitive or productive purposes. Several hundred islands, at least, actually have a small number of permanent inhabitants but do not have formal organization and are not, therefore, included in the normal statistical tabulations in a way that they can be mapped or documented.

Historically the islands of the Philippines were occupied by boat-traveling peoples who tended to be mobile and to occupy the coastal littorals. From this point of view bare rocks, bare reefs, marshy flats, and volcanic piles offered little. Steep shore fronts, mountain islands, exposed or storm-swept coasts made little appeal. Islands in the centers of island groups and interior hinterlands of large islands lacking waterways were less attractive than those littoral situations surrounded by good fishing grounds and inviting coastal lowlands. Often small islands on the fringes of large islands combined the advantages and made the most attractive sites. At the time of Spanish entry into the Philippines it is likely that the distribution of population showed a zone of concentration along the littoral, with attractive coastal lowlands being zones of marked population, and with many small islands located near large islands being more heavily populated than the large islands themselves. Spanish influence was directed landward to potential agricultural environments where sedentary and permanent settlement could spread. As the Philippine population has grown the island interiors have become settled, and population distribution has tended to spread away from the coastal littoral. There still is, however, a considerable preference for the littoral location (fig. 19), so the number of islands permanently inhabited has risen steadily. In the modern period this is a marked development, as indicated in a comparison of the statistics for 1903 and 1960 in appendix table 1.

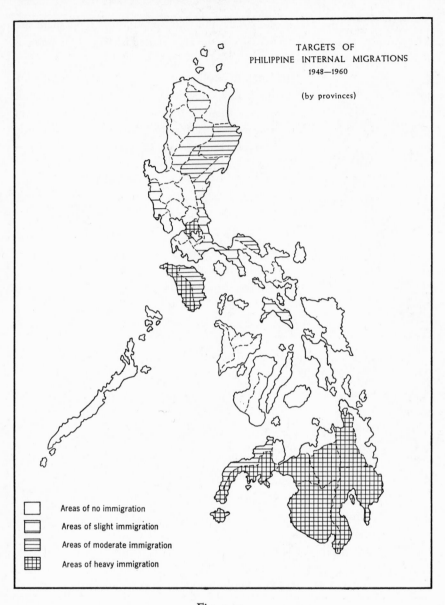

TARGETS OF
PHILIPPINE INTERNAL MIGRATIONS
1948—1960

(by provinces)

Areas of no immigration
Areas of slight immigration
Areas of moderate immigration
Areas of heavy immigration

Fig. 24a.

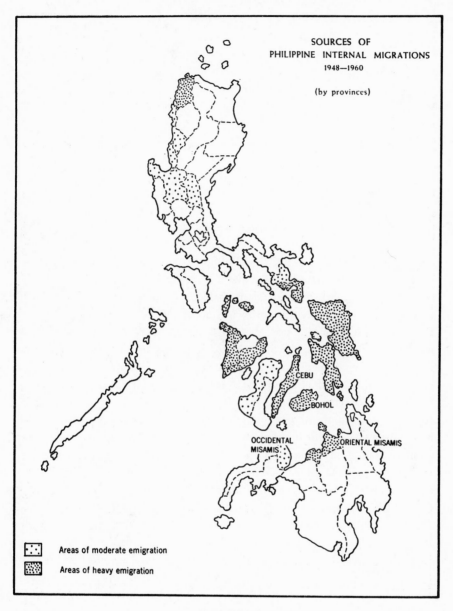

Fig. 24*b*.

DENSITY AND INTERNAL MIGRATION

In a country lacking marked immigration and emigration the concentration of population in specific regions becomes a matter of historical growth, balanced by the tendencies to internal mobility.[3] The original mobility of the Filipino was lessened by early Spanish influence, but mobility is rising again in the modern period. Regional population density, therefore, becomes a matter of cultural habits and cultural pressures upon the population. There are four habit-pressure factors that have affected the modern regional densities of population in the Philippines. These are the pull of the town and the city, the historical economic tie to the land, the existence of vacant and near-vacant reserve lands, and the economic balancing of high regional density through interregional transfer of economic aid. Each factor has been of historical importance and each is of contemporary significance.

In the sixteenth century the Philippine population density was a low one, amounting to between four and five persons per square mile, though certain localities and small islands probably had comparatively higher densities. In 1960 the arithmetic density was about 235 per square mile, whereas the physiological density was about 1,000 per square mile.[4] For a strictly agricultural society such densities could be serious, but the Philippines is no longer purely an agricultural society. There remains a considerable reserve of cultivable land, and the Philippines is in the process of industrialization.

The pull of the town and the city began with the Spanish program of founding towns and promoting sedentary settlement; this influence has been a continuous one, with the current trend to urbanism being expressed more strongly than at any time in the past. Cities all over the islands are growing rapidly, though the numerical increase of the Manila metropolitan region stands out above that of any of the lesser cities. The tendency is to pull people from all rural areas, thereby lessening the rate of increase in the rural density.

The impact of the Spanish was to increase the sedentariness of the Filipino in all territories of Spanish control. On Luzon and in such Visayan islands as Cebu, Bohol, Panay, and Leyte the evolution of sedentary agricultural economy during late Spanish times produced increasing regional densities. The growth of commercial export agriculture early in the twentieth century increased this pattern of rural density, both in the regions engaging in export agriculture and in those areas engaging in domestic food production. The growth of landed estates having tenant- and cash-labor forces increased local densities through the tendency to tie local populations to the land. Panay, Negros, Cebu, Bohol, Leyte, southern Luzon, and the Central Plain of Luzon built up marked regional rural densities.

The essential mobility of the Filipino continued to express itself in such areas as the Ilocos coast of northwest Luzon, and to some extent in Cebu, Bohol, and Panay, from which many people began filtering into empty areas even before 1900. The same process was at work locally in the Sulu Islands. This trend to internal migration has been accented during the twentieth century as roads into island interiors were built and interisland shipping services increased. The impact of these movements can be seen in the growing population totals for the Mindanao provinces. Since 1948, in particular, internal migration has built up the population of Mindanao, Mindoro, and northeast Luzon. Many of the medium-to-small islands are now growing rapidly as the spread of population affects all parts of the islands. (See appendix table 9 for data on language patterns as a result of migration, and see also appendix table 15.)

Economic balancing of local economics through the interregional transfer of funds has tended to continue the buildup of regional population densities in areas of heavy population. Such areas as the Ilocos coast of northwest Luzon, or Bohol, Cebu, and Leyte, could achieve such densities with their own agricultural resources only by lowering the level of living. With the support of family members who migrated toward the empty lands where economic opportunities were larger, the residents of the older centers have absorbed increased population densities without undue privation.

Tagalog peoples from the Central Plain and southwestern Luzon have been less willing to break their local ties to families, barrios, and land than have the Ilocanos of northwest Luzon, and thus have tended to remain in their home areas. To some extent this has been true of the Bicolano peoples of southeastern Luzon. Cebuanos from Cebu were reluctant to migrate in the earlier periods, as were the peoples of Bohol, Leyte, and Panay, but all these groups have shown an increasing willingness to migrate in recent decades.[5] Such ethnic variations, and the variant workings of cultural and historical processes, have produced marked differences in local regional densities. Pampanga Province in 1960 was one of the most densely settled sectors of the Central Plain of Luzon, and the province contains no significant reserve of cultivable land. The province had an arithmetic density of 733 people per square mile in 1960, and a physiologic density of about 1,900 per square mile. For Ilocos Norte these figures in 1960 stood at 218 and 1,780 respectively; for Ilocos Sur, at 339 and 2,300 respectively; and the corresponding figures for Cebu were 678 and 2,350. Bukidnon Province in interior Mindanao showed 1960 figures of 60 per square mile for arithmetic density and about 310 per square mile for physiologic density. The latter figure illustrates the scale of enterprise at which the pioneer settler operates when migrating from an overcrowded region, for the province contains a large reserve of unclaimed, cultivable land.

The use of agricultural and physiologic density measures is reasonable for much of the Central Plain of Luzon, for Mountain Province, and for Bukidnon in interior Mindanao. These are not very effective measures throughout most of the Philippines, however, for populations of the coastal littorals include significant numbers of full and part-time fishermen, aquatic products supply a significant share of the Filipino diet, and the very extended coastlines of the islands provide significant fishery potentials.

There has been serious crowding of the rural section since early in the present century in northwest Luzon, the Central Plain, southern Luzon, and some sectors of southeastern Luzon. Similarly, the coastal littorals of Panay, western Negros, Leyte, Cebu, and southwest Bohol have been overcrowded. Many of the small islands of the Visayas have suffered serious crowding. The government has encouraged internal migration in various ways since about 1913, but the complementary developments of interisland water-transport and road systems into island interiors have been inadequate. Few strong population movements took place in the years prior to 1948, though the Ilocanos of northwest Luzon and the peoples of Cebu, Bohol, and Leyte were learning the pioneering tradition and tending to move more easily than did other Filipinos. Perhaps the experience of "refugeeing into the jungle" while fleeing from the Japanese during World War II helped, but the postwar development of transportation facilities, both interisland and on land, has been a significant stimulus.

Since 1948 a very significant pattern of internal migration has developed within the Philippines which is reflected in the statistics of the 1948 and 1960 censuses. This pattern of regional redistribution of the rural population is presented in figures 23 and 48 and in appendix table 15. It can be expected that this pattern of movement will continue for a significant period of time. Mindanao has been the chief recipient of this internal movement, along with some of its fringe islands to the northeast. Southern and interior Mindanao, in particular, have been the regions to which most migrants have gone recently. Palawan and nearby islands have received small numbers of in-migrants. Masbate, its associated small islands, and southern Negros Occidental are the only Visayan islands to have received a significant in-migration, the Visayas generally being a zone of out-migration. Mindoro has been a zone of heavy in-migration. Catanduanes, Polillo, Alabat, and other small islands off southeastern Luzon, along with some localities of southeastern Luzon, have been areas of moderate in-migration. Zambales and Mountain provinces, in northern Luzon, have received moderate numbers of new settlers. Northeastern Luzon has been the other region of heavy in-migration, as the Cagayan Valley and its fringes has been the region to which many settlers have gone from the northern Central Plain of Luzon and the southern Ilocos coastal zone. The metropolitan region of Manila, of course, stands by itself as a region of urban growth through in-migration, as discussed above. The zone into which this urban flow has moved affects the southern part of Bulacan Province, most of Rizal Province, northwest Laguna Province, and most of Cavite Province, as these surround the political district of Manila proper.

Ethnic and Cultural Backgrounds [6]

The term "Filipinos" connotes a unified people, one having a common historical background, a unitary racial composition, and a relatively common culture, but the term is little more precise in these respects than is the term "Americans." Spanish influence countered the earlier tendency to increasing diversity by stimulating unification of certain sectors of culture among a part of the population; but twentieth-century influences are operating more widely, both in regard to the whole population and in regard to the whole spectrum of culture. The divisive influences of a multiple-island environment have been continuously operative, but are countered by such modern unifying influences as political nationalism, a common educational system, and radio broadcasting. The following discussion of the ethnic and cultural backgrounds of the Filipinos takes into account factors making for both homogeneity and heterogeneity.

ETHNIC STOCKS AND ETHNIC COMPOSITION OF THE FILIPINOS

It is customary to classify the early Filipino ethnic mixture into three separate racial stocks: the Negrito, the proto-Malay, and the Malaysian. Such culture groups as the Chinese, Japanese, Indonesian, Indian, Spanish, and American also contributed to the historical admixture as ethnic stocks already somewhat mixed in genetic terms. It is clear that the Filipinos are a people derived from diverse ethnic stocks, even though the largest number of Filipinos share rather uniformly the Malaysian or Indonesian ethnic element. There is a degree of utility in the old Spanish classification of Filipinos as *negrillos, indios,* and *moros.* Negrillos were the little black people; indios made up most of the population; and the moros were the Moslem element of the far south, toward whom the Spanish were traditionally antagonistic.

The oldest living racial stock found in the Philippines is the Negrito, a member of the Negroid racial group. The Negrito became widely scattered throughout the islands at a very early date, but has never been very numerous. Different groups must have entered the Philippines at different times over separate routes of entry. The Negrito stock belongs to the true pygmy group, averaging under five feet in height. Kinky hair, blackish skin pigmentation, and broad-headedness are other physical attributes of the Negrito. Possessing a simple culture, and depending on hunting and gathering, the Negritos were and are mobile peoples without permanent settlements and other cultural habits associated with a sedentary life. They have suffered pressures from the expansion of peoples with more sophisticated culture, and at the time of the coming of the Spanish, were already being restricted as to the territorial ranges they occupied. They often have been called upland forest dwellers, but this is a result of the pressures placed upon them; although they do appear to prefer forest environments, they did live in lowland areas when permitted, and not all Negritos even today are uplanders.

Since the arrival of the Spanish, at least, the number of Negritos has been declining, and in the 1960's there are thought to be less than 15,000 relatively pureblooded Negritos remaining. Both very early and later ethnic mixture has occurred, and the Negrito gene complex is rather widely spread throughout the island population. In the modern period relatively little mixture is taking place, and the Negrito share in the Filipino bloodstream is distinctly declining. In the 1960's Negritos are still resident in the Zambales-Bataan sector of western Luzon, in much of the lower mountain country of eastern Luzon, in the upland interiors of Panay and Negros islands, in northeast Mindanao, and in upland sections of northern Palawan.

Many scholars agree that an ethnic stock that may be distinguished as proto-Malay came early into the Philippines. The proto-Malays are thought to have come from several specific sources, at different times, and to have distributed themselves in different parts of the islands. The proto-Malay are considered less Mongoloid than the Malay, and probably are derived from various intermixtures in southeastern Asia. At the same time, the precise definition of proto-Malay, in anthropometric terms, differs markedly, and cultural data often are brought to bear upon the distinctions made. The proto-Malay and the Malay obviously are peoples fairly closely related, and the chronology of their movements and the cultural heritage of their groupings are the chief distinctions that can now be made between them. In broad terms both sets of groups are Malaysian and both are from southern Asia. To attempt to further distinguish the two sets of groups at this time is either to deal in characteristics not fully agreed upon or to depend upon historical, cultural, and regional data. The following paragraphs do all these things.

The proto-Malay peoples appear to have been agricultural peoples who were inclined toward a relatively sedentary life. According to their specific patterns of culture, including agricultural systems, they ranged from the lowlands into the higher mountain country. If they ever had a liking for the coastal littoral, this choice declined under the impact of the later streams of Malay immigrants, and the proto-Malay became dwellers of island interiors, hill-country regions, and in northern Luzon, mountain dwellers. The Spanish made little headway with these hinterland peoples, who were either warlike or reclusive, and for the most part, these groups remained outside the Spanish pale. Their descendants in the modern Philippines are still often referred to as "pagan peoples." Many of these groups were relatively small in numbers, loosely articulated as to political systems, scattered as to locality, and practicers of shifting cultivation, which gave them some degree of mobility. Historically, in the southern Philippines such elements were raided by the Moslem groups; they then became even more reclusive in nature, and declined in numbers.[7] North of the zone of Moslem raids, small populations of proto-Malay groups remain viable at the present time. In northern Luzon the proto-Malay peoples established a strong hold over much of what is today Mountain Province, and they now form a large population.

Ethnic mixture between proto-Malay and Malay peoples has been fairly continuous on a small scale, and the proto-Malay share in the modern Filipino bloodstream is a very significant one. Where modern religious and secular culture contrasts are too strong there are preventives in this mixing process which were not present in an earlier era, but among those groups adopting Christian religious and secular practices the mixing of ethnic elements continues. Such proto-Malay groups as were large enough in numbers and sufficiently cohesive in culture to maintain their identity to the present day speak individual languages, possess discrete bodies of culture, and retain their individualities. Thus Bontoc, Ifugao, Kalinga, and Apayao in northern Luzon stand for ethnic stocks, languages, cultures, populations, and to a degree, regions.[8] Manobo, Bagobo, and Tiruray in Mindanao do the same, though these are smaller populations less concentrated in occupance areas, and more easily subject to the disruptive impact of the immigrant Christian population.[9] The Mangyan of Mindoro and the Tagbanua of Palawan are, to some degree, intermediate between the two other situations.[10] Some culture groups entered the Philippines early enough to be labeled proto-Malay in ethnic terms, but because of their conversion to Christianity in early Spanish times, they have become so merged in the Hispanicized Malay bloodstream and culture that they are now almost indistinguishable. There has been recent questioning of the true genetic distinctions between the proto-Malay and the Malay. The suggestion has been made that the refusal of Spanish Catholic culture by selective elements of the lowland-littoral population caused the retreat and resettlement of such elements into hinterlands and highlands, such as northern Luzon, and that such apparent distinctions as recognized early in the twentieth century may have derived more from historico-cultural causes than from physiognomic-genetic differences in origin. If this interpretation be taken, it does not disturb the basic generalizations stated above.

The Malay element among the Filipinos includes those Indonesians who entered the islands after about A.D. 300 from the southern Asian mainland and the western half of the Indies. They are thought to represent a more Mongoloid mixture than the proto-Malay, which gives them certain physiognomic characteristics that set them apart from the earlier immigrants. It is, however, chiefly in their patterns of culture and ways of living, and in their occupance of the littoral environments, that they differ from the proto-Malay. Their languages show merely technical differences, but their habits of dress also vary, and there are differences in their architecture, their use of boats and aquatic gear, and in their dietary systems. Almost all of the Malay groups north of Mindanao and Palawan became Christians, which in itself sets them apart from the proto-Malays of the Visayas and Luzon. In Mindanao, Palawan, and Sulu almost all the Malays are Moslem, another primary point of distinction.

The former distinctions between proto-Malay and Malay are breaking down on all grounds. The 1960 census indicates that slightly over 70 percent of the population of Mountain Province, Luzon, is of the Christian religion, whereas almost 75 percent of the population claims as a mother tongue one of the languages traditionally associated with the pagan proto-Malay ethnic-culture groups. Though speakers of about seventy languages and dialects, including European and southern Philippine languages, were tabulated by the 1960 census for Mountain Province, the Christian Ilocanos from the lowland west coast of Luzon made up about 20 percent of the population of Mountain Province. The acceptance of Christianity is a critical step toward dissolution of the distinctions between Malay and proto-Malay. Somewhat over 50 percent of the total population could speak English and/or Tagalog; about the same number were literate; and about 80 percent of the population had entered the educational system. These are all steps in the merging of the population into a common culture pattern that will eventually carry with it enough intermarriages to blend the proto-Malay and Malay elements.

It is difficult to suggest actual proportions of ethnic mixture from the many other sources that have contributed to the Filipino bloodstream. Late Indonesian immigration certainly brought in important Indian components and small amounts of many others. Chinese contact with the islands has been nearly continuous for at least a thousand years, and the tendency for resident Chinese males to take local wives is very old in all of southeast Asia. To some degree the Japanese did the same thing for a period of time. The Spanish intermarried with the Filipinos, and the Americans have done the same in this century. Not only have these contacts added to the ethnic mixture; they have compounded the culture complex. The "Christian way of life" brought primarily by the Spanish and the Americans has altered the basic structure of culture in the same way that the "Moslem way of life" has done in the south. In the 1960's the pattern of Filipino culture is oriented predominately toward the "Christian way of life"; the Moslem pattern is maintaining itself in a rejuvenated frame; and the pagan elements are declining.

LINGUISTIC PATTERNS

Occasionally an educated, urban Filipino expresses the thought that the Philippines may be the third-largest English-speaking country in the world, ranking after the United States and Great Britain.[11] A somewhat poetic thought, the comment has substance in that English has been the language of instruction in the schools for over half a century, the primary newspapers have long been published in English, most American moving pictures are run with their original sound tracks, and much radio broadcasting employs English. Spanish has dropped to a minor position as a language; college students now study Spanish as a foreign language, and the 1960 census reported Spanish as a spoken language for just over a half million people. Chinese also is a minor language in the islands, and only about 150,000 inhabitants acknowledge it as a mother tongue. The census reported almost 11,000,000 people (about 40 percent) able to speak English, and just over 12,000,000 (about 44 percent) able to speak Tagalog. Although English remains the language of instruction in the schools, the Tagalog figure is indicative of the popular and educational campaign to eventually make Pilipino the primary language of the Philippines. (See appendix table 9.)

The 1960 census lists more than seventy languages and dialects, each spoken by more than 200 persons as a mother tongue. Many of these are dialects only, and others are dying languages. Depending upon the manner of grouping these languages, there are about thirty-nine languages having more than 10,000 speakers each. Some of these are regional languages spoken by local populations, and of the thirty-nine, some thirty-one languages are spoken by over 50,000 persons each. Mountain Province, the Visayan Islands, Mindanao, and Sulu share in these patterns. In addition, eight of the thirty-nine native languages include the mother tongues of about 23,300,000

Filipinos, or about 87 percent of the total population. Table 9 in the appendix gives an approximate record of this language pattern.[12]

The Philippine languages all belong to the Indonesian family of languages. Their separation and elaboration represents both a historical and an environmental development. Whereas Ifugao is an old arrival in the islands and is now spoken in inland north Luzon, Tausug is a recent arrival spoken in parts of the Sulu Islands in the far south. Pampangan and Pangasinan are two closely related languages that have spread in adjacent regional positions in the Central Plain of Luzon. Masbate and Aklanon, the latter spoken in northwest Panay, have become differentiated in time owing to their separated insular locations and different histories of population growth. Iloko is spoken rather widely throughout the islands because of the fact that the Ilocanos of northwest Luzon have migrated to many parts of the islands in the past two centuries. Cebuano, native to Cebu, is spoken widely throughout Mindanao for the same reason. Although related, not all these languages are mutually intelligible, and English, Tagalog, and Cebuano often serve as lingua francas. English is used widely in this regard; Tagalog is used in Luzon and the northern Visayas; and Cebuano, from the central Visayas southward. Tagalog has been chosen as the base for Pilipino, the future national language, because it is the language of central Luzon surrounding the political capital and the center of modernism.

Not all inhabited islands have their own languages, despite a tendency toward insular individualism (fig. 25). Bicolano is spoken as a mother tongue by over 99 percent of the population of Catanduanes Island, and Tagalog is the mother tongue of the same percentage of inhabitants on Marinduque. Palawan has several mother tongues of long standing. Negros reflects historical settlement in its language pattern. Panay-Hiligaynon, from southeast Panay Island, dominates western Negros, whereas Cebuano, from Cebu, is even more dominate in eastern Negros; the two languages accounted for over 99 percent of the mother tongues spoken by the Negros residents in 1960. As Tagalog-speaking settlers move into Mindoro, Tagalog is becoming increasingly dominant as the mother tongue and the common language.

In certain local regions, mother tongues are becoming either remnantal or dialect evolutions of something else. Although Negrito was recorded as a language in the 1960 census, it is neither a discrete language, as such, nor is it everywhere the same, since Negrito is a dialect version of some other regional language. Caviteño, recorded in the census as a mother tongue in Cavite Province, is a Hispanicized Tagalog.

The Manila metropolitan region lies within the zone where Tagalog is the mother tongue, but over seventy languages were recorded as mother

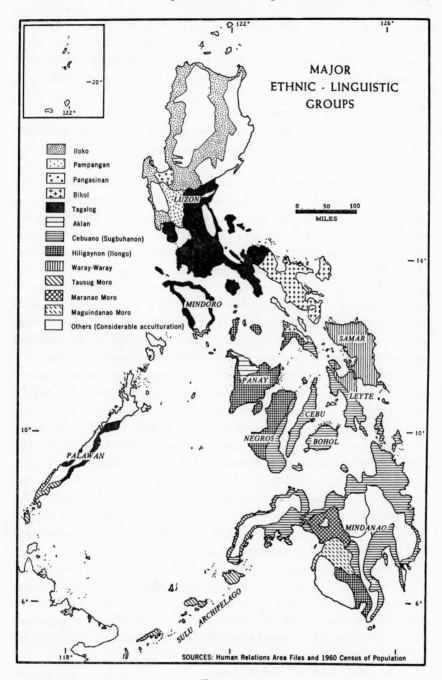

MAJOR
ETHNIC - LINGUISTIC
GROUPS

Iloko
Pampangan
Pangasinan
Bikol
Tagalog
Aklan
Cebuano (Sugbuhanon)
Hiligaynon (Ilongo)
Waray-Waray
Tausug Moro
Maranao Moro
Maguindanao Moro
Others (Considerable acculturation)

0   50   100
MILES

LUZON

MINDORO

PALAWAN

PANAY

SAMAR

LEYTE

CEBU

NEGROS   BOHOL

MINDANAO

SULU ARCHIPELAGO

SOURCES: Human Relations Area Files and 1960 Census of Population

Fig. 25.

tongues of this metropolitan population in 1960. In all, twelve languages, including Chinese, were the mother tongues of over 25,000 persons each. Almost the entire population (over 97 percent) could speak Tagalog, and well over a half (about 70 percent) could use English (appendix table 9).

REGIONAL CULTURE GROUPINGS

The cultural regionalisms of the Philippines are numerous, based upon quite different criteria, and exhibiting significant variation. There are three obvious and basic patterns—pagan, Christian, and Moslem—historical in origin but regional to a degree. Another basic pattern that still is real in the islands is the urban-rural pattern, though not all demographically urban settlements are as yet culturally urban. Smaller towns and cities distant from Manila and the main traffic routes still retain rural attributes. A new kind of cultural distinction coming into being is the industrial as opposed to the older agricultural. Many of the language groupings express cultural groupings also, since the languages are regionally concentrated in environments that differ in several respects (fig. 25). About many of these features there has accrued a possessive pride in particular attributes, tending to crystallize them and preserve them as regionalisms. These divisive tendencies operate in spite of the unifying tendencies of education, consumer goods, and systems of communications.

To the degree that political structure and organization becomes interrelated with religious organization, theological concepts, and cultural mores, the pagan cultural pattern of the Philippines is tending slowly to decline and faces eventual extinction. Christian missionaries, both Catholic and Protestant, continue to evangelize the pagan groups in all parts of the islands. The Moslem elements earlier did the same in their southern sector. The Moslem way of life, theological and temporal, is too strong to succumb to Christianity, but the sharply militant antagonism between the two is largely a thing of the past. Religious architecture, clothing styles, religious practices, and cultural mores distinguish the two groups, and these will be carefully perpetuated both by leadership and by the populace.

Climatic regionalism, carrying with it differences in economic crop plants, economic practices, dietary habits, and cultural mores, tends to produce regionalisms that can be culturally fostered. The presence of the coconut palm and the abaca plant, of cotton growing and weaving, and sugarcane production all have their impact upon the domestic homestead, habits of food and drink, clothing customs, and handicraft production.

The littoral location, with its beaches, shore waters, boats, and seafood diets, contrasts rather markedly, even in an island environment, with the hill-country location or the interior lowland rural scene. There are markedly different patterns in the location and positioning of settlements and family homes, and in daily habits. These regionalisms often are more localized than the larger and more formal patterns that attach to climatic or linguistic regionalisms.

Working against the operation of such localisms today are the school system, the daily paper, the radio broadcast, the transport systems, and the commercial system. The impact on elementary school students of the use of the same textbook throughout the islands is strengthened by the easy availability of the same confection, toy, tinned food, or "storebought" clothing, and by the uniformity of what the radio set will bring in broadcasts out of Manila.

RELIGIOUS GROUPINGS

Reflecting its historical Spanish orientation, the Philippines is overwhelmingly Roman Catholic. The integration of secular and religious government was a distinctive feature of Spanish control in the Philippines. Remaining outside Spanish control were the pagan populations, possessing their own local and regional patterns of animism—patterns that continue in declining numbers into the present. The Moslem religion was brought into the southern Philippines slightly earlier than the Roman Catholic, and with the traditional antagonism between the Spanish Roman Catholics and the Moslems, Islam remained a militant and thorny problem for the Spanish. Although Moslems were widely scattered in small numbers at the coming of the Spanish, their zone of dominance lay in Palawan, southwestern Mindanao, and Sulu.

American influence in the Philippines separated church and state in the same manner as has obtained in the United States. This gave license for the entry of the Protestant missionary groups, and Protestantism has been added to the Philippine scene. In the Islands the term is pronounced "pro-TEST-ant" and socially reflects an attitude of rebellion to traditional Roman Catholicism. American influence permitted the establishment of two other protesting religious organizations, the Iglesia Filipina Independiente, generally known as the Aglipayan church, and the Iglesia ni Kristo. The former group arose out of the political rebellion against Spain in the last years of the nineteenth century, the formal organization of the church dating from 1902. The latter church group dates from 1914, featuring tight socioeconomic integration of its adherents. Both the Aglipayan church and the Iglesia ni Kristo are Philippinized Catholic sociotheologies.

Within the sociocultural structure of the modern Philippines, therefore, there are four significant groupings in which religious thought extends into a way of life. These are: pagan, Roman Catholic plus Filipino Catholic,

Protestant, and Moslem. The 1960 populations represented are shown in appendix table 10. The pagan way of life is declining in influence as its number of adherents decline. The Moslem pattern remains regional but distinctive and active, both socially and politically. The influence of the Filipino Catholic and Protestant groups is increasing more rapidly than their increase in population alone would indicate. The Protestant influence is far greater than its number of church adherents, as it has worked as a leaven in the realm of education and cultural development generally. With the exception of the Moslem concentration in the southwestern Philippines, and to a degree the Aglipayan church, other patterns are today widely distributed (figs. 26a, 26b and appendix table 10).

Features of Settlement

The dominant element of pre-Spanish social organization was the barangay, essentially a kinship grouping most commonly of some twenty to about a hundred families, most of whom usually resided in a primary settlement that may be termed a village.[13] The group functioned socially, economically, politically, and regionally. In the latter sense the barangay represented an independent territorial unit having, for practical purposes, political autonomy. Seasonally occupied houses often were scattered singly or in small clusters at varying points throughout the territorial area of the barangay. Filipino family structure, in socioeconomic terms, has long utilized a variably articulated structure of "kindred" patterns superficially resembling the extended family system; but the nuclear family has been the basic unit of residence, and a village normally has consisted of a group of single-family houses.[14]

The Spanish acted to stabilize the social and political structure of the barangay, strengthening the class stratification and turning the datu or chief into the hereditary *cabeza de barangay* or headman. Gradually the Spanish recognized the scattered clusters of seasonally occupied houses as the sitio, or hamlet, a residence site remaining subsidiary to the barangay in all respects. In political and territorial terms the Spanish turned the barangay into the smallest unit of local government and the smallest unit of political area. This is the modern barrio. On top of this native structure the Spanish established towns and cities as centers of residence, and towns, municipalities, and provinces as superior units of political structure.

This basic pattern survives in the modern Philippines in respect to political structure and in terms of settlement pattern. The political units have expanded in number on the several levels, and American influence has added only the chartered city to the basic political structure.[15] American influence is evident in the changing physical shape and layout of recent settlement patterns. The building of an extensive road system has produced linear patterns of settlement along roads and has facilitated dispersed settlement in some rural areas. At the same time, American influence is changing the basic plan of towns and cities and significantly encouraging urbanism. In the more recent period, however, such actions have been in the hands of the Filipinos themselves, who have modified American influence in their own manner.

DOMESTIC HOUSING

The traditional Filipino house has been a structure of bamboo, thatch, and matting set off the ground on hardwood pilings, a light and airy single-family house easily built but not very durable. It could be constructed as a single room and porch, or it could be extended into a rambling structure of numerous rooms and partitioned sections. Such a house could be built over shallow water along a coast or riverbank, or it could be placed at some inland point. There was little regional styling in pre-Spanish days among the Malaysians or among the proto-Malays, though the two groups built their houses differently, and the Negrito built hardly more than simple rain and sun shelters. In time, both regional styling and differences in raw materials available at inland points produced variations in the traditional bamboo and thatch architecture; an Ilocano house now differs somewhat from a Sulu Island house, and both differ from an Ifugao house. Much of the housing of the Philippines continues to be built of light materials in the traditional manner, but numerous cultural influences have been at work to modify basic patterns.

The Spanish introduced a new form of architecture and a new settlement layout to the Philippines. Massive stone construction of a lower story, topped by a wood and tile second story, produced quite different buildings that were grouped around a central plaza filled with decorative plantings and ornamental sculpture. In time, carving techniques decorated the wood sections, decorative ironwork was variably employed, whitewashed plaster became common, and stone masonry replaced wooden pilings under native houses. More recently cement has replaced stone. Officials and members of the upper classes lived around the plazas in rather formal, ornate buildings, but in the blocks away from the plazas only modifications in floor plans or elevations off the ground changed traditional styles. To admit light, window and door construction employed translucent shells set in small panels in a wood frame, with the windows sliding to permit wide openings. Sliding wood shutters sometimes were added to the better houses to ward off rain without closing up houses.

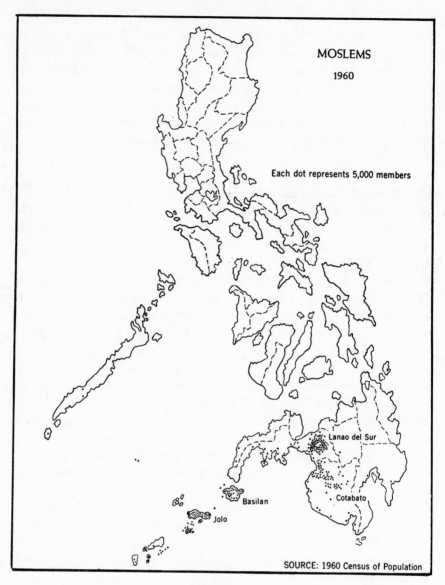

Fig. 26a.

In more modern periods the galvanized roof has often replaced thatch, solid wooden floors have replaced split bamboo, hinged windows of wood and glass have replaced the sliding panel windows and varying kinds and amounts of furniture have been added to the interiors of houses. As piped water systems have been built in the Philippines during the present century,

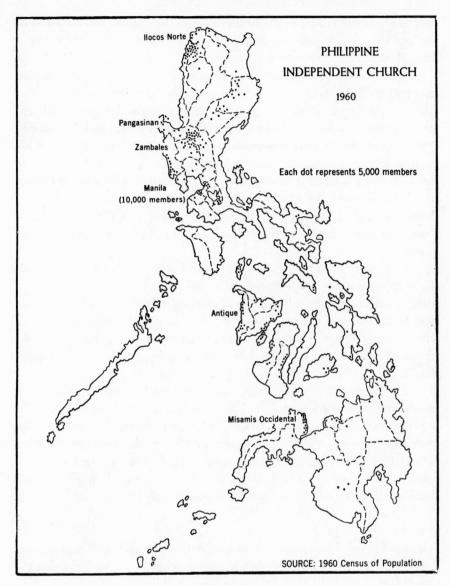

PHILIPPINE
INDEPENDENT CHURCH

1960

Ilocos Norte

Pangasinan

Zambales

Each dot represents 5,000 members

Manila
(10,000 members)

Antique

Misamis Occidental

SOURCE: 1960 Census of Population

Fig. 26b.

showers, flush toilets, and kitchen sinks have been added to the urban housing pattern. Paint has been employed on wooden surfaces, window screens have come into use, and cement or solid-wood steps have replaced the bamboo ladders leading to the front porch or entry hall. Floor plans have been expanded to allow functional space separation of the house interior. But in the rural countryside, in the smaller villages, the hinterland sitios, and in the poorer sections of cities the lightly built traditional Filipino architecture is strongly preserved.

After World War II, with its massive destruction, domestic Filipino architecture was altered again. Particularly in the Manila metropolitan area, but to some degree in many other cities and towns also, residential suburbs resemble those of American cities, with ground-level houses and decoratively planted yards, in the recent styles and materials of American domestic architecture. Houses now display much of the interior design of the American home, both as to space separation and furniture. Air conditioning is closing the formerly open Filipino construction, and the appurtenances of a modern home are those of contemporary United States. And yet there is a difference inside the house; these are Philippinized American houses in many different ways.

Little of this modernization of domestic architecture has penetrated the far rural countryside, for it is dependent on new skills and upon electricity, upon changing family culture and advancing patterns of income not yet widely available. In the towns and villages near cities, varying amounts of change may be seen, and the tempo of change is increasing; but the simple thatch-on-bamboo pile dwelling still is home to large numbers of Filipino families.

The seasonally occupied house, still a common feature, may often be a rather simple structure, sometimes barely more than a sleeping shelter. Built and used by agricultural folk practicing shifting cultivation at a distance from their primary homes, these seasonally occupied houses also are not uncommon among truly urban residents of the upper classes. A secondary home in a barrio village often is a relatively traditional house, more cheaply built and less formally arranged than the primary house in a large town or city.

PUBLIC ARCHITECTURE

The pre-Spanish Philippines was singularly free of public buildings of any kind, and the barangay village showed neither religious nor secular construction.[16] Roman Catholic churches, government buildings, fortifications, monuments, bridges, and other public building, patterned after similar structures in Mexico or Europe, spread with the Spanish into the Philippines. Massive stone construction was common, with plaster, whitewash, slate, and tile construction also employed. Early American influences introduced new types of public building, such as the local schoolhouse, and brought new stylistic patterns.[17]

Expressing itself chiefly in the period of reconstruction after World War

II is the process of Philippinization in public architecture. Filipino architects began to demonstrate skill in adapting modern building materials and structural patterns to the Philippine environment, retaining many elements of traditional styling. This is notable in all forms of nonresidential building, and both regional and cultural forms are slowly maturing. Modern Roman Catholic churches differ markedly from those of earlier centuries, and Moslem architectural styling in the southwest employs traditional motifs in new combinations and materials. Blends of traditional and contemporary are creating an individual Philippine regional architecture that, at its best, is both attractive and suited to the region.

THE VILLAGE AND THE HAMLET

The traditional barangay of the lowland Malay Filipino was a straggling collection of houses forming a rural residential village. Handicraft manufacturing and barter trade required neither specialized facilities nor structures. If located along a shoreline or riverbank, a village might be an elongated settlement no more than two or three houses deep and ten to fifty or sixty houses long. Coconut trees, banana plants, and other useful or nonutilitarian vegetation might partially separate house sites, and garden patches were interspersed among the trees and houses on the inland side. Fishing boats, gear, and drying racks fringed the shore or bank, and this open zone was the meeting ground of adults and the playground of children. Since shifting cultivation was part of the economic system, garden sites located inland, on nearby islands, or at other favorable spots often required seasonal departure from the base village, resulting in dispersed houses or sitio hamlets being scattered throughout the territory of the barangay. When the village was located on a small marginal island such garden sites often were on the "mainland" of the nearby larger island. In favored local environments barangay villages were not many miles apart, but along some coastal zones the favored spots were widely separated.

By the time of the Spanish entry into the islands most proto-Malay groups were inland residents of interior valleys, hill country, or mountain country. The barangay village often was sited at some easily defended point, and perhaps even fortified in some traditional manner. Among unwarlike groups, the utility of a village site was related to water sources, cultivable lands, or other subjective factors. Villages often were straggling clusters of houses or even loosely articulated hamlets. Since many proto-Malay groups were primarily shifting cultivators, their village sites might be shifted periodically, or dispersed houses or hamlets might be scattered throughout the territory of the group. Among village dwellers such site shifts were not aimless and frequent; sometimes periodic shifts took place within a repetitive orbit related to the territory of the group in question. In north Luzon those proto-Malay peoples who carried on irrigated wet-rice culture on permanently terraced lands occupied permanent villages. Some of these were rather large, but seldom was there any formality in the arrangement of houses. Many north Luzon groups also carried on shifting cultivation on nearby garden sites, and often they too established seasonally occupied houses singly or in hamlets at some distance from the base villages. As the Moslem immigrants moved into the southern Philippines, militant Moslem raiders in Mindanao, Palawan, and Sulu forced some culture groups inland away from the coasts, causing some to adopt dispersed patterns of residence in which housing sites were chosen for inconspicuousness, and others, who retained the village settlement form, to shift to defensive and fortified sites.

The Spanish found the high degree of mobility and the wide scattering of barangays, sitios, and seasonally occupied sites incompatible with their political, economic, and ecclesiastical aims for the native population. Agricultural produce, labor contingents, and the tribute taxes were difficult to accumulate, and the Christianizing of the widely scattered population was almost impossible with a small cadre of priests. Spanish influence, therefore, was exerted to nucleate settlement into larger units. This took two general forms: the founding of new settlements on "central" sites, and the relocating of barangays within reasonable distances around the central settlements. The new central settlement was early termed a *cabecera* or *pueblo,* later called a poblacion, a term still in use for the central sector of a Philippine town. Around the cabecera, barangay villages were located at convenient distances when this could be done. Such villages were not given formal plans in most cases, but there frequently resulted elongated string villages, clustered ford and bridgehead villages, or loosely clustered villages focused on a *visita* chapel built for periodic religious services performed by a priest on circuit from a cabecera church.

The Spanish were not able to completely substitute sedentary agriculture for the traditional shifting cultivation, so scattered sitios, dispersed homesteads, and distant barangays continued to be occupied. Often the barangay, as a political district, contained no significant village settlement, but instead contained a number of scattered sitios. The Filipinos offered resistance to Spanish desires for, and programs of, resettlement into large, centralized villages. Some success attended the program in Camarines Sur, Laguna, and the Ilocos coast provinces; and the Tagalog-populated southern Central Plain, near Manila, showed the greatest success of all. In the Visayan Islands considerable resistance to resettlement was augmented by the continued raiding of the southern Moslem groups, and in Mindanao the program showed almost no results beyond a few points defended by Spanish arms. In the interior hill and mountain sectors, also, the Spanish never succeeded in a resettlement program. Despite the lack of general success, the Spanish efforts at resettlement did alter the settlement structure of the Malay groups of Filipinos. Population movement toward island interiors took place when there were agricultural lands available there, and village settlement spread into such interior situations.

The barrio village is the principal settlement form of the Philippines today. Scattered hamlets continue the sitio tradition, and seasonally occupied dispersed houses still are used by the barrio folk who cultivate caingins in traditional shifting cultivation. Sitios of fishermen are scattered along coasts and on small offshore islands, and those of lumbermen or miners are scattered in the mountain country. American influence in transport and in communications has kept alive a tradition of dispersed permanent settlement, particularly along routes serviced by bus systems. The modern barrio retains its territorial significance, inherited from the barangay, and settlement within any given barrio may involve a village, a number of sitios, or hamlets, and a certain share of permanently occupied dispersed homesteads. There continues a significant amount of seasonal residence away from the main homestead. This may involve the traditional dispersal into the rural countryside of the regular residents of the barrio village or the hamlet, but today it also includes a seasonal movement of urban residents to the barrio village and the hamlet.

The traditional barangay village often ranged from about 85 to perhaps 700 inhabitants; there were some large villages, but probably the most common number of inhabitants was less than 200. The sitio, or hamlet, often contained from five to perhaps fifty inhabitants, and sitios of about twenty people each were very common. As the Philippine population has increased, some barrios and villages have grown to several thousand inhabitants, with the former sitios becoming villages.[18] More common, however, has been the hiving-off, or splintering-off, tendency of the Filipino, which has resulted in the founding of new sitios and new villages, followed by the creation of new barrios as local political districts. Each census has reported an increased number of barrios, and the 1960 total was not far from 26,000.[19] Most barrios now contain one primary village and numerous sitios, though some newly created or isolated barrios still may contain only a few sitios. At the creation of a new barrio district one sitio becomes the administrative center, thus attaining status as the primary village. Although the barrio and the village often are identified, it is necessary to distinguish between them as to the number of inhabitants. The average population of the barrio political district

in 1960 was probably about 900, whereas the average primary village population probably was close to 600. Both barrio and village totals are growing
larger; in 1903 about a third of all villages contained less than 200 people
each, whereas in 1960 only a few primary villages were that small.

TOWNS

No town or city, in the modern sense, existed in the pre-Spanish Philippines.
Large and active trader settlements were present at Manila, Cebu, and a site
or two in the Sulu Islands, but the town proper has been a creation of
Spanish administrative effort. By the mid-seventeenth century about 200
settlements, *pueblos de Indios,* had been founded. These could be labeled
towns by virtue of their planned layouts, their cabecera churches, their
secular administrative headquarters, and their occupance by Filipino families.[20] A central plaza and a gridplan set of streets were notable features.
Around the plaza were grouped the church, the church residence and school,
government buildings, and the homes of the upper classes. A marketplace
came to be located close by the plaza. The earliest pueblos were relatively
compact settlements, in the Mexican manner, but the inflamable nature of
traditional bamboo and thatch housing led to the enlargement of town sites so
that houses could be more widely spaced in gardens to prevent extensive fires.
It also led to gradual alteration in the construction of town houses for the
upper and middle classes, and many houses near plazas were built of stone
and wood, with tile roofing.

The first towns were relatively small in size, comprising anywhere from
100 to 300 houses. Later, population increases filled in vacant building sites,
and irregularly shaped suburbs accreted around the central settlement as
barrios. Often some families declined to reside permanently in the pueblos,
but maintained houses there to which they could come from village or hamlet
for Sunday services or for other special church functions. A Spanish priest
and, sometimes, Spanish soldiery were regular residents of the pueblo.

As a secular center the pueblo exercised jurisdiction over outlying
barrios, evolving gradually into the municipio of the present day which serves
as the capital of the municipality.[21] The territory of the cabecera church, and
its resident priest, normally correlated with the secular limits, and the priest
operated a circuit of periodic religious services in visita chapels in outlying
barrios and occasional sitios. Pueblos normally were situated in agricultural
lowlands when possible, with the objective of relocating numerous barangay
villages round about in order that the largest possible Filipino population
could be brought under both secular and religious control. In a very general
sense each of the Spanish towns eventually served as a "central place" in that

it provided services to a local district, though the spacing and location of the towns represented little real organization.

Spanish effort in the founding of towns and Christianized communities was spread as widely as possible, but achieved only uneven distribution throughout the Philippines.[22] Almost sixty towns were located in the Visayan group of islands, achieving only a semblance of control over the widely scattered population. Nearly thirty locations in the southern Bicol sector of southeastern Luzon afforded a better coverage. About twenty towns were scattered along the Ilocos coast of northwest Luzon, providing coverage of the coastal lowland. About a dozen towns scattered in the Cagayan Valley of northeast Luzon achieved very little regional control or coverage. The largest number of towns was founded in the southern Central Plain of Luzon, extending southward into Batangas Province. The region from Laguna de Bay northward past Manila into Pampanga Province was the most effectively covered region, giving a concentration of Spanish influence and control. Elsewhere little was achieved by the early Spanish efforts to organize administration, resettle the population, or turn them into Christians.

Almost every Spanish pueblo grew into a modern town.[23] The pattern created by the first foundings was repeated in later time as Spanish influence spread more widely throughout the islands, and the late towns closely resemble the earlier ones. American influence in the twentieth century maintained the framework of territorial and political structure, but the physical plan of the newest towns has often departed from the traditional pattern. Recent towns founded by the Filipinos themselves also have departed from the classic patterns, as many of the most recent towns took over existing barrios and merely regularized their physical plans to a variable extent.

There were, in 1960, more than 1,300 towns in the Philippines, ranging in size from about 600 population to about 15,000. Around Manila some of the old towns have merged into the metropolitan region and are not included in the above generalization. Although the smallest Philippine town barely fits the definition, each of these settlements serves several functions for its surrounding political district. The town is the seat of political administration and the center of political power. The town houses secondary economic functions, commercial undertakings, and is the center of regional accumulation and distribution of commodities and consumer goods. The town normally is a transportation center and contains such communications facilities as exist. Customarily such services as medical and dental care are available only in towns. In addition, the town serves not only as the primary place of residence for a population but as a secondary area of periodic or short-term residence for inhabitants of outlying villages and sitios.[24]

THE CITY OF MANILA

Manila, as the focal point of Spanish influence, soon distinguished itself from the pueblos of the provinces. Already a large and fortified settlement before the arrival of the Spanish, it increased in size, population, and cultural function. Given a royal charter in 1574, Manila has had separate governmental control. A European walled city, the Intramuros, replaced the native fortifications by 1600, and came to contain the government buildings, the headquarters of the several religious orders, a number of churches, and the residences of the leading Spanish and Spanish-Filipino families.[25] A specific sector of the city, outside the Intramuros, housed the Chinese, Japanese, Indonesians, and such other Asiatics as visited and resided in Manila. This section also contained the trader shop-houses, commercial establishments, warehouses, and the handicraft manufactories. A large Filipino population gathered in suburbs, comprising both well-to-do families attracted to Manila and the large service population needed by the Spanish. The size of the city varied periodically, sometimes depending upon whether the Chinese were in favor or were subject to persecution by the Spanish and Filipinos alike, but population totals of 30,000 to 50,000 characterize the very early references.[26] Almost from the beginning of Spanish control, Manila was the dominant center of political power, of wealth, of commerce, and of Spanish and Chinese influence.

Manila continued to grow steadily as the chief center of the Spanish island empire. Although the suburban sectors never were subject to integrated formal planning, several cabecera settlements were independently sited at different points in suburban sectors, each containing its plaza, church, government buildings, residential core, and barrio suburbs. In time these several towns simply grew together to form the larger part of the city of Manila. Sixteenth- to eighteenth-century stone churches, government buildings, and high-class residences were repeatedly destroyed or damaged by earthquakes, and native sectors often burned, so that frequent rebuilding was required. Late nineteenth-century administrative rules required private residences to be built of wood above the first story.

In many ways Manila was not a striking city in the early period. Many of the recreational and cultural amenities accumulated around local centers in the suburbs from an early date, and the core of the city was reported to be a dull place. The primary business center of the city grew up north of the Pasig River, across from the Intramuros, as a crowded and drab area. Though a few wharfs and quays were built along the Pasig River near its mouth, the river was too narrow and too shallow to serve as a port for early ocean shipping, so its facilities became the center of interisland trade. No effective seafront port facilities were ever developed under Spanish rule, for open international trade was not in favor. The flat bay shore, the shallow bay waters, and the open roadstead situation required offshore anchorage and lighterage handling of passengers and cargo. The small harbor at Cavite was found far more satisfactory for primary refuge from typhoon storms, and for ships' repairs. Despite these facts Manila came to dominate the interisland trade, and continued to be the center of the Spanish trade monopoly with the islands.

By the mid-nineteenth century Manila had become a large city of over 200,000 population, though it fluctuated both in nationality and in total numbers. It had become a multicentered city, with several patterns of decentralization and locality concentration, all oriented toward the mouth of the Pasig River and toward the Intramuros.[27] The decentralization and the locality concentrations crystallized further during the nineteenth century, so that at the advent of American control Manila consisted of a dozen recognized districts bound into one large urban settlement. Local administration of civil matters remained decentralized, though general police power and certain urban services extended outward at variable distances from the Intramuros core. Depending upon where authority drew its outer line, the population of Manila around the year 1900 varied from about 220,000 to about 350,000.[28] Early American influence added little to the urban sprawl, though it began the development of a port, a more clearly articulated road system, and a commercial and financial district. Later American and more recent Filipino influences have continued the development of port facilities, the high-rise architecture of the business core, and the suburban zoning of residential and industrial buildings.[29]

The area of Manila as a city was set at 20 square miles in 1901, but was later reduced to 14.3 square miles at which figure it remains. Except for the variable controls exercised by Manila authorities, the outlying urbanized areas continued under their previously established local governments until Quezon City was chartered in 1939 and Pasay City in 1947. No further political reconstitution of the urbanized zone took place for some years, so that in 1960 the metropolitan region of Manila included three separate chartered cities, perhaps twenty nearby municipalities, and a large number of barrios.[30] The urbanized area in 1960 was approximately 150 square miles, and the urban population approximated 2,200,000, though an additional commuting population resided outside the urban region itself. In 1963 Caloocan municipality was chartered as a city, and in the future other suburban towns may well become chartered cities also.

Long the political capital of the Philippines, the chief port for international trade, the chief center of non-Filipino population, Manila has also become the chief manufacturing center. The modern port function remains within the political limits of Manila itself, and here too remains the business and financial heart of the country. Quezon City was named the political capital in 1950, and manufacturing has spread throughout much of the urbanized region into the open rural spaces around the city.[31] Rather than decentralizing the manifold functions of the "city," however, such trends merely serve to enlarge the urbanized zone, to create a still larger metropolitan region. Within the port area and the central business district permanently resident populations have been stationary or declining, and a normal pattern of flight to the suburbs has been taking place.[32]

OTHER CITIES

Before discussing other cities, a distinctive Filipino political phenomenon concerning urbanism must be clarified. The city, as an institutional development, has become part of the national political system of the Philippines, and is subject to political and administrative manipulation in such a way as to obscure the interpretation of the growth of urbanism in the islands. Manila was given a special charter in 1901, confirming its former status under the Spanish regime, and Baguio was similarly chartered in 1909 as the summer political capital. Both settlements were then taken under the direct administration of the United States Governor General, and were separated from the normal patterns of provincial and local government. No other cities were chartered until after the institution of the semiautonomous Philippine Commonwealth in 1935. Beginning in 1936, however, additional cities were given special charters on the patterns applicable to Manila and Baguio, the Philippine president thereby assuming ultimate control of the political administration of all such chartered cities. In 1963 the number of chartered cities stood at 39. The act of chartering a city removes it from the control of the provincial government and places it under presidential administration.[33] To some extent, therefore, city administrations become part of the presidential machinery of political patronage and power. (See appendix table 14.)

Cities are ranked according to the size of the taxable base supporting their financial and political structure, and the salaries of city officials are fixed according to the rank of the city. As a city is being chartered, there is great incentive to include as much territory as possible in order to raise the tax base and to achieve as high a rank as possible. In some instances the area included within a city charter involves large tracts of rural countryside having no aspect of urbanism in the normal sense.[34] Chartered cities become territorial units for many types of statistical reporting, including all reporting by the

Bureau of the Census and Statistics. For reasons of internal Philippine politics, therefore, many cities contain much larger areas, and larger populations, than would be the case under a normal consideration of urbanism. Perhaps the outstanding case is that of Zamboanga City, chartered in 1936, which involved 1,139.47 square miles and included all of Basilan Island and a great chunk of the southern peninsula. The 1939 census reported Zamboanga at 131,455, whereas the actual urban area of the town contained perhaps 18,000 people. In 1948 Basilan Island was given a separate charter as a city, and the area of Zamboanga City was reduced to 622.3 square miles, for which the census of 1948 reported a total population of 103,317, some 20,000 of whom lived within a plausible urban setting. The 1960 census reported Zamboanga City at 131,411, but a fair portion of the increase over 1948 represents an increasing rural agricultural population; the urban zone in 1960 perhaps held some 30,000 people.[35]

Cebu, on the east coast of Cebu Island, was perhaps the only other Philippine settlement, after Manila, worthy of being considered a city during the late Spanish era. Much early effort went into making Cebu a Spanish stronghold, even after primary attention was transferred to Manila. Cebu had a protected location behind Mactan Island, was a relatively populous locality, and was an important interregional trade center when the Spanish arrived. Within the Spanish island empire, Cebu came to function as a primary cultural and military base in the Visayan Islands region, and became a southern entrepôt in the interisland trade pattern. The city grew to a population of about 46,000 in 1903, and expanded from its original site only gradually. In 1936 Cebu was made a chartered city, and its area was expanded to 128.3 square miles, including some 75 square miles of rural, agricultural hill country. The 1963 area of the city was reported as 108.4 square miles. Of the 1960 recorded city population of 251,000, close to 200,000 may be considered as belonging properly to an urban entity. Much of the modern city represents twentieth-century expansion of urban settlement, both north and south, along the narrow coastal fringe. Cebu shows many of the characteristics of the city, though some of them are not highly developed. No real manufacturing district had developed prior to 1960, though fabrication and agricultural-processing activities were increasing. Warehousing and branch-plant assembly-finishing in the interregional wholesale trade are important economic functions. A significant business district had emerged, but the skyline was rising only slowly, and residence within the central area was not yet declining. Cebu City is a land-transport–trade center for the island of Cebu, a major entrepôt for the interisland trade and communication traffic, and the second-ranking international port of the Philippines.[36]

Iloilo, on the southeast coast of Panay Island, was a locality in which pre-Spanish villages were numerous, as the alluvial lowland was extensive, the Jaro (Iloilo) River allowed access to the hinterland, and the coastal littoral was protected by Guimaras Island. Spanish control of the coastal region developed early, though few Spanish residents located there. Iloilo grew into a minor entrepôt and the local center of Panay Island trade, but remained just that until the Spanish opened the port to foreign trade in 1855. It then grew relatively rapidly as a regional trade center, and in 1903 had a population of about 50,000. Early American development of port facilities gave impetus to growth, and Iloilo rivaled Cebu as the Visayan entrepôt, while also handling some foreign commerce until the 1930's. A compact urban core of three- to five-story buildings produced a distinct central district. Compact village settlements on the plain littoral were incorporated into the urban district with fewer than the normal scattered fringes, resulting in several plaza-market-church subcenters to the city. The modern city of Iloilo did not incorporate a large rural hinterland upon chartering, and its 21.6 square mile area in 1963 was more fully urbanized than is the case with many Philippine cities.

Davao, in southeastern Mindanao, represents a twentieth-century urban development built upon a late and small Spanish townsite. The general region remained one of the least populated areas of the islands until late in Spanish times, with native tribal groups scattered through the hinterland. The town of Davao held 6,000 people in 1903, and it grew slowly until the 1930's, though an immigrant Visayan population was spreading into the hinterland and bringing significant volumes of produce to Davao for shipment to northern points. The city was incorporated in 1936, and by inclusion of some 748.1 square miles, recorded a population of 95,000 in 1939. Enlarged to 853.7 square miles by 1963, the 1960 census recorded a total of 225,000 population. Of this, some 85,000 is included within the urban zone. The city has evolved around its port in a somewhat haphazard pattern that resembles the American city more than that of the classical Orient. Agricultural-processing facilities for the products of the regional hinterland, particularly in the abaca industries, and an increasing number of wholesale warehouses and assembly stations, are giving Davao the status of an interregional port. As the highway network expands beyond the local hinterland Davao may well reach major status as a center of interregional trade, processing, and distributing. Relatively rapid growth and expansion of the city may be expected in coming decades.

Bacolod, on the west coast of Negros Island, is gradually becoming a city in respect to many of the usual criteria. Although the coastal littoral nearest southern Panay shared patterns of native settlement with that island, interior Negros was heavily forested and inhabited mainly by Negritos when the Spanish arrived. Agricultural development of the island began only after 1800, when sugar planting began along the plains of both the east and west coast. Bacolod was not, in itself, an important early sugar center, but it was a location convenient for gathering traffic to Iloilo. It became a municipio, a late Spanish garrison center, and an important political center of island rebellion against the Spanish, maturing into the political capital of the province of Negros Occidental. The growth of modern road transport has made Bacolod a land-transport center, as a result of its political status. Chartered as a city in 1938, its whole municipality was included, making a total of 62.3 square miles. The inland zone is agricultural, with numerous plantation-labor villages. Bacolod City grew rapidly after about 1920, and in 1960 the central urban sector included about 92,000 people. Interpreting the city according to American methods of judging metropolitan regions, the northern and southern littoral suburbs of the settlement increase the total to about 107,000 as of 1961. Numerous cultural, recreational, service, and business activities have centered in the city, and wholesaling and technical agricultural service-centers have developed. The outport of Pulupandan is a somewhat lesser feature of the city's importance, as it is overshadowed by Iloilo.

Most of the other chartered cities of the Philippines are smaller in size, incomplete in terms of multiple urban functions, and political in their patterns of status. There are numerous towns that are growing in size, some of which are political capitals, and they are acquiring various characteristics of cities. Urbanism is an increasingly important feature of Filipino society, and will continue to be as the earlier small agricultural society becomes a modernized, culturally complex, larger society. Many settlements that are just large towns at present will become cities in the full sense of the word in a few more decades. Political practice may change, altering the patterns of territorial organization and bringing with it changing bases of statistical tabulation. Industrialization, as one particular spearhead of cultural modernization, undoubtedly will be a significant factor in creating new centers of urbanism in the Philippines. The areas and populations of the chartered cities are given in appendix table 14.

Diet, Health, Mortality, and Growth

Situated just off the edge of the Asian mainland, the Philippines has not been an integral sector of the classical Orient in respect to the varied conditions affecting domestic life, health, disease, and population growth. In general the Philippines has been a healthy environment and one in which pestilence, famine, war, and socioeconomic segregation have taken no heavy toll.[37] Brief consideration of several topics under this heading may round out the discussion of population.

FILIPINO DIETARY

In traditional terms the Philippines is a region dominated by a rice-and-fish-staple dietary pattern, a pattern regionally complemented by particular variations in the staple or complementary foods. Traditional complementary food crops included the yam, taro, and sugarcane group of crops, and a series of fruit crops among which the coconut and the mango were predominant. The Spanish brought a large group of new food crops to the islands, the most significant of which were the sweet potatoes, maizes, and maniocs. Minor items included a wide range of tropical and subtropical fruits. The water buffalo, locally distinguished as the carabao; pigs; south Asian mixed breeds of cattle; the jungle fowl, chicken of pre-Spanish origin; and new stocks of goats and chickens from Spanish sources rounded out a list of primary animal food sources. Post-Spanish agricultural economy regionalized and blended this varied food-source complex fairly effectively, so that the Filipinos have been able to draw on a varied and productive range of food-crop sources yielding a reasonably balanced dietary.[38] In the economic and agricultural history of the island almost the full range of food products, in regional terms, has been available to the whole population of that region; and there has not developed the strong stratification of consumer patterns whereby economically deprived elements are forced to live on a narrow range of products yielding an unbalanced dietary.

In modern times the Filipino dietary preferences have been changing, but most of the changes are of the same kind as those found in other parts of the world; the resulting dietary problems are not unique to the Philippines.[39] A liking for foodstuffs traditionally associated with the mid-latitudes has been growing in the Philippines. As most of these products must be imported, they promote financial problems affecting island economy, but they have not, in themselves, created any unique health problems affecting population patterns. The liking for wheat breadstuffs and cereal preparations, for dairy products, for mid-latitude fruits and their preparations, for the mid-latitude vegetables, and for modern kinds of confections has brought a healthy widening of the dietary ranges in all parts of the islands.

Beginning in late Spanish times the growth of export agriculture has led to certain imbalances in the Philippine agricultural economy. In producing coconut products, sugar, abaca, tobacco, and a range of minor products for the world export market, the allocation of land to rice production has lagged, so that the Philippines has become a rice importer. Sugar export earns foreign exchange, and the allocation of the crop to the domestic market has been niggardly in recent times. Wheat products, much of the dairy products, and the mid-latitude fruits must be imported, and only an inadequate supply of the mid-latitude vegetables can be grown in highland locations. The frequent discussion of the unbalanced agriculture of the Islands concerns imbalances in the Philippine financial structure which are serious, but these imbalances do not actually cause widespread dietary imbalances affecting the health of the population.

THE PUBLIC HEALTH SITUATION

Pre-Spanish Philippine culture possessed no complex tradition of medicine, but because of its position apart from the Asian mainland, the archipelago did not suffer the chronic epidemics of serious diseases common to the mainland. Early Spanish influence brought no scourges. As freer contact was permitted during the nineteenth century, cholera and smallpox did reach epidemic proportions a few times through introduction from the mainland. Late nineteenth-century Spanish practices brought the beginnings of modern medicine, and on this base American public and private programs built rapidly and effectively. Controlled water systems, improved disposal of wastes, and general procedures of modern medical practice in both the public and the private sectors developed widely. Filipinos took easily to the whole of modern medical theory and practice, and the professional level of procedure has been relatively high, as the medical professions have been among the preferred callings among Filipinos. The Philippines in the twentieth century is a generally healthy region.[40] The Philippine population has been free from seriously restrictive inroads made by disease. There has been imbalance between the urban and rural availability of health services, but this has not been such that population-growth rates have been seriously affected.

BIRTH AND MORTALITY PATTERNS

Vital statistics as to birth and death rates for the Philippines have never been complete, and the census reports provide the best gauge of what is happening to the population. The balance of in- and out-migration is quite stable in the modern period, adding an insignificant total to the population. This is not true for the earlier centuries, and as late as the end of the seventeenth century it is likely that there was a steady in-migration taking place from the south. All but a small share of the population is Catholic or Moslem; hence, little change has probably occurred so far in the modern period with regard to family limitation. The widespread, and effective, availability of medical services in the modern period has meant a declining death rate among all age categories, but particularly has the infant mortality rate declined in the more recent period. Judging from some recent sampling, and from the census reports, it appears likely that the birthrate has long averaged over 40 per thousand; some authorities place it closer to 50 per thousand. The death rate, by 1960, may have dropped below 20 per thousand; opinions here range between 22 and 12 per thousand. If, in fact, the recent rate is near 20, a further decrease in the death rate is not improbable, as there are several diseases now having fairly high mortality rates which could be attacked by improved medical programs. A birthrate that continues at a high level, coupled with a death rate that could decline still further, suggests that the rate of population growth is climbing.

THE GROWTH OF POPULATION

It is notable that Spanish rule in the Philippines did not contribute to significant depopulation of the islands, as was the case in parts of the New World. The various Spanish military activities against the Dutch and the British provoked regionally centered economic exploitation that may have resulted in some local depopulation, since such exploitation undoubtedly produced economic privation, but the overall demographic effect was not great. The Spanish conquest was not a bloody one; the Spanish brought no epidemics of new diseases, and the drafting of labor for plantations and mines was comparatively insignificant.[41] It is hard to assess the demographic impact of the long-continued Moro raids upon the Visayas, though the emotional effect was extremely strong, and there clearly was a retarding effect on the southward movement of population surpluses from both the Visayas and Luzon. If there was an actual demographic impact, this effect may well have been offset by the continued in-migration of Moslem peoples into the southern islands of the archipelago at least until 1800.

The conclusion is almost unescapable that from the onset of Spanish rule, the Filipino population grew steadily. Spanish influence certainly lessened the patterns of tribal wars and established a kind of stability in civil affairs within the islands that made for potential population increase. The statistics of the Spanish era are incomplete, but the data suggest a steady increase on the order of 1.5 to 1.8 percent per year.

Whether the first American census in the Philippines, that of 1903, was really accurate is an arguable matter, but it must be accepted as a reasonable approximation. The detailed analysis of the 1960 census still is not available, but the available summary data suggest that the most recent trend involves the highest rate of growth since the arrival of the Spanish, an intercensal rate of increase since 1948 of 3.0 percent per year. Growth rates during the American period appear to have been higher, at all times, than during the earlier era. The recent rate of growth is one of the highest in any country for which data are available.

An improving modern dietary, an increasingly effective private and public health program, the absence of epidemic diseases, a steady reduction in the mortality rates among persons approaching, or in, the childbearing age bracket, a continued high birthrate, and the absence of significant emigration all point to a continuing high rate of population increase for the Philippines. Projections suggest a rate of 3.4 percent per year by the early 1970's. A population total in the vicinity of 55,000,000 to 60,000,000 for A.D. 2000 is one possible result. Against these factors making for increase must be placed others that may tend to lessen the projected rates of increase, although these are less predictable for the Philippines in the near future. The tendency for educational levels to increase, the trends toward urbanism, the weakening of the traditional bonds of Islam and Catholicism, a marked Filipino tendency to "keep up with the world," and the lessening of very early marriage among urban and better-educated Filipinos may all combine to slow down projected rates of increase. Although none of these factors can be statistically demonstrated from available data, they form a group of culturally predictable trends that could become effective in future decades.

SIX

~~~~~ # The Several Agricultural Economies

Almost all generalizations concerning the agricultural economy of the Philippines emphasize the unbalanced pattern by which an overconcentration upon commercialized export crops results in an underproductive domestic sector and a significant dependence upon imported food products. Such generalizations normally discuss rice and corn as the basic food staples, and emphasize the dominance of sugarcane, coconut, abaca, and tobacco as export crops that support the economy. There is truth in such generalizations, but such judgments obscure significant elements of the whole agricultural picture by using the approach of the dollar balance of international trade. To insist that the Filipinos at present grow too much sugarcane at the expense of their rice production is to ignore the fact that the small area of sugarcane lands would be less productive if devoted to rice or corn. This view also ignores such facts as the increasing preference for wheat products and for mid-latitude fruits, which cannot easily be grown in the Philippines, and the rising pattern of urbanism (from whence an increasing share of the rice deficit derives) which has been moving faster than the rate of basic improvement in the agricultural economy. There presently is an imbalance in Filipino agriculture, but this is a complex situation resulting from historical patterns of agriculture, from modern developments in commercial agriculture, and from relatively recent changes in Philippine culture patterns. Whether a balance is restored between domestic and export agricultures in the future depends far less on simple considerations of planting schedules and crop acreages than upon fundamental improvements in agricultural technology, shifts in patterns of economic control of agricultural land, structural improvements in Philippine economy, and fundamental changes in Filipino living habits.

One simple and significant fact is that Filipino agriculture is not very productive at best; its per-acre and per-capita yields are among the lowest in southern and eastern Asia, and rank low in world comparisons. Despite the growth of a significant export agriculture and the continual expansion of the agricultural landscape, the technology of crop growing remains simple and not greatly influenced by the elements of modernization which have appeared elsewhere in the world. This is as true of the technology behind export agriculture as it is of the technology employed in the production of domestic food and raw-material crops. The patterns of expansion in crop acreages and yields, as simple totals, have obscured the facts concerning relative productivity.

Whereas significant changes have taken place in the areal distribution of agricultural production and in the patterns of crop production over the last century, it must be noted that Philippine agriculture has not participated in the production revolution that has characterized the agricultural history of some other parts of the earth during the same period. The Philippines badly needs an agricultural revolution to accompany the industrial revolution that is setting in, and to complement the cultural revolution that has taken place in the island world during the past century. If Philippine per-acre yields of rice were equal to Japanese yields, there would be no imbalance in Philippine agriculture; or if Philippine sugar yields and copra quality were commensurate with American productivity patterns, the commercial sector could easily support importation of foods not grown in the Philippines.

Historical Patterns of the Growth of Agriculture

The present agricultural economy of the Philippines is compounded by several varieties of cropping systems, land-control systems, labor systems, and trade-consumption systems. The earliest of these relate to the early history of occupance of the Islands. Most widely distributed upon the arrival of the Spanish was the caingin system of shifting cultivation employed by a low-density population scattered throughout the archipelago. This pattern employed chiefly rice, yams, and bananas as staples; minor crops such as coconut, abaca, and sugarcane were grown as complements; and jungle gathering further complemented the dietary. Along the island littorals the main population practiced an agricultural-fishing economy in which some caingin cropping occurred in the immediate hinterlands, village gardening patterns obtained around sedentary villages, and fishing in offshore waters served as a basic complement. Rice, yams, bananas, and abaca were grown by caingin methods, whereas coconuts, fruits, and a few spices, vegetables, and sacred crops were grown in village gardens. In the uplands of northern Luzon an irrigated-terrace agricultural system combined sedentary cropping on the controlled wet terraces with caingin cropping on adjoining unterraced slopes. Here and there, as along the Ilocos coast of northwest Luzon, some intermixing of native systems occurred in that simple irrigation was employed in the seasonally dry coastal lands. Around the wet margins of Laguna de Bay and Manila Bay, and in the wet lowlands of southeast Panay, rice was grown on wet lowlands in what must be termed a wet-field system, though it was more a natural swamp system than one of well-controlled wet fields.

Whereas the north Luzon terracers and some of the littoral dwellers had evolved land-control systems approaching private ownership of permanently settled lands, all caingined lands were controlled by territorial groups with local tenure by usufruct only. Political systems in operation involved differentiation of rights and duties with regard to land, labor, service, and tribute among the different social strata present in local areas. Hostilities between island and regional groups, based upon both ethnic and political elements, in some regions resulted in the enslavement of captured persons, further elaborating the labor structure. The entry of Moslem Indonesian settlers and immigrants, just prior to the coming of the Spanish, brought additional patterns of militant contact, extending northward through the islands, with Moslem outposts established as far north as Manila Bay.

The variable frequenting of the western coasts and westernmost islands by Japanese, Chinese, Indonesian, and, perhaps, Arab traders in the pre-Spanish period had introduced most of the compatible Asian crops. It also resulted in the establishment of short- and long-term trading emporia, initiating very small movements of interregional trade in varied products, and a rather minor international trade in special agricultural products as well as jungle extracts. Such items as coconuts, abaca, rattans, rare woods, pearls, coral, and exotic jungle extracts flowed out of the islands in exchange for porcelains, silks, copper and brass ware, lacquers, and other manufactures. In the south a small trade in slaves was traditional.

The Spanish introduced significant new elements into the crop systems, into land-control systems, into social structuring, and into local and regional movements in products. Among the new crops were corn, sweet potatoes, manioc, agave, pineapple, and a whole series of American fruits and roots, as well as varieties of livestock. Of these, perhaps corn has been the most significant, as it could become a crop staple in some areas not well suited to rice. In broad terms, the Spanish introduced the system of private ownership of land (plus the accompanying institutions of deed, title, land tax, and private sale of land) and the land-related system of the encomienda, estate, plantation, or large private farmholding. The Spanish resettlement system stimulated patterns of movement in agricultural products from producing localities to consuming localities, engendering the beginnings of local and interregional trade. Through Spanish influence (essentially in the hands of Filipinos) the traditional social structure was both modified and crystallized, and a kind of trichotomy was developed among the Christian, the pagan, and the Moslem sectors of the populations. Late in the Spanish period, minor efforts in constructing irrigation systems had some local impact on agricultural production. It is notable, however, that Spanish influence had little effect on agricultural technology, and therefore did extremely little to alter the basic production systems of Philippine agriculture.

American influence began with the issue of land-control systems, making an effort at ownership reform and the limitation of landholding size. Reform efforts were short-term and regionally centered only, but the size limitation effectively prohibited the appearance of plantation agriculture in the Philippines. The introduction of a title system, a survey system, and the regularization of title disputes through court systems provided effective means of land control, but these beginnings were neither extended throughout the Islands nor perpetuated into effective results. The new systems were entirely alien to the Filipinos and were of advantage chiefy to the educated upper classes. The introduction of new crop varieties and the institution of a skeletal system of agricultural extension services and experiment stations yielded some benefits to production technology. The incorporation of the Philippines within the American tariff boundary gave a strong impetus to an export trade in selected agricultural products, thereby initiating the elements of imbalance in domestic agricultural production. Trends in domestic American agriculture, such as the big-machine tools, commercial fertilizers, toward enlarged farm sizes, and continual introduction of new crops, were neither feasible in the Philippines nor were they compensated by alternative influences or technologies effective in Philippine agriculture. American influence upon agricultural production technology was relatively minimal during the period of American control of the Islands, whereas the impact upon the processing of agricultural products has been rather significant.

The marked growth in Philippine population has been accompanied by the extension of the agricultural landscape, but there has also been an overconcentration of population in some regional centers, yielding a severe tenancy problem that in the early 1960's, still plagued the economy. Contemporary Philippine agriculture has a large residue of traditional patterns, practices, and systems, for all the changes that have appeared. Production technology remains almost traditional, and the caingineros are still widely distributed and numerous and produce at a very low level. Changing population distribution has created large product-deficit regions that are now supplied by product-surplus regions in a marked domestic flow of agricultural products. Production technology is beginning to change for the better, but it is far behind the demand. Agricultural production cannot respond to consumer demand in such things as wheat products and mid-latitude fruits, and it has responded inadequately to consumer demand for dairy products and mid-latitude vegetable products. Although change has come to Philippine agriculture in the last four centuries, the needed agricultural revolution in production systems does not yet appear to be well under way.

Cropping Systems and Combinations

In the contemporary period five crop plants form the bases for all regional patterns of agriculture in the Philippines. These are rice, corn, yams and sweet potatoes, bananas as food staples, and coconut as an all-purpose plant whose mature fruit serves primarily a commercial purpose. The crop plants account for all but a small share of the cultivated acreage. The table of crop frequencies (appendix table 17) indicates the frequency of occurrence on farms for 1948 and for 1960.[1] Rice and bananas are almost always present in the agricultural landscape throughout the archipelago, and almost all cropping combinations involve either one or both. Regional specialization adds some one crop or group of crops to the rice-banana base in a particular manner, either as locally dominant items or as shared complements that bulk significantly in the acreage patterns and in the regional economy.

After about 1750, corn became accepted as a crop and a food, and it has risen steadily in importance as a crop staple. In the Visayas, southeast Mindanao, and northeast Luzon, corn has become a regional dominant, and in the Visayas it has replaced rice as the primary food item. The sweet potatoes and manioc have joined the yams both in use and regional concentration. Manioc (cassava) has become a garden and small-patch complement rather than a basic staple of field-grown proportions. Such American fruits as the papaya and the avocado have spread widely to join the pattern developed by the jackfruit and pomelo, but none of the fruits truly rivals the bananas, and none either singly or in combination, has risen to the status of a primary crop in any regional context. Coffee and cacao have risen steadily in status, and the 1960 data indicate a higher farm frequency than the 1948 pattern.

Sugarcane has declined notably in its relative frequency as a complementary crop as the modern commercial sugar industry has developed. Its occurrence as a farm crop suggests that it is a regional specialty and far less widely planted than its commercial importance as a leading export crop would suggest. Abaca has also declined in relative frequency of planting because of climatic restrictions, commercial specialization, and recent regional disease problems. Tobacco has always been a restricted crop, having been formerly a Spanish Crown monopoly; but in the American era it spread as a garden or small-patch crop. Recent development of Virginia-leaf tobacco as a Philippine crop for a legally protected Philippine market has lifted its importance as a primary crop in northwest Luzon.

Mixed farming, as the term is employed in American agriculture, is not really significant in the Philippines. Most of the crops listed in the table of crop frequencies occupy small acreages and properly are complements in cropping combinations and systems. They show up as garden plantings on small farms, patch plantings, field-boundary plantings, or interplantings on larger farms. Most of the farms classed as "others" in the table of crop frequencies are small farms and part-time farms. Market gardening, specialty farming of distinctive items for limited markets, flower growing, specialty seed growing, and other particularistic elements common to American regional agriculture are notably lacking in Philippine agriculture. Market gardening is quite recent in island agriculture and often is confined to fringes of urban areas containing significant numbers of Chinese. Not properly represented in the 1948 data is the recent increase in the cultivation of mid-latitude vegetables in the North Luzon Highlands, but the 1960 data shows its expansion there, cabbage, potatoes, string beans, carrots, onions, cauliflower, and lettuce occupied a total area of over 10,000 acres in Mountain Province in 1960. This is a regional feature not likely to spread to all parts of the islands.

Combinations of the chief crops in major regions and minor localities give distinctive patterns clearly visible in the landscape. Northern and western Negros Island is an agricultural landscape in which sugarcane assumes a dominant status, and in which rice, coconut, bananas, papayas, and mangoes are employed as complements occupying marginal positions in the agricultural landscape. Southeast of Manila, coconut plantings dominate the landscape, and complementary crops show up in patches, gardens, and homestead plantings. Corn and coconut appear to dominate the landscape in much of

Cebu, whereas the root crops present an open landscape in the typhoon-swept Batan Islands. South of central Luzon the coconut tree has long closed in local landscapes, and as the frequency of coconut planting increases throughout much of the Philippines, its effect on the landscape is increasing. For all the regional specializations, however, rice, bananas, corn, yams, sweet potatoes, and coconut dominate the cropping systems and the agricultural landscapes of the Philippines.

In the development of modern cropping combinations, except for coconut, Filipino farmers do show a tendency to differentiate between domestic-use crops and commercial-export crops. This is most notable in the production of sugarcane, which has tended to become a product of a few large farms and associated, smaller size growers who are on contract. In recent years tobacco, as a commercial crop, has joined sugarcane in becoming an agricultural specialty crop. Abaca shows some of this same tendency. Coconut is grown as a specialty crop, but it is also planted as a commercial complement by farmers of other kinds of crops in all areas except the north and the highlands.

Systems of Land and Water Control

Although the Philippines has matured into a modern political state, the Filipinos have never learned the complex technology of fully advanced agriculture, and it is only in the very recent period that some progress is being made toward this end. Highly productive agriculture involves complex and integrated procedures of land control, soil management, and water control, but very few of these procedures are common in the Islands. Historically, both lowland shifting cultivators and highland terracers who practiced complex soil management and water-control engineering have long occupied the islands, but the lowlanders never learned and applied the techniques of the highlanders. The Spanish, coming to a humid landscape that seemed to present no serious problems, did almost nothing to change the casual handling of agricultural procedures in the lowlands, and made no real contact with the highlanders of north Luzon. During the American period, soil management, erosion control, and water-control practices developing in the United States were not applied in the Philippines. Most American effort concerning water was expended in ensuring potable water supplies around towns and cities and in extending sanitary procedures concerned with public health.

Lowland wet-field rice cultivation in the Philippines is generally carried on without those effective practices that keep rice fields flooded with water throughout the whole growing season. The bunding of wet-rice fields did become common; this bunding serves to retain such precipitation as falls into the fields or inadvertently drains into them, but it is common for fields to dry out during a short dry spell before the end of the growing season. The careful practices of the north Luzon highlanders cover small acreages only, and are a clear exception to the generalization. Late in the Spanish period a few small irrigation systems for wet-field rice and other crops were developed in the regions around Manila, but the installation of irrigation systems lagged far behind the increase in rice-field acreage as the agricultural landscape was extended. Little progress was made during the American period in increasing the development of irrigation facilities proportionate to the increase in total rice-growing acreage. In recent years government programs aimed at developing small irrigation facilities for local communities have led to a considerable increase in acreages of irrigated land devoted chiefly to rice growing, and there is a public impression that real progress is being made in the improvement of Philippine rice agriculture (fig. 27). Through the installation of powered pumping facilities, small-dam diversion schemes, canal systems, and field-bunding systems it is true that areas of nonirrigated rice land are being converted to irrigated rice lands, with consequent improvement of yields. The extension of rice acreages on the pioneer margins of settlement, however, has in recent years far out-paced the growth of irrigation facilities, and the great majority of this new rice acreage is on nonirrigated land; hence, the total acreage of rice land is growing at a rate faster than the introduction of irrigation facilities. Significant portions of the annual increases in rice acreage involve nonlevel lands in rolling country and hilly regions, on which upland rice is being grown; such situations permit no provision of controlled water supplies. Despite the government programs converting nonirrigated rice lands to irrigated lands, therefore, it remains true that Philippine rice agriculture is not making the strong improvement in its water control that is needed to bring about the increase in productivity for a food staple.[2]

Terraced landscapes of some age do occur in many localities throughout the islands, aside from those of north Luzon, but they occur in small units or in lightly developed patterns. Careful terracing of a nonlevel landscape, as it was brought into cultivation, has never been normal practice in the Philippines, and the intricate terracing of north Luzon has no counterpart elsewhere in the Islands. Such terracing is not necessary for growing other crop plants, but for a cropping system employing rice the provision of level fields and integrated water control historically has been the only procedure that could guarantee high-level yields for permanently cropped lands. That the agricultural landscape of the Islands is not now a mosaic of small terraces does

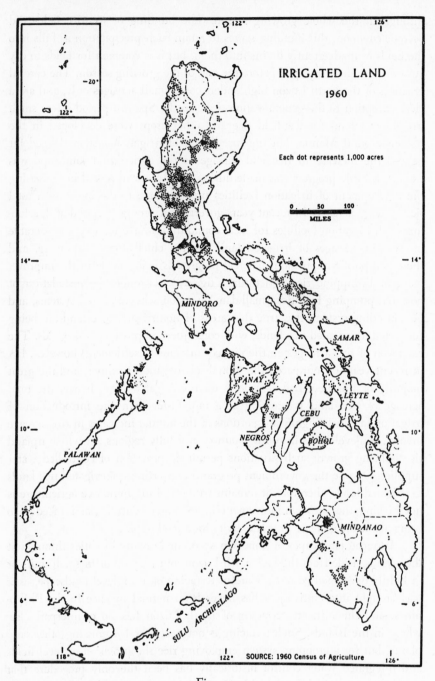

Fig. 27.

make possible the relatively easy mechanization of farming operations on these lands, but mechanization is not yet the chief answer to problems of wet-field rice production in the Islands.

The Filipino farmer, by and large, has been a planter and reaper who has seldom incorporated into his cropping practices any form of technology that could maintain or improve the inherent qualities or characteristics of the soil. This remains true in the contemporary era, and many areas of farmland today suffer from both soil depletion and soil erosion. In a general sense those regions farmed longest at a relatively high density rate show the greatest amount of deterioration. Some of the Visayan islands, areas around and southwest of Manila, and the northwest coast of Luzon show the most severe impact of soil erosion and soil depletion, with the great majority of farmland in those areas having heavily eroded and severely depleted soil. Many of the regions recently serving as zones of settlement and agricultural expansion show only light effects largely because they are still new farmscapes.

Traditionally, the Filipino lowlander was a shifting cultivator. Under the influence of the Spanish, the settled areas became zones of permanent cultivation, but shifting cultivation continued on the margins and on the frontiers. With the extension of settlement, civil government, and the patterns normal to sedentary society, the earlier zones of shifting cultivation progressively became zones of sedentary agriculture following permanent cropping practices. The shift in cropping practices, however, brought no accompanying improvement in procedures of soil management. Declining yields have usually accompanied permanent cropping practices, so that low yields became a permanent feature of Philippine agriculture. American influence had some small effect, and contemporary Philippine government agencies are working steadily to improve soil management, but the country-wide level of practice still is low. Cover-cropping, crop rotation with soil-building crops, composting, contour cropping, manuring, the application of commercial fertilizers and soil builders, and other related productive practices have relatively slight countrywide application.

Systems of Land Ownership and Tenure

The traditional concern of the Filipino with land was in terms of its use, not in terms of its ownership, in the sense the term carries in the modern occidental world. Ownership was vested in a communal group, meaning a society, a people, a tribe, a clan, or some other organizational entity among a given population. Ownership went with occupance of a territory by the population unit. The tenure of land was by usufruct, meaning the right to use land for any of several purposes but not the right to alienate that land in any way. Tenure operated for several purposes in specific ways according to the social structure of the particular group. Among socially stratified peoples or tribes there were classes or persons at the lower extreme who were excluded from particular rights of tenure, whereas at the upper extreme there were classes or persons who could demand tribute in labor, service, or a share of the yield produced by the exercise of particular tenure rights from either the whole population or given classes below them. Between these two extremes were varied patterns by which most of the small population held tenure rights to use land for any purpose and to retain the products thereof. Shifting cultivation, hunting, food gathering, appropriation of forest and mineral resources, and fishing all operated within this general framework of ownership by a group and tenure by usufruct. Among the north Luzon highlanders modifications of this traditional pattern approached concepts of private ownership in the limited sense that tenure applicable to permanently cropped terrace lands was held during the continued occupance of any given field.

The Spanish introduced into the Philippines sixteenth-century European land-system concepts and some of the concepts and practices they had developed and applied in their New World colonies. Not all New World practices became fully developed in the Philippines, and certain of those applied at first, were later discontinued at various dates during the period of Spanish control. The subject of Spanish land systems in the Philippines is an intricate one, and only certain aspects of it will be discussed here. The primary point at issue is that Spanish practice introduced what, in final effect, became private ownership and private tenure with right of alienation into a region in which there had been only ownership by a group and tenure by usufruct. The actual ways in which this was accomplished are of less concern than the end results. As the Spanish altered the settlement structure of the Philippines, turning shifting cultivators into permanent-field farmers with fixed village and town residence, the Spanish system gradually replaced the traditional system in the regions and areas the Spanish brought under effective control. Beyond those areas of effective control, traditional systems continued in force. Although the Spanish legally recognized and theoretically honored the traditional communal system, Spanish civil administration never really enforced the maintenance of the communal system, and in the long run, the Spanish system prevailed to the exclusion of the traditional system in the regions of Spanish civil control.

Too much has been made of the encomienda system as the spearhead of Spanish control over land which resulted in the creation of great private, family, and church estates, thereby turning the Filipinos into a victimized

tenant population. The encomienda system, which was a New World practice, had far less to do with any such development than did the Filipino
adoption of the Spanish systems of landownership and tenure during the
eighteenth and nineteenth centuries.[3]

Filipino adoption of Spanish land-system concepts was one aspect of
their embrace of Spanish culture. Tribal leaders and upper-class persons and
families took advantage of their positions and greater knowledgeability in the
whole process of Hispanization to acquire ownership of land in the fee-simple
pattern by which the Spanish system chiefly operated. Some Spanish and
some Chinese, of course, did the same, as eventually did some Americans.
The Catholic church used the same opportunities, and in that many church-
owned lands lay around towns and cities in areas of stable Spanish control,
church-owned lands later became a focal point of dispute. As the Filipino
population grew, however, and the farm landscapes expanded in total area, it
was chiefly Filipinos who became the landowners by the new system. Those
lower classes that had traditionally been excluded from various tenure rights
had fewer opportunities to acquire land under the new legal systems. The
large expansion in population and in land taken into farmsteads during the
nineteenth century permitted the acquisitive, the knowledgeable, and the
privileged to use the power of civil government to the end that increasing
areas of land passed from legal control by the traditional system into control
by private ownership under the newer system. The traditional position of the
less-privileged Filipino classes with respect to tenure right became enforced
by the procedures of Spanish civil government, operating through Filipinos
who formed its bureaucracy. Late nineteenth-century Spanish decrees formalized land titles and urged their claiming. Knowledgeable Filipinos, not shy of
the law and having access to its machinery, were the chief beneficiaries of the
decrees. A good deal of land occupied and cultivated by small farmers passed
into the ownership of those who could secure title, and the occupants found
themselves in the status of tenants. Peculiarities of Filipino social custom
concerning the relationships in patronage between patron and obligee worked
to restrain and prevent retaliatory action by the small farmer who was
unfamiliar with legal provisions and legal machinery. Thus, traditional native
practice, traditional social custom, Spanish legal developments, and the
aggressiveness of Filipino upper classes tended to develop a pattern of tenancy
under a new legal system which became far more extensive than had ever
been the case in pre-Spanish times.

American concepts of land systems reinforced Spanish patterns. American practice introduced the Torrens title system, by which past disputes could
be settled once and for all by those who would use the courts; it introduced

the land-survey system, and specific procedures by which land ownership in the now well-established private-ownership system could be acquired. These practices all favored those familiar with the law and willing to use its machinery; the rural small farmer, uneducated in the law and unfamiliar with its machinery, was reluctant to use that machinery. American land law instituted a limit on the amount of land to which any single owner could acquire title, and thereby, did head off the appearance and growth of the corporate plantation system as that system operated in other parts of southeast Asia. American practice in land reform did reduce church ownership in certain areas near Manila, but it did nothing about reform of tenancy on the large tracts of land held by a far greater number of existing Filipino landowners. American legal provisions did not prohibit a large extended family from acquiring, in the aggregate, a large holding by the simple procedure of securing title to a maximum amount of land for each member of a family. American practice ruled against the recognition and protection of the traditional communal system as it still operated in these frontier, marginal, or newly developed areas of the Islands, and permitted the further displacement of that traditional system.

With the continued rapid growth of population, a share of that new population remained in its home territory, giving rise to very strong pressures on land in some areas and resulting in a further increase in tenancy under several different systems. In such areas as the Batangas Peninsula, the Manila hinterland, the Central Plain of Luzon, the Ilocos coast, southeastern Panay, and western Negros Island tenancy problems grew steadily more pronounced all during the American period, resulting in a crisis situation in the first years of Philippine independence. In Pampanga Province, in the lower Central Plain of Luzon, the most pronounced development of tenancy by 1948 had reached the point at which some 86 percent of the agricultural holdings were under some system of tenancy.[4] It is not the purpose of this section to discuss at length the tenancy question, but the conclusion emerges that in densely populated regions of long agricultural occupance the problems surrounding landownership and tenure became severe and troublesome. These problems bear strongly on the agricultural economy of the Philippines, and the fragmentation of agricultural land into small holdings operated by tenants, often under exacting rates of rental, has much to do with the relatively low productivity of Philippine agriculture.

The Philippines has recently taken strong steps in the matters of land survey, the expediting of issuance of deeds and titles, the throwing open of new lands for settlement by private initiative, and less effectively, the arrangement of resettlement programs by governmental action.[5] For the present the tenancy crisis perhaps has eased somewhat, and there is both considerable opportunity for landless Filipinos to acquire land and considerable understanding of the legal basis for the operative system of private landownership and private tenure. There still are, however, many landless Filipinos in densely populated sections who are not afforded easy opportunity to participate in the system now operative, families who stand in debt-social obligatory status to landlords, and families who are reluctant to migrate from their home regions even though local conditions are difficult. There also are local regions in which remnant tribal peoples still maintain their traditional systems of communal ownership and tenure. Some of these regions are coming under increasing pressure from settlers moving out of crowded areas, and the conflict between the two systems is not yet resolved. Both these situations constitute landownership problems that will continue to cause difficulty in the future.

The expansion of survey facilities has permitted the increased issuance of titles, and the migrational data suggest large numbers of people moving from former areas of heavy tenancy. The natural presumption is that in the settlement of new lands in the pioneer regions by persons emigrating from zones of heavy pressure on land, the new settlers will not reproduce the conditions operative in their former home regions. It is expectable that they will become landholders on properties large enough for the provision of improved economic conditions. The evidence available, however, does not bear out this expectation. The physiologic density figure previously cited for Bukidnon Province, in the midst of plentiful open and available land, suggests that the Filipino pioneer settler actually often operates very small holdings. Field evidence from southern Mindanao suggests that on the pioneer fringe there is a strong tendency for the new settler to slip back into the position of a tenant on a too-small holding after only a short period of occupancy on his new land, even when open and available land is to be found locally. There are several economic and technologic factors operating to bring this about, but it appears as an unfortunate result. Different data, on the other hand, suggest that in key areas of high tenancy ratios the problem increasingly becomes more serious. These data suggest that the countrywide tenancy average has increased from 37.4 percent of all farmers in 1948 to close to 50 percent in 1960.[6] In a country developing a trend toward urbanization and industrialization, which processes tend to take the pressures off land and the agricultural economy, the present countrywide average may prove bearable, so far as major social and political problems are concerned. This would be true providing that conditions in any local region could be rectified to a satisfactory level. So far as the agricultural economy itself is concerned, however, the kind of tenancy which operates in the Philippines to fragment land into very small pieces and to set patterns in such a way as to inhibit improvement in agricultural productivity will continue to be a drag upon that agricultural economy. One step in the route toward greater productivity of agriculture involves enlarging the size of operative farm units sufficiently to make economically practical many of the modern complex agricultural practices. The whole legal setting of landownership and tenure, and the present tendency to break up so-called landlord estates into small holdings does not augur well for the development in the Philippines of that advanced, mechanically powered, and high-productivity motivated modern agriculture which is actually so necessary.

Crops: Acreages, Regions, and Production Patterns

Although it is customary to divide Philippine agriculture into domestic and export sectors, not many farmers operate so exclusively. The farmer of southern Luzon who plants coconut seedlings and grows upland rice as an intercrop may be classified as engaging in domestic production until the trees begin to bear. Until the growth of the trees makes rice intercropping impractical he will produce in both the domestic and the export sectors. His mature coconut farm will be classifiable in the export sector. The southeast Luzon farmer who produces rice, abaca, coconut, and sweet potatoes as his major crops may sell most of his rice, abaca, and coconut to commercial markets, at which point wholesale dealers dispose of the rice in the domestic market and the abaca and coconut in the export market. This commercial farmer has kept small shares of each of the major crops for home use or local barter trade, saving his sweet potatoes for home use and local barter. But around his homestead he has also produced small volumes of such vegetables as taro, eggplant, and tomatoes, and such fruits as bananas, papaya, lanzon, and avocado. Most of this volume will be eaten at home, but some of it will go to friends, and some will enter the local barter market. His dozen hills of sugarcane provide chewing cane for relaxed evening snacks but do not make him an export producer just because sugarcane is primarily an export crop. His pig and a dozen chickens provide local consumer or barter products at the proper times. The small volume he sells or barters at the local town market helps provide the complementary staples, the regular fish purchases, and the occasional odd purchases.

There are farmers and landholders who produce one crop to the practical exclusion of others, but these form a minority of all Philippine farmers. In the Central Plain of Luzon first-crop rice growing dominates the farm landscape, and other crops occupy quite small acreages. In Batangas, Iloilo, and Leyte more than half of the rice farms report bananas, and the agricultural census statistics show many other crops are present on farms in small plantings. Similarly, in the heart of the commercial sugarcane-growing sector of western Negros Island, rice, corn, sweet potatoes, and manioc show up on the farms in significant areas, along with small plantings of many other crops, and only a very few of the largest cane farms approach the true monocrop pattern.

Further comment is appropriate here on matters pertaining to the modernization of Philippine agriculture. Structured within the Department of Agriculture and Natural Resources for decades have been such bureaus as Plant Industry, Animal Industry, Soil Survey, and other divisions and agencies charged with aiding agriculture. There have been provincial experimental stations, agricultural high schools, and a College of Agriculture within the University of the Philippines. Many changes have been brought to Philippine agriculture since 1900 by these agencies, but the programs have been skeletal ones constantly struggling against apathy, the shortage of manpower, and the shortage of funds needed to carry out truly aggressive and effective programs. Such changes as have taken place have been at rates lower than the rates of population increase, changes in levels of living, and changes in general standards of living and economic operation. Those farmers who were inclined to take advantage of the opportunities have benefited thereby. In general, however, the small Filipino farmers of the rural districts, the poorer and less well-educated farmers, and the tenant farmers have not had the benefit of aggressive programs brought to them in a form they could utilize. Commercial sugarcane growers, through their tight associations with millers and refiners, have had private experiment stations and technical laboratories that brought to all commercial growers such improvements as were developed, but such activities have not affected many other segments of agriculture. Foreign and domestic companies marketing fertilizers, powered machinery, and less complex agricultural tools have carried on campaigns and programs in advertising, education, and propaganda, but these have had little appeal to the poorer, smaller, and more distant rural farmers. Well-educated and prosperous farmers holding large acreages have been able, for some decades, to take advantage of experimental operations, the mechanization of technology, and the utility-of-scale procedures, to the end that there have been marked variations in yields per acre, farm incomes, and economic profits between the large farmers and the small farmers. Too often, however, the large landholder has been willing to let his tenants carry on their traditional practices, so long as the tenancy fees were forthcoming.

Beginning in the late 1950's newly initiated government programs affecting many aspects of agriculture, but particularly relating to crop breeding, have been organized. For example, there now are integrated programs in experimental rice growing which combine soil manipulation, provision of irrigation water, improved seed stock, fertilization, weed control, pest control, and improved planting and harvesting technologies.[7] Publicizing of the results of such programs is beginning to have an effect in the regions exposed to such publicity, and improved agricultural procedures are catching on in localities where most of the farmers have become well indoctrinated and have the means to finance changes. Perhaps it is fair to say that an era of significant change has been introduced, and that within the next decade or two such innovations will spread widely, with corresponding increases in productivity and rural prosperity. As of the mid-1960's, however, such changes are in only the very early stages, and the impact on national per-acre crop averages and total productivity has been negligible when compared to the rates of population increase. Such beginning patterns of change should not be disparaged, but realistic assessment of the rates of change in the rural backcountry leads to the conclusion that agricultural improvement still does not affect those who need it most. Provided these programs of improvement can be carried forward on strongly aggressive patterns for two or three decades, Philippine agriculture may well undergo the revolution it so greatly needs.

CROPS OF THE DOMESTIC SECTOR

As a matter of convenience the customary division into domestic and export crops is accepted in this and the following discussion. As food staples three crops dominate the domestic sector of agriculture—rice, corn, and the yam–sweet potato group, in that order. All other crops may be considered complements, supplements, snack foods, or specialty crops of seasonal or unusual consumption. There are regional patterns in the production agriculture of many of the crops of all the above groups, and there are regional patterns of use by consumers of the staples and the complements. The recent development of transportation and commercial organization operate to make available in all parts of the Islands both the staples and the complements, but it is particularly true of the supplements, the snack foods, and the specialty items. For example, rice may be purchased in any town market on the Islands if the consumer prefers it as a staple. The mangosteen, on the other hand, was grown as a specialty item on only 2,414 farms in 1948, although these were distributed throughout all but one or two provinces. On the 5,100 bearing trees in 1948, well over 3,000 were in the four provinces of Lanao del Norte, Lanao del Sur, Zamboanga, and Sulu, in the far south. For a short period in

June and July the mangosteen appears in commercial markets in a great many towns throughout the Islands, the main supply moving from the far south throughout the whole archipelago. Even in its production area the mangosteen is a specialty item available only during a short period.

Rice. Referred to as *palay* in the Philippine agricultural pattern, rice is the traditional staple food of the Philippines and it retains that position today in the agricultural economy. Rice is the primary crop on almost half the farms of the Philippines and is grown on more farms than any other single crop. Occupying a little less than half the total cultivated land, rice is the food staple of about three-fourths of the population, who eat it at least once a day. Although grown almost everywhere in the archipelago, the primary production patterns shows regionalization; this is indicated on the accompanying maps (figs. 28, 29). The Central Plain of Luzon is the largest regional producer, but Mindanao is the source of the largest surpluses in the 1960's. Southwestern Luzon, eastern Panay, and the Bicol Peninsula follow the Central Plain as heavy producing regions, and Bohol, Leyte, and the Cagayan Valley appear as secondary producers. No one sector of Mindanao ranks with the above regions, but rice is widely grown in many parts of the island.

Rice has few environmental restrictions in the Philippines. Temperatures are suitable everywhere except in the highest mountain country. A few upland locations along the east coasts of Luzon and Mindanao are too cloudy for productive rice-growing. Elsewhere, the operative environmental factors can be negated by planting during the rainy seasons or by provision of irrigation water. Rice requires between 50 and 60 inches of water, in most Philippine situations, during the period from field preparation through mature grain-setting, and the volume of water should be rather evenly distributed throughout the whole period.

As previously mentioned, Filipino farmers have not provided the culturally controllable circumstances for high-yielding rice agriculture, either in terms of soil and water management or in production technology. Philippine yields, therefore, rank among the lowest for the world rice producers. Until very recently these national yield patterns were not improving, and despite the steady increase in rice acreage, production patterns have not kept pace with increasing consumer demands. The Philippines began importing rice in the late nineteenth century, and modest annual imports to compensate for rice deficits have been the rule with few recent exceptions.

Most primary rice farms grow a single annual crop of long-season rice as a lowland crop in fields that may be bunded to hold water but seldom have provisions for supplying water deficits. Seedbed germination during the period of field preparation is followed by hand-transplanting of seedlings at

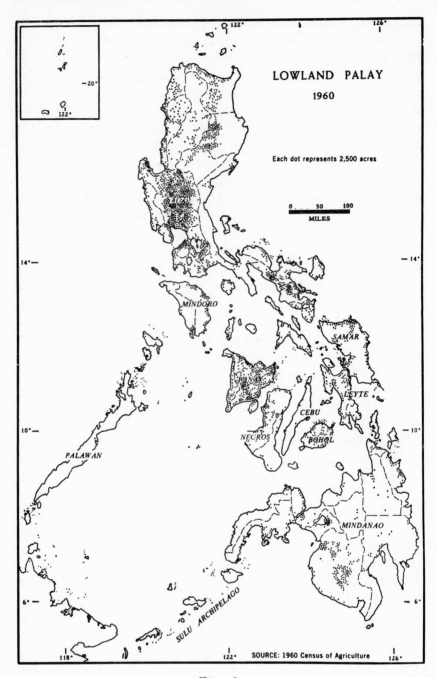

Fig. 28.

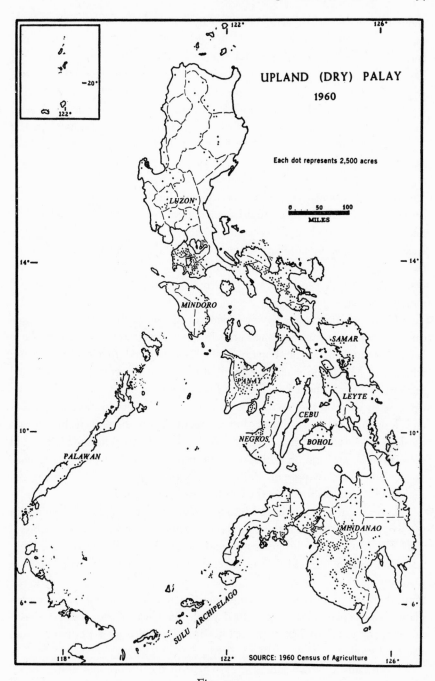

UPLAND (DRY) PALAY
1960

Each dot represents 2,500 acres

Fig. 29.

about 65,000 "sets" per acre. Weeding by hand is normal, and the largest share of the crop is hand-harvested. Depending upon the local circumstances, between 20 and 26 man-days of labor expenditure per acre is normal for lowland rice. Long-season, single-crop yields average close to 1,300 pounds per acre. About a fourth of the rice farms plant a second crop of shorter-season lowland rice which may average close to 900 pounds per acre for about the same labor expenditure. On a little less than half of the farms classed as rice farms, upland rice is grown as a field-seeded crop dependent upon rainfall and soil moisture. Average yields reach almost 700 pounds per acre with about half the labor needed for lowland rice. Much of the upland rice is grown on permanently cleared and occupied fields, but some is planted by the cainginero on land either cleared for short terms only or on land cropped in rice at the start but planted to coconut or other crops for long-term occupance. Rice yields on newly cultivated forest clearings at the expanding margins of the agricultural landscape often return almost double the normal yield the first year, but a descending yield pattern soon reduces the yield toward the national average.

There is little good reserve rice land available, so the growth in acreage cannot continue at the past rate. Farms in the crowded sections of Luzon have been growing smaller, and many have been reduced to close to 2 acres; whereas in Mindanao many rice farms still average 15 acres. In the crowded sections of Luzon about half the rice farms are worked by tenants. Both the decrease in size and the tenancy factor make for difficulty in increasing yields and lowering costs. A drastic improvement in production technology is needed. But also needed is a change in land-control practices which would permit the larger farm on which an improved technology could operate with greater efficiency. At present, Philippine rice-production costs are among the highest cost-patterns found in the world's rice-growing regions.

Corn. Corn was introduced into the Visayan sector of the Philippines in the sixteenth century, and the crop then spread to other parts of the archipelago.[8] Known in the Philippines as *mais,* corn eventually proved a highly adaptable crop plant, useful in many ecological situations as a complement to rice and the yams. Gradually its superior potential in the zones of erratic rainfall and on the drier soils brought corn to a regional dominance as a crop plant. Its acceptance as a basic food staple, in place of rice, cemented this dominance, and corn has risen steadily in importance as a Philippine crop and food staple.

Corn can be grown almost everywhere in the Philippines and is being planted somewhere during every month of the year. Those regions with year-round precipitation usually raise three crops per year, but elsewhere corn is a rainy-season crop. Although all types and varieties of corn are grown, the flint corns are most common, being best adapted to the making of "corn rice," and to the rather low level of storage technology employed.[9] Corn suffers from a wide range of diseases and pests in the mild Philippine environment, and though physical yields are often fairly high, harvested yields may be rather low, particularly for second- and third-crop plantings. Per-acre yields vary widely, from 300 pounds per acre to 800 pounds in regional terms and in first- to third-crop returns, but the national average is slightly under 600 pounds per acre. This is an extremely low figure for the second-ranking food crop, and it is the result of poor soil management, employment of poor seed and variety patterns, and low-level technology.

It is in the Visayan islands of Cebu, Bohol, Leyte, and Negros that corn is the dominant food crop. (See fig. 67 for Cebu Island.) As settlers from these islands migrated to Mindanao they carried their corn-growing and corn-eating customs with them. The margins of Davao Gulf form a major producing region and a source of surpluses for the Visayan deficit areas. The accompanying map of the distribution of corn (fig. 30) indicates a number of secondary regional producing centers, such as the Cagayan Valley of northeast Luzon, the Batangas Peninsula of southwest Luzon, the Sorsogon Peninsula of southeast Luzon, eastern Panay Island, and a broad zone of western Mindanao. All of these secondary regions are commercial, surplus producers, shipping corn to the Visayan deficit area and to Manila markets.

Corn is still grown primarily for human consumption, but its use in poultry feeds and in industry has been increasing during the recent period. As an agricultural product corn is cheaper than rice but contains about the same food value. Its total acreage has expanded steadily, and in the early 1960's it stood close to 5,000,000 acres per year. There is reserve land suitable for growing corn, but soil erosion-depletion in the Visayan islands of Cebu and Bohol has reduced yields so severely that increased plantings elsewhere are needed to maintain the regional food supply. The consumer demand will continue to rise, and unless improved technology and land management can stay the decline in yield on long-cultivated lands, the reserve land will soon be needed to match the increased consumer demand. In the past there has been a surplus of corn, but ultimately a national deficit may appear. The Philippines could become a regular importer of corn products unless striking changes can be brought about in the productivity of the corn-growing agricultural pattern.

Root crops. Traditionally a wide variety of root crops—the yams and taros—formed what was probably the oldest group of food crops grown in the Philippines. Long before the arrival of the Spanish, however, rice had

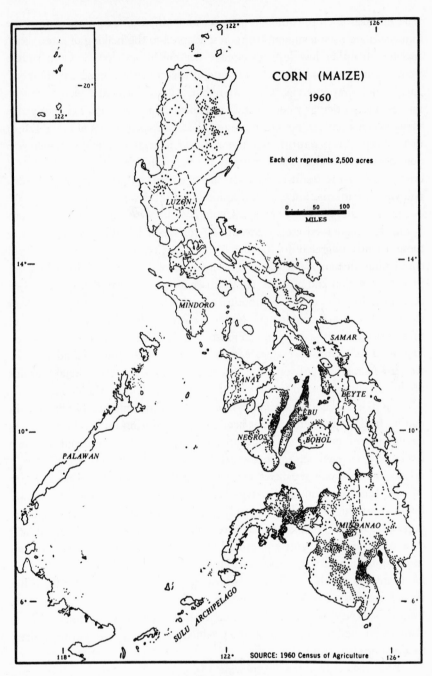

Fig. 30.

replaced both the yams and the taros as the preferred food crop. The older crops assumed complementary roles in most areas but retained their dominant positions in particular regions. The Spanish introduced sweet potatoes, manioc, and the peanut, as well as a few minor items, to expand the root-crop group. The sweet potato, known as *camote* in the Philippines, significantly displaced the yams in those regions in which they had remained important. Manioc, commonly known as cassava in the Philippines, achieved a standing as a lesser complementary crop almost throughout the islands. The peanut was accepted as a minor complement and became widely distributed but not very commonly grown. In the modern period the peanut has gained accept-ance in the form of peanut butter or as a whole-nut snack food and is increasing somewhat in popularity as a crop.

In the contemporary period the root crops, as a group, generally form a complementary element in cropping and in food acceptance. As appendix tables 17 and 18 indicate, sweet potatoes are widely grown, followed in order by manioc, yams, and peanuts. All show up in small acreages in almost every part of the Philippines. The distributions of cassava and camote are shown in figure 31. As a group the root crops are a staple food for the poor, the thrifty, and the early-stage frontier settler, or they serve as a hard-time crop. As an occasional complementary variant of the diet, as a seasonally used item, or as a specialty snack food, each of the crop plants has a particular role and steady utility among all classes.[10]

On Bohol the sweet potato shares with the yams and manioc a fairly significant position in the agricultural scene. All classes of Boholanos, who are the most Scots-thrifty of the Filipinos, eat the root crops regularly, selling into commercial markets their higher-priced crops. The sweet potato, the yams, and manioc are widely grown on small plantings in the hill country of Leyte and the Sorsogon Peninsula of southern Luzon. In the windswept Batan and Babuyan islands, the root crops are basic staples for the small population. In highland Mountain Province, northern Luzon, the sweet potato is either a local dominant or a significant complement among the terracers. On Negros and Mindanao manioc is widely present as a reserve patch-crop to be eaten by the human population if the crop year is not a good one, but to be fed to the pigs if the harvests are bountiful. Throughout the Sulu group of islands manioc is widely grown, and on Jolo Island it assumes regionally significant status, since the crop is present on more than half the farms in small but locally important plantings.

The total acreage of all the root crops has, in recent years, averaged about 700,000 acres. Philippine yields in each root crop are somewhat lower than comparative yields in other areas of the world where each is a significant

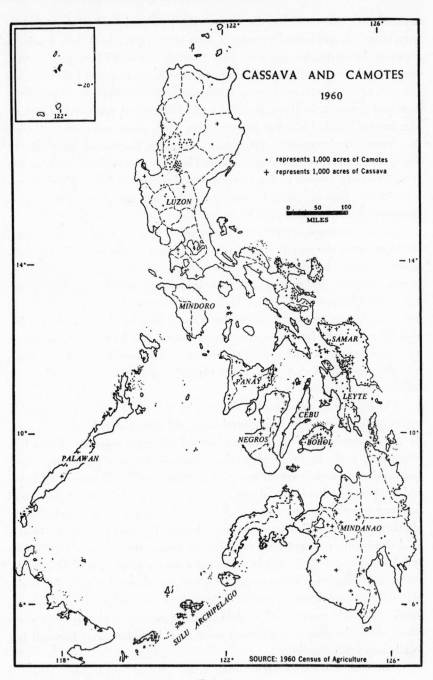

Fig. 31.

crop. As none of the crops represents a strongly preferred food crop, there is little effort to improve the yield pattern or production technology, and procedures remain traditional and not highly productive. There is a large reserve of rough or marginal land that could be devoted to several of these crops, but it is not likely, in the face of their decreased general acceptance, that their production will be greatly expanded if any other way can be found to improve Philippine agriculture.

Vegetable crops. The growing of vegetable crops has not been a highly developed aspect of Philippine agriculture because the shifting-cultivation background employed gathering of wild products as a complementary aspect of the dietary economy. Most greens and seasonings were near at hand and could be had for the taking.[11] Modern Filipino agriculture, therefore, has no highly developed zonal patterns of market gardening, truck farming, or specialty cropping. Most homestead or kitchen gardens in hamlets and villages came to contain a few "greens" producers, such as herbs, vines, or trees, and a few producers of mild seasonings. The spices and seasonings, however, have not been strongly significant to native Filipino cookery, and many of the items in contemporary use were introduced by the Spanish, the Chinese, or the Americans. The Chinese introduced a variety of vegetable plants from the Asian mainland; the Spanish brought some from the Mediterranean or from the New World; and the Americans introduced a wide range of leafy vegetables, root vegetables, or fruiting vegetables from many different sources.

In general the whole vegetable crop sequence has been growing in popularity among Filipinos as a dietary development, augmented by both growing familiarity and knowledge about diet and nutrition. Around many of the larger towns and cities there is now an area that can be classified as a market-garden zone. This is particularly true, of course, around Manila, with a cosmopolitan consumer-population drawn from all over the world; but it is a general growing response to a rising urban consumer demand.

During the middle part of the American period Filipino consumers began to make use of mid-latitude vegetables that could not be grown on the Philippine lowlands. These were supplied by the import trade at relatively high prices, but later some small-scale development of market gardening made it possible to produce some of these in the hill country of north Luzon, at altitudes above 4,000 feet. This acceptance of mid-latitude vegetables has grown steadily, augmenting the import of foodstuffs. During the 1950's there began the expansion of market gardening in the north Luzon hill country, centered in the Trinidad Valley near Baguio, to fill the urban demand for salad vegetables and other items now popular in Filipino cookery. A regionally significant, somewhat exotic, agricultural pattern has developed and is spreading within the hill country. This pattern can never spread to the lowlands, but there are many upland interiors throughout the islands high enough and cool enough for such upland market gardening to become widespread.

Table 18 in the appendix lists the few vegetables that are widely distributed on Philippine farms. The squash and tomato are of New World origin, and the mung bean is from China; but the eggplant, taro, ampalaya, and patola are old items in the Islands. Bamboo is included in this sector of the table in reference to the edible bamboos from which the young shoots are cut to provide a vegetable, though these same bamboos have other uses when the canes mature. According to 1960 data, no other vegetable crops occupied many acres or were grown on many farms, but the total list is long, over fifty different plants that play a small local or regional role in patterns of cropping. Recent data indicate the expansion of highland market gardening, particularly in Mountain Province, with cabbage and onions as leading items.

Fruit and nut crops. Some sixty different fruit and nut plants, grown as vines, shrubs, and trees, are found on Philippine farms, although census data is gathered for only about forty of these. Some are native to the Philippines, a good many came in long ago from the Asian mainland, and a good many are of New World origin and more recent in local cultivation. The non-native plants have been repeatedly introduced over time. Almost all of the native plants are to be found growing in wild areas or on nonfarm lands. Most of them had long been utilized by shifting cultivators and were fostered or formally planted on lands returned to regeneration after a cycle of use as cropland. From many of them there is still gathered a significant volume of wild fruits. In the cropping sequences throughout the Islands, none of the fruits or nuts has risen to dominance as a primary crop in the farmscape scene, but the whole group fills a significant role as a complement to the basic patterns of cropping. Coconut is an exception to this generalization in the sense that it has become a commerical crop. In the domestic use pattern, however, coconut is only a complement or specialty item, never a basic staple food; thus in this sense it is not an exception to the rule. Table 19 of the appendix indicates the rank and frequency of cultivation of the 22 fruits and nuts grown on more than 50,000 farms in 1948. The dominant position of the banana has been commented on previously, but it should here be noted that there is little regionality to the distribution of the banana. Most other fruits show some tendency to regional centering of production, although every one of the items listed in table 19 is reported from every province in the Islands.[12] For example, the mango tree is grown everywhere in some numbers, but its economic significance is important only in those sectors having dry seasons at the set period of the year in which the tree blossoms and bears fruit. The west coast of Luzon, and Panay and Cebu islands form the leading producing regions for the commercial mango. The lemon, although grown everywhere in the Philippines, is regionally centered in the Bicol provinces of southeast Luzon. The orange, on the other hand, is rather evenly scattered throughout the Philippines so far as its plantings are concerned.

Special comment is necessary on the position of pineapple. Introduced by the Spanish at an early date, the plant spread widely in a variety producing a very small, sweet fruit and long, slender leaves. Its primary native use came to be in the fiber known as piña, which is extracted from the long leaves, and for this the green fruit is cut out to encourage the growth of longer leaves. The crop is fairly widely grown as a minor fruit-fiber complement; however, one sizable commercial planting of large-fruited varieties established by the Philippine Packing Corporation in northern Mindanao produces a large volume of canned pineapple which forms a significant export from the Islands. The Dole Corporation has now initiated a large planting in Cotabato Province. So far, however, no really significant effect of this has shown up elsewhere in domestic agriculture, although in the commercial market-garden zone around Manila pineapple has long been grown for the fresh-fruit market.

Considering the whole group of fruits and nuts, the data suggest that the coastal sectors around the Lingayen Gulf, the Batangas Peninsula, the southern Bicol sector of southeast Luzon, Cebu and Bohol islands, and southeast Panay Island, in the Visayas, are the regions in which the largest variety of fruits are to be found on farms in considerable plantings. Parts of Pangasinan and Batangas display the nearest approach to what may be termed the orchard landscape. Encouragement of commercial fruit-growing by government agencies is producing a gradual development of more specialized agriculture; but in general, the Filipinos have preferred small homestead or patch plantings of a wide variety of fruits, and commercial horticulture is neither technologically advanced nor highly productive. Although significant to Philippine agriculture and important to local economy, the contribution of the fruit and nut crops is far less than it could be. There is considerable reserve land that could easily and advantageously be adapted to horticulture, but the task of educating the Filipino farmer in this respect is a considerable one.

As complements to agricultural production, and to domestic economy, the fruits and nuts are employed in a wide range of uses. The fruits are eaten fresh in season, and they are made into preserves, candies, and confections. Many of them are used in making ice creams and ices. Many of the green fruits are employed as pickling and seasoning elements, and edible oils are extracted from the seeds of several. Local native practice also finds use for them in what are best termed tropical delicacies.

Beverage crops. Perhaps the wide-ranging dependence upon the coconut palm forestalled Philippine domestication of what is generally classified as a beverage crop, but in any case, there is no native crop plant used for that purpose only. The milk from green-to-ripe coconuts, and the sap extruded from the lopped-off growing tip of the tree, can be consumed as a sweet, fresh drink, or they each can be fermented into an alcoholic drink. *Tuba* was perhaps the nearest approach to a traditional national drink. The alcoholic version of this is made by slightly fermenting coconut sap and variably dyeing it with mangrove bark, but the resulting beverage must be made daily and consumed promptly. A certain number of coconut trees in almost every locality are tapped for their sap until the trees die. Tuba can also be made from the sap of the buri palm or from the sap of the nipa palm, and a certain volume is regularly produced from all three sources.

The introduction of coffee and cacao as more normal beverage plants dates well back into the Spanish period. Both plants spread fairly widely, but neither beverage caught on sufficiently to be promoted as a strong agricultural producer, although the Batangas region of Luzon produced a considerable volume of coffee in the nineteenth century until disease reduced the plantings. In the recent modern period both beverages have risen markedly in popularity, and import volumes of cacao and coffee have grown steadily. During the 1940's government encouragement of plantings in each crop resulted in increased cultivation. Both plants can be widely grown in the Philippines, although there are some regions ecologically better-suited to each; but Philippine technology did not develop the careful procedures needed to succeed in a highly profitable manner. Continued government encouragement to stimulate production sufficient to eliminate the import volumes of both products resulted in new waves of plantings during the late 1950's and early 1960's. The pattern in farm frequency may be seen in the listings in table 20 of the appendix.

By the early 1960's cacao was present on 42,000 farms in small plantings totaling just over 23,000 acres. Cacao prefers a year-round humid climatic regime on the lowlands or lower hill country, some shade, and considerable care, since it suffers from strong winds and numerous diseases. Philippine planters have not yet found the most satisfactory regional niche in the agricultural environment, and it is unlikely that production technology has risen to the high level needed either to grow or to process the raw crop. Recent plantings range from the Cagayan Valley of northeast Luzon to the

Sulu region in the far south, generally avoiding localities with strong typhoon effects and areas having pronounced dry seasons. Continued experiment with planting areas and with technologic procedures will take place, and there well may be marked shifts in acreages and regional centers of production before the agricultural pattern becomes stabilized. If such a pattern can be established, the Philippines may well develop sufficient production to avoid the import of the product in the future.

Coffee has had much the same history as cacao. Recent government stimulation of domestic production has been pronounced, as the Filipinos have recently taken to drinking coffee in large amounts. Coffee planting in the Philippines should do best in the lower hill-country areas having a short dry-season during the coolest months of the year, but the history of planting has not yet clearly indicated the most suitable ecological environments for significant production. Whether Filipino horticultural technology succeeds well with extensive plantings of coffee is also not yet clearly indicated. In 1960 some 150,000 farms had set out coffee-plant stock in several varieties over about 75,000 acres distributed all over the Islands, and the annual production may have approached 70 million pounds. This amount is still well short of the annual consumption, and the use of coffee continues to expand. Continued government stimulation, and agricultural experiment, may well develop coffee into a significant Philippine crop, but at the date of this writing, a considerable import of coffee is still required to meet consumer demand.

Fiber crops. In the traditional pattern quite a number of fiber sources were utilized by home and handicraft industry consumers. Kapok trees, abaca and banana plants, palm trees, bamboos, and a variety of vines provided a wide range of fibers, from soft and short to hard and long, for many uses. Abaca was perhaps the most significant of all, and it provided strong fibers that yielded almost the whole range of textile qualities from soft and fine fiber to coarse, hard fiber. The modern use of abaca in rope and heavy mattings has obscured its traditional role as a clothing textile. Since it has become an important export item, abaca will be discussed further with the crops of the export sector.

The Spanish brought New World maguey and the pineapple to the Philippines. Maguey, which produces a fiber similar to that of abaca, spread throughout those regions having pronounced dry seasons. The pineapple spread in the moister regions as a minor fruit, but was grown chiefly as a source of fine, medium-length fiber, the product of its long spinelike leaves.[13] Pineapple fiber, or piña, found its chief application in very fine clothing and table textiles, partially replacing abaca in this range of fine handicrafts as abaca became reduced to a rope-and-matting fiber. Jute, hemp, flax, cotton, ramie, kenaf, and various other fiber plants have been introduced at one time or another. Each has been experimented with and scattered into the agricultural landscape, but few of them have risen to important status. In the modern period the significant domestic sources of fiber have been kapok, abaca, maguey, and pineapple, so far as agricultural production is concerned.

Maguey plantings are scattered through most of the Philippine provinces, but the plant has never developed into a major crop. Its peak period was in the early twentieth century, when over 50,000 acres were in maguey plantings. In 1948 some 20,000 farms reported about 20,000 acres in maguey, with Cebu possessing about two-thirds of the total. The reported 1960 acreage had dropped to about 9,000. The fiber yields serve a domestic market and make a small contribution to the export trade, but the production trend is languishing.

Although the ramie plant (*Boehmeria nivea*) is not really new in the Islands, a campaign to popularize it as a potential fiber source has recently produced a small extension in plantings. Technologic problems in decortication are a stumbling block to the small farmer, and there has been little acceptance of the crop plant. There has been some extension in plantings since 1948, when data indicated only 590 farms growing ramie and a total of about 1,500 acres. By 1960, however, the area devoted to ramie had increased threefold over 1948, a trend that continued to accelerate in the early 1960's. The plant was reported in 1948 from 35 provinces in very small plantings; the significant plantings were in Cotabato, Agusan and Lanao provinces of Mindanao. By 1960 commercial production had centered in Davao and Cotabato with a total of 3,500 acres devoted to ramie in these two provinces.

Kapok, traditionally grown as a fiber for stuffing pillows, mattresses, and other items, and also used by the furniture industry in the modern period, is a very widespread crop tree. In 1948 it was present on 137,000 farms in every province of the Islands. In most areas the planting consists of only a few trees, for the restricted utility of the fiber and the slight demand for it in traditional economy made large plantings unnecessary. Cebu and Bohol are the center of contemporary production. The modern demand for kapok remains restricted, with only 8,000 acres devoted to its cultivation in 1960, and its future potential is little greater than in the past.

Cotton is an old crop plant in the Philippines, although there is some doubt as to the actual fiber meant by the earliest Spanish references to cotton. Cotton was grown in central and northwest Luzon in mid-Spanish times, and Spanish developmental plans included its expansion in the nineteenth century. The rise of modern industrial cotton-textile manufacturing, and the great expansion of international trade in cotton textiles, killed off the domestic cotton industry before it became soundly developed, and plantings and the handicraft industry declined to very minor levels. Despite encouragement, cotton growing has not regained any of its former status in the Philippines. Attempts to popularize the crop during recent decades have failed largely because there has been no market for unprocessed raw cotton available to the farmer. Small plantings of cotton were reported in 1948 from almost every province, but the total number of farms growing it was reported at 9,180, and the total acreage was about 3,000. The Ilocos coastal zone of Luzon and Cebu Island represented the largest share of this small activity. An expansion of 6,500 acres of commercial cotton took place in Cotabato Province during the late 1950's and early 1960's.

These data suggest that government stimulation of planting programs for fiber crops is insufficient, in itself, to develop a sector of the agricultural economy. The lack of marketing facilities and primary agricultural-processing facilities, and the pattern of international trade competition, can hinder the initial production efforts and prevent the expansion of production of a crop. Also, in the Philippines the traditionally dominant position of abaca worked against the easy spread of other fiber crop plants.

Minor crops. There are many crop plants not included in prior commentary, most of these falling outside the previous groupings. A long list would be needed to include all the minor exotics, such as the 70 acres of strawberries now grown in the North Luzon Highlands for a select Manila market. The more important and diagnostic items include betel nut; the various beans, peas, and pulses; rubber; ginger; the peppers; and forage grass.

As shown in table 21 of the appendix the betel palm is widely distributed on Philippine farms, a few trees per farm. It is a holdover from the day when Filipinos, like the peoples of southeast Asia, were betel-chewers. The betel habit has largely disappeared among younger Filipinos, but the nut and the rest of the "makings" are still widely available in local markets to accommodate an old-fashioned minority.

The various beans, peas, and pulses, aside from the mung bean previously mentioned, occupy a notable, if small, place in the Filipino dietary. Only some 27,000 acres of about fifteen varieties of the group were reported in 1948, scattered throughout the Islands in very small patch-plantings in either market gardens or kitchen gardens. The 1960 data indicate a combined total of 226,000 farms cultivating at least one kind of bean, approximately half of which raise mung beans. Beans involved 193,000 acres, reflecting a fairly strong increase in the acreage of mung beans. One very old remnantal plant from the very early crop-cultivation era, the pigeon pea (*Cajanus cajan*), has almost disappeared from the Islands, although there is a curious preservation of it in local hard-times patch planting in southern Panay Island.

Unlike other parts of southern and eastern Asia, the Philippines grows very few spices and hot condiments, for the Filipinos are not spice-eaters. Chili pepper, black pepper, mustard, and ginger account for a total of about 10,000 acres, half of which is in ginger, a favorite of the resident Chinese. The other spices and hot condiments are so sparsely planted that there are almost no data on them.

As in other parts of the Orient, however, controlled pasturelands occupy no formal space in the Philippine agricultural landscape.[14] A very minor crop found around the outskirts of the older towns and cities is forage grass, grown almost entirely for the town-kept horses used to pull the several varieties of taxi-carts. In 1948 a total of 1,144 farms reported about 1,200 acres of this crop, but its decline had already set in as the "jeepney" taxi converted from war-surplus jeeps became popular. Livestock on farms traditionally are fed straw, plant wastes, and bran millings; they are allowed to range the grassy margins of roadsides and crop fields and to browse the stubble of harvested fields.

Rubber is but a very small item in the Philippines because American legislation against large landholdings coincided with the beginnings of southeast Asian rubber planting. In 1948 rubber trees were being grown on 2,880 farms, on a total of 12,700 acres, and were found in every province of the Islands. The only commercial plantings were in Zamboanga Province, southwest Mindanao, which has had small commercial plantations since the 1920's. With the modern rise of the rubber industries, the Philippines is now interested in a domestic rubber industry, and within the land-law limits, there is government encouragement for the agricultural planting of rubber trees. The 1963 data indicate the crop was being grown on 44,000 acres. Most of this large expansion of rubber-tree planting has come about since 1960 (when there were only 12,800 acres) on plantations in Zamboanga del Sur, Cotabato, Davao, and Bukidnon. The rubber tree can be grown widely throughout the lowland regions that are humid all the year, and as there is ample land for rubber-tree planting, the industry undoubtedly will expand even more in coming years. The recent establishment of commercial plantations in Cotabato Province, on Basilan Island, and elsewhere on Mindanao certainly are but the forerunners of that expansion.

Livestock and poultry. Pigs, chickens, and water buffalo are animals of traditional importance to the rice economy of the Philippines; other animals are complementary additions of relatively minor importance.[15] The keeping of cattle by shifting cultivators was traditionally a matter of religious and social ritual and not an economically motivated activity. Ducks, pheasants, geese, and pigeons have long been minor, but established, elements in the economy on the southeast Asian mainland, and they are a similar part of the Philippine pattern. Spanish, Chinese, and American influences upon the Philippine cultural complex have added certain elements to the traditional economy, but in part, these influences have been felt more strongly on the consumer side than on the production side.

Most Philippine farmsteads support a pig or two and a number of chickens; and most farmers seek to maintain one or two carabao. The smallest farms, particularly those of tenants in crowded areas, may not possess the carabao, but must rent animal draft power as needed, or do without it. Table 24 of the appendix indicates that in 1948 most farms reported chickens, pigs, and carabao, in that order. Ducks and geese were reported on far fewer farms, but were scattered throughout the Philippines. Table 24 also indicates the 1960 populations, and the postwar regeneration in numbers is clearly evident.

The Spanish introduced horses, goats, sheep, and additional cattle stocks to the Philippines. Repeated reintroduction of varied breeds of all these animals has taken place. Cattle and goats have often been brought in from the Asian mainland, and horses have been brought in from China, Japan, Timor Island, and varied other sources. American reintroduction of the turkey was accompanied by reintroduction of American breeds of chickens.

To the traditional rice-fish-pork-chicken dietary the Spanish added beef, goat, and mutton; and American influence accented this tendency, so that beef and lamb or mutton consumption has increased steadily in the Philippines. Both cattle and carabao contribute to the beef supply, and goat meat and sheep meat are both sold as lamb or mutton. The modern trend is such that current demand for beef steadily threatens to make inroads upon the working-animal populations of carabao and cattle.

Although terms referring to cattle ranching occur widely in the literature of both the Spanish period and the modern era, cattle really have not found an effective ecological niche in the Philippine environment or in the traditional economy. The Spanish gave up the attempt to create a pastoral economy in the Islands. Gradually, with the expansion of the dry-field side of agriculture, in corn farms, coconut farms, and upland rice farms, a place for cattle as draft animals has been found. Added to the demand for cattle as beef, the draft-animal use has definitely produced a complementary role for cattle in the present Philippine economy. Livestock farming as a specific agricultural operation, however, is not yet widespread nor it is technologically well developed. The consumer demand for beef puts a steady pressure upon the draft-animal population and the power supply available to farmers. In the absence of controlled pasturage lands, hay-crop lands, and feeder-fattening operations, there is also a heavy demand for grain supplies which is met by taking from the rice and corn supplies, thus worsening an already deficit situation. The tropical grass-grown parangs and grasslands do not constitute true pasturelands, and for those farmers owning the most animals, those grasslands are not available.

Horses found little place in the Philippine agricultural scene as agricultural draft power, but fitted gradually into the rural, village, and urban scenes as transportation power, pulling the light carts serving to transport passengers and make light deliveries. This pattern did not develop significantly until the late nineteenth century, and remained fully operative into the twentieth century until the growth of motorized transport began to restrict horse transport around the main urban areas.

Goats and sheep are not at home in the Philippines. Although the goat has been able to thrive in the expanded cultivated landscape, the sheep has remained an exotic animal in this near-tropical environment. Of the 326,000 goats reported in 1948, nearly one-half were in the Visayan Islands, and the rest were scattered all over the archipelago; the number of goats has increased steadily since then, reaching 617,000 in 1960. Sheep reached a peak number of not quite 40,000 in 1939, but were decimated for food supply during World War II; in 1960 almost one-third of the 15,000 animals were in the provinces of the western Visayas.

In the traditional pattern domestic chickens and ducks seldom received much care, but they were provided a protected home and sources for food-scavenging. Egg yields were low, birds were light in weight, and the eggs and meat added only minor food supplies to the dietary. More interest lay in the cocks, for cock-fighting, than in the hens as egg producers. Increased attention and care, and improved breeds, have accompanied the steady increase in bird populations, and eating habits have grown to include chicken and eggs as a nearly normal element in the dietary; but farmstead chicken-raising remains at a rather low technologic level. Poultry farming, in the developed sense, is but recent in the Islands, a result of American influence. Around urban zones poultry farming is expanding with a relatively high level of technology. Its steady increase puts further pressure on the total grain supply, as the raising of specific poultry feeds is not a developmental element in the agricultural complex.

Local regional custom, chiefly around Manila, provides a snack food for a population grown accustomed to it; this is the preparation of *balut,* almost-hatched duck eggs cooked in boiling water in the shell. Manila duck-raising activity aims at heavy production of eggs for this specific purpose, and eggs are shipped in from Rizal, Laguna, and Batangas to augment the supply.

Dairying, as a productive enterprise, is only slightly developed in and around the larger cities. In the towns and rural areas it is only a casual affair. On the other hand, the acceptance of dairy products has been strong in the twentieth century, and the consumer demand continues to increase, requiring the import of large amounts of dairy products.

The animal-economy phase of Philippine agriculture presents a number of strongly underdeveloped elements, in which consumer demands have arisen without the evolution of satisfactory productive facilities because these did not fit well into either the environment or traditional practice. Although animal economy can be improved and increased, it is likely that a deficit situation will continue for a long period.

CROPS OF THE EXPORT SECTOR

There are a number of crops that contribute in some degree to the export markets held by the Philippines, but several of these have extremely little significance and are not dealt with here. Those to be considered are: coconut, sugarcane, abaca, and tobacco. Each of these also contributes a share of its yield, of course, to domestic consumption. In the case of tobacco it may be questionable whether, in the 1960's, the crop should be considered primarily a domestic one or chiefly an export, as changes have taken place in the patterns of governmental tobacco controls.

Coconut. Native to some part of southeast Asia or Malaysia, the coconut palm was a village- and homestead-planting tree in the pre-Spanish Philippines. It served a very wide range of uses domestically, and its fruit was sold into the China trade. The tree apparently was planted all over the lowland Philippines in small patches.

The coconut palm prefers a near-tropical temperature regime with no extended low-temperature periods below 65°F., a humid precipitation regime providing at least 60 inches of rainfall per year without extended dry periods, moist edaphic situations without waterlogging, reasonably good soils that permit root development but firm root footing, light and air provided by tree spacings at fair distance, and protection from damaging windstorms. Although the tree will grow in situations failing in one or more of the above preferences, it will respond by declining in the yield of fruit. Yields of 40–50 nuts per year are high, but average Philippine yields from 30 to 35 nuts per year, and noncommercial homestead yields of under 20 nuts per year are not uncommon. If high yields are to result, the combination of ecological preferences restricts the tree to the well-drained lowlands having year-round precipitation regimes and to those regions not suffering heavy typhoon damage. In cultural practice the spacing of trees is required, and for the continued health of the tree through its long life span, the ground surface under the tree should not become littered with decaying vegetation, nor should too much undergrowth be permitted.

Few of these ecological requirements were known when the Spanish ordered additional plantings of coconut trees around the new settlements into which they gathered such of the Philippine population as they could command. A traditional planting practice of cluster plantings was continued, and little care seemed to be needed for the trees to yield a steady return of coconuts. Thus, there evolved planting practices that have accompanied the steady expansion of coconut acreage to the end that the Philippines is a world leader in coconut products. In recent decades, as more of the ecological preferences have been determined, modification of planting practices has come about, showing up in the widely spaced, clean-kept patterns of the younger plantings. Meanwhile, in plantings that cover large areas of the southern Philippines, epidemics of disease and pests have begun to take their tolls. *Cadang-cadang*, a virus disease, is making inroads in southeast Luzon, and in several areas, but particularly Zamboanga, beetles and fungus diseases combine to damage large areas of plantings. Breeding experiments with virus-resistant stock is producing coconut varieties that may prove immune to cadang-cadang, and one of the most promising results is that they may also produce a dwarf variety that will be less susceptible to wind damage and be cheaper to harvest and maintain.

Important commercial coconut production lies south of the most serious typhoon zone—south of Manila and extending into the Sulu region (fig. 32). The total coconut acreage amounted to about 3,349,000 acres in 1960, and coconut ranks third among Philippine crops in terms of area. Young plantings do not produce a return until after seven or eight years, and they reach mature yield patterns only after twelve to fifteen years. Interplanting of young coconuts is normal. Labor requirements, after planting, are not heavy, although in mature plantings they must be fairly continuous, for coconuts may be harvested right around the year. Over 90 percent of the Philippine yield is processed into copra. Sun drying and smoking still are normal, which accounts for the low quality of the Philippine product on the world market, although some local areas, such as Cebu, have a good reputation for sun-dried copra. Desiccated-coconut manufacture takes a small volume of the total yield, and domestic consumption of fresh coconuts takes perhaps 3 or 4 percent of the total yield.

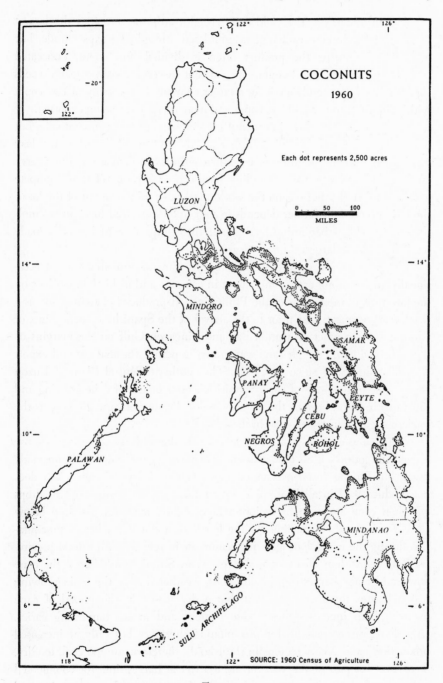

Fig. 32.

Taken altogether, the yield from coconut cropping provides the largest segment of the foreign exchange accumulated through the export trade, but in statistical returns the product often is divided into copra, desiccated coconut, coconut oil, and copra cake, so that in certain years sugar exceeds copra. The current tendency is for a larger amount of processing of raw copra within the Philippines and less copra and more coconut oil being exported.

Philippine technology in coconut growing is not high comparatively, but it has appealed to the Filipino farmer as "the tree of life" and as the lazy man's crop, and the planting of coconut continues to increase as the reserve lands are filled in by the expanding farmscape. Coconut oil must compete with a number of other oils on the world market, so improvement of the lot of the Filipino coconut farmer depends in part upon improved low-cost technology. So far only a beginning in this pattern of improvement has been made on the part of the largest number of growers.

Sugarcane. In early pre-Spanish times sugarcane probably was an occasionally grown minor-crop complement in caingins and in kitchen gardens on the lowlands in most areas of the Philippines. It produced chewing cane as a snack food or sweet. Just prior to the arrival of the Spanish, at such points of Chinese trade contact as Manila Bay and Lingayen Gulf on the margins of the Central Plain, enough cane was grown to permit the making and export of small volumes of sugar to China. The southern Central Plain of Luzon became one of the areas of early Spanish encouragement of cane growing and sugar making, and became the primary regional center of cane growing as the modern sugar industry evolved in the Islands.

Sugarcane can be grown everywhere in the Philippines except in the higher hill country if all that is desired is chewing cane or a little homemade sugar, but for the cost-conscious modern sugar industry the cane plant does not produce well in all Philippine environments. The sucrose content drops off when cane is grown in regions where nightly temperatures drop below 60°F. for intervals, in regions having less than about 50 inches of precipitation during the main, long growing season, or in regions with a total precipitation of more than about 75 inches per year. Strong winds knock the cane down and make harvesting difficult. Dry weather during the main growing season lessens the sucrose content, but a dry season at the period of cane maturity both increases the sucrose content and makes harvesting easier. Irrigation can compensate for precipitation shortages but only at increased production costs. Many regions in the Islands, therefore, are too cool, too dry, or too wet for part of the year, or are too wet at harvesttime for commercial sugarcane. Soil requirements are significant for commercial cane growing and many regions have soils too heavy, too sandy, or too low in quality for cane. Much of Luzon is thereby ruled out, and even the Central Plain, southern Laguna, and western Batangas are not ideal, even though cane is now grown in all three areas (figs. 33, 70, 71). Northern Cebu, northern and western Negros, and eastern Panay islands, in the Visayas, have close to ideal conditions for cane growing and today are the chief sugarcane growing districts, with higher yields of sugar per acre than the Luzon districts. Both Leyte and southwest Mindoro stand in a median position as to situation and production. There are other regions with the proper climatic regimes in which cane could be grown commercially, but these have not been utilized.

Spanish encouragement of sugarcane-growing gradually increased during the nineteenth century until in the 1890's the annual export of sugar was approaching 300,000 tons per year. The Central Plain, southern Laguna, and western Batangas, on Luzon, formed the older cane-growing regions. About 1850, cane growing began in Negros, and later in northern Cebu and in north and eastern Panay; and the Visayan region dominated this industry by 1900. Cane growing became a labor-intensive agriculture, in the early period consuming up to 50 man-days per acre for the required production cycle of 12–18 months.[16] Increasingly cane growers became specialized farmers employing seasonal labor during the harvest period and in the following replanting period. Primary acreage patterns trended toward the monocrop pattern, with other cropping combinations gradually declining to the status of complements. Technologic specialization significantly became part of cane-growing agriculture. Cane-processing devices began as very simple hand-operated or animal-powered presses, and sugar-reducing devices amounted only to simple boiling pots, molasses draining-vats, and other simple machinery, all of cheap local manufacture. Increasingly cane-milling and sugar-reducing machinery grew more complex, power-consuming, specialized, and costly. By 1900 the processing end of the operations began to dominate the agricultural operations. Simple farmers growing cane no longer could cope with the technologies and capital requirements of the milling and sugar-reducing operations. These even began to regulate the cane-growing activities. Heavy fertilization of fields gradually became necessary to maintain satisfactory sucrose content in cane yields of 15–20 tons per acre. Timing schedules of planting and harvest began to be important as milling operations became more exacting. Early in the American period the whole sugar industry took a new turn in which operations in cane milling and sugar reducing became centralized industrial procedures employing modern technologies and corporate financing and ownership; these operations became geared to an

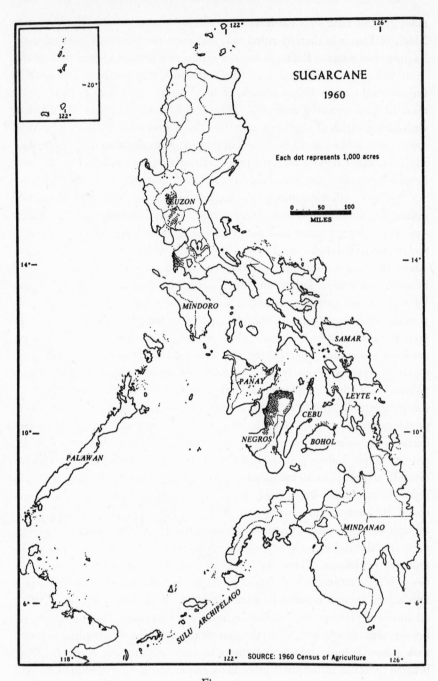

Fig. 33.

export market politically structured with the United States. This development turned cane-growing agriculture into a tributary activity fully controlled in almost every aspect.

Nineteenth-century export and domestic sugar was *muscovado,* unrefined raw brown sugar, either in loose crystal form or in any of several molded shapes and sizes; it was produced by simple boiling devices and shaping procedures. After 1900, upon entry into the American market, muscovado commanded only low prices, not being competitive with Cuban and Hawaiian sugars produced and refined by industrial reducing procedures. Land laws prohibited entrepreneurs from developing large cane-growing plantations, but potential industrial sugar-producers needed guaranteed amounts of cane production to justify high-capital investments in industrial plants capable of producing high-grade sugars. By 1912 the modern system began to take shape, involving long-term growing contracts between groups of individual cane-growers and corporate concerns that milled the cane, reduced the sugar, and handled the export. A quasi-legal area, the Sugar Growing District, was created. Outside the district no farmer could secure a cane-growing contract. Farms ranging from 10 acres to quite large holdings participate, although small farms are more common than large ones. A unique Philippine system has evolved among world cane-sugar producers, a cooperative system involving contract planting and corporate processing in which contracts specify almost every detail of the agricultural operations.[17] The whole sugar industry is, furthermore, controlled by governmental agreements between the United States and the Philippines as to the volume of Philippine export which may enter the United States under preferential customs duties.

During the period from 1912 to the early 1960's various changes have taken place in the whole sugar industry, thus affecting the agricultural patterns of cane growing. Steady expansion in the number of sugar centrals (combined cane mills and sugar-reducing plants), each with a group of contract planters, expanded the acreage patterns of cane growing until the outbreak of World War II. Postwar replacement of war-destroyed sugar centrals was slow and never complete, and new treaty arrangements limit the export of Philippine sugar to the United States.[18] In 1941 there were operative 45 centrals supported by 24,000 contract cane-growers cultivating about 410,000 acres. In 1960 there were only 23 sugar centrals operative, although the capacity of these plants approximated that of the prewar list, and the total acreage amounted to close to 600,000. The regional location of cane growing has changed but little, but its technology has become partially mechanized. The number of cane farms itemized in the 1948 data in appendix table 17 reflected the incomplete restoration of sugar centrals, without the services of which cane growing as a commercial venture was relatively useless. The number of farms growing cane in table 17 reflected the 1948 position of sugarcane as a minor crop complement in the noncommercial aspect of agriculture. The 1960 data indicate the crop as 598,000 acres, which suggests a continuing expansion of commercial cultivation.[19]

Contemporary sugarcane agriculture, therefore, is a product of rather formally arranged economic and political developments. Expansion in cane growing is not freely open to farmer-selection, to spontaneous development of a good farm-cropping combination, or to the comparative regional economics of land use, since disposal of a cane crop depends upon the possession of a contract agreement with a miller who is himself dependent upon an export-quota limitation; the volume of domestically consumed sugar is supplied by the millers as a calculated surplus over the United States export quota. Cane growing as a minor complement crop for use or sale as a snack food (as chewing cane or in minor use in beverages and desserts) is widespread but has quite restricted consumer demands at present.[20] In the future increased productivity through the mechanization of cane growing and harvesting, through improved agricultural technology, and through increased efficiency in the system of land holdings and cane growers will be required if the sugar industry is to become competitive on world markets. During the 1970's there may well take place some changes in cane agriculture. As per-acre sugar yields on Luzon are lower than those on Negros, and as there is evidence that some Luzon growers and millers are mining the land for what it is worth until the date of full-duty assessment, a decline may well take place in Luzon cane growing, and perhaps in that of Leyte, Cebu, and Mindoro. It is likely that northern Negros Island may continue as a cane-growing region, although technological change may occur and crop diversification may alter the regional crop landscape of local areas.

Abaca. The abaca plant, *Musa textilis,* is a member of the banana genus, producing an inedible fruit but a very long and strong, hard fiber resistant to fresh and salt water. All varieties of abaca are more delicate than the fruiting bananas, and are more demanding as to the ecological requirements for successful growth and fiber production. A warm-to-hot environment, rainy and humid the year around, is basic. Strong winds damage the plant; a dry season restricts its growth or kills it, but waterlogging cannot be tolerated; and the plant is demanding as to soil quality and texture. This ecological combination finds its most successful situation on well-drained alluvial soils with groundwater supplies in the lower foothills and upper alluvial plains in the southern half of the eastern Philippines. An endemic plant and native domesticate, abaca was a very old source of fiber for clothing, string, matting, netting, and rope among the Filipinos. Very fine grades of fiber were used in clothing, leaving the coarser grades for other items. Some abaca varieties produce fine fibers in lesser amounts, whereas other varieties yield coarse fibers of greater length. A little pre-Spanish trade in abaca exported the fiber throughout eastern Asia, but the plant was then chiefly a village-garden or caingin source of fiber for home use, grown very widely south of Manila.

Abaca did not appeal to the Spanish and no encouragement of its production occurred until the 1820's when American demand for it as a marine cordage fiber started its rise as a commercial export crop. Southeastern Luzon, being nearest to the chief port of Manila, became the regional center of a growing pattern of commercial production, and the fiber became known as manila hemp, from its port of export. The plant was grown by small farmers in mixed plantings of trees and other tall crops that gave wind protection. By 1900 the acreage had expanded markedly in the peninsular sectors of southeast Luzon, with a small scattering of plantings in the eastern Visayan Islands down to the north coast of eastern Mindanao, and abaca had become the leading export of the Philippines. Problems of plant disease in south central Luzon caused its decline there around 1900, but the crop expanded steadily in more southern regions, finding its most congenial environment in coastal plains marginal to the Gulf of Davao in southeast Mindanao. By the 1930's the Davao region had become a primary center of abaca production through Japanese development of large landholdings that were either leased or held through Filipino agents in subversion of the land laws. The Sorsogon Peninsula of Luzon and the Davao Gulf margins were the primary, and concentrated, production regions, with Leyte a secondary region, and the coastal lands of eastern Negros, the whole of the Samar coast, and the coast of northeast Mindanao possessing a wide scattering of plantings.

The crop acreage, its commercial significance, and its export volume all reached a peak just prior to the outbreak of World War II. Lack of maintenance of the then massed plantings in many areas during the war promoted a series of new plant diseases into epidemic patterns, spread further by careless exploitation immediately after the war. The inroads of plant diseases, coupled with the confiscation and exploitive mining of abaca on former Japanese holdings, turned the acreage and the production downhill, and the decline has continued into the 1960's. The rise in importance of other export crops has meant that abaca has lost rank as an export; it accounted for only a small share of the total export value in the early 1960's.

The Davao region shows marked shifts in the location of the abaca-producing lands from the shores of the Gulf to northern inland locations, but the importance of the whole Davao region is dropping markedly as settlement fills up the region and abaca mosaic drives out the healthy stock. With the decline of Davao, Leyte, Samar, and Negros, the provinces of the Bicol Peninsula (Camarines Sur, Albay, and Sorsogon) and Catanduanes Island regain their leading positions (fig. 34).

The growing of abaca is not a labor-demanding task once the plants have grown to a height that their leaves shade the space between plant-settings to keep down weed growth. The harvesting process is not labor-demanding either, as it may be scattered throughout the year. There is no strong seasonality to harvest periods when the plant is grown in its preferred environment, so abaca production fitted well into small-farm cropping combinations and productive patterns. The processing of the fiber, however, can be a very labor-intensive process and must be done promptly after the cutting of the stalks. Decortication by fully mechanical procedures has not, so far, succeeded in replacing hand-stripping of the fibers for the production of the highest-grade fibers because it removes too high a percentage of the fibrous material present in the stalk. A low-powered, semimechanical decorticating machine (*hagotan*) is today rather widespread, but hand-stripping (through a combing device) is still commonly used to produce the highest grades of abaca fiber. Hand-stripping normally yields about 15 pounds per man-day against 175 pounds with a hagotan, so that cordage prices for abaca fiber make hand-stripping a low income-producer.

The rise of commercial production of abaca for the rope trade, involving production of medium-grade fibers, and the appearance of competing fibers for clothing textiles, have driven down the production of very fine fiber and have replaced it in most uses. The domestic demand for a variety of ropes, strings, and mattings has meant that the crop is not produced solely for an export market.

The future of abaca-growing in the Philippines is not really dependent on world demand, which is ample, or on available land, which also is ample, but it is to be determined by the control of plant diseases. Filipino farmers are not yet a well-disciplined lot, and they have not been cooperative in the expensive disease-control quarantine programs that must be applied in massive regional measures; the future of abaca in the agricultural economy of the Philippines depends upon this control of plant diseases which, so far, has not been made effective. On the other hand, there is price competition for abaca in the rope and string fields, so abaca production must remain economically competitive, and the costs of disease control may be self-defeating if Filipino farmers fail to cooperate sufficiently within a reasonable period.

Tobacco. As a Spanish sixteenth-century introduction from the New World, the tobacco plant fitted into no familiar pre-Spanish application in the

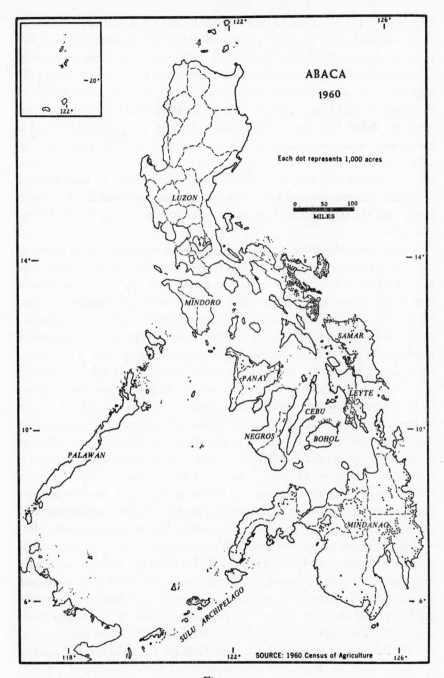

Fig. 34.

Philippines. The plant spread rather widely at an early date, but the usages of tobacco spread more slowly. By the mid-eighteenth century, however, the cultural adoption of smoking had become widespread, and tobacco was being grown widely as a minor crop throughout most of the Islands. At that point the Spanish colonial government chose the tobacco industry as a means of financing colonial government, previously hindered by the dependence upon grudging deficit financing from Spain or Mexico. The establishment of a government monopoly system over the growing, processing, and marketing of tobacco in the 1780's introduced government regulation into this segment of the agricultural economy, a condition that has continued to contemporary time with intermissions and variations. This governmental role has had much to do with the importance of tobacco as an agricultural crop in the Philippines.[21]

Since the mid-eighteenth century tobacco has been very widely grown as a kitchen-garden or caingin-patch crop. Grown for home use or for small-scale barter-trading as leaf tobacco in local markets, there has been little control over it at any time, and the crop today shows up on a large number of farms. Its frequency in 1960 is indicated in appendix table 17. As a significant, commercially grown field crop, on the other hand, the pattern of government regulation has led to regional centering of production in particular ecological, environmental situations. Recent government stimulation of tobacco growing is reflected in the fact that in 1960 tobacco was being grown on 175,000 farms. In simple terms the plant can be grown anywhere in the Islands except in the highest mountain country, as neither temperature nor precipitation regimes operate against the growth of the plant; however, for the production of particular types of tobacco leaf, in terms of aroma, color, leaf-texture, leaf-strength, burning qualities, inherent "tobacco quality," and the other elements significant to consumer acceptance in the whole modern tobacco industry, certain climatic regimes, soil patterns, edaphic conditions, and cultural technologies are particularly important. Fertile, loamy-to-sandy alluvial soils, medium amounts of precipitation, and a dry season toward harvest-time favor production of high-quality leaf, but different types of leaf result from different ecological situations. North and northwest Luzon contained the first areas of extensive development, possess the preferred environmental conditions, and continue as the chief producing regions at the present time. Specifically, the Cagayan Valley of northeast Luzon, the Ilocos coast region, and the Pangasinan margins of Lingayen Gulf are the chief regional centers of tobacco growing, despite the wide distribution of the planting of tobacco.

The early development of the Spanish tobacco monopoly was around Manila. As experimental patterns matured, tobacco growing spread northward, under monopoly control. The Cagayan Valley produced the highest quality of the leaf preferred in the nineteenth century for use in cigars. The Philippine export of cigar leaf, and cigars, became a noted element in world tobacco trade and consumption. The abolition of the government monopoly in 1882 led to a marked short-term increase in tobacco growing but also to a chaotic situation with regard to quality production, processing activities, and domestic and export market situations. Late nineteenth-century corporate domination of the tobacco industry was directed primarily to Spanish markets for leaf tobacco. Early American influence in the Islands expanded production significantly and reoriented marketing toward the United States. The governmental role became chiefly one of regulating quality standards and improving tobacco varieties, although the indirect impact of the new free-trade rules were, in themselves, significant governmental influence.

Changes in American consumer demand (toward lighter tobaccos and cigarettes, away from the heavier cigar leaf), World War II, and the postwar flooding of Philippine domestic markets with American cigarettes significantly altered Philippine tobacco production and manufacturing. Government aid to farmers, a government purchasing bureau, agricultural experiment work, tobacco processing work, the introduction of Virginia tobacco varieties, and import controls all had combined by the late 1950's to rejuvenate and to reorient Philippine tobacco growing. The Ilocos coast has now become an important producer of Virginia-type cigarette tobaccos for the home market, where it forms a valuable cash-crop addition to the regional economy.[22] American government embargoes on Cuban tobaccos in the early 1960's redounded to stimulation of Philippine production and export. Philippine government taxation of tobacco yielded significant government income, and government has a strong stake in the role of tobacco-growing in the Islands.

The Cagayan Valley, the Ilocos coastal region, and the northern Central Plain of Luzon continue as the chief tobacco areas, but in the future, the experiment with other local environments may well spread tobacco-growing in restricted regional terms. Philippine production first serves a domestic market for tobaccos, but the export market is again a significant one, important to the overall economy. Government stimulation of production will work toward the maintenance of, and the expansion of, the export market so long as a significant world market in tobacco remains open. There is ample land in preferred environments, tobacco-growing yields a high per-acre return, and the acreage needed does not bulk heavily in terms of total agricultural land. Tobacco often is grown as a second crop in the seasonal cycle on small or medium-sized farms where family members may contribute a large share of the labor needed. The current production of the Ilocos region is in this pattern. As a commercial crop (the first crop being a food crop for home use or local barter) tobacco provides the farmer a cash income, whether the product ends in the domestic market or is exported. In 1960 the acreage had expanded to 237,000 acres, 128,000 of which was Virginia type, and 109,000 of which was native variety.

Minor crop products. There are a few minor crop products that contribute variably to the export market in most years, but these are chiefly token items whose return is far outweighed by the value of the import volume in closely related products that cannot be produced in the Islands and for which there is a consumer demand.

The chief minor-crop export is pineapple, which is actually a ranking export. The export production in 1960, however, was entirely from one American-owned holding in northern Mindanao, and its contribution to Filipino income is minimal. A second large holding was being developed in the early 1960's. The distribution of the pineapple as a crop plant is country-wide, but it is grown as a fruit only for kitchen-garden or local fruit-market barter. It is still grown in very small quantities for the production of piña fiber, yielded by the spiny leaves of a down-graded fruiting variety of the pineapple.

Maguey, as an American-derived agave, is widespread, but it has never flourished as a crop planting in the Islands. It contributes a small volume of export fiber beyond the amount that is used domestically. Kapok has also produced a small export volume over the years.

Taking the fruits and nuts together there is intermittent small export of several of these, such as mangoes, bananas, fresh coconuts, lanzons, but never does such a volume balance the import of mid-latitude fruits and nuts.

Rubber production has not been a significant industry in the Islands. The present stimulation of this industry is for home consumption rather than for the export market.

Summary

Philippine agriculture in the early 1960's occupied about 60 percent of the working population, but produced only about one-third of the national income, and provided a level of living well below the standard of living aspired to by the Filipinos.[23] In simple terms the agricultural economy produces enough root crops, corn, and vegetables, on the average; is deficient in rice, fruits, meat and poultry, and the beverage crops; produces no wheat crops to meet the current demand; and produces but little of the large dairy-product requirement. There are large surpluses in coconut and sugar, and smaller surpluses in abaca, tobacco, and pineapple. The agricultural exports more than pay for the agricultural imports, but this surplus of purchasing power from agriculture is far lower than it should be in an economy that is so strongly dependent upon agriculture and that is attempting to finance industrialization from domestic sources.

Although it is possible to divide agriculture into domestic and export sectors, this dichotomy is little more than a retained convention. It is somewhat unrealistic to assert that Philippine agriculture is overextended in cultivation of export crops, since each of these is now used domestically in increasing proportion, and since as a whole, such crops bulk high neither in acreage nor in total share of the national income derived from agriculture. It is true, of course, that coconut, sugar, abaca, and tobacco provide a large share of the annual earnings of Philippine foreign exchange, but as yet there is no other major source for such earnings. It is equally true that conversion of lands producing annual export surpluses in each of these crops to the production of domestic-use food crops would not increase the annual national income, would not provide the imported food supplies, and would not place the Philippines in a sounder international economic position.

Philippine agriculture currently suffers heavily from low productivity in almost every comparison. This is significantly a historical matter deriving from the low technological levels of the pre-Spanish period and the only slight improvement during the Spanish era, but it is a current matter that the twentieth century shows a strong lag behind the rates of growth in some other parts of the world. In comparative terms the rate of technological improvement in Philippine agriculture shows a lag behind the rates of growth internationally, behind the growth rate of Philippine population, and behind the rates of growth in other sectors of Philippine culture. This lag in growth rates is to be seen in the low per-acre crop yields, in the high per-man and per-acre labor requirements, in the low per-acre applications of power resources, in the high per-unit costs of some products, in the small per-operator farm size, in the low per-operator and per-farm incomes derived, and in the low competitive received-prices of exports on the international market. Further, the lag is to be seen in the high incidence of soil erosion-depletion, and in the low per-acre applications of any kind of fertilizer or soil-building material.

Increased effort of governmental agencies to improve productive ability in agriculture is to be seen in the building of fertilizer plants, in the rates of irrigation development, in the programs to control plant pests and diseases, and in the programs to open reserve lands. Private initiative is showing increasing rates of change in several directions. There were signs in the late 1950's and early 1960's that significant improvements were beginning to take place in agricultural technology. It is, however, an open question whether the rates of change will soon exceed the rates of population increase and general cultural demand placed upon the agricultural economy. It will take critical review of the data of about 1975 to determine this point.

Filipinos are chiefly small farmers, with about a half of all farms being under 5 acres in area. The farmers throughout much of the country do not have free and easy choice of the crop they will grow, owing to environmental situations, to the developmental history of the farms themselves, and to economic factors limiting cropping choices. Poultry-raising is perhaps the most productive of all choices, but it cannot be elected by all farmers. Sugarcane is one of the most productive crops, but it too can be elected by only certain farmers, owing to the grower-miller relationship controls. Tenant farmers often are even more restricted in their crop choices than are owner-farmers. Diversification is increasing, with more attention being given to more highly productive crops, but the choices are not numerous nor are they free. The major crops rank in approximately the following order in per-acre net returns of 1960 Philippine pesos: Sugarcane = 300, Vegetables and Fruits = 250, Cacao = 250, Coffee = 200, Rice = 150, Coconut = 125, Abaca = 80, Corn = 70, and Root Crops = 70.[24] Philippine agriculture, therefore, is somewhat tied to cropping combinations yielding only modest returns, whatever the major crop. Thus long-range improvement in the agricultural economy lies in the direction of marked improvement in agricultural technologies (in the broadest sense) and in sharing the proceeds among smaller numbers of farmers.

SEVEN

~~~~~ *Resource Exploitation*

Fisheries: Resources, Practices, and Yields

The Indo-Pacific realm is the greatest center of fish life in the world, and the Philippine position is one that shares in this rich aquatic resource. A total of more than 2,100 species of fishes known to frequent Philippine waters have been catalogued, and this total will probably reach 2,400 different species with more complete knowledge.[1] The total area of fishing waters in and around the archipelago is several times the land area of the Philippines. Although Philippine waters support a tremendous variety of fishes, this wealth in variety is not accompanied by a corresponding wealth in quantity relative to modern demand, although the volume was more than adequate to earlier requirements. The numbers of suitable species available, in quantities sufficient to warrant commercial exploitation, are quite limited. (See appendix table 6 for list of species commonly caught.) Modern ruthless exploitation through overfishing, dynamiting, and poisoning has further reduced the commercial fish resources in nearby waters.

The traditional and basic Filipino diet is one of rice and fish. Fish and fish products supply the bulk of the protein consumed, and in one form or another, fish appears daily on the family table for more than one-half of the Filipinos. The average per capita consumption of fish in the Philippines in 1962 was 38 pounds, a quantity representing only 64 percent of the normal requirement as recommended by the National Research Council in 1959.[2] The Philippine fishing industry did not, in 1960, provide fish sufficient to meet even the inadequate national consumption. Substantial quantities, approximating 38,000 tons of fish and fish products, or 8 percent of the total amount actually consumed, had to be imported. Production of fish and fish products in the Philippines has been increasing, however, as a result of growing demand, and the 1962 production was more than double that obtained in 1950. Nevertheless, fishery production has steadily fallen farther behind the increases in demand created by a growing population. Since inshore and inland waters are limited and already producing at near capacity, further increases in production will have to come through expansions of offshore (deep-sea) fishing and estuarine fishpond operations.

The larger share of the Filipino population traditionally was resident along the littoral, and except for a small sea-gypsy element, divided its time between what may be termed land occupations and aquatic occupations. Almost every family did some fishing, either regularly or seasonally, and aquatic commodities were a normal product-component in traditional economy; the high per-capita consumption of fish among Filipinos derives from this historical pattern. The share of the population engaging in aquatic occupations has decreased as the population has grown, as settlement has moved inland, and as secondary occupations and urbanism have developed and expanded. Consequently the role of the professional fisherman has increased; but among the Filipinos the professional occupation has been slow to respond to the consumer demand, with the result that demand has exceeded supply. In the years since World War II, government stimulation of the fishery industries has been considerable, and the trend is upward. Fishing and associated occupations now are significant employers of full-time and specialized labor. Over one-half million Filipinos are engaged full time in the fishing industry; approximately 350,000 as fishermen, 117,000 as caretakers and workers of fishponds, and 30,000 in industries closely allied to fishing.[3]

The Philippine fishing industry consists of three types of operations: (1) commercial fishing, which includes all fishing from vessels over 3 tons gross licensed by the Bureau of Fisheries, (2) municipal and sustenance fishing, accomplished either in vessels under 3 tons gross or without the use of vessels, for subsistence purposes, and (3) fishponds for the controlled production of selected fish species. Sustenance fishing covers a wide range of activities and occurs in shallow shore waters, in lakes, ponds, reservoirs, and streams, and in rice fields, irrigation ditches, and seasonally water-covered surfaces. All elements of the population may engage in it. Shore-water fishing from small boats, or through the use of simple traps and nets, seldom is statistically tabulated, but may now be significant to the dietary of populations resident along the littoral just as it was in earlier periods. Except for the few larger

lakes and rivers, to be noted later, inland fishing produces only small complements of fishery products to the dietary pattern or to the annual consumption.
The relative proportion of the total Philippine fish-catch produced by each
type of fishing operation is 31 percent commercial, 56 percent sustenance, and
about 13 percent fishponds.

COMMERCIAL FISHES [4]

The scad furnishes the Philippine commercial fishing operators with their
largest volume of catch. The round scad and big-eyed scad, called *matang
baka* in Tagalog, together supply 28 percent of the commercial fish-catch.
The scads are small fish, 10–12 inches in length, which lend themselves to
drying. Primary fishing grounds for the scad are in the Sulu Archipelago and
in the waters near Palawan (fig. 35). The slipmouths, known locally as
sapsap, hauling, or *dalangat,* furnish 13 percent of the total commercial catch.
Especially abundant in the Visayan Sea and Manila Bay areas, the slipmouth
is usually marketed fresh. The *dilis* or anchovies make up 5 percent of the
commercial catch and a very large share of the municipal and sustenance
catches. Although important in all Philippine waters, the anchovy is particularly abundant in the Visayan Sea, Sulu Sea, Samar Sea, and the waters
north of Palawan. Considerable quantities of anchovies are dried or processed
into a salted preparation called *bagoong.* Sardines or *tamban* also occur
widely through the islands, but are particularly numerous in the Sulu and
Visayan seas areas. This small but tasty fish does not keep well and is more
often cured, dried, or salted into a product called *tinapa.* Sardines contribute
approximately 6 percent of the commercial catch, and a much larger proportion of the sustenance catch. The caesio or *delagang bukid* is generally caught
over coral reefs in Sulu or Palawan waters after which it is prepared into a
dry salted product called *daeng* in the nearby settlements of Sitangkai, Bongao,
and Bacuit. Herring or *tunsoy* are plentiful and constitute one of the most
important municipal and sustenance fish. Some herring reach the market as
fresh fish, but most of the catch is cured, salted, and smoked and sold as
tinapa. Herring are particularly numerous in Visayan waters. The nemipterid
or *bisugo,* another small fish common to Sulu, Visayan, and Manila waters,
furnishes an additional 6 percent of the commercial catch and a substantial
portion of the sustenance catch. Numerous other species of fish are important
in the Philippine fishing industry, such as surgeon fish, croaker, lizard fish,
mullet, bonito, mackerel, and tuna.

Philippine coastal waters also contain other forms of marine life suitable
for food. Crustaceans are relatively abundant and contribute approximately 5
percent of the total Philippine fish production. Shrimps are found throughout

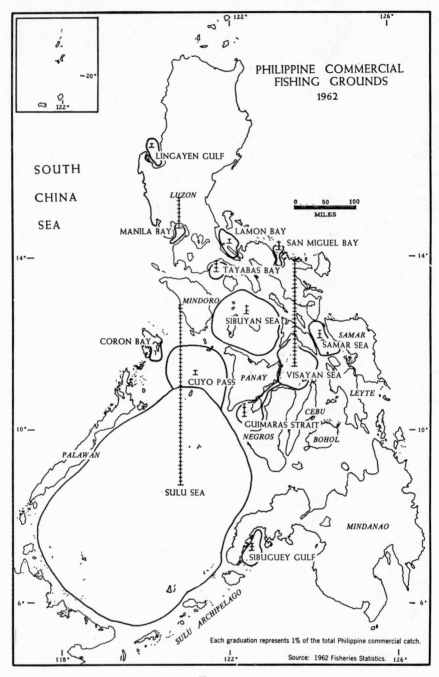

Fig. 35.

the archipelago, but especially large quantities are harvested in the Visayan Sea, Manila Bay, Sulu Sea, and in Guimaras Strait. The waters surrounding Samar are rich in crabs. Trepang, produced from sea cucumbers found in the Sulu group, is an important minor item of export. Sponges and pearl oysters of good quality also are produced in the Sulus. Edible seaweeds are harvested in the waters off northwestern Luzon.

FISHING GROUNDS

Although virtually all Philippine coastal waters provide sources of fish and fish products, not all waters are of equal commercial significance. The Philippine Bureau of Fisheries delimits forty-four fishing grounds of which three (Southern Sulu Sea, Sulu Sea near Palawan, and the Visayan Sea) accounted for 67 percent of the total catch made by commercial fishing vessels in 1962. Twelve of the fishing grounds produce commercial fish catches in excess of 1,000 tons annually, and together these twelve are responsible for 93 percent of the total commercial catch (fig. 35). The more important commercial fishing grounds, in addition to the three already mentioned, include Manila Bay, Guimaras Strait, Tayabas Bay, San Miguel Bay, and the Samar Sea. Fishing vessels operating in Philippine fishing grounds are based either locally, on nearby coastal settlements, or upon more distant, large markets, such as at Manila, Iloilo, and Bacolod. It is significant that the majority of commercial fishing operations, and in general, most of the sustenance and small-vessel operations also, are concentrated in the waters in the central, western, and southwestern sectors of the Philippines. The waters adjacent to the northwestern, southeastern, and eastern coasts either are lacking in significant fish resources or have not been developed to their potential. The dominance of certain fishing grounds over others is, to a degree, ephemeral. Overfishing and other abuses, such as dynamiting and fish poisoning, quickly deplete fish populations necessitating the transfer of fishing operations. The depletion of important fishing waters such as those off northwestern Cebu near the small island of Bantayan has been the direct result of ruthlessly exploitive practices.[5]

COMMERCIAL FISHING METHODS AND EQUIPMENT

The commercial fishing equipment and techniques used in the Philippines differ depending upon the scale and capitalization of the operation, the species of fish sought, and the specific fishing ground. The otter trawl (*galadged otter*) and bag net (*basnig*), and to a lesser degree the trap net (*muro-ami*) and round haul seine (*ilaway or sapiao*), dominate the larger-scale commercial fishing operations, whereas handlines (*kawil and kawil moderno*), trolling (*sibid-sibid* or *sibid-sibid moderno*), gill nets (*panta*), beach seine (*pukot pang-gilid*), and various corrals (*baklad*) are associated with the smaller-scale commercial operations and municipal and sustenance fishing.

Otter trawls, which include about 500 vessels, produce approximately 40 percent of the commercial catch. In this operation a conical-shaped bag or net is dragged over the sea bottom at depths reaching 200 feet. The catch consists mainly of bottom-dwellers, such as the slipmouth, nemipterid, shrimp, and lizard fish. An almost equal share of the commercial catch is contributed by bag-netting operations, which include more than 742 vessels. A bag net consists of an inverted bag-shaped net that is lowered into the water. Fish are attracted at night by lights, and when sufficient numbers are present the bag is lifted and emptied into the boat. The bag is designed to catch pelagic fish such as anchovies, sardines, herrings, scad, and mackerel. Introduced from Japan, the trap net is formed with two wings arranged in a V-shape leading to a bag or pen. The fish are driven into the trap, which is laid in shallow water, usually over coral reefs. The principal species caught include the caesios, surgeon fish, and the prized lapu lapu. The trap net contributes approximately 7 percent of the commercial fish caught. The round haul seine is similar to the bag net—a huge dip net for pelagic fishing. Of the various commercial-fishing equipment, the trap net is much the more productive, the bag net and round haul seine are intermediate, and the otter trawl least productive, per unit.[6]

The kawil, or handlines, are simple multihook lines suspended in waters over reefs or other areas known to be frequented by fish. Snappers, mackerel, and groupers are usually caught by this method. Trolling implies the trailing of a simple fishing line or lines with attached lures behind a slow-moving boat. Mackerel, tuna, and barracuda are the principal fish caught. The gill net, a close mesh of stout netting, is operated as a drift or set-net curtain into which fish swim and are gilled. Catfish, crevalles, mullets, and gobies are commonly caught. The gill net can be used for both freshwater and saltwater fishing. The beach seine is a universally used fishing gear in the Philippines. The net is set out from the beach in a large semicircular pattern and then hauled toward shore, trapping anchovies, sardines, herrings, and other fish that live in the waters close inshore. The fish corrals employed in the Philippines take many varied forms depending upon fishing conditions, availability of capital, and local custom. Fish corrals are extensively employed throughout the archipelago because building materials can be obtained locally and at relatively low cost. Usually the corral is built of bamboo poles with a matting of rattan or bamboo, and consists of one or more guiding barriers and enclosures. There are five basic types of fish corrals employed in the Philippines: *paugmad, aquila, inagcla, bungsod,* and *hasang.* The paugmad is the simplest corral and consists of a single enclosure with a V-shaped entrance. A landing platform is constructed on one side of the enclosure. Both demersal and pelagic fish are caught. The aquila is erected primarily in tidal-flat areas and attracts crabs, shrimps, and mullets. It consists of one or more enclosures with a small collecting crib. The aquila is often transferred from one place to another during the season. The inagcla is a simple fish corral shaped in the form of an anchor. It operates in both shallow and deep waters. The bungsod is used primarily in moderately shallow southern waters, 30–40 feet in depth, near Zamboanga. It is especially designed for tuna, sardines, and mackerel. The hasang is the most elaborate of the fish corrals. It may be rectangular, triangular, or diamond-shaped and usually employs several chambers or enclosures and various ingenious entrances. In a variety of modifications the hasang is used throughout the Philippines and is probably the most effective fish corral.[7]

Most of the fish caught in the various Philippine fishing waters are not shipped great distances to markets. Subsistence fishing or small commercial operations are the more typical fishing operations, and in general, they serve to supply only the local markets. Large-scale, organized commercial-fishing enterprises operate out of Manila, including the small fishing ports in neighboring Bulacan and Rizal provinces, Bacolod and Cadiz on Negros, Iloilo and Estancia on Panay, Balud on Masbate, and Catbalogan on Samar; approximately 75 percent of the total Philippine commercial catch is landed at one of these ports. Manila is the largest market for fish and over its fish wharves and the nearby ports of Navotas and Malabon in Rizal is landed more than 60 percent of the total national commercial catch. The lack of readily available capital for the purchase of icing and refrigeration equipment, larger boats, and more expensive nets has limited the expansion of large-scale commercial-fishing enterprises.

FISH PRESERVATION

Many special preserving techniques have been devised by the Philippine fishing industry in order to combat the generally poor keeping qualities of the native fish and their rapid spoilage in the moist tropical climate.[8] Approximately one-half of the Philippine fish catch is consumed fresh—a form of fish marketing and consumption which generally is highly restricted by season and then confined only to the coastal settlements and larger cities. Although some fish is preserved by canning, far more common is preservation by drying, salting, and smoking.

Simple drying processes probably account for approximately 25 percent of the total fish-catch. Usually the larger fish are split, cleaned, and laid out on racks to dry in the sun for periods of from two to three days or until the flesh is firm. This dried fish product is marketed as daeng. Usually the smaller fish are dried directly as caught, and the resultant product is called *cuyo*. Occasionally the fish to be dried is first soaked in large vats of brine and then dried. Sun-drying is practiced throughout the archipelago wherever fish are caught. The resultant dried fish product will keep for a period of from two to three months. Salting, and wet-salting with subsequent fermentation, accounts for about 20 percent of the catch. Drying and salting of fish is particularly important in those fishing areas relatively remote from large markets, or in those areas that need to preserve much of their catch because of the highly seasonal fishing season. Fishing settlements along northern Luzon near the mouth of the Cagayan River are the principal drying, salting, and bagoong-producing centers; other important processing centers are located in Iloilo, Cebu, Masbate, Batangas, Rizal, Manila Bay, Sulus, Capiz, and Samar. Smoking fish, or the preparation of tinapa, is accomplished by brining, cooking, and smoking, and the main locale of its production is concentrated in the areas surrounding Manila Bay, particularly in the provinces of Bataan and Rizal. Several specially preserved fish products have markets throughout the archipelago; for example, bagoong, a fermented salted fish paste made from anchovies and other smaller fishes, and *binoro,* a preparation made from salted sardines.

Nineteen small fish canneries were in operation in the Philippines in 1958, sixteen of them in the Manila area, two at Catbalogan on Samar, and one in Iloilo.[9] The total amount of fish canned in the Philippines is very small, and imports of canned fish from the United States and Japan continue to be substantial. Generally the preservation methods employed in the Philippines result in an inferior produce, one that spoils in a short time.

Freshwater fisheries. Philippine freshwater resources have been seriously depleted by destructive exploitation. Several commonly caught freshwater species, however, continue to constitute an important resource for local fishermen living along the larger rivers and lakes of the country. The several varieties of mullets, catfishes, carps, mussels, and perches are the principal species. The more important Philippine inland fishing areas are Laguna de Bay, Lake Naujan on Mindoro, Lake Bato in southeastern Luzon, and Lakes Mainit and Lanao on Mindanao. The Laguna de Bay fisheries are particularly significant to the shoreline towns and to the Manila metropolitan market. The Agusan, Rio Grande de Mindanao, Cagayan, Abra, and Pansipit rivers also are of considerable significance.

FISHPOND CULTURE

A large deficiency in fish production as compared with recommended levels of fish consumption continues to plague the Philippines. It would appear that fishing in coastal and inland waters has reached near capacity. The high seas offer a possible solution to the need for expansion of pelagic fishing, but an even greater possibility is the expansion of fish production in culturally controlled ponds. The potential of the archipelago in the latter method is tremendous. The spread of *bangos,* as the brackish-water fishponds are called throughout the archipelago, has resulted in major shifts both in total production contributed by fishponds and in areas of fish production in the years since 1946. Whereas the area devoted to bangos amounted to approximately 132,000 acres in 1946, the following ten years saw this area double, and by 1962 a fishpond area of 318,000 acres was supplying 12 to 13 percent of the total Philippine fish production. It is estimated that approximately 1,400,000 acres of freshwater and mangrove swamplands, excluding foreshore areas, are available for fishpond development—an area more than four times that now being utilized. Extensive areas of undeveloped fishpond lands exist in Mindanao, particularly in the provinces of Cotabato, Zamboanga del Sur, and Agusan, and in the Visayas and parts of Luzon.[10]

Bangos use only estuarine waters, coastal swamplands, tidal flats, and shallow bays where brackish waters exist. The fishponds vary considerably in size from less than an acre to several hundred acres. Privately owned fishponds average about 20 acres in size, whereas those on leased government land are somewhat larger. Fishponds are found in all but a few of the provinces; however, the past concentrations of ponds have been in the Manila Bay area (25 percent) and in the western Visayan islands of Panay and Negros (25 percent), with lesser areas along the shores of Lingayen Gulf, southwestern Luzon, northern Bohol, and southern Mindanao. Nearness to markets undoubtedly is a primary concern in the location of bangos, but if they are to be successful several environmental factors must be satisfied. Because fishponds in the Philippines concentrate on cultivation of the milkfish, a species requiring saline or brackish waters, their distribution is confined to littoral locations. The type of soil is of critical importance, for it must be impermeable in order to impound the waters. Those areas in which the parent material is of coralline origin generally are unsuited for fishponds.

The milkfish does not reach sexual maturity in captivity. Therefore, the fry, the eventual planting stock, are caught in shallow inshore waters, usually during the period from March to August. The west coast of Luzon north of

Lingayen Gulf, Bataan Peninsula, and certain Visayan coastal waters are sources of milkfish fry. The planting stock is sold to nurseries where they grow to fingerling size. After transfer to rearing ponds the fish will attain commercial size, approximately 1½ pounds, in three to six months' time. A well-managed fishpond should produce about 1,200 pounds of milkfish per acre annually, although average archipelago yields are closer to 500 pounds of fish per acre.

Recently the *tilapia*, a freshwater fish indigenous to Africa but introduced into the Philippines from Thailand in 1950, has made rapid advances as a "cultivated" fish in backyard fishponds. Maturing and reproducing in captivity, the tilapia reach commercial size in about four months, each fish weighing about ½ pound. Yields from tilapia ponds are greater than those obtained from bangos; however, the fish is extremely bony.[11]

Although Philippine fishery production continues to increase, imports continue to rise. In 1962 the Philippines spent approximately $17,000,000 for imported fish and fish products. Most of this import consisted of canned fish, mainly sardines and anchovies from Japan, British Africa, and the United States.[12] The export of fishery products from the Philippines in 1962 totaled approximately $500,000 and included shellcraft, fish sauces, seaweeds, trepang, reptile skins, and shark fins.

SUMMARY

The Philippine fishing industry has been unable to supply the nation with seafood sufficient to meet even its present inadequate consumption. Inshore and inland fishing grounds generally are producing at capacity. Deep-sea fishing grounds and fishponds offer potential fish production sufficient to meet present-day and future needs if properly developed and utilized. Increased Philippine production and consumption of fish and fish products is extremely important in order to balance the present protein-deficiency in the Filipino diet.

Forest Industries: Logging, Timber, and the Minor Products

The forest industries constitute one of the five most important industries of the Philippines. Not only are forest products basic to the domestic economy, by supplying building materials and the raw materials for countless home industries, but the export of forest products, particularly lumber, logs, and plywood, normally ranks third in value among the country's exports. The total annual timber-cut amounts to nearly 3 billion board feet. Logs and lumber are the principal products of the forests both in volume and value. There are several minor products of the forests which are produced in significant quantities, such as poles and pilings, railroad ties, mine timbers, rattan, bamboo, firewood, charcoal, and gums and resins. Approximately 450 million board feet of lumber were sawn in 1960, together with 188 million square feet of plywood and 244 million square feet of veneers. The 1960 combined daily capacities of the 368 Philippine sawmills was 3,281,000 board feet, a daily capacity nearly double that of the prewar period. These sawmills represent a total invested capital of over $27,000,000. Forests and industries associated with their exploitation—furniture manufacturing, gathering of gums and resins, and charcoal preparation—furnish employment for nearly 100,000 Filipinos, and are the main livelihood of an additional 400,000 dependents.

PHILIPPINE FOREST RESOURCES

Prior to the era during which man began to clear land for agriculture in the Philippines, perhaps 90 percent of the total area was covered by what might be judged today as commercial forest. Even then the plant cover of some of the western fringes of the westernmost islands probably did not carry thick stands of heavy timber trees, owing to seasonal aridity. Traditional crop-growing systems in the archipelago chiefly employed shifting cultivation, which in some areas began the gradual reduction of the plant cover toward savanna parklands dominated by pyrophilous tree species and heavy tropical grasses. Even before the arrival of the Spanish, timber cutters were seeking out selected woods of special qualities for export to the mainland. Such activity probably did little to reduce the areas of forest, although it may well have affected the frequency distribution of certain tree species. Throughout the Spanish period shifting cultivation continued as one of the basic cropping systems, and the Spanish introduced several varieties of browsing animals and varying combinations of livestock raising. By the late Spanish era there were numerous large herds of cattle and it was the common practice to burn off the grazing ranges. The Spanish did little to develop lumbering as an industry until quite late in their period of control over the Islands. Then, Spanish "building code" requirements in towns initiated a domestic lumbering industry and started to increase the general rate of consumption of timber products. At the same time, expansion of the agricultural landscape increasingly ate into the forest cover. All of these varying practices served, by the end of the nineteenth century, to reduce the area of commercial forests to something in the neighborhood of 70 percent of the total area of the Islands. In the year 1902, the total lumber-cut amounted to about 50 million board feet, and over 700 different woods were brought to market. During the twentieth century the total area of land in permanent farms has increased, the practice of shifting cultivation has continued, the mining of commercial timber has gone on at an increasing rate, and livestock ranching has expanded. Although forest conservation practices have been initiated, a considerable sector of the "forest primeval" has been reduced to the status of "cultivated landscape."

Commercial forests in 1960 covered approximately 50 percent of the area of the Philippines, although some of these forests have had many of their special woods logged out by past extractive procedures (figs. 16, 17). The volume of merchantable timber is impressive. Estimates of the total volume of standing timber vary considerably, from a conservative 240 billion board feet [13] to a perhaps overly optimistic 447 billion board feet.[14] At current market prices for logs and lumber, these forests represent a capital resource that can be conservatively valued at 20–25 billion dollars. The estimated annual growth of the Philippine forests may be as high as 6 to 8 billion board feet.[15] (See appendix table 7 for a list of species commonly logged.)

Members of the dipterocarp family,[16] principally the white lauan, red lauan, tangile, apitong, yakal, and guijo, make up the majority of the dense stands of mature timber upon which most of the Philippine forest industry is based. These large dipterocarp trees, frequently running 15,000 to 25,000 board feet and more to the acre, supply the bulk of the high-quality woods for general construction purposes as well as for cabinet and furniture manufacture. The dipterocarps often occur in relatively pure stands and comprise 75 percent of the total volume of commercial timber in the forests of the Philippines. Particularly extensive dense stands of dipterocarps are found in the northern sections of the Cordillera Central, in the foothills around the margins of the Cagayan Valley, in the Zambales Mountains, and along the east coast of Luzon. Approximately 20 percent of the total Philippine standing-timber volume is represented on Luzon. Most of the island of Mindanao is heavily clothed in this tropical rain forest. The extensive forests on Mindanao comprise 55 percent of the volume of commercial timber in the archipelago. Approximately 15 percent of the Philippine timber volume is located in the Visayan area, especially on the islands of Samar and Negros. Interior Mindoro and some of Palawan are densely forested and they contain most of the remaining commercial forested area.

About 4 percent of the commercial forests in the Islands belong to the molave forest association. These forests are more open and dry than a typical rain forest, and do not produce as much timber volume as the dipterocarps; however, they provide woods noted for their natural beauty and extreme durability. The valuable narra, tindalo, dao, ipil, and molave, the latter the tree from which the forest association takes its name, are the dominant species. The largest remaining stands of molave forest are found on Palawan and Mindoro and in the northeastern corner of Mindanao. The molave woods are especially prized for furniture and decorative veneers.

Commercial pine forests, which occupy approximately one million acres, are all located in the mountains of northern Luzon at elevations ranging between 3,000 and 6,000 feet. These pine forests, which represent the only source of true softwoods in the Philippines, may be cut only in limited quantities because many of the larger rivers of Luzon form in these mountains and the forests are needed for watershed conservation. The pines are used primarily by the mining industry in the Benguet and Bontoc areas in northern Luzon.

The mangrove forests that border many coastal areas throughout the Islands are used primarily as a source of firewood, and to a lesser extent as source of tannin materials. The wood of the mangrove requires about one week to season, splits easily, and makes a lasting hot fire. Because the mangrove forests grow along easily accessible coasts, they have been ruthlessly exploited. Formerly more extensive, the mangroves, together with swamps and marshes, now cover only 2 percent of the area of the Philippines. At present the mangrove forests are particularly extensive in Zamboanga del Sur Province on Mindanao.

LOGGING AND SAWMILLING

The most important industry of the Philippine forests is logging and sawmilling. Approximately 70,000 workers are presently employed in this segment of the forest industry. Lumbering in the Philippines received its greatest impetus from the large-scale rebuilding and construction projects initiated by the incoming American administration during the early twentieth century. Until World War II the industry was characterized by lack of mechanization, except in a few notable instances. Most of the felling of trees and their bucking into logs in the forests was done by handsaws, and the carabao supplied most of the transport. A great deal of damage was done to Philippine sawmills and equipment during World War II, partly through actual destruction and partly through the neglect of machinery. Part of the present industry is rebuilt and modernized upon the prewar framework and part of it consists of new postwar installations. Today the logging operations employ the use of power equipment, such as tractors, log-loaders, trucks, and power saws. In a few instances private rail facilities are still used, or logs are floated down to the mill sites on the rivers. Usually the new mills have located quite close to, or actually in, the forests to avoid added transportation costs, or they are located along island shorelines. Approximately one-third of the total Philippine timber-cut is processed into lumber. Most of the Philippine sawmills are of small capacities. Sawmills with daily capacities of 2,000, 4,000, or 6,000 board feet are common, and with few exceptions, they are below 15,000 board feet daily capacity. Many of these small mills are located in the larger cities where the market exists, particularly in Manila (fig. 36). There are a few large sawmills with daily capacities ranging from 25,000 to 100,000 board feet. Almost without exception the larger installations are located near their sources of timber rather than being market-oriented. The largest sawmill in the Philippines is located in northern Negros, and other large mills are located in southeastern Luzon and on Mindanao. The leading lumber-producing provinces (with their percentage of the national sawmilling capacity in 1960) included: Agusan (9 percent), Zamboanga del Sur (7.7 percent, Quezon (7.1 percent), and Negros Occidental (6.5 percent).

Logging procedures in the Philippines, as in most tropical forests, differ slightly from those employed in temperate-land forests. Because of the frequent occurrence of the broad buttresses or flanging of the lower part of the tree, many of the tropical trees must be cut several feet about the ground, thus leaving a high stump. The fallen timbers are then sawn into convenient lengths, usually 16-foot logs, and hauled to the mills. Most logging operators employ trucks for transport, although railroads or animals may be employed. Usually the work in the forest is done under the *paco* system, which pays the fallers by the piece, or by thousand-board-feet units, rather than by a daily or hourly wage. At the mills the logs are sawn into cants or, in some cases, into 2-inch-wide planks. The lumber is then stacked outside and air-dried for periods ranging from thirty to ninety days, by which time the moisture content of the wood has been reduced to 30 or 40 percent. At this moisture level the lumber is suitable for general construction purposes. Lumber that is to be used for furniture, doors, casings, and floors requires further reduction of the moisture content to 15 or 18 percent; this is accomplished in kilns. The lumber is transported from the mills to the markets by trucks or interisland vessels. Of the Philippine timber-cut processed into lumber, approximately 80 percent is consumed domestically. More than one-half of the Philippine timber-cut, however, is not processed into any finished or semipermanent form, but is directly exported as raw logs. These logs are transported short distances from the forests to the nearest coastal landings and floated out to overseas vessels lying offshore. Most of the raw logs are shipped to Japan. Exports of raw logs not only represent a very large volume of Philippine timber upon which the benefits of further processing in the Philippines have not been realized, but they also include some of the best-quality timber.

An increasingly greater share of the capital investments in Philippine

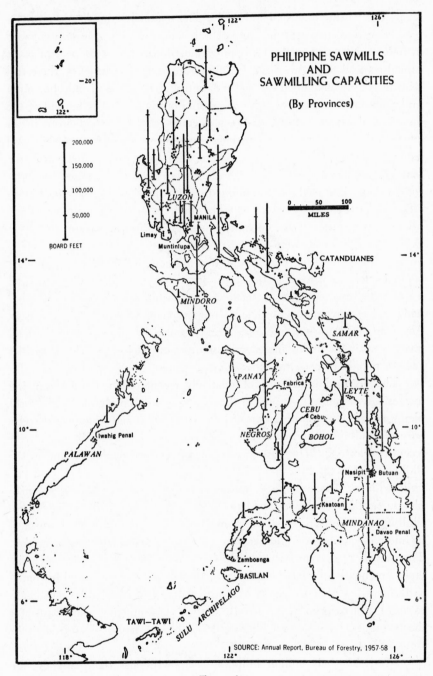

Fig. 36.

sawmills is passing into the hands of Filipino nationals, stimulated by Philippine laws stipulating that any corporation, company, or partnership engaged in forest exploitation in the Philippines must have at least 60 percent of its capital controlled by American or Filipino interests. Nevertheless, there still remains considerable alien capital and control of the sawmill industry, often under "dummy" ownership. Filipinos control outright some 35 percent of the total capital invested in the nation's sawmills, and they participate in an additional 24 percent of the capital investment in joint-ownership and management with other nationalities. The Chinese control a large part of the remaining sawmill capital through their marriages to Filipinos, minority corporate interests, or through dummy directorships. American financial interests are represented in sawmills in which there is joint ownership, and these usually represent the larger sawmills. There are also small amounts of Swiss, British, and Spanish minority-capital represented. Wholly Filipino capital finances 62 percent of the sawmills, or 229 establishments, representing approximately 50 percent of the sawmilling capacities. The Chinese control 67 sawmills representing 21 percent of the sawmill capacities. On the other hand, these companies with a large proportion of western capital, that is, American and European interests, are represented by 38 percent of the total investments in the Philippine sawmill industry, but their sawmilling capacities amount to only 15 percent of the industry's total.

The plywood industry is of relatively recent origin and is becoming increasingly significant. At present there are over a dozen plywood and veneer plants operating in the Philippines. The manufacture and widespread acceptance of Philippine plywood and veneers in world markets is a relatively recent development. The large expansions of plywood manufacturing in the Philippines date from the end of World War II. The first plywood plant was built at Limay, Bataan, in 1936; however, by 1941 there were only three small plants, and their combined production was relatively insignificant. Today the Philippines manufactures plywoods in quantities sufficient not only to meet its internal consumption, but also to supply an ever-growing overseas market. The timbers most commonly used for veneers are tangile, lauans, and palo-sapis. Frequently, the more exotic dao, banuyo, and narra are used for fancy surfacings. The plywood plants are mostly located in the Manila area, southeastern Luzon, and on Mindanao. Recently a plant utilizing wood wastes for the manufacture of pressed fiberboard has been established at Nasipit in Agusan Province.

Nearly one-half million Filipinos—employees and their families—are dependent upon the logging and sawmilling industry in the Philippines. Because both the larger logging and sawmill operations require large permanent labor forces, there is a tendency, as with the mining industry, toward the development of small company towns or logging and mill camps. Often these towns become quite large and are given political status as a municipality or barrio. The larger companies provide housing, medical facilities, and company-operated commissaries as added inducements to employment. Since most logging operations are conducted in remote locations, their forest-cutting operations have often resulted in an unwelcome encouragement to settlement in the recently cut-over lands. This rapid and often uncontrolled settlement is not altogether a blessing. Indeed, so quickly has much of the cut-over land been occupied that the settlers and their clearings, on occasion, actually precede the loggers. These overly eager settlers, and the omnipresent caingin agriculturists, wreak considerable havoc upon the valuable forests with their clearing fires, and millions of board feet of prime timber are destroyed annually in this manner.

One of the largest users of the better-quality and harder-grade Philippine mahogany is the Philippine furniture industry. Although there are a few large factories, mainly in the city of Manila, most furniture manufacturing is carried on in small shops, and each shop's production is usually contracted on special order. Although there are over 450 separate furniture establishments registered in the Philippines, more than 100 of the larger factories are located in or near Manila. The industry employs more than 8,500 workers. Tangile, dao, and red and white narras are the principal woods utilized in furniture manufacturing. Red narra is the favorite wood because of its durability, ease of working, and beauty; the red narra from northernmost Luzon is most highly prized. Abaca and kapok are the main native upholstering materials. The largest furniture-manufacturing factory is the Muntinlupa Penitentiary near Manila in Rizal Province. Here more than 1,000 inmates fabricate various items of furniture, producing mainly for the various government offices. The lumber for Muntinlupa is prepared at the Davao and Iwahig Penal Colonies. Philippine furniture made by actual craftsmen are products of true beauty.

Minor forest products. Not all forest workers are employed in the logging and lumbering phases of the industry. There are countless thousands of additional people who gain at least part of their livelihood from gathering and processing of minor products from the Philippine forests. Usually they are people whose homes lie close to the margins of the forests and who supplement their meager farm incomes by the cutting of firewood, preparation of charcoal, or by the gathering of rattans, bamboo, bark, and gums and resins.

The cutting of firewood and the preparation of charcoal, although usually carried out by individuals or small groups, are very important to the Philippine economy, for other possible fuels are either deficient or completely lacking in the archipelago. In the large cities of Luzon, such as Manila, the bundles of firewood, called *rojotas,* are usually brought from Mindoro and constitute the principal sources of fuel for cooking purposes.[17] Cebu's needs are supplied from Bohol Island. Limited quantities of charcoal are used either as cooking fuel in the better restaurants or in the preparation of industrial oxygen. The mangrove tree supplies the favored fuelwood, but significant quantities of tengel, sagasa, and ipil-ipil are also used. The best charcoal is prepared from mangrove and tengel.

Bamboo and rattan are the principal so-called minor forest products. Undoubtedly, for domestic purposes bamboo is the most useful and versatile plant in the tropics. Bamboo is a member of the grass family. A very tall grass, it grows rapidly, and after cutting, can quickly regenerate itself, often more abundantly than before cutting. The plant is composed of a hollow stem with numerous cross sections or partitions at the internodes. It is used for a multitide of purposes. Homes can be built almost entirely of bamboo; furniture, matting (called *sawale*), boats, roofing, bridging, fencing, fish traps, and even water containers are but a few of its many uses. Many varieties of bamboo are grown throughout the Philippines; however, the highest quality bamboo comes from the forests of Bataan and Zambales provinces and from the lower slopes of the Cordillera Central in northern Luzon. Bamboo is not only a product of the Philippine forests; it is widely cultivated as a crop and is found growing in clumps, especially along the boundaries of fields, throughout the archipelago.

Rattan, a variety of climbing vine found growing in the dipterocarp forests, provides a valuable raw material of particular use in the furniture industry. Rattan is found growing in 300- to 600-foot lengths with very little taper throughout its length. The vine possesses a remarkably high degree of tensile strength and can even be used as a substitute rope. It is easily bent under steam and pressure into sharp curves, and holds its new shape well. The valley of the Agusan River in northern Mindanao is the best rattan area in the Philippines. There are also considerable quantities of rattan harvested from the forests of Luzon, Catanduanes, and Palawan. A rather large furniture industry, centered in Manila, is based on rattan, and a very high-grade Philippine rattan furniture is produced.

Other minor forest products that are, or have been, produced in small quantities in the Philippine forests include Manila copal, gutta-percha, cutch, cinchona, and rubber. Most of these gums, resins, and barks have had histories of extreme fluctuation in supply and demand. Copal, the sap from the almaciga tree, is used to add brilliance to high-grade glossy varnishes and lacquers. Synthetic substitutes have cut into the demands drastically and the present small production, originating mainly from Palawan and Quezon provinces, satisfies a small domestic market and finds a limited overseas demand in Europe. Gutta-percha, a gum extracted from the tree of the same name, is used as an insulating coating on underground and submarine electric cables, as it is not affected by moisture or acids. The wholesale felling of the gutta-percha trees in order to secure the latex has almost destroyed the source of supply. Only a small quantity of gutta-percha now enters the domestic market, coming mainly from Mindanao and the island of Tawi-Tawi in the Sulu Archipelago. Cutch and cinchona are produced from the barks of two forest trees found growing in the Philippines. The former is the bark of the mangrove tree which is a source of tannin; the latter is the source of quinine, used in the treatment of malaria. In the past the production of cutch has been of considerable export value, but many of the mangrove forests have been overexploited, especially in Zamboanga. The present cutch production is sufficient for the Philippine tanning industry; some 60,000 hides annually are processed into leather in Bulacan Province outside of Manila. The Bureau of Forestry has maintained a 550-acre cinchona plantation at Kaatoan, Bukidnon, since 1929; however, competition offered by synthetically produced malarial suppressives has operated against any further large expansions in cinchona acreage. Wild rubber trees are widely dispersed throughout the Philippines, but commercial rubber cultivation centers on seven relatively recently developed rubber concessions, totaling 44,000 acres, in southern Mindanao and on Basilan Island. Philippine rubber production falls far short of supplying internal demands. Again, the synthetic rubber product has offered keen competition to any substantial increases in natural rubber production aimed at an international market, although some expansion in the acreage will probably take place to satisfy domestic demand.

SUMMARY

It appears in the light of even the more conservative estimates of annual forest growth that the Philippine forest industry is based upon a firm and sustained foundation. At present, however, too much of the best timber is being exported without the benefits of even the most rudimentary processing. The Philippine economy, and the livelihood of countless thousands of additional workers, would benefit from further processing in the Philippines. Caingineros and overly eager, often illegal, settlers pose the most serious immediate threat to the Philippine forest industry.

Mineral Industries: Minerals, Distribution, and Mining

In spite of its small size the Philippines is an important producer and exporter of minerals.[18] The list of minerals is quite long, including several metallic ores such as chromite, iron ore, manganese, copper, gold, and silver, along with certain nonmetallics as sand, limestone, salt, gypsum, rock asphalt, and marble. Unfortunately, the mineral fuels appear to be in short supply, insufficient for even the present modest internal demands.

Although minerals and their recovery and processing form an important segment of the modern Philippine economy, they serve primarily an overseas market. The Philippines has not progressed industrially to the stage at which many minerals are significantly processed and consumed within the country. Nevertheless, the contribution of minerals to the whole economy should not be minimized. The total value of mineral production in 1961 exceeded $163,000,000, and mineral exports ranked fourth in value, following the Philippine export mainstays of sugar, coconut products, and timber. Approximately 150,000 to 200,000 dependents are supported by the 33,000 workers employed directly in mining operations.[19]

The actual Philippine mineral-resource base is still rather imperfectly known. Only slightly more than 10 percent of the area of the Philippines has been systematically surveyed for minerals. As surface and subsurface geologic structures and composition become better known, there is every indication that the present number of proven mineral reserves will be increased tremendously. Most mineral deposits occur within two highly mineralized belts: one running approximately north–south through the archipelago, roughly along western Luzon from the Cordillera Central through Zambales and Batangas to Mindoro, Panay, Negros, Cebu, and Mindanao; and the other running northeast–southwest extending from southeastern Luzon through Masbate and Samar and into eastern Mindanao (fig. 37). Gold, silver, chromite, and copper are especially significant in the east. The Cordillera Central in northern Luzon continues to be the most important single mineral region in terms of value of total mineral production. Whereas other Philippine mining areas are located close to tidewater, the northern Luzon region lies within a relatively inaccessible highland area.

Metal technologies were not highly developed in the Philippines in the immediate pre-Spanish era. Although bronze and gold artifacts turn up very widely in archaeologic finds, it appears that mining and processing skills were rather limited at the time of Spanish arrival. There are early references to gold-working in northern Luzon, and gold was being produced at several

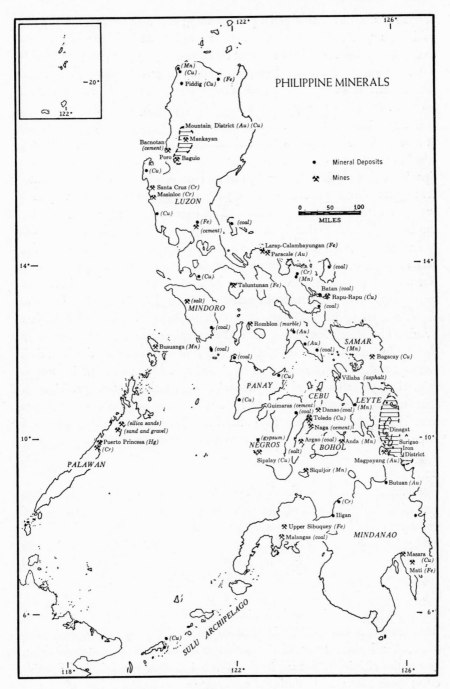

Fig. 37.

points in Luzon by both alluvial placer mining and lode mining; but the raw gold was a regular trade medium between Filipinos and Chinese or Japanese traders in the lowlands along the west coast, and most of the product probably left the country. Gold was also produced in Samar, Masbate, Panay, and northeastern Mindanao, and used as a trade medium along the coasts of those islands. References to copper appear rather late in Spanish times and may indicate Chinese influences. Small amounts of iron apparently were worked at several points throughout the archipelago.[20] The precious metals were of real interest to the Spanish, but no striking fable of an El Dorado led the Spanish on, as it had in the Spanish New World. Several seventeenth-century expeditions penetrated Luzon gold-mining hill country, but very little success attended them. Numerous mining concessions were granted during the late eighteenth and early nineteenth centuries, but in general the gold-gathering and gold-mining activities were spasmodic and quite unsuccessful. Some mining of Bulacan hematite iron ores was done in late Spanish times, but this too proved unrewarding. In the Philippines the whole history of terrain exploration for hoards of metals, and the exploitation of labor forces in the mines, was quite unlike the pattern that developed in the Spanish New World. The search for, survey of, and development of mineral resources in the Philippines belongs essentially to the American era and the twentieth century, and it was accomplished by Americans. Direct Filipino interest in mineral exploitation, and the financial and technological participation therein, was somewhat slow to develop. It has been only in the post-World War II period that concern for industrialization has made development of mineral resources of popular concern to the country as a whole.

GOLD AND SILVER

Gold mining has been the leading mineral industry in the Philippines generally, both in terms of the value of the product and the number of employees. Gold regularly contributes 20–25 percent of the total value of Philippine mineral production, and its recovery employs approximately one-quarter of the total mining labor force. The Philippine mines yield approximately 1 percent of the world's total gold, an amount sufficient to rank the island republic eighth among the gold-producing nations of the world.

Gold extraction in the Philippines dates back to the pre-Spanish era with small hand-operations, chiefly in secondary alluvial deposits, in the mountains of northern Luzon, at Paracale in southeastern Luzon, on Masbate and Cebu, and in the vicinity of Butuan in northern Mindanao. The principal Spanish effect upon gold mining during the 300 years of control was one of general neglect. Periodically mining was intensified in those areas already worked, particularly in Paracale, but there was no sustained production. The gold-mining industry was given tremendous impetus during the American administration by revised monetary policies in the United States and Great Britain during the years 1928–1933. Primary deposits were the main targets, and production soared. By 1940, the Philippines ranked sixth among the world's gold producers, with an annual production of 1,100,000 fine ounces. Mines and equipment sustained considerable damage during the war years, 1941–1945. Costly rehabilitation and abnormal economic conditions slowed resumption in the postwar period, and production has varied between 400,000 and 500,000 fine ounces annually.

Twentieth-century gold mining has centered in the geologically complex highlands of northern Luzon from which has come more than three-fourths of Philippine gold. Gold is obtained by the gold-mining companies from the processing of low-grade ores, or as a by-product from copper-concentration operations. Six or seven major producers of gold have their operations in the northern Luzon mountains. Ore is mined using shaft- and drift-mining techniques with separation of the metallic gold by cyanidation.

The amount of gold recovered as a by-product from what are basically copper mines in the archipelago amounts to 17 percent of the total gold production. The large copper mine on Cebu produces by-product gold in quantities sufficient to rank the island as a poor second after Luzon. Lesser quantities of gold are obtained at Magpayang and Masara on Mindanao and occasionally at Paracale in southeastern Luzon. Large-scale gold mining has been abandoned on Masbate, where approximately 12 percent of the Philippine prewar production originated. All gold produced in the Philippines is now sold on the "free market." Small quantities of silver, averaging 500,000 troy ounces annually, are recovered from the major gold operations.

The premier position gold has long retained in the Philippine mineral economy is being challenged by the increasing copper production; however, in light of large possible and probable gold-ore reserves, and providing cost and price ratios do not worsen, the Philippines should remain among the important gold-producing countries, and gold will continue to occupy an important position among Philippine minerals.

COPPER

Post-World War II development of the large copper deposits has brought significant modification to the relative composition of the Philippine mineral economy. Although large-scale extraction and concentration of copper ores actually began in 1937, there were only two producers until the war, and annual production did not exceed $2,000,000 in value. By 1959 six new producers had commenced operations, and capacities have so increased that the value of copper production exceeds $39,000,000 and in certain years challenges gold as the leading mineral. High postwar prices and increasing world consumption were prime factors stimulating this large copper production.

Again, as with gold, the mountains of northern Luzon were the site of early copper mining, and two producers continue to operate in this rugged upland area. The copper content of the northern Luzon ores generally exceeds 3 percent, and the area appears to contain substantial reserves of ore. The bulk of the ore is concentrated at Mankayan, 60 miles north of Baguio; copper concentrates are trucked to the port of Poro, La Union, which necessitates a 90-mile truck haul over exceedingly rough mountainous topography. The largest Philippine copper mine, and the leading producer of copper, is located in west central Cebu in the municipality of Toledo. These large deposits of low-grade copper ores, averaging 0.7 to 0.9 percent copper content, are strip-mined, concentrated at the mine, and trucked only 10 miles downgrade to loading facilities at the west coast port of Sangi. Other low-grade copper deposits are being mined at Sipalay in southwestern Negros and at Masara in southeastern Mindanao. Smaller, but very rich, deposits of copper are being worked on Rapu-Rapu Island, off southeastern Luzon, and at Bagacay in central Samar. Other commercial-sized deposits of copper ores are known to exist in the Philippines, but they are not presently under development for one reason or another.

Generally prior to shipment abroad, the Philippine copper ores are treated in flotation mills so as to obtain a 21–23 percent copper-content shipping concentrate. As a by-product, sulphuric acid and sulphate are extracted from the residues at the Cebu mine for processing into ammonium sulfate fertilizer. Pryites from Rapu-Rapu are processed into fertilizer at Iligan, Mindanao. The recovery of gold from the smelting of the copper concentrates is an important additional source of income. No copper smelting is performed in the Philippines. Smelters in Japan, and to a lesser extent in the United States, are the principal customers for Philippine copper.

Copper ores and ore reserves in the Philippines are substantial with an estimated 130,000,000 tons of mill ore.[21] Providing world marketing conditions remain favorable, copper should continue as one of the nation's leading minerals.

CHROMITE

In terms of value of total production, chromite ore normally ranks third among Philippine minerals, providing 15 percent of the total mineral production. Reserves of commercial-grade chromite, particularly refractory ores, are very large. The Islands lead the world in the production of refractory chromite, supplying almost three-fourths of the United States requirements, and they rank sixth among the world producers of metallurgical chromite.

Reserves of chromite in the Philippines in 1958 were estimated at 11,000,000 tons of 32–33 percent refractory-grade chromite and 2,500,000 tons of 42–49 percent metallurgical-grade chromite ores; but exploration is incomplete.[22] The largest chromite deposits lie in the Zambales Mountains adjacent to the coast, with smaller deposits located near Lagonoy Gulf in southeastern Luzon, near Opal and Lourdes in northern Mindanao, and on the islands of Palawan and Dinagat. Virtually all refractory-chromite production centers in the large deposits at Masinloc, Zambales, which are estimated to contain 10,000,000 tons of ore. Refractory production from these deposits has averaged about 500,000 tons annually since 1952. The majority of the ore is recovered through bench mining and other forms of surface mining. Approximately one-third of the ore production is direct-shipping grade; the remainder must be concentrated prior to shipment. The principal metallurgical-grade chromite mines are located in the municipality of Santa Cruz, also in Zambales, and they yield approximately 85 percent of the nation's production. Here operations are underground in a 2,000,000-ton reserve. Smaller metallurgical chromite mines are in operation on the island of Palawan and near the city of Baguio in northern Luzon.

All Philippine chromite ore is exported, principally to the United States, with smaller shipments to Japan, Canada, and the countries of northwestern Europe. Reserves of chromite are proven, or suspected, in quantities that are sufficient to last many years at the present rates of extraction.

IRON ORE

Iron ore ranks fourth in value of production among Philippine minerals. At present all Philippine iron ore is exported to Japan, and varies in quantity from 1,000,000 to 2,000,000 tons annually.

The existence of modest-sized deposits of iron ore in the Philippines has been known for a long time. Small deposits in Bulacan and in northwestern Luzon at Piddig were worked, in small measure, even in pre-Spanish times. Large-scale mining, however, began in 1934, and except for interruptions during the war years, has been continuous. Reserves are of two types: (1) small scattered deposits of hematite and magnetite ores located in Luzon, Marinduque, Samar, and southeastern and southwestern Mindanao, and (2) large deposits of lateritic ores, possibly totaling 1.5 billion tons of 46 percent ore, in Surigao and adjacent offshore islands.[23] At present, mining centers in the hematite and magnetite deposits, particularly in the Larap-Calambayungan deposits in southeastern Luzon. The deposits at Larap consist of hard, porous hematite and primary magnetite, which can be recovered through bench- and shaft-mining techniques. Reserves of commercial-grade magnetite, containing an estimated 57 percent iron content, are relatively small, and are estimated at 35,000,000 tons, but the ore bodies lie practically at tidewater. These deposits yield more than 75 percent of the Philippine iron-ore production. Smaller deposits of hematite and magnetite under commercial development are located at Sibuguey and Mati on Mindanao and at Taluntunan on Marinduque. These are much smaller deposits with reserves of 2 million to 8 million tons of shipping ore each.

The big enigma of the Philippine iron-ore picture lies in the future development of the large lateritic deposits of Surigao Province. Whereas these ores have been successfully processed, metallurgically, in Japan, the processing has not been economically profitable. The ore is basically limonite and occurs as an overburden over a 60-square-mile area of northeastern Surigao, and on Manicani and Homonhon islands in Leyte Gulf. The ore is quite high in nickel also, actually representing a potential source of this metal. Although discovered in 1912, the Surigao iron-ore body has remained undeveloped because there are adequate reserves of better-grade ores elsewhere in the Philippines.

The significance of Philippine iron-ore reserves undoubtedly will undergo considerable reevaluation in the years ahead. The ores, now wholly exported, will find some domestic market with increasing industrialization in the Islands. The plans for the development of an integrated steel complex near Iligan in northern Mindanao will require Philippine iron ores. Undoubtedly, the reserves of high-grade hematite and magnetite ores will be further increased by additional systematic exploration.

MANGANESE AND OTHER BASE METALS

The production of manganese ore in the Philippines has fluctuated sharply, reflecting the marginal character of many of the ore deposits and operations, and the changing economic conditions that effect world demand. The majority of manganese deposits are low-grade, and most of the ores must be concentrated before shipment. Small deposits of manganese are scattered throughout the archipelago; however, production has centered in two areas: (1) Busuanga, where direct-shipping ores are mined, and (2) the low-grade deposits on Bohol and Siquijor islands. Since World War II, manganese ore production has fluctuated between 5,000 and 33,000 tons annually. Total reserves of manganese in the Philippines are modest, although at present rates of exploitation they should be sufficient to last for many years. Because of the marginal economic character of the deposits, production will continue to fluctuate widely with increasing or decreasing world supplies and prices.

Other base metals produced in the Philippines include mercury, refined from deposits of cinnabar near Puerto Princesa in Palawan, and small quantities of lead, zinc, and molybdenum. Most of the Philippine production of base metals is exported, although small amounts of copper ore are used by wire factories in the Manila area. Almost all mineral processing accomplished within the islands is for purposes of ore concentration. If an internal demand for mineral consumption can be developed through the establishment of an iron and steel industry or a copper-smelting industry, these developments would bring about a healthy reorientation of the entire Philippine minerals industry.

FUELS AND NONMETALLIC MINERALS AND MINERAL PRODUCTS

The Philippines appears to be rather poorly endowed with fossil fuels. There have been no significant commercial petroleum discoveries, and the deposits of coal are both small and of inferior quality. More than 80 percent of the present Philippine coal production comes from the island of Cebu. The Cebu fields are located at Danao, Argao, and Uling in central Cebu, and consist mainly of subbituminous grades. Coal is also mined at Malangas in Zamboanga del Sur where the best quality Philippine coal is obtained, some being of coking quality. Small amounts have been mined on Batan Island, off southeastern Luzon. Coal deposits are known in at least twelve provinces, and total reserves are estimated at 67 million tons. Annual coal production varies between 150,000 and 250,000 tons with 90 percent used in the cement industry. The Malangas field acquires added significance because it is located near deposits of high-grade magnetite at the Upper Sibuguey field.

Cement is the leading nonmetallic mineral product of the Philippines. The first modern cement plant was established by the government at Naga, on Cebu, in 1924. It was based upon local limestone and coal. The product was shipped by water throughout the archipelago. Later, a second government plant was established to better serve Manila and northern Luzon markets at Bacnotan, La Union. Limestone occurs locally, and coal is shipped to the plant by water from the Malangas field. The finished product reaches the market by truck and rail. The three nongovernment cement plants, two located near Manila and one on Guimaras Island, between Negros and Panay, are based on local limestones and imported bunker oils. Philippine cement production amounts to more than 1,000,000 metric tons annually, an amount generally adequate to satisfy local demands. The resource base for cement production is essentially limitless, for only gypsum must be imported;

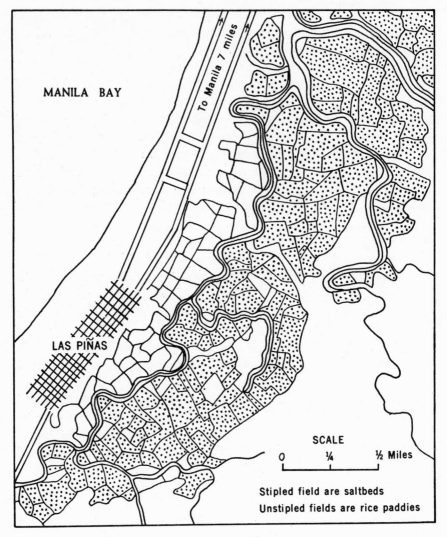

Fig. 38. Salt beds of Manila Bay.

and cement production doubtless will continue to increase as new demands, and possibly overseas markets, are created.

The Philippines is essentially self-sufficient in salt for human consumption, although the quality of domestically produced salt is very poor. Virtually all of the salt produced in the Philippines is through the solar evaporation of seawater. Most of the production comes from small salt beds located in littoral areas of northwestern Luzon on the Ilocos coast or near Lingayen Gulf and around Manila Bay where the long drought period favors evaporation (fig. 38). Salt for industrial uses is generally deficient and, at present, constitutes an annual import of 20,000 tons. The largest salt beds are found in western Mindoro and eastern Negros, where industrial salt is produced. Mining of salt in these latter areas was established in conjunction with food processing, soap manufacture, tanning, and the manufacture of caustic soda. Salt production amounts to 150,000–200,000 tons annually.

Several other nonmetallic minerals are mined in the Philippines in small quantities. Rock asphalt from Villaba, Leyte, is used locally for road surfacing. Some silica sands for glass manufacture in Manila are mined in Palawan. Marble, some of considerable beauty, is quarried on Romblon. A small gypsum deposit has been opened recently in southwestern Negros. Clays and limestones are mined in small quantities throughout the archipelago. All of the nonmetallic mineral production is consumed within the country, although increased cement production could seek foreign markets.

SUMMARY

The mineral industries of the Philippines operate almost exclusively for foreign markets. The resource bases for most minerals are good, and with continued exploitation a prosperous industry appears assured for many years. Systematic geologic reconnaissance should add considerable reserves. Only with mineral fuels does there appear to be cause for serious concern. Unfortunately, very little processing of minerals is accomplished in the Islands prior to their export, and today the mineral industries of the Philippines are almost wholly extractive.

EIGHT

~~~~ Secondary Production Patterns

Land, Sea, and Air Transport

Historically, most of the Filipinos have been littoral dwellers, boat users, and people concerned with both the land and water fringes of the coastline. As they were village and sitio dwellers carrying on a relatively localized economy, small boats served their daily purposes and formal transport centers were not required. Interregional cargoes of trade goods were in small volumes that could be handled on beaches, and the interregional watercraft themselves required almost no special facilities. This traditional pattern began to change late in the Spanish period both on sea and on land. The Spanish introduced interisland shipping that began to concentrate some patterns of traffic at scattered entrepôts, but they did extremely little in the way of developing port facilities as such. As the Filipino population grew larger at inland locations on the larger islands there arose the need for land transport with both vehicular mechanisms and patterns of roadbeds. A small development of roads, and horse- or carabao-drawn vehicles, characterized the late Spanish era, most notably in the hinterland of Manila. The Spanish also permitted the beginnings of a rail system, centered on Manila, which seemed to suggest a future pattern of development.

The Philippine Archipelago has always presented a peculiar set of physical conditions. The earliest Filipino residents accepted these conditions and developed their boating patterns, but developed almost no land-transport system. Late Spanish efforts began to modify the traditional system. During the early twentieth century, Americans modified both land- and sea-transport systems still further, but left both quite incomplete. The Filipino population has not yet strongly formulated a set of concepts in transportation-communication that effectively binds the island world together either in terms of sociocultural ties or in patterns of economic development. To a degree the population is "making do" with transport systems that serve poorly, and are accepting the physical facts of their environment, rather than turning those facts to the best advantage. It would be possible to unify the whole archipelago with a water-transport system that took advantage of the lengthy and often deeply embayed coastline and the extensive system of protected waterways between many of the islands. Several of the larger islands present landscapes that lend themselves to the development of effective systems of land transport. The whole archipelago presents conditions that could permit of an extremely effective system of air transport. In communications the regular broadcast stations are effective, but other forms of communication technology suffer seriously from the lack of effective development.

In the Philippines the contemporary demands for transportation are generated by potential cargo and passenger movements in response to four different kinds of economic pressures.[1] First, a very significant demand for intraisland and interisland transportation service is generated by the necessity for concentrating at certain of the ports the various products destined for export. Throughout the Philippines large quantities of minerals, timber products, and commercial agricultural crops such as coconuts, coconut oil, copra, abaca, sugar, and tobacco are produced. Although many of these products are shipped overseas directly from the production zones, there are significant quantities that must be moved to one of the open ports prior to final export. One-quarter of the more than 7 million tons of minerals produced annually in the Philippines is exported, the remainder is consumed within the country. Likewise, most of the nearly 3 billion board feet of timber-cut and the over 2 million tons of commercial agricultural produce must enter into local transportation, at least in part. Thus, an estimated 6 million tons of commodities intended for eventual export are transported over the internal transportation network annually.

A second large demand placed upon Philippine transportation is generated by the need to distribute the various imported goods throughout the Islands. Generally the imports are unloaded from foreign vessels at Manila, although on occasion the ports of Cebu and Iloilo receive foreign shipments directly. These imports, generally consisting of manufactured goods, enter into local transportation in significant quantities; however, they never bulk as large as the tonnages of export products. Often the distribution of the imports furnishes return cargoes for an otherwise empty carrier. The largest import tonnage is petroleum and its associated products, representing approximately 2 million tons, which are distributed to various depots throughout the archipelago, and from these depots to the actual consumers.

The internal exchange of commodities from producers in one area of the Philippines to consumers in another furnishes the third, and largest, amount of cargo for the Philippine carriers. Perhaps 55–60 percent of the total tonnage transported within the Philippines is composed of foodstuffs and various products produced in different centers of the country. Generally this movement is one-way—from the less densely settled rural and pioneer areas toward the larger urban centers, or to those areas that are primarily concerned with producing for foreign markets and thus deficient in the basic subsistence foodstuffs.

Last and perhaps most important, in the Philippines, as in much of southern Asia, there is a very large passenger traffic. The Filipino has become a rather mobile individual; he is quick to move into areas of greater economic opportunity, thirsty for the glitter and more numerous cultural facilities of the larger cities, yet intensely loyal to his "town" or birthplace, which he attempts to visit periodically. Students, merchants, sales representatives, migratory workers, and visitors overflow the facilities of the buses and interisland steamers, especially during the holiday season. Millions of passengers use the Philippine transportation system each week.

Difficult terrain, constant heat and heavy precipitation, and limited financial resources have made the establishment of an effective and efficient transportation system more difficult. The Philippine government and the Philippine transportation industry have not been able to keep pace with the demands placed upon the various transport media. Today the transportation system of the Philippines must be considered inadequate for the demands of the nation as a whole.

WATER TRANSPORTATION

Present-day Philippine interisland shipping and the resultant over-water trade patterns are the result of a gradual evolution and continued adjustment to meet the challenge of changing economic conditions within the archipelago. For the Philippines, water transportation will always be of greater importance than land transportation, as the straits and channels that separate the islands are the arteries through which flows the lifeblood of commerce.

A total of 6,000 to 7,000 vessels, including sailboats, powercraft, barges, and lighters, are registered for commercial coastwise operations in the Philippines. This commercial shipping fleet represents approximately 350,000 gross registered tons of shipping.[2] Although a few vessels are being designed expressly for the interisland fleet operations, a large segment of the principal commercial vessels was acquired, virtually in toto, from the surplus wartime shipping of the United States government, since the entire Philippine interisland shipping fleet had been destroyed during World War II. These vessels were designed as military craft and, therefore, are not suited to general commercial use.

The bulk of the Philippine interisland freight is carried by a group of 125–150 larger ships referred to as the core fleet. Vessels of this core fleet operate on regular schedules, travel fixed routes, and call at the major ports. Manila and Cebu are the main foci of Philippine interisland shipping and trade, and the ship movements between these two ports, and from these ports to their trade hinterlands, provide the basic framework of Philippine water-borne commerce (fig. 39). Relatively frequent service is maintained also with the ports of Iloilo, Tacloban, Dumaguete, Cagayan de Oro, Surigao, Zamboanga, Jolo, and Davao, and through these latter ports into their regional hinterlands. Intraisland water transportation is relatively insignificant, excepting possibly the routes between Manila and the ports of southeastern Luzon, and around the circumference of Mindanao, for the slower water transport has been unable to compete with highway carriers.

In the light of what must continue to be a major dependence upon water transportation, the Philippines has failed to develop the port and terminal facilities necessary for minimal use. Only the port of Manila has modern loading and unloading equipment. Other ports, and they number approximately 500, only provide berthing facilities permitting operation of ship's tackle; and many of the important ports are nothing more than protected anchorages for lightering cargoes in the stream. (See appendix table 37 for list of ports.)

Ports in the Philippines are classified under four categories: ports of entry, national ports, municipal ports, and private installations. The ports of entry are open to foreign shipping, staffed by Customs Service personnel, and have facilities usually considerably above the national average. There were eighteen ports of entry in 1965. Manila is the leading Filipino port in the volume of its foreign commerce, ranking second in the volume of its domestic trade. South Harbor, Manila's foreign-shipping terminal, provides berths for fourteen oceangoing vessels. This port area is served with modern equipment, including fork lifts, motor trucks with lifting cranes, electric floor-tractors, and several heavy-duty cranes. North Harbor, available to interisland shipping only, is provided with eleven piers, but no shore-based loading equipment. Cebu is the leading interisland shipping center of the nation, and is also an important port of call for overseas vessels. The remaining ports of entry consist of quays and wharves, warehousing, lighterage, quayside transport, and bunkerage facilities. National ports include all ports of primary importance to foreign, interisland, and interprovincial commerce, excepting

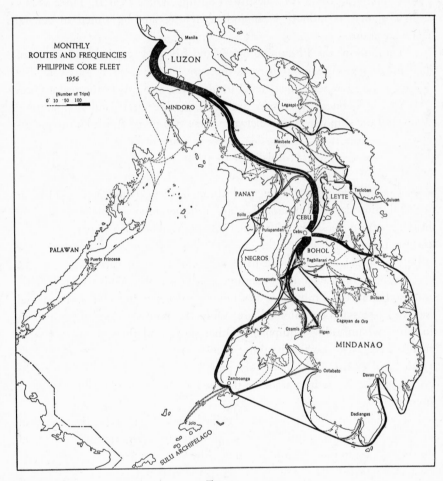

Fig. 39.

the ports of entry. Improvement and maintenance of these ports is financed by the Philippine government.

Port facilities at most national ports are primitive, often consisting of no more than a single wooden pier extending only a short distance seaward. Usually only the smaller, shallower draft vessels can come alongside to load and discharge; such ports are seldom equipped with warehouses, lighterage, or bunkerage facilities. Despite these handicaps, most of the national ports have become important regional trade centers.

The municipal ports usually consist of a single wooden pier, not always extending beyond low tide, or a protected anchorage that will permit lightering or use of the beaches by small craft. Municipal ports are built and maintained by the various municipal councils. These ports represent the final destinations, of the points of origin, for Philippine interisland commerce.

Although the great majority of the private port facilities offer little in modern equipment, several of them, particularly the ore-shipping ports of Masinloc, Larap, Sangi, and Malangas, afford conveyer-belt loading facilities.

The ports of entry, principally Manila, Cebu, and Iloilo, and to lesser degree Zamboanga and Davao, are the major collection centers for the interisland-transported export commodities: sugar to Manila, Iloilo, and Cebu; abaca to Manila, Cebu, Legaspi, and Davao; and copra to Cebu, Manila, Zamboanga, Legaspi, Jolo, and Iloilo. Manila also receives and consumes, or transships, approximately 85 percent of the Philippine imports. Mindanao Island acts as the principal point of origin for domestic foodstuffs, particularly large quantities of rice, corn, and cattle, which are shipped into the populous Visayan Islands and to the other major urban centers of the Philippines. Mindanao also places large shipments of abaca, copra, and other coconut products into interisland commerce.

Philippine water transportation today generally is inadequate for the demands placed upon it. This inadequacy stems from deficiencies in the number of vessels, inefficiencies in shipping itself, and in the generally low standards of the terminal facilities.

LAND TRANSPORTATION

Philippine land transportation is also generally inadequate to meet the developing national economy. The present highway and railroad networks are too slight in total mileages and in locational distributions; many areas are connected only by trails, and the quality of the facilities leaves much to be desired.

In the Philippines, railroads have never played the important role they have in so many other countries. Unquestionably, rail is an excellent means for bulk transport, but in the Philippines the archipelagic nature of the land areas restricts the length of the railroads and seriously hinders their effective integration. There is a total of 695 miles of 42-inch-gauge public railroad in the Philippines.[3] Most of the commercial trackage is on Luzon where the Manila Railroad Company, a government-operated corporation, operates 582 miles of rail lines connecting Manila with the Central Plain northward as far as Bacnotan, La Union, and with connections to southeastern Luzon as far as Legaspi, Albay. The remainder of the public rail network is on the island of Panay. This rail line connects the port city of Iloilo with Roxas City on the north coast. Prior to World War II approximately 57 miles of track were used on the island of Cebu between Danao and Argao, but the Cebu railroad was not rehabilitated.[4]

The Philippine rail system was not fully completed until 1938. This late completion date did not allow time for the railroads to become sufficiently entrenched to be able to withstand the intense competition from buses and trucks. Work was begun on the Luzon railroad system in 1887 under British direction and with British capital; however, in 1917 these assets were transferred to the Philippine government, where they have remained. The Manila-North line is essentially the "sugar road," whereas freight on the southern line is somewhat more diversified, with considerable revenues from the transport of sugar, forest products, and petroleum. The line north from Manila is under considerable competition from bus and truck operators because of the relatively dense highway network in the Central Plain. As yet, southeastern Luzon is not connected with Manila except by a very poor road. Passenger traffic is quite heavy on both extensions.

The railroad on Panay has been in operation since 1907, although it has undergone considerable reorganization and is now under governmental administration. Sugarcane, centrifugal sugar, and molasses from landlocked sugar-producing areas to the north, as well as a modest general freight and a large passenger traffic, are the bases for continued profitable operations.

The few railroads in the Philippines are performing an economically and socially useful function. It is, however, extremely doubtful if further expansion, other than modernization of the present system, could be justified economically. For several years there have been tentative plans for extending the railroad line from San Jose, Nueva Ecija, across the Caraballo Mountains to Bayombong, Nueva Vizcaya, and then to Santiago, Isabela, and terminating at Tuguegarao, Cagayan. Such a line would be approximately 220 miles long. Transportation-research teams have argued against the construction of this extension, claiming that future revenues are insufficient to permit economic operations.

A large share of the intraisland freight and the great majority of the passengers are transported by carriers operating on the Philippine highway system. The road network is also of importance in providing the connecting links between the various parts and their hinterlands. Both the density and quality of the Philippine highway system vary considerably from island to island, and even within the individual islands (fig. 40 and appendix tables

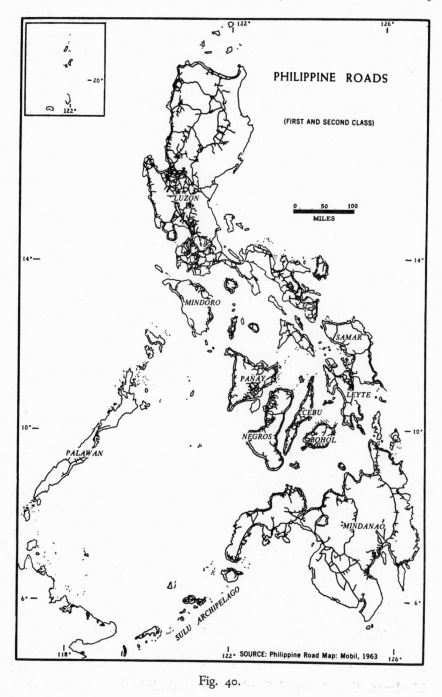

PHILIPPINE ROADS

(FIRST AND SECOND CLASS)

Fig. 40.

27, 28). In general the road network of central Luzon is reasonably adequate in its overall length, particularly on the Central Plain; however, the quality of many Luzon roads, several of them of primary importance, is below that desirable, and many areas are very inadequately served. The roads on many of the Visayan islands and on Mindanao are considerably below minimal standards, in terms of both overall length and road quality.

In 1960 there was a total of 22,292 miles of first-class, second-class, and third-class national and provincial roads in the Philippines.[5] Only 18 percent of the roads, however, were concrete or asphalt-surfaced, and an additional 34 percent had some stone or gravel surfacing. Few of the highways have permanent bridges, and many rivers still must be forded. In 1958 only 63 percent of the 19,000-odd Philippine barrios were connected by roads with the outside world.

In many sections of the Philippines the lack of roads has greatly retarded economic development. This is particularly the case on the island of Mindanao. Whereas Luzon, in 1958, had 46 percent of the country's road mileage on 36 percent of the land area, Mindanao, which contains 33 percent of the area, had only 16 percent of the roads. The importance of road construction to the settlement of Mindanao is attested to by the rapid settlement preceding and immediately following the construction of the recent Davao-Agusan highway in eastern Mindanao. This highway traversed what had been an extensive and virtually uninhabited lowland area between Davao Gulf and the mouth of the Agusan River in the north. Construction engineers were continually encountering new settlers taking up occupance along the highway right-of-way.

In light of the small number of motor vehicles, the present Philippine highway system can probably be considered as generally adequate, with a few important exceptions. Little of the road network, except in the metropolitan Manila area, supports a dense traffic flow. In 1960 there was a total of 150,000 motor vehicles in the Philippines; approximately 55 percent of these vehicles were private automobiles, the remainder were trucks and buses. Three-fourths of the vehicles were registered in Luzon, and 31 percent were registered in just the city of Manila alone. The Visayan area had 16 percent of the vehicles, whereas Mindanao had only 9 percent.[6] The latter percentage was almost wholly trucks, buses, and jeeps.

Public buses carry a very large number of passengers. Although most of the passenger traffic is for short hauls, usually to nearby market towns, there are several long-distance through-carriers, particularly on Luzon and Mindanao. Saturdays and Sundays are particularly busy traveling days, although local factors such as market days or barrio fiestas will cause seasonal variations. Most of the buses are owned by small transportation companies with three or fewer operating units; however, the larger companies have the greater passenger-mileage traffic. The majority of Philippine buses have capacities of from 20 to 45 passengers. The more numerous small companies are intensely competitive, as are several of the larger operators, and they have created chaotic competition with their ruinous rate-structures and rebate arrangements. The smaller companies are usually satisfied to obtain a bare daily income sufficient for living costs. They do not feel obligated to follow fixed routes or schedules. Their drivers often race one another at dangerously high speeds to pick up passengers. Maintenance is minimal and breakdowns along the road are frequent. Most towns that are located on highways are served by frequent and relatively inexpensive bus transportation. The buses also transport considerable quantities of cargo.

AIR TRANSPORTATION

With their archipelagic structure and form the Philippines are particularly suited to the development of commercial aviation. Because of the higher costs of air transportation, however, the commercial aviation industry does not occupy a favorable competitive position in freight traffic when compared with trucks, buses, and water transport. Approximately 85 percent of the current revenues of commercial aircarft operations comes from their passenger traffic, which is a rather selected clientele.

One commercial airline, the government-controlled Philippine Air Line, monopolizes domestic aviation in the archipelago, although there are several small airlines, and charter aircraft are available from other companies. Generally scheduled operations by PAL are conducted by two-engined DC-3 aircraft for local travel and turboprop or four-engined propeller aircraft for the longer flights; jets were beginning to appear early in 1966.

Through the offices of the Civil Aeronautics Authority, the Philippine government maintains eighty-one airfields scattered throughout the country (fig. 41). Most of these airports, however, are inadequate even for twin-engined operations. The Manila Airport maintains highly adequate facilities, including repair shops, and is the principal point of takeoff and destination for domestic and international flights. Lahug Airport at Cebu is the second busiest, and while serving as an alternate field for international flights, maintains an entrepôt position with respect to Mindanao and the Visayan area. A new international airport has been constructed recently on Mactan Island, adjacent to eastern Cebu. Bacolod, in western Negros, and Davao, on Mindanao, also have busy air terminals.

Passenger traffic by air is particularly heavy between Manila and Cebu

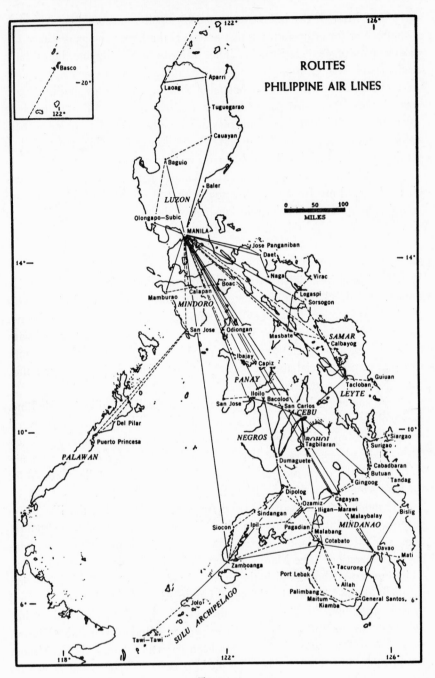

Fig. 41.

and between Cebu and points in northern Mindanao. Air-freight movement is especially concentrated between Manila and Bacolod, and to Manila from Cebu, Davao, Iloilo, Cotabato, Zamboanga, and Baguio. The Philippine Air Line is also an important carrier of mail.

The potentials of interisland passenger transport and of interisland cargo movements for high-value and perishable products by air are great. The major reasons for the limited development of air transportation have been the deficiencies in physical facilities and the relatively high rate-structure.

SUMMARY

The Philippines has the basic framework for an adequate transportation system. Improvements in existing facilities and the additional construction of a few carefully considered new facilties should make it possible to meet the many varied demands for national economic integration. Better port facilities, more efficient carriers, and a greatly expanded road network, particularly on Mindanao, are the most immediate needs. In 1956 the Stanford Research Institute's transportation study strongly recommended the creation of an integrated system of large ferries operating between the more important islands; this suggestion has not been implemented. These ferries could carry large freight trucks from the road system of one island to that of another. Ferries could provide a cheap and practical bridge system between the various main islands.

Manufacturing and the Growth of Industry

Although some manufacturing has been a traditional, historical accompaniment to the economy of every people, it would appear that the pre-Spanish Filipinos did relatively little manufacturing in comparison with some mainland peoples, and their small accomplishment was neither broad in range of product nor in range of processes utilized. Every local culture group in the Islands made textiles in some amount, and processed woods, bamboos, rattans, and leaf fibers in various ways. Every group processed stone into tools and utensils, and every group was variably skilled in basketry; but not every group processed pottery clays, and only a few groups processed metals. Housing was simple, furniture was scant, apparel was tribally distinctive and often relatively scanty, tools were simple and few, and transport equipment was almost limited to watercraft. Basic needs were few, levels of aspiration set low limits, and trade supplied many of the desired amenities, both as internal trade and as foreign trade. Chinese, Japanese, Indonesian, and other traders brought into the Islands many of the manufactured commodities that were in use. Just prior to the coming of the Spanish, the Moslem immigrants in the south began bringing in new commodities and new processes, but these had not spread widely when the Spanish arrived.

The Spanish introduced whole new ranges of processes and commodities, needs and desires, and during the first two centuries of their presence in the Islands, established a whole new range of manufacturing. The permanent residence of significant numbers of Chinese at Manila and a few other points in the earlier period was a part of this development. Manufacturing remained handicraft in pattern, but the commodity and process ranges were greatly extended. Public architecture and town housing took on new forms, the patterns and styles of apparel expanded greatly, transport equipment began to involve land movement, and new kinds of marketing-exchange began to operate. These processes operated selectively, both in regional terms and among socioeconomic classes. For an upper-class resident near Manila, becoming a Christian Filipino involved participation in many aspects of the new economic patterns, whereas for the rural occupant of a distant sitio lightly touched by Spanish influence the participation was very slight; and for many of the pagan peoples who resisted the new elements of Spanish control during the early period, participation was almost totally lacking.

To the degree to which the Spanish periodically prohibited Filipino participation in certain economic activites, favored or suppressed Chinese economic activities, exacted products from the residents within encomienda grants, recruited Filipinos into the military services, exacted labor service from the Filipino population, and encouraged or discouraged Filipino participation in trading operations, there developed varieties of skills among Filipinos and degrees of Filipino development of manufacturing.[7] Around Manila, Cavite, Cebu, and Ioilo the presence of Chinese and the parallel employment of Filipinos in different economic activities widened the range of manufacturing operations, but the general reluctance of the Spanish to settle in, and develop, "the provinces" retarded the spread of these changes and retarded the general growth of all secondary elements in the island economy.

In the nineteenth century there began a pattern of marked economic change, the result of the failure of Spanish monopoly-company trading. Elements in the change were the relaxation of the Spanish rules on foreign trade, increased foreign entry into the Islands, the settlement of Chinese in various provincial towns, and the beginnings of Filipino participation in economic operations. The rise in the export volumes of tobacco, coconut products, abaca, and sugar led to the development of agricultural-processing activities. The rise in importation of foreign commodities, as finished manufactures, led to the decline of many of the basic handicrafts, but also led to the rise of lateral manufacturing and processing operations.[8] The relatively slight amount of entrepreneurial experience and participation by Filipinos, and the aggressive activity of the Chinese in the absence of effective Spanish government rules thereon, led to the rapid rise of the Chinese to a position of dominance in foreign trade, wholesaling, distribution of imports, and the collection of exports. Filipino participation often lay in the roles of unskilled labor, skilled labor, or primary producer-consumer rather than in entrepreneurial operations. These changes focused rather strongly on a few port cities, such as Manila, Cebu, Iloilo, and a very few others to which foreign traders were occasionally admitted. The changes affected hinterland communities around each port to variable degree, but often did not reach far into the rural backcountry. Spanish citizens participated in the changing economic activities, and a few upper-class Filipino families also participated, but it is customary to say that by the end of the nineteenth century the Chinese were dominant in all secondary aspects of the Philippine economy. The nineteenth century saw, therefore, the extensive growth of industry on a level that remained largely handicraft manufacture, but which set the stage for the evolution of modern industry in the Philippines.

THE RISE OF MODERN INDUSTRY

During the latter half of the nineteenth century developments began to occur which were instrumental in the evolution of modern industry in the Philippines. One of these was the application of mechanical power to agricultural processing of rice, sugarcane, corn, and occasionally other products, and to sawmilling in the lumber industries. The building of the Manila Railroad, and the employment of powered shipping bottoms, was followed by the slow development of power in road transport. There also began the modern organization of financing, trading, and manufacturing by the establishment of corporate organizations. For example, the Banco Espanol-Filipino dates from 1852, the Compania General de Tabacos de Filipinas (Tabacalera) dates from 1883, the Compania Maritima dates from 1886, and the San Miguel Brewing Company dates from 1890. Some of these early organizations remained restricted to the field in which they began, but others, such as the San Miguel Brewing Company, gradually expanded and diversified their spheres of operations to include wide ranges of manufacturing activities.

Early American governmental influence expressed itself in the furtherance of free-trade regulations, which greatly stimulated the export of such commodities as sugar, coconut, abaca, and lumber products, resulting in the rather widespread distribution of increased amounts of agricultural process-

ing, the growth of the apparel industries, and the expansion of the embroidery industries. American influence stimulated the real beginnings of the
mining industries and related economic operations. American influence was
also felt in such matters as the restriction on large landholdings and the
limitation of foreign corporate participation in certain activities, but it did not
do very much directly to stimulate Filipino entrepreneurial activity, and it did
little to restrict the strong position of the Chinese. Although there was a
steady increase in Filipino-controlled manufacturing enterprises, many of
them were small-scale operations, owing to the lack of strong capital investment, and they tended often to be related to the handicraft backgrounds in
which Filipinos had been participating. This latter relationship, particularly,
makes it difficult to unravel the early growth of industry, since early statistical
tabulations included all kinds of manufacturing establishments regardless of
their size, number of employees, volume of output, financial structure, or
product.[9]

With the beginning of the commonwealth period, in late 1935, there
began a new era of industrial development in the Philippines.[10] There was
recognition of the scarcity of Filipino-controlled capital resources and the
inability of private enterprise to initiate significant industrial undertakings
rapidly and on sufficient scales. One result was the establishment of government-owned corporations that set up industrial plants and initiated production in several kinds of operations.[11] Some of these government organizations
were primarily intended to sponsor and finance private industrial beginnings
or international trading operations, but others actually engaged in production
and trade; it was hoped that when the several industrial operations reached a
successful level of achievement, privately organized capital would take over
most of the government-initiated industries. Basic policy orientation was
toward private control, ownership, and operation of the machinery of industrialization, with government operating only as sponsor, initiator, and tariff
protector.

Another result of the commonwealth period was the gradual adjusting of
trade relationships and tariffs between the United States and the Philippines,
as these affected both the industrial operations pertaining to export products
and the operations relating to imported consumer goods and capital equipment; these relationships also affected the patterns of capital investment in
Philippine industry by American concerns.[12] New political and economic
agreements satisfactory to both sides were only slowly developed, and Philippine industrialization suffered from crosscurrents. Just prior to the outbreak
of World War II relative control of Philippine industry stood at approximately 40 percent in the hands of Filipinos, 30 percent in American hands,

and 25 percent in the hands of Chinese, although Spanish and Chinese interests in some portion of the total listed as Filipino probably prevailed. The total volume of capital investment in industrial facilities stood at only just over $200,000,000. The American participation lay largely in mining, public utilities and power development, and in agricultural-processing industries producing exports for the American market.[13] Chinese capital investments were strong in commercial phases of industry rather than in manufacturing as such. Much of the Filipino investment represented government participation, and few of the private Filipino concerns were large or highly capitalized.

World War II, of course, created havoc through the whole of the Philippine economy, and the reconstruction pattern was not able to fully carry out all policy lines previously laid down. War-damage funds, mainly from the United States, financed much of the immediate postwar rehabilitation, but the tendency of Filipinos to put such funds into consumer goods, commercial activities, and secondary speculation rather than into primary investment hindered rehabilitation, and the reluctance of the government to take the stringent economic steps necessary created a series of economic crises that significantly affected postwar industrialization.[14]

Philippine economic policy sets a high value on industrialization, particularly in the development of a strong manufacturing sector. It is committed to the development and maintenance of private entrepreneurship, although government funds are frequently employed in the creation of large government corporations that operate in what is normally considered a private sector of the economy. The formation of these corporations encourages the flow of private capital into those sectors of manufacturing in which it is reluctant to enter. Strong government protection has been afforded certain developing industries, through foreign import and exchange controls, through the recent decontrol of the Philippine peso, and through partial tax exemption for the so-called new and necessary industries. The policy of encouraging the growth of the manufacturing sector of Philippine economy has resulted in a very rapid expansion of those industries which can be termed import substitution.[15] Most rapid growth has occurred in the manufacture of food and beverages, clothing and footwear, cigarettes, pharmaceuticals, petroleum refining, and the assembly of appliances and transport equipment.

The average annual growth rate of the real national income through the 1950's, and especially since 1955, was approximately 7 percent. Value-added to the national income by manufacturing has risen at an annual rate of 14 percent. This high rate of growth in the manufacturing sector through the 1950's enabled industry to increase its share of national income from about 10 percent to 16 percent.[16] Unfortunately, the growth of Philippine private capital has been relatively slow; many wealthy Filipinos are reluctant to invest their capital in any enterprise other than land; and several areas of the nation's economic structure have not been developed, for example, the actual manufacture of most basic manufactured items required for assemblage. In other words, much of the present Philippine manufacturing is mere assemblage, and much of this does little more than place the sugarcoating on the pill. Among the better-developed segments of present Philippine manufacturing are the lumbering and plywood industries, mining and mineral processing, including the production of fertilizers and cement, food processing and beverages, the sugar-industries, and textiles. Government corporate firms have been particularly active in shipbuilding and ship repair yards; rolling mills; transportation, particularly rail; the development of hydroelectric power; and certain other quasi-public sectors. In all probability the government will remain dominant in these high-investment industries.

THE CONTEMPORARY MANUFACTURING INDUSTRY

The discussion of contemporary Philippine manufacturing is restricted by the data available. The *Philippine Statistical Survey of Manufactures* includes data on only those establishments employing five or more workers. It is organized by ten regional units, and generally follows the United Nations standard classification system. It provides some data on twenty major groups of manufacturing.[17] In applying the international system of manufacture classification to the Philippines, such items as the manufactures of abaca disappear into the category of textile manufactures, being only partially recoverable by subcategories of internal separation. Reporting suppresses data not considered effective and data that might reveal organizational identity, and it itemizes only certain kinds of totals. Appendix tables 30–34 supporting this section provide, therefore, only a partial tabulation of the annual returns for 1960. Comparable data for periods to 1955 do not exist, so longer-term trend patterns cannot be pinpointed.

The dominance of Manila and its urban region stands out very clearly in the data for number of establishments, total manufacturing employment, financial returns, and energy consumption (fig. 42). Generally, the region listed as metropolitan Manila accounted for approximately one-half of all reporting establishments and total manufacturing employment, slightly less than one-half of the total value-added by manufacturing, and slightly more than one-half of the total value of manufactured products in 1960. Furthermore, many of the establishments tabulated as being in the two adjacent regions of central Luzon and southern Luzon, are actually located not far beyond the limits of the Manila metropolitan area, and their addition to the

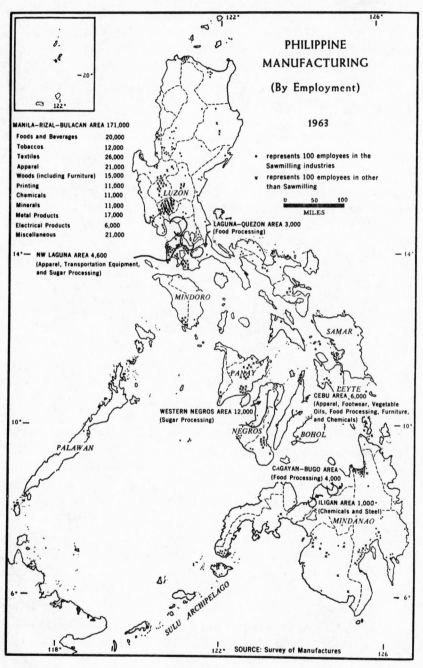

PHILIPPINE
MANUFACTURING

(By Employment)

1963

• represents 100 employees in the
   Sawmilling industries

× represents 100 employees in other
   than Sawmilling

MANILA–RIZAL–BULACAN AREA 171,000

Foods and Beverages	20,000
Tobaccos	12,000
Textiles	26,000
Apparel	21,000
Woods (including Furniture)	15,000
Printing	11,000
Chemicals	11,000
Minerals	11,000
Metal Products	17,000
Electrical Products	6,000
Miscellaneous	21,000

LAGUNA–QUEZON AREA 3,000
(Food Processing)

NW LAGUNA AREA 4,600
(Apparel, Transportation Equipment,
and Sugar Processing)

WESTERN NEGROS AREA 12,000
(Sugar Processing)

CEBU AREA 6,000
(Apparel, Footwear, Vegetable
Oils, Food Processing, Furniture,
and Chemicals)

CAGAYAN–BUGO AREA
(Food Processing) 4,000

ILIGAN AREA 1,000
(Chemicals and Steel)

SOURCE: Survey of Manufactures

Fig. 42.

Manila totals would make the dominance even more pronounced. One of the more noticeable shifts of manufacturing activity in the Philippines in very recent years has been the move from Manila to suburban Manila, and then to the area around suburban Manila in southern Luzon.

Beyond the central region, centering on Manila, the distribution of manufacturing is widely scattered over the Islands. Although the tabular data do not clearly distinguish it, important local concentrations of manufacturing occur around the larger established urban entities of Cebu and Davao, and perhaps a dozen or more lesser centers. Such a concentration has clearly taken shape around Iligan in northern Mindanao as a result of the partial developing of the hydroelectric power of the Maria Cristina Falls. It is in Iligan that the large, government-financed integrated steel mill is planned.

The great majority of municipio towns now have electric power available, and small manufacturing plants no longer classifiable as handicraft operations are springing up very widely as all elements of Philippine society pursue the goal of industrialization. Minor concentrations of manufacturing are developing at many regional centers throughout the Islands. Lumbering and plywood manufactures are widely distributed, as are various mineral industries, food processing, and textile industries. The Dole and Del Monte canning operations on Mindanao are important pioneering food-processing industries that employ thousands. The Mindanao Development Authority (MDA) and the Program Implementation Agency (PIA) are but two of the government divisions created to foster the development of Philippine industries.

The Manila metropolitan area, as defined in 1960, consists of the four cities of Manila proper, Pasay City, Quezon City, and Caloocan, and the four Rizal Province municipalities of Makati, Mandaluyong, Parañque, and San Juan del Monte.[18] Beyond this statistical unit there is a suburban fringe becoming increasingly urbanized and industrialized which is sometimes referred to as Greater Manila and which would add one or more of the municipalities of Malabon and Navotas on the north, Marikina on the east, and Pateros, Pasig, and Taguig on the southeast.[19] Considering the issue historically, the city originally consisted of the Intramuros (the walled city), with the port on the bay side and in the Pasig River mouth, and suburbs of the inland fringes. The extension of the city of Manila to its present limits, 14.3 square miles, included the port area and the original suburbs. The chartering of Pasay, Quezon, and Caloocan cities, have been added steps in the extension of the city as a functional urban unit.

Manila has been the chief entrepôt for domestic and international commerce. Both secondary and tertiary industries have tended to locate here.

Market-oriented manufacturing activities were also attracted by the large population of the city and its surrounding hinterland. Imported raw materials and machineries from abroad have attracted resource-oriented activities. Labor, market, transportation media, foreign capital, and initial impetus have all contributed to the continual growth and growing complexities of Manila's industrial infrastructure.

The development of manufacturing, and the location of industrial plants within Manila, has proceeded historically. Several generalizations can be stated about the distributional patterns of manufacturing within the Greater Manila region. Although many handicraft operations were carried on within the Intramuros in the earliest period, by the nineteenth century a great many of them had developed locational foci either in the port area or in suburbs on the inland side of the settlement. Shipping, warehousing, and wholesaling occupied the port area frontage along the bay and lined the Pasig River mouth. Within the Pasay area the tobacco-manufacturing operations became concentrated in small establishments in what originally was a suburban fringe. Food and apparel manufacturing developed small establishments in San Nicolas, Binondo, and Tondo, north of the Pasig River. In the early twentieth century different kinds of manufacturing establishments began replacing residential buildings in various sections of the city area. Generally, the small space requirements of many small factories and processing plants permitted them to locate well within the urban limits, whereas residential expansion continued on the fringes. The port area became more formalized, and its resident population declined. The bay section north of the Pasig River became the area reserved for domestic shipping, the North Harbor. South Harbor, south of the Pasig, became the sector utilized by foreign shipping, and the wholesaling, warehousing, and assembly activities continued their developing concentration in the port area. The Pasig River originally served a port function, but its shallowness has blighted its more recent development, and commercial functions have tended to crowd out shipping functions.

In more recent periods as large plant establishments became organized, only a few locations within Manila proper were open in effective size-units, but some replacement of residential housing has continued, most notably in the port area, and around the railroad terminals. The recent trends, therefore, have been for the larger plants to locate in the suburban fringes. The suburban municipalities consisted of concentrated poblaciones, scattered barrio nuclei, and open agricultural lands, so large industrial sites have lain chiefly in the open tracts between the older settlement sites. Light manufacturing and service industries have accumulated in and on the fringes of the old poblaciones, along primary roads, and in the various old barrio centers.

There is relatively little functional concentration in the development of industrial districts; instead there is a tendency for all kinds of industries to scatter into all suburbs according to criteria related to local transport, the availability of land, and various other temporary deterimants of site location.

In broad terms it may be said that the larger and more modern plants and the more recently developed industrial operations are located around the fringes of the industrial area, with older, more traditional, and smaller establishments located within Manila proper and within Pasay City. Quezon City was originally intended as the site for the national capital, public buildings, and residential quarters for civil servants, but much of the open land was available for industrial occupance and Quezon City now houses a significant share of the whole industrial function. The recent development of the port area correlates, of course, with the development of the suburbs because a section of the port area lies on land filled in on the bay side of the Intramuros. There is a tendency for such operations as printing and publishing to concentrate within the city, close to the consumer demand, or in lesser commercial subcenters in the larger area. There is continuing change as older residential localities give way to the inroads of commercial or manufacturing activities. The siting of new residential tracts, communities, and zones in the suburbs is somewhat competitive with the siting of industrial activities, as large open-land areas are needed by both. The result is a rather mixed residential, commercial, industrial urban complex in which all kinds of activities occur in all kinds of areas.

Philippine manufacturing industry still clearly shows its origins in agricultural processing and in the clothing industries. Food manufactures, and beverage, tobacco, and apparel products still account for a relatively large share of the value added by manufacture (about half the total in 1960); they also account for a large number of the industrial employees, and involve the largest number of manufacturing establishments. Although large plants are to be found in each of these divisions, a great many of the establishments still are small, low in capitalization, and low in the number of employees. Some of the manufacturing activity in agricultural processing is not closely related to large urban entities that are port cities or centers of other kinds of manufacturing. This is particularly notable with regard to sugar milling, coconut-product processing, and the rice-corn milling operations. Negros Island, for example, has considerable sugar-milling activity located in towns not otherwise notable for manufacturing, although there is a trend toward the eventual establishment of by-product manufacturing. Rice milling is found everywhere in rice-growing regions, and corn milling is scattered through the regions of primary corn production.

During the late nineteenth and early twentieth centuries the range of manufacturing increased steadily, and at independence the Philippines possessed a total manufacturing establishment of considerable breadth and depth, although the volume output in many lines amounted to much less than the annual consumption. Since independence a primary goal has been to increase the productivity and output in nondurable goods toward the annual consumption requirement; thus a considerable recent increase in establishments has occurred in lines already present. Many of these new plants have located in, around, or close to, the Manila metropolitan area. Textile manufacturing, apparel industries, rubber products, medical products, cosmetics, soaps, cleansers, and many of the metal fabrications and electrical manufactures fall into this group. Locations in or near Manila find skilled labor and power supplies available and wholesale distribution markets close at hand, as Manila is a major internal-trade distribution center.

Since independence industrial expansion has also spread into manufacturing lines not previously present or well-developed in the Islands. Veneer and plywood in the category of wood products, paper products and paper manufactures, refined petroleum products, iron and steel, and several of the metals products fall into this grouping, which represents new patterns of industrialization for the Philippines. The further development of many of these lines of activity is dependent upon the maturing of large-scale power-development projects, so their regional location will increasingly tend to correlate with power development. The new industrial region around Iligan, in northern Mindanao, is an example of this growth pattern, and the Iligan region may well become a center of heavy industry. In the wood and paper products line the factor that tends to influence location is raw material supply, rather than power supply, so industrial establishments are being developed in otherwise nonindustrialized localities.

The index of industrial activity is rising both steadily and rapidly, and manufacturing clearly is the most rapidly expanding segment of the Philippine economy at the present time. Between 1956 and 1960 the real increase in output of the manufacturing sector could be placed at approximately 12 percent per year. The index ratings for recent years are given in appendix table 33. From a position of accounting for less than 10 percent of the annual national income in 1948, manufacturing has risen steadily to a level approaching 16 percent of the total national income. But the process of Philippine industrialization is only fairly under way, in reality, and its contribution to the economy of the Islands can be expected to increase rapidly within the coming two decades as the country forcefully pursues the present program of expansion.

Foreign Commerce and Domestic Trade

The patterns of exchange of goods and commodities for the island realm of the Philippines show distinctive elements related both to the geographical regionalism of the Islands and to the political history of the realm. There is the concentration of foreign commerce and domestic trade at the port of Manila, the heavy role of interisland shipping in the gathering and distributing trade, the strong orientation toward an American market as regards exports and imports, and the entrenched role of Chinese wholesalers in all aspects of exchange. Historically there has been changing emphasis in this regional exchange pattern, an era of dominance by Spanish influences, a tremendous rise in the volume of commodity flow after the late nineteenth century, the rise of the American market, and the contemporary effort of Filipinos to gain control of Philippine trade movement and orientation of the markets. Foreign commerce is an aspect of total exchange which has both stimulated and ordered the patterns of domestic trade, as prior to the rise of foreign commerce the amount and kind of domestic trade was comparatively small.

THE BARTER BACKGROUND

As a geographic region located on the margin of the Asian continent, the Philippine Islands were both a convenient landfall for far-ranging mainland sea traders, and an excellent meeting ground for the traders from different seas and far trade realms.[20] The Sulu Archipelago was a fabled meeting center for these voyagers; such points in the Visayan zone as Cebu, Butuan, and Iloilo, and some ports in southern Mindoro were entrepôts; the Polillo Islands off southeastern Luzon were a frequented meeting ground; and numerous bays, harbors, and river mouths along western and northern Luzon formed landfalls or anchorages for numerous traders, and the towns behind them became seats of residence for foreign traders.

Barter-trade patterns between Filipinos and foreign visitors ranged through many groups of commodities and goods. Raw commodity items such as coral, pearls, shell, and gold; crop items such as coconuts, abaca, kapok, yams, and native fruits; such jungle extracts as rare woods, waxes, resins, rattans, and medicinals; and manufactures such at mattings, nettings, basketry, and textiles from several fibers formed an export series of commodities and goods. Raw products such as pigs of copper, bronze, and iron; and manufactures such as porcelains, utilitarian metal fabrications in copper, bronze, and iron, varied kinds of fine textiles, assorted lacquer goods, and ornamental goods such as glass objects, goldwork, and jewelry made up a broad category of imports. Entrepôt exchanges, in the in-transit sense, took place in spices, perfumeries, peppers, medicinals, and sundry exotics, and in manufactures of a regional or specialty nature.

Filipinos participated to a limited degree in the carrying trade, and were active in the entrepôt exchange of in-transit goods, but the chief traders and entrepreneurs were Chinese, Indonesians, Annamese, and Indians. The Japanese entered the regional trading pattern in the fifteenth century, chiefly frequenting ports in western and northern Luzon, and in the Polillo Islands. Moslem Indonesian traders were vigorously renewing and expanding their trade contacts in Sulu and the Visayan zone, and were reaching northward in the late fifteenth century. Undoubtedly there were favored islands and localities within the island realm, and entrepôts varied in importance, but it is notable that in the pre-Spanish era there was no archipelago-wide dominance over commerce by any one leading entrepôt or locality. Political patterns were territorially restricted to islands or small regions, although strong chiefs levied tribute upon regions and groups of lesser strength. Some militant raiding, privateering, or piracy appears to have been present, and slaves constituted one of the commodities of exchange.

Although the total population of the Philippines was small in pre-Spanish times, and although the majority of the population lived near island coasts, there was interregional trade between islands and also between coasts and island interiors. Many of the jungle products came out of the interiors, or from smaller hinterland islands, and many of the goods brought into the Philippines filtered out from the entrepôts and meeting grounds into these trade hinterlands in a thin trickle, constituting a pattern of domestic gathering of exports and distribution of imports.

When the Spanish arrived in the Philippines they found a variety of goods of interest to them moving in established patterns of commerce. Spanish political influence operated to abolish regional tribute levying, to attract traders to Spanish ports, and to initiate their own control over trade in those parts of the Islands over which they could establish military and political control. Spanish mercantilist theories of commerce substituted new kinds of monopoly controls, but the competitive position of the Spanish Philippines was unfavorable compared with that of Mexico, and early-period Spanish trade never expanded in line with its potential. The Manila Galleon Trade, repeated suppression of Chinese resident traders located at Manila, the first and second efforts to form a Royal Company of the Philippines (both ending in financial fiascos) were expressions of the urge to restrict monopoly of trade. During the early Spanish era the chief commodities in commerce were oriental manufactures brought into the Philippines, usually from the China mainland, for shipment to Mexico and Spain, and mostly paid for with silver dollars. Only a very small volume of exports consisted of products of Philippine origin, and the import of manufactured goods also was extremely small, so few of the benefits of commerce accrued to Filipinos. Liberalization in trading regulations came about only slowly during the nineteenth century, although non-Spanish European traders began to be admitted into Philippine ports just prior to 1800.

MODERN PATTERNS OF COMMERCE

During the late nineteenth century Spanish merchant trading with the Philippines increased markedly, but the significant motivation in the growth of Philippine commerce came from British and American merchant shippers engaged in the carrying trade, in the financing of foreign commerce, and in import-export businesses in their own right. The reluctance of the Spanish to finance Filipino participation in commerce, and the inherent inability of the Filipinos to do so, permitted the Chinese to increase their role in the total commercial operation. The significant element in the growth of late nineteenth-century commerce was the export of products of Philippine origin, giving to Filipino producers a source of purchasing power with which to buy for themselves an increasing range and volume of imported goods. By the end of the nineteenth century the basic structure of modern Philippine commerce had become established. Essentially, raw materials provided the exports and manufactured goods formed the imports. Agricultural commodities, abaca, sugar, tobacco, and coconut led the export list, followed by forest products, timber, sawn lumber, rattans, and gums-resins-extracts; a small range of manufactured goods formed small-volume export patterns.[21] On the import side, such manufactures as textiles and clothing, machinery, construction materials, transport equipment, and iron and steel products led the list, but food products such as rice, wheat flour, and fish products had a significant position in the import commerce (see appendix tables 35, 36).

Since the late nineteenth century the commerce of the Philippines has been subjected to a variety of influences affecting its volume, directional movement, composition, and balance. Just as the modern structure began to take shape the sovereignty of the country passed from Spanish to American hands, in late 1898.[22] The American initiation of commercial mining activity early in the twentieth century brought mineral products into the export list. The beginning of free trade within the American tariff boundary in 1909 made commerce with the United States dominant in the total Philippine pattern. World War I and the era of the Philippine Commonwealth had effects of minor importance. World War II, of course, seriously disturbed all aspects of Philippine foreign commerce, and the period of recovery was of some years duration. Philippine independence, in 1946, promised to alter the tariff structures and boundaries, but the readjustment in these patterns was arranged so as to be gradual, and the impact upon Philippine foreign commerce will be long-term in nature. The receipt by the Filipinos of a large volume of war-damage funds from the United States soon after independence, and the payment of Japanese reparations over a longer period, have been important elements in the total foreign-trade structure. Changing industrial technologies, and the appearance of new kinds of commodities, have affected the nature of Philippine commerce, and the changing consumer habits and economic aspirations of Filipinos have accompanied these technology-commodity shifts. The contemporary evolution of programs of national industrialization and economic development will prove to be strong factors influencing the foreign commerce in coming years.

The postindependence revision of tariff structures between the United States and the Philippines was designed to promote independent economic growth of the Philippines and the development of a broadly directed foreign commerce. It was to include the imposition of progressively higher American duties on Philippine exports to the United States and protective Philippine duties on United States exports to the Philippines. Such rate changes were to begin in 1956, as the base-date of operation, and to reach maturity in 1974, at which date no economic favoritism would remain in either direction; but provisions of the basic acts have been stayed by repeated legislation on both sides which continues the favored position of the Philippines in the American market. There is some question as to whether the Philippines really wishes to move outside the American tariff boundary, and whether Philippine tariff policy may contribute significantly to the accomplishment of Philippine objectives.[23] Directional movement, annual volumes, and commodity patterns in the total foreign commerce of the Philippines may well continue to reflect short-term changes in United States–Philippine tariff structures.

Until well into the nineteenth century Manila was, in theory, the only port through which foreign commerce could move legally, and Manila had the only operative customs office. In practice, Asian small-craft traffic continued a limited foreign commerce touching many parts of the Islands, as Spanish control could not be made absolute. The areas outside Spanish control continued old practices: the Sulu Archipelago remained a meeting ground for barter trading, and the Moslem trader-raider-pirate pattern continued in the southern islands. Customs offices were opened in Zamboanga in the early 1830's, in Cebu in the 1840's, in Iloilo in the 1850's, and in Legaspi and Tacloban in the 1870's; and foreign shipping was admitted reluctantly.[24] The port of Manila was opened to regular foreign commerce in 1834; it was already the leading port of the Islands in Spanish-operated foreign commerce. The concentration of Spanish shipping on Manila, the existing pattern of interisland trade, the stronger position of the Chinese at Manila than elsewhere, and the relatively better facilities at Manila than at outports all served to place the port of Manila in a dominant position in Philippine foreign commerce well before the end of the nineteenth century. Imports were chiefly handled by Spanish firms and shippers until the end of the nineteenth century, whereas foreign firms and shipping were permitted to participate in the export trade, both from Manila and from Cebu and Iloilo, during the late nineteenth century.

During the twentieth century numerous ports have been opened to foreign commerce, with periodic shifts in the list. Since World War II there have been a few changes in the list, and in the 1960's there were twelve ports of entry regularly open to foreign shipping.[25] The lack of good port facilities at most of these serves to continue the historical emphasis upon Manila as the focal point for Philippine foreign commerce. During the 1960's only the ports of Manila, Cebu, and Iloilo have carried on a significant pattern of cargo movement, and the programs of port construction continue to place Manila in a position so dominant there is little question that Manila will remain the chief port of the Philippines in respect to foreign commerce.

From a level of $833,000,000 in 1949, by which time a certain degree of normalcy had been restored following World War II, Philippine foreign trade had increased to $1,420,000,000 in 1962. Most of this expansion had taken place in the field of exports, a factor vital to the expanding Philippine economy because these exports have been the means for financing economic development. The United States has dominated Philippine foreign commerce, both before and after Philippine independence. The high point of American domination was reached immediately after the war (1946–1953), and since that time there has been a gradual, but steady, decline in the relative share of the United States. The greatest relative increases in the purchase of Philippine exports have occurred in the countries of northwest Europe, particularly Holland, Germany, and the United Kingdom (combined they took 16 percent of the exports in 1962), and in Japan, which alone received 24 percent in 1962. These same countries supplied 36 percent of the Philippine imports in the same year. The United States remains the single most important nation, both in exports (51 percent) and imports (43 percent), but its share is declining. It is clear that total volume will continue to grow and that although the United States will remain a dominant market for Philippine products and the dominant single supplier of Philippine imports, Philippine foreign commerce is, nevertheless, broadening in directional movement and range of commodity.

As the period of modern foreign commerce developed, the plant fiber abaca became the first export to achieve importance, and it led the list during the late nineteenth century. Movement of abaca into American markets for marine hawsers and other types of rope formed the first significant flow in the export trade toward the United States. Sugar exports increased steadily during the late nineteenth century, and the United States replaced China as the chief market. By the early twentieth century sugar was leading abaca as an export commodity. Coconut products did not become really significant export items until after the establishment of free trade with the United States in 1909. Coconut exports are normally summarized under several headings, but copra became a ranking export after the 1920's.[26] Tobacco held a ranking export position from the late eighteenth century into the twentieth century, but its volume export and value total did not keep pace with those of the newer exports. Various kinds of forest products were significant exports during the nineteenth century, but the export trade in logs, timber, and sawn lumber is a phenomenon of relatively recent decades.[27]

There are a number of export commodities that have become important in the total export trade during the twentieth century. Gold, silver, and copper, although old in mining history, have grown significantly in production during the present century. Gold, as a component of the export commerce of the Philippines, has varied in position according to government regulations controlling its disposition, and the smuggling of gold out of the islands has been important in the long-range trend. Iron ore, chromite, and manganese are relatively recent in the export list. Such items as embroideries, pearl-shell products, canned pineapple, fresh fruits, and the varied manufactures of rattan, abaca, and furniture are relatively recent as significant items in the total export trade, although pearl shell, rattan products, and abaca cloth were of historical trade significance. Several of the export products moving toward the American market have maximum quotas for duty-free entry, and this has served to limit both production and export.[28] Although processed and manufactured goods are appearing in the export pattern in increasing significance—for example, plywood, veneer, tinned foods, coffee and cacao preparations, rubber products, and textiles—the overall composition of Philippine exports remains chiefly unprocessed raw materials and semiprocessed products.

In the Philippine import trade in the nineteenth century, China held a leading position, as Chinese products had formed a goodly share of the traditional Philippine-Mexican-Spanish trade pattern. Close behind were other countries of the Orient, supplying speciality products for that traditional trade. In the development of modern trade patterns Spain first began supplying the Islands with manufactured products, but Great Britain rose rapidly to a position of chief supplier in the late nineteenth century. The transfer of sovereignty from Spain to the United States, and the development of the free-trade market, quickly brought the United States into the position of chief supplier of the Philippine market for manufactured goods—a position that nation has retained in the contemporary period, although Japan, Germany, and the United Kingdom are increasing their shares of Philippine imports. The import trade pattern has grown at about the same general rate as the export pattern, although there have been year-to-year variations in the balance between the two flow patterns.[29] The composition of the import trade has varied with the patterns of industrial technology and product manufactures; automotive products ranked low in the early decades, as did certain other manufactures. New commodity groups, such as electric refrigeration equipment and radios, have appeared in the list of Philippine imports quickly after their volume appearance on the American scene. This is to say that Philippine import patterns have kept pace with industrial technology and commodity production patterns, particularly in the American system.

Rising consumer demand, through growth of population and changing preferences for textiles and styles in dress, led to a strong development of textile imports in the early twentieth century.[30] The development of domestic textile-manufacturing in recent years has not yet caught up with consumer requirements, and textiles remain an important import. Similarly, leather imports showed significant increases during the twentieth century as preferences in footwear changed. Several other elements in the import pattern show these same relationships.

With the growth in import of manufactured goods has gone an increasing import volume in food products of mid-latitude variety and pattern of processing, reflecting both another kind of consumer change, and an undersupply of domestic foods. Wheat flour; tinned and dehydrated dairy products; tinned fish and meat products; condiment foods such as peanut butter, margarine, confections, and vitamin extracts; beverages such as the soft drinks, coffee, chocolate, and beer; drug and cosmetic items such as the toothpastes, lipsticks, and "wonder drugs" all occupy a strong position in the import trade. To a degree these imports reflect purchasing power, but in good part they also reflect changing aspirations and preferences among Filipino consumers.[31] The import of rice has been quite regular since the nineteenth century, although the total volume was small until 1962 and fluctuated inversely with the total domestic production in any given year. In 1965 a large quantity of rice, totaling more than 500,000 metric tons, was imported to meet anticipated shortages caused by adverse weather conditions and the failure of the rice acreage to expand in consonance with the rapidly expanding population. It appears that large rice imports will be a permanent item of Philippine import unless rice agriculture achieves a revolutionary improvement in production technology.

In many of the import commodity groups the establishment of branch production plants, or assembly plants, in the Philippines had led to a decline in particular imports over the decades; but newer items have often taken the place of older ones, and there is a cyclic element to the rise and decline of specific imports. In 1953, finished textiles were the number one import; in 1962 they had fallen to eighth. In general terms the development of Philippine manufacturing has not, until recently, kept pace with rising consumer demand for manufactured goods, so the import total has slowly continued to rise, fluctuating with the political climate. In certain specific products the development of domestic manufacturing capacity has cut off the direct import trade and will continue to do so. Involved with this whole import structure, of course, is Philippine economic policy with regard to exchange control, import control, tariff control, and the program of industrialization within the Islands. Such policy aims at import substitution, that is to say, making domestic manufacturing able to satisfy domestic demand in an increasing range of consumer goods and semi–consumer goods. To the degree that Philippine policy is able to achieve its ends, the import trade will strike a balance in many commodity groups; however, changing industrial technology, changing commodity manufacture, and changing consumer demand will serve to provide a large import market in the foreseeable future. The long-range trend in imports is a gradual shift from consumer goods to producer goods.

In the long-range trend of modern foreign commerce the position of the United States is a dominant one. Economic policy controlling commerce shifted from one of Spanish restriction and monopoly to one of American theoretical free trade and nonrestriction. The workings of the American system, however, were such as to direct the great majority of Philippine exports into the American market. Producers of some products found it more convenient to structure production to American duty-free quotas than to seek international markets or compete on over-quota competitive pricing. In practice, Philippine imports tended to derive from the American source, abetted by growing Filipino familiarity with American products and by American entrepreneuring and merchandising in the Philippines. Although other suppliers of the Philippine market maintained such markets, their increases were not proportionate to the increase in total imports. The relative scarcity of Filipino entrepreneurs and shippers in foreign trade worked against the broad development of non-American markets. By the onset of World War II Philippine commerce was tied to the United States almost as tightly as a smaller commerce had been tied to Spanish control in the earlier period. Postwar policy has been directed toward the establishment of a broader Philippine market for exports and the cultivation of other suppliers for imports, as well as the development of domestic manufacturing capacity for the home supply of many imports.[32] The breaking of a near-traditional and entrenched pattern of foreign commerce, however, will be both difficult and slow. Despite the increased trade with Japan, Indonesia, Australia, Great Britain, and several other countries, it is likely that much of the foreign commerce of the Philippines will continue to be with the United States.

DOMESTIC AND INTERISLAND TRADE

Although the patterns of domestic trade for an area such as the Philippines in which population has grown steadily, show features normal to any diverse regional assemblage, the lines of movement in an island realm such as the Philippines are very different from those in regional assemblages consisting of contiguous land areas. On the one hand, regions of surplus production in food supplies move those surpluses to deficit regions in quite normal sequences; specialty products flow from source regions to consuming regions in regular manner; export commodities move from production centers to points of export in usual systems. On the other hand, in the island world of the Philippines, the lines of movement of all forms of domestic exchange assume patterns directly related to the basic disposition of the more than 1,100 inhabited islands scattered over a large total land-sea area. In this internal flow of domestic exchange two distinct but complementary elements are operative. There is the island coast–island interior set of movements which is unique to the particular Philippine situation, but in which there is a somewhat similar repetition of the basic pattern from island to island, in descending complexity from large to small islands. Complementing this system of flow is an interisland set of movements which also is unique to the particular placement of islands in the archipelago, but which has developed historically in a pattern determined by political arrangement and growth of population. The first aspect, coast-interior, is an automatic consequence of islands being inhabited; this movement of trade is inevitable, in a sense, although its particular volume, composition, direction, and method of movement depends upon the size and nature of the island, its population, and its economic development. The complementary phase of trade, interisland movement, is also automatic in an island world, but had the Spanish made Davao, in southeast Mindanao, their political, military, and commercial center the patterns of interisland trade flow would be very different from what they are today. The importance of Cebu in interisland trade movements derives in no small part from the location there of the first Spanish base of operations, and from its continuing early importance to the Spanish, although its central location with respect to the rest of the archipelago also was of considerable significance. Had free-trade concepts, rather than mercantilist concepts, dominated early Spanish thinking, Manila would never have achieved its early dominance; the whole historical development of cities and ports would have been different; and the patterns of interisland trade flow would today have a very different shape in complementing the coast-interior flow of trade.

Such speculative theory on internal development and flow of trade for an area such as the Philippines can postulate several different historical sequences of development, but the Spanish did make Manila their central base of operations almost to the exclusion of the development of other centers, so the discussion must relate to the historical pattern. As a center of commerce Manila grew on the basis of foreign trade; internal trade and the associated flow patterns were consequently matters of secondary importance. Spain never controlled the whole of the archipelago, and settlement history, economic development, and the resulting internal trade reflect this fact. Much of the system of interisland movement long preceded the Spanish, and as mentioned previously, in pre-Spanish times there was no dominant trade center. On the other hand, the Spanish influence made for more inland settlement patterns, as opposed to the dominance of coastal, littoral settlement patterns of the pre-Spanish era, so the long-term influence has been one of increasing coast-interior patterns of movement. The prevalence of islands lacking internal waterways is significant in this coast-interior movement system.

In an archipelago such as the Philippines, therefore, domestic trade and its patterns of movement take shape in a manner related both to the insular situation and to the historical sequence of development. In this circumstance, water transportation will always be more significant than land transport; the operations of trade will always involve centering of economic activity in settlements that are more frequently ports than centers of land transport; and the economics of trade will reflect the development of, or the absence of, a dominant center of interisland trade. As the Spanish did develop Manila into a dominant central port and center of financial control, the patterns of physical movement of trade, and the economics of trade, center on the Manila metropolitan region.

In early Spanish times domestic trade continued on a traditional basis of very small volumes of local exchange and coast-interior exchange. The only significant development was the beginning of the movement of local surpluses from regions around Manila into the urban area; these included food supplies, fuels, construction materials, and ship-building materials. During middle Spanish times this movement increased steadily, if slowly, and small amounts of export materials were drawn into Manila. During the early period the Spanish did almost nothing to develop either land transport or interisland shipping. During the middle period a little Spanish shipping began circulating between Manila and the Visayan Islands. The development of modern patterns of trade and trade movement was a product of the breakdown of Spanish monopoly control during the nineteenth century. This involved opening of Philippine ports to foreign commerce, the growth of interisland shipping, the beginning development of inland transport, the growth and shift of population, the appearance of deficit regions in food supplies, and the development of agricultural surpluses both in food supplies and in commodities available as export products. The opening of ports to foreign trade, however, was not accompanied by any program of port development as such, except for the development of facilities at Manila. By the end of the nineteenth century, except for the island of Mindanao, the basic structure of domestic trade, its regional centering, and its patterns of movement had significantly taken shape. As Elliott puts it: [33]

> The natives carried on their small interisland trade by means of primitive sailing crafts and the Spaniards sent their crazy little steamers wandering in and out among the islands, picking up the products of the country as opportunity offered and carrying them to Manila, Cebu, and Iloilo, where they were turned over to the exporting houses. Neither the ships nor their methods of doing business were subject to any form of effective government inspection or control.

The developments of the twentieth century have been steady in terms of the growth of facilities for movement of goods, both on land and water, the growth and shift of population, the development of Mindanao and other lightly populated islands and regions, the accentuated development of deficit regions and regions of production surpluses, and the continued dominance of Manila as the focal center of both domestic trade and foreign commerce.[34]

Modern domestic trading operations have grown out of a barter background that has not entirely been replaced at the local sitio and barrio levels, on small islands distant from market centers, or among some of the pagan ethnic groups. Until very late in the nineteenth century only a few Filipinos had accumulated financial resources of a kind that could be applied to nonbarter, commercial trading operations. As the modern pattern of commerce and trade took shape Filipinos took relatively little part in it, but Chinese took advantage of their previous connections with Spanish commercial operations to enter the wholesale trade and to become middlemen operating at the ports and other points of breakage in trade movements. Developing interconnections with foreign firms, chiefly at Manila, Chinese family firms came to dominate much of domestic trade. They financed purchases of commodities moving toward the export market often at the first-stage level of wholesaling and gathering, and in turn, financed and handled the distribution of imported goods moving out of Manila into the regional trade hinterlands through the last-stage wholesale distribution points. Chinese commercial establishments scattered out over the Islands, locating their terminal agencies in poblacion centers in most towns throughout the Islands.[35] On the gathering end, moving local surpluses toward markets or wholesale centers often involved purchases from primary producers. On the distributing end, Chinese wholesalers sold to, and often financed, Filipino retailers who operated small *sari-sari* stores, shops, market stalls, dressmaking establishments, and other kinds of operations. Chinese often engaged in retail business while operating wholesaling activities in poblacion centers.

In areas of high-tenancy ratios some of the trading operations have taken the form of crop sharing, payments in kind, financial loans to be repaid by deliveries of crops, and other types of arrangements that permitted landlords to function almost as wholesale gatherers of trade products. In areas where labor shortages develop in agricultural operations there still are active systems by which agricultural labor is paid with a share of the crop, thus serving to distribute commodities on the local regional level. Many such variations in these patterns throughout the Islands maintain old elements of barter-exchange at the present time.

Within recent decades there has been an increasing development of Filipino entrepreneurship in foreign commerce and in domestic trade. Corporate structures at the upper levels, and family concerns at the lower levels, have taken an increasing role in both the gathering trade and the wholesale distributional trade patterns. The trends toward national economic development are increasing these developments steadily, and both the variety and the volume of commercial trading operations is increasing, reaching further into hinterlands formerly carrying on only barter-exchange.

The spread of population through overcrowding of long-settled regions has increased both the range and the volume of domestic trade. The earlier migrants to undeveloped lands and relatively empty regions produced few surpluses, but as agricultural landscapes have developed, surpluses of primary products have created outward flows of food and commercial products, to be paired with inward flows of consumer goods. Mindanao particularly demonstrates this, although the trend is widely operative today. Accompanying this development of new trade regions has been the growth of trade development in long-settled regions and the continued growth of the Manila metropolitan region. Such areas, of course, take increasing volumes of imported or domestic manufactures, but they also form food-deficit areas toward which large volumes of food surpluses regularly move in interisland trade.

The Manila metropolitan region lies at the center of domestic trading operations, in terms of physical movements, commercial organization, financial structuring, and as a primary market. Historically, as domestic trade has grown Manila has maintained its pattern of dominance in all respects, so that in the hierarchy of trade regions and trade centers, Manila stands out as the national center. Manila leads as a market for regional surpluses, whether for domestic consumption or for export. As the point of arrival for imports from abroad, Manila is completely dominant, functioning as the primary break point in wholesale distribution. In this respect Manila dominates the whole of Luzon, Mindoro, Palawan, and the associated lesser islands, and ranks as the only strong interregional center for the northern part of the archipelago.

Cebu stands as the second-ranking trade center of the Philippines. Considerable foreign export movement in abaca and sugar passes through Cebu, and Cebu is a major port of export for copra. But Cebu operates chiefly as an interregional center in the gathering and distribution of domestic trade products. Large volumes of corn and smaller volumes of rice, livestock, fish, fruits, and vegetables move through Cebu to a consuming population on Cebu Island. Cebu serves as a major point of distribution for manufactured goods moving to lesser centers within the trade hinterlands. Cebu is a major point of passenger movement, both by ship and by air. Its hinterland includes the eastern Visayan Islands and about the northern half of Mindanao. Its position on the interisland shipping lanes, and on the interisland air lanes, facilitates this role.

Iloilo serves as an interregional trade center for the western Visayan Islands, but its hinterland is a small one, being cut off on the north and west by Manila and on the east and south by Cebu. Formerly an important port in foreign commerce, Iloilo retains a role in the export of sugar and its products, but Iloilo serves today chiefly as an interregional center in domestic trade, gathering and shipping rice and corn, and distributing manufactured consumer goods.

Davao is the fourth-ranking center of interisland trade and is a growing center for southeastern Mindanao. Relatively recent in development, and restricted in hinterland, Davao serves primarily as the gathering point for regional surpluses of corn moving to Cebu, Negros, and the Manila area, and for abaca moving toward foreign markets. The growth of Davao since 1935 has been notable, but in the 1960's the city entered into a new burst of growth that will be reflected in its larger role in interisland trade.

Zamboanga serves a partial role as an interregional trade center, owing primarily to its position on interisland shipping lanes. An old port, it serves as a regional center for inbound rice shipments and for outbound copra and fish, as well as smaller volumes of timber, abaca, and fruit products.

Within the regional hinterlands of these five major interregional trade centers are developed a series of lesser trade centers and transport orbits for the movement of domestic trade.[36] Within Luzon, north of Manila, these trade regions are divided between landlocked trade regions centering upon a city that functions as a land-transport center and trade regions fronting on a coast and centering on a port city. Elsewhere in the Islands, to date, all these lesser trade regions are areas fronting on a coast, centering on a port or ports, and consisting of area units that extend toward the interior of an island. Even Mindanao still shows in the 1960's this orientation to the coastal port, but as the population of the large island builds up, the growth of interior trade regions is certain to take place. This predominant orientation of trade regions toward coastal port centers reflects the physical nature of the island world, but it also reflects the fact that water transportation systems were more easily arranged to serve even large islands than were internal systems of land transport. Road development on such islands as Bohol, Cebu, Negros, Panay, and Mindoro tended to follow the coasts, and even that on Mindanao did the same at the earlier stages. Such road systems operated as feeder systems connecting ports to coastal regions of the hinterlands, with first trails and later feeder roads penetrating into interior hinterlands. (See figs. 39, 40.)

Within Luzon, chiefly north of Manila, the comparatively early development of the road systems, and the building of the Manila Railway, tended to develop landed trade regions centered upon towns and cities serving as land-transport centers. As the interior population densities built up in the Central Plain of Luzon and in southwestern Luzon, the agricultural productivity of the landscape yielded surpluses of products and provided markets for manufactured goods similar to those patterns of other landed regions. The development of the Cagayan Valley in more recent time has shown the same trend, and in a lesser way the economic orientation toward trade is developing in the North Luzon Highlands. In this whole zone the growth and structuring of trade regions is related to the major physical lineaments of the country and to the transport network that has evolved. From the Central Plain there is a strong southward movement of rice from the country zones into the cities, and from the cities toward the Manila metropolitan region, with smaller surpluses of other products following in the wake of the rice trade. Outward, by rail and by road, flows the whole range of manufactured commodities. The Cagayan Valley, as a producer of large surplus volumes of rice and corn, with lesser volumes of tobacco and other agricultural products, does not have a good water-transport situation, and has developed chiefly a road-transport connection with central Luzon, terminating in the Manila region.

Although the road systems of the large islands are incomplete as yet, and although the national and municipal ports throughout the archipelago present only minimal port facilities, the systems of trade movement that have developed within the island region serve rather effectively to move local and regional surpluses to deficit regions and points of export. Similarly these systems distribute manufactured goods and food supplies throughout the Islands and to the several deficit regions rather effectively. In addition to the movement of commodities, the transport systems move a surprisingly large passenger traffic, the air services considerably augmenting water and road facilities. It is true that facilities of transport into the hinterlands, into interiors of larger islands, and to smaller islands are not yet really effective. Transportation of export items from hinterland barrios to export points, and of imported or Manila-manufactured commodities from import points to those same barrios, is still relatively expensive and somewhat inefficient at several points. Since World War II, however, there has been a steady increase in the evolution of the physical elements of transport, correlated with a tremendous increase in the economic organization and structuring of trade, which does permit an archipelago-wide flow of agricultural products, nonagricultural raw materials, domestic manufactured goods, and imported products, so that Filipinos everywhere now have regionally available to them both markets and consumer goods.

The Philippines presents the picture of a relatively small but distinctive island world in which a small population has grown into a significant population while altering its cultural orientation twice in rather marked patterns of change. Although the growth in population is a matter common to other regional areas, the relatively peaceful aspect of culture change characterizing the Philippines forms a notable instance in world historical development.

The pre-Spanish Philippines held a relatively small population with somewhat diverse levels of cultural development, but all of these were of relatively simple organizational development in almost every respect. The population was oriented chiefly to a littoral environment in which a marine economy was complemented by a land economy in multiple locality-structurings centered on individual islands. Village settlement, tribal and confederacy political organization, and basic subsistence economies complemented by restricted barter-exchange patterns characterized the whole region. Contrasting elements were smaller groups of even simpler cultures that were not yet fully agricultural or sedentary in even the simple sense. An orientation toward the Malaysian world of southeast Asia provided the primary motifs to culture systems. Although certain elements in this overall pattern were very old, much of the population resident along the littoral had arrived relatively recently, and many groups were still finding their preferred regional situations and localized living systems. Penetrations northward, and toward island interiors, had not taken the Malaysians everywhere in the Philippine world by A.D. 1400, and groups of Negrito or proto-Malaysians were widely scattered. Chinese and Malaysian trade contacts with particular island localities were operative but involved little permanent accretion by settlement.

In the fifteenth century new peoples came into the Sulu Islands bringing new elements of culture; they were the Moslem Borneans and other peoples from the Malaysian and Indian worlds. These movements brought militancy, new political structuring, a new religion, and new elements of economic organization which rapidly flowed northward as far as Manila and which took over island hegemony in the far south. Changes were beginning to take place which could have been far-reaching had they been allowed time for absorption; that the new elements were quickly followed by still another pattern of new introductions cut off this possibility of cultural expansion.

The Spanish arrived in the Visayan Islands sector of the Philippines in the sixteenth century as the bearers of a quite alien set of culture patterns. Their relatively rapid achievement of hegemony over Luzon and the Visayan Islands came without actual militant conquest, although considerable militancy developed between the Christian Spanish and the Moslem Borneans and Indonesians which set up a long-standing dichotomy in island life that was shared by the native populations of both sectors. The Spanish orientation was toward land-living and sedentary, village-dwelling, agricultural life in which the population gathered into church-centered settlements. Changes came gradually but peacefully to the coastal zones, the smaller islands, some islands of linear shape (such as Cebu), and the zones of broad lowlands. The Spanish did not succeed with the peoples of mountainous interiors on the rougher islands or on those with large upland interiors, such as northern Luzon, Mindoro, and Palawan, but they did prevent the further ingress of Moslem Bornean culture patterns beyond Sulu and the fringe of Mindanao. The interior of Mindanao, the second largest island in the archipelago, remained a relatively empty buffer zone between the Moslem and Christian fringes of littoral occupance until well into the late nineteenth century.

Under the Spanish, the population of the Islands grew steadily, and a quiet but effective Hispanization of Malaysian peoples took place, producing a village- and town-dwelling, Roman Catholic, agrarian population carrying on an archipelago-contained economy. By agricultural occupance the population spread out over the areas of easy access from those island littorals along which pre-Spanish settlement had provided nuclei; land-based populations created farmscapes, hamlets, villages, and towns over considerable areas in the Philippines by the late nineteenth century. By 1900, however, the seven million Filipinos had by no means taken over all available arable lands, and many islands and local regions were still almost empty. This domestic agrarian pattern was but little affected by the Spanish-Chinese international trade program characterized historically as the Manila Galleon Trade, but the Spanish permitted no alternative in areas under their control. The Moslem south, under the patterns of local rulers, both heckled the northern Christian sector and carried on its traditional marine economy complemented by patterns of interregional raiding-trading. The Spanish disinclination and inability to develop a progressive internal Philippine economy in the face of growing pressures from outside traders, commercial influences, and maturing Filipino cultural patterns had, by the late nineteenth century, produced strains in Spanish control of the Islands. This culminated in the somewhat accidental American takeover of political control in the Philippines in 1898.

American systems of political, social, and economic government peacefully introduced new and far-reaching changes into Philippine living patterns which stimulated the expansion of a land economy to the extent that the Filipinos quickly became volume exporters of a few products and importers of a wide range of manufactured products, consumer habits, and culture customs. The growth of domestic political democracy blended traditional Malaysian, Spanish, Hispanicized, and American institutional elements into a new and distinctive system that now functions as a national system, despite some internal imbalances and incompatibilities. The growth of such social institutions as the American-oriented educational system added English to the multilingual system as a lingua franca, making possible the further growth of an updated national culture well oriented toward the modern world in many respects but also distinctly American-oriented. The growth of a commercial economy created some new developments in agriculture while leaving other aspects changed but little from the level of Spanish local subsistence systems, and it created an internal imbalance that persists in contemporary economy patterns. The growth of land-transport systems facilitated the continued spread of agricultural settlement into island interiors, and the growth of water-transport systems has tied the island world together into one operative unit centered on Manila. The preservation of economic institutions derived from the Malaysian cultural tradition, first Hispanicized and then Americanized, facilitated growth and development of a modern Philippine economy while also heightening internal pressures in such problem zones as agrarian tenancy, capital control, political structure, and social custom.

With political, social, and economic independence the modern Philippines has resisted the pressures that would change the country into a social-ized state in political, economic, and social terms, and the national interest now is centered upon processes and procedures of industrialization, modernization, and national economic independence from the former too-close relationships with either Spain or the United States. The internal development of resources, both of natural resources and of capital and technology, is directed toward the improvement of the Filipino level of living, the articulation of the Philippine national state, and the preservation of individual initiative and private ownership so far as these can be developed in a small state in the twentieth century. The dichotomy of the earlier Moslem Bornean–Christian Malaysian orientations has been bridged in the main; Mindanao is rapidly filling up with migrants from too-heavily populated parts of other Christian sectors of the Islands; and distribution of the more than thirty million Filipinos is showing evidence of "evening-out" through occupance of the hitherto empty zones, and by the growth of urbanism in many parts of the island realm.

There remain numerous large imbalances in Philippine living systems, production systems, culture systems, and subregional systems. Small groups of Negrito and proto-Malaysian peoples still live by ancient economic systems, whereas many residents of cities live by strictly contemporary, cosmopolitan systems. Although a technological revolution is bringing industrialization to cities typical of the twentieth-century world, rural agriculture at large has not effectively participated in the agricultural revolution occurring in some parts of the world; thus, the basic economy of the Islands remains seriously handicapped. Philippine economic life is still tied rather too closely to the American realm, but it may remain so through economic choice, despite the urge to independence. Despite these and other imbalances the Philippines has grown into a regional entity in which distinctive man-land and culture-environment relationships obtain in almost all aspects. The Philippines today constitutes a viable geographic region in which Filipinos can look forward to progressive development in the future with excellent prospects, although there will be serious problems to be solved in the near future if an upward spiral of economic and social growth is to be shared effectively by the whole population.

PART THREE

The Regional Environments

NINE

The North Country: Northern Luzon and Beyond

An Introduction to Philippine Regions

Among large archipelagos of the world, the Philippine Islands are unusual in that they constitute a single political unit. The several large islands and thousands of small islands of the Philippines, which extend over 17 degrees of latitude and 10 degrees of longitude, are essentially an integrated culture and economy; however, this integration is by no means complete, and the variants give rise to diverse regional landscapes. *The keynote of Philippine geography is diversity.*

The very insular character of the Philippines lends itself to the development of considerable regional diversity. In a very real sense, each island constitutes an individual region—an impractical regionality, it might be pointed out, for by latest count there are 2,773 named and 4,327 unnamed islands in the archipelago.[1] Furthermore, each of the larger islands contains many contrasting landscape types. The four major lowlands of the archipelago—the Central Plain and Cagayan River Valley of Luzon, and the Agusan and Cotabato river valleys of Mindanao—have each developed their own occupance patterns, as has each of the several hundred lesser lowland areas scattered throughout the archipelago. And these lowland areas contrast sharply with the adjacent high mountain areas, such as the Central and Eastern Cordillera and the Zambales Mountains of Luzon, the highlands occupying the interiors of most of the larger islands, and the high complex mountain systems of Mindanao. Additional topographic diversity is contributed by the presence of several extensive plateau lands, such as the Bukidnon-Lanao Plateau in north central Mindanao.

Diversities in the physical environment, however, do not end with the regional differences of physiography. Climatic differences also have regional expression, as annual precipitation ranges from a low of only 35 inches in the northern Cagayan Valley, to over 200 inches along certain exposed eastern littorals. Climatic variety is further heightened by the different regimes of precipitation and drought experienced in various sections of the Philippines. In general, western and central sections of the archipelago receive strong summer precipitation maximums, whereas areas in the east are exposed to northeastern air movements and receive their maximum precipitation during the low-sun period. Much of the southern Philippines experiences a relatively even distribution of rainfall. Periods of drought vary both in duration and severity from one locale to another. The typhoons, or tropical cyclones, so important to Philippine climatology do not strike all areas equally.

Soils and vegetation, as they are in large part reflections of climate, relief, elevation, slope, and parent-rock material, are also very diverse. A bewildering mélange of soils occurs throughout the Philippines, and soils range from the relatively fertile, derived from certain volcanic and alluvially deposited parent materials, to the relatively infertile, if not sterile, soils developed on hard metamorphic rocks. Vegetational associations range from the tall, dense stands of dipterocarp climax monsoonal forests, such as those found in northern Negros and in many parts of Luzon and Mindanao, through the sparser noncommercial forest growths and highland pine forests of Mountain Province, to the extensive grasslands found on many of the islands.

These important variants in the Philippine physical environment are matched by equally diverse elements in the cultural setting. In spite of the recognition of a Filipino ethnic type, there is considerable ethnic diversity among Filipinos. In general, the earliest immigrants to the Philippines, the Negritos and proto-Indonesian groups, today occupy the more inaccessible interior regions into which they have retreated under pressure from later arrivals. Peoples of Malayan ethnic stocks occupy the lowlands, but even within this relatively homogeneous group there are major cultural differences, based upon religion, language or dialect, economy, and varying degrees of acculturation. The strong Moslem orientation of the population of the southwestern corner of the archipelago has created a major stream of cultural divergence. The varying degrees to which the various regions of the Philippines were exposed to Spanish culture also has resulted in different cultural environments. Generally the Spanish influence was greatest in the Manila area, in the Bicol Peninsula, on the Ilocos coast, and on the islands of Cebu, Negros, and Panay; it was negligible in the areas of predominantly Moslem occupance—Cotabato, Sulu, Lanao del Sur, and Zamboanga del Sur—and among the pagan groups of Mountain Province, the Cagayan Valley, Mindoro, and Palawan. Basic to much of the internal cultural diversity is the presence of some seventy-six major and minor ethnolinguistic groups in the Philippines. Although generally Malayan in origin, these dialects are frequently not mutually understandable. Thus, on many of the larger islands the people living on one side cannot communicate with those on the other side, except through the medium of English.

The population of the Philippines is very unevenly distributed.[2] The densest settlement area is in metropolitan Manila and the surrounding strongly urbanized province of Rizal. The latter province had an average density of 2,028 persons per square mile in 1960.[3] Intermediate densities are encountered on the Central Plain of Luzon and on the Visayan islands of Cebu, Negros, Panay, and Leyte. At the opposite end of the demographic scale are the relatively empty lands of Palawan, with 28 persons per square mile in 1960; Occidental Mindoro with 37; and Bukidnon and Agusan in Mindanao with about 60 persons per square mile. Even small islands show diverse densities. Many small littoral islets hold high densities, whereas hundreds of islands are totally uninhabited.

The physical and cultural environmental differences in the Philippines are sufficiently strong that a marked regionality has developed in the economy. Commercial agriculture vies with subsistence agriculture; food crops complete with nonfood crops; and regions of agricultural sufficiency, or surplus production, contrast with deficit regions. Modern scientific agricultural techniques are applied alongside techniques that have been used for centuries. Large landholdings and high land-tenancy conditions may exist in one area, such as in the provinces on the Central Plain of Luzon, whereas in Mountain Province and on the islands of Palawan and Mindanao most farmers own the lands they are farming. In the socioeconomic sense, the mature landscapes of the Central Plain, Ilocos coast, and Bicol areas stand in sharp contrast to the pioneer-like occupance patterns characteristic of the Cagayan Valley and interior and southern Mindanao. Perhaps nothing heightens regional economic differences more than the unevenness of distribution of the facilities for land transport. As a nation, the Philippines has an overall road density that approximates the average road density for the world as a whole;[4] however, the densities of these facilities vary considerably through the archipelago. Whereas the road mileages of the provinces on the Central Plain of Luzon reach a density only slightly less than that of the United

States average, the road networks on Palawan and in many parts of Mindanao, particularly in the provinces of Agusan, Cotabato, and Zamboanga del Sur, are practically nonexistent.

The extreme diversity of the Philippine landscape permeates the whole fabric of land and society, and is so distinctive that it calls for regional analysis—analyses of smaller, relatively homogeneous units that will facilitate a more detailed understanding of the many aspects of Philippine geography.

A simple, but distinct, regionality in the Philippine landscapes is very apparent to those with only a cursory knowledge of the Philippines. These "macroregions" are perhaps more sensual than definable. The larger islands, isolated as they are from one another, contribute the basic regional character of the archipelago. Luzon, Mindanao, the Visayan Islands, and Mindoro and Palawan, and their island festoons, provide the basic regional framework. Yet each of these major units possesses as much, or more, diversity within itself than is to be found in comparison with the other macroregions. Any attempts toward developing quantitative criteria for delimiting the more obvious Philippine regions, that is to say regions possessing significant individualism sufficient to warrant separate regional status, is a task fraught with difficulty, one that usually ends in the use of a multiplicity of criteria, and one that is quite beyond the purposes of this study. There are Philippine regionalizations that can be based upon physiography, climate, agriculture, ethnic, or linguistic homogeneities, to mention but a few. It is not our purpose to propose an ultimate regional subdivision of the Philippines, nor is the subdivision of the Philippines necessarily a desired end product. Our purpose is rather to recognize certain basic differences that have areal expression and to use these differences to gain a deeper understanding of the geography of the Philippines.

In keeping with this objective, a regional subdivision of the Philippines into twenty-three distinctive units is utilized (fig. 43). The criteria for these regions, and their boundaries, vary considerably and usually depend upon the character of the individual region. The small Batan and Babuyan islands off northern Luzon constitute a first region. The large island of Luzon is subdivided into eight major regions with a ninth representing the urban sprawl of metropolitan Manila. The Visayan Islands are grouped into four regions. The islands of Mindoro and Palawan are each treated separately and apart from either Luzon or the Visayas. The southern Philippines are divided into six regions on the island of Mindanao, with a seventh comprising the Sulu Archipelago (table 4).

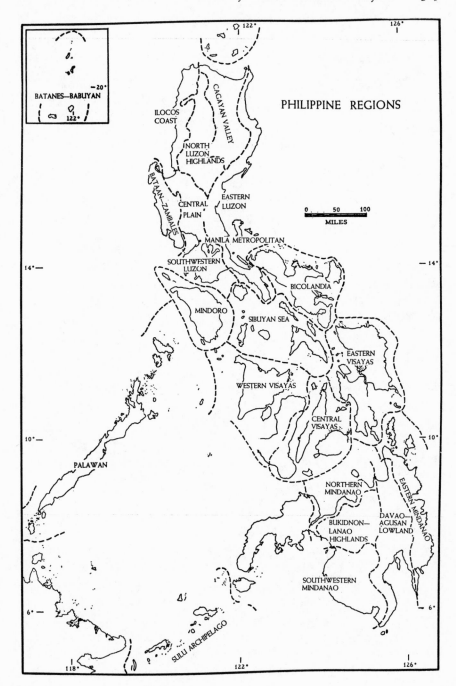

Fig. 43. Regional system employed in this volume.

Table 4   PHILIPPINE REGIONS

Region	Area (in sq. mi.)	Crude population density	1960 population
Batan-Babuyan	312	513	16,000
Cagayan Valley	5,500	175	961,000
Ilocos coast	3,600	282	1,016,000
North Luzon Highlands	6,200	86	533,000
Bataan-Zambales	2,900	176	515,000
Central Plain	5,900	536	3,165,000
Metropolitan Manila	800	3,243	2,595,000
Southwest Luzon	2,500	696	1,741,000
East Luzon	5,600	74	415,000
Bicol Peninsula	5,400	380	2,055,000
Mindoro	3,900	80	313,000
Palawan	5,700	28	162,000
Sibuyan Sea	2,450	238	582,000
East Visayas	8,400	243	2,041,000
Central Visayas	5,880	461	2,713,000
West Visayas	7,350	393	2,887,000
North Mindanao	2,850	306	873,000
East Mindanao	4,600	97	444,000
Davao-Agusan	10,100	107	1,079,000
Bukidnon-Lanao	5,000	119	595,000
Southwest Mindanao	8,850	116	1,029,000
Zamboanga Peninsula	6,100	168	1,027,000
Sulu Archipelago	1,100	297	327,000
Highlands (not included)	4,600	–	–
	115,600	234	27,084,000

The Far North: The Batan-Babuyan Islands

To the north of the main island of Luzon and lying between that island and Chinese Formosa are two small island groups that are the northern outposts of the Philippines, yet are structurally affiliated with the Philippine Archipelago.[5] These two insular outliers are the Batan and Babuyan islands, about 30 islands, islets, and rocks in all (fig. 44).

The Batan Islands are the northernmost of the two miniature archipelagos, a group composed of the three larger islands of Itbayat, Sabtang, and Batan, and numerous small islands, including Y'Ami, North Island, Mabudis,

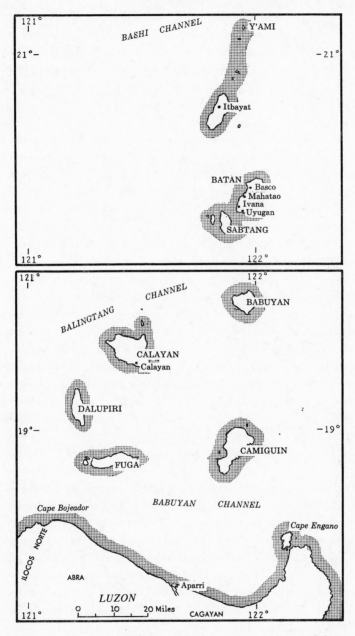

Fig. 44. The Batan-Babuyan Islands of the northern Philippines.

Siayan, Diogo, Ibuhos, and Dequey. Uninhabited Y'Ami, the northernmost of the group, lies only 100 miles south of Formosa and is separated from the nearest land to the north, the Chinese island of Hungtung (Little Botel Tobago), by the deep, 53-mile-wide Bashi Channel. The total land surface of the Batan Islands is 81 square miles, most of which falls on the four inhabited islands, that is, the three larger islands and Ibuhos.

The Babuyan Islands, comprising the remaining area of the region, lie to the south of the Batan Islands and are separated from them by the 42-mile-wide Balintang Channel. The Babuyan group is made up of larger islands than those of the Batan group, and collectively they represent a total land area of 231 square miles. The Babuyan group consists of the five large islands of Camiguin, Calayan, Babuyan, Fuga, and Dalupiri, together with several very small uninhabited islands and islets. Only a 20-mile-wide stretch of water, the Babuyan Channel, separates the Babuyan Islands from the northern coast of the large island of Luzon.

Politically, the Batan Islands are grouped together as the province of Batanes, the smallest of the Philippine provinces, with its capital at Basco on Batan Island. The Babuyan Islands, excepting the island of Fuga, are administered as a municipality of Cagayan Province on Luzon. Fuga is a barrio of the Luzon municipality of Aparri in Cagayan Province.

Although the islands of the Batan-Babuyan region are scattered through two degrees of ocean surfaces, latitudinally, the similarities in their physical and cultural environments suggest a single regional treatment. Both of the island groups are rather effectively isolated from the rest of the Philippines by distance and by the lack, or difficulty, of communications; however, the Babuyan Islands are isolated to a lesser degree than the Batan Islands. The distance factor, coupled with the lack of an important hinterland owing to the small and fragmented land area, the extremely rugged topography of many islands, the general lack of arable lands, and the lack of exploitable resources, are reflected in a poor level of economic development which, in turn, results in infrequent and tenuous economic and cultural ties with the remainder of the Philippines. The islands present rugged, steep coasts that often are fringed by coral reefs. The coasts are generally lacking in harbors and this, together with the prevalence of typhoons in the area, discourages contact by sea. Most of the islands afford only open roadsteads at best. The entire shoreline of the island of Itbayat is formed by steep, rugged cliffs with neither beaches nor protected anchorages. The only landing, which is along Itbayat's western coast, has steps cut into stone which climb up the steep cliffs to a trail that leads to the interior of the island. Volcanism has played an important role in the creation of the larger islands of the region. Mount Iraya reaches to nearly 3,300 feet on Batan Island, the twin-coned volcano on Babuyan reaches to 3,500 and 2,200 feet, and Mount Camiguin rises to 2,400 feet. Basco, on Batan, and Calayan have the only ports provided with regular, although infrequent, interisland shipping service from Aparri and Manila on Luzon. Typhoons preclude the regular maintenance of even this service during the period from September to February.

Extreme isolation from other Philippine areas and the lack of products to exchange on the main islands have resulted in the development of a strong, regional economic self-sufficiency in the Batan-Babuyan region.

The Batan-Babuyan region has been an area of virtual demographic stagnation, insofar as regional population growth is concerned. Limited land area and limited land capabilites for agricultural purposes have seriously restricted population growth in the region. Whereas the Philippines showed an overall increase of 86 percent in the thirty-year period from 1918 to 1948, the population of the Batan-Babuyan region increased by only 23 percent in the same period, that is, from 11,000 to 14,000 persons; and between 1948 and 1960 the province of Batanes saw an actual decrease in population which was offset by a small increase in the Babuyan Islands. Total numbers and densities of population are much higher on the Batan Islands than on the Babuyans, in spite of the larger size of the latter. In 1960 the Batan Islands supported a population of approximately 10,300 persons divided politically into the six municipalities of Itbayat, Sabtang, Basco, Ivaña, Mahatao, and Uyugan, the latter four located on the island of Batan. Whereas neither the total numbers nor densities of population are particularly striking when compared to average Philippine conditions, the provincial physiological density of 720 persons per square mile of cultivated land is dangerously high when compared to the limited capabilities of the land. Arable land and land already under cultivation are essentially synonomous. The Babuyan Islands, on the other hand, appear to offer far greater agricultural potential, yet their population is considerably less than in the Batan Islands. Only 5,400 persons lived permanently in the Babuyan Islands in 1960, and nowhere do population densities approach those in the Batan group.

It would appear that the strong land ties of the Batan Islanders have discouraged migration, whereas the strong cultural ties that many residents of the Babuyans have with northern Luzon encourage migration to the still lightly settled and economically more attractive section of the main island. Nearly all (99.6 percent) of the Batan population regards Ivatan, a local dialect quite distinct from the dialects spoken on Luzon, as its mother tongue. Less than 1 percent of the resident population of this province has immigrated from elsewhere in the Philippines. Approximately one-third of the persons born in the Batan Islands lived elsewhere in the Philippines in 1960. The majority of off-islanders resided in the provinces of Tarlac and Rizal.

Agriculture provides the base of the livelihood structure of the Batan-Babuyan region. The soils of the region do not appear to encourage the cultivation of rice. The total amount of land devoted to rice cultivation is very small and the yields obtained are quite low. Rice production within the region is confined to an area of only a few thousand acres and the production represents less than 10 percent of recommended consumption levels. Corn, which is commonly grown in other parts of the Philippines where rice does poorly, is not regarded as a favored food crop. Yields and per capita consumption of corn approximate the rather low national levels. Thus, neither of the two basic grain crops of the Filipinos are important in the diet of people in this region. The prevalence of strong winds, particularly those associated with typhoons, operates against high productivity for these two crops.

Root crops, on the other hand, are extensively cultivated and their combined acreages equal that of the two grains, as compared with a ratio of 1 acre of root crops to 13 acres of corn and rice, nationally. Camotes (sweet potatoes) are the main staple food for the Batan-Babuyan region, particularly in the Batan Islands where the annual production of camotes is equivalent to nearly 800 pounds per capita. The surpluses of camotes support a fairly large livestock industry in the region, particularly cattle, carabao, and hogs, and occasional shipments of livestock are made to Aparri and Manila. Coconuts, taro (gabi), yams (tugui and ubi), bananas, papayas, and citrus fruits supply additional foodstuffs.

The waters around the Batan Islands do not appear to be rich in fish, or if they are the situation does not lend itself to exploitation by small fishing operators. The quantity of the fish catch in the Batan area is insufficient for local consumption. The fishermen from the Babuyan Islands, on the other hand, participate in the relatively rich Babuyan Channel fishing grounds. Within these latter islands, fishing vies with agriculture on fairly equal grounds as the principal economic activity. Any surplus fish caught in the Babuyan area finds a ready market in northern Luzon. Most of the settlements on the Babuyan Islands are essentially small fishing villages, providing bases for the fishing fleet and racks for drying and preserving the catches.

The most unique cultural item that can be seen in the Batan area, at least to the visitor familiar with other areas in the Philippines, lies in the type of house construction. An almost universal use of stone and tile in domestic architecture lends an "un-Filipino" character to the landscape. Climatically, the Batan-Babuyan region lies along one of the main typhoon tracks of the western Pacific. Not only are these islands visited by frequent typhoons, but the typhoons in the northern Philippines are generally more severe than their southern Philippine counterparts.[6] The strong winds accompanying these storms have called for more permanent construction materials than those used in other parts of the Philippines. These fairly substantial houses are usually located in the bottom of swales or amidst trees for shelter from the strong winds.

Basco, the provincial capital of Batanes, is the only town of any size or commercial importance in the region. The town is located on the western side of Batan Island at the base of volcanic Mount Iraya. Basco is the major port for the province and its principal commercial center. Commercial ships call infrequently. The Basco airfield is served by commercial carriers from Luzon. In 1960 the town had a population under 1,000. Calayan is the largest town in the Babuyan Islands with a population of only a few hundred persons. Calayan is a minor fishing center, and its small port is a shipping point for cattle, hogs, goats, and small quantities of lumber from Calayan Island.

The Batan-Babuyan region is one of the most isolated areas of the Philippines. Population has been relatively static for several decades, and is marked by neither in-migration nor out-migration. The region does not participate significantly in the national economic scene. Arable land is severely limited and the region produces little beyond its local needs.

An Introduction to Luzon

Luzon, the largest island of the Philippines, stretches in overall length for more than 530 miles southeastward from Cape Bojeador in the northwest to the northern shores of San Bernardino Strait between Luzon and the Visayan island of Samar, over a latitudinal distance of approximately six degrees. The island's width varies from a slim 8 miles across the Tayabas Isthmus in the south to over 135 miles along the 17th parallel between Palanan Point and the Ilocos Sur coast. The island embraces a land area of 40,420 square miles, a figure that represents nearly 35 percent of the total land surface of the Philippine Archipelago.

Luzon has a very irregular form with a coastline over 3,000 miles in length. Its attenuated form is deeply indented by several major water bodies, including Lingayen Gulf, Manila Bay, and Ragay Gulf on the west, and Lagonoy Gulf and Lamon Bay on the east, and numerous smaller bays. There are several major peninsulas also, particularly in the southeast.

Luzon is an island for Philippine superlatives. Its central and eastern cordillera lands contain the highest and most massive mountains of the Philippine Archipelago. The Cagayan, Abra, Agno, Pampanga, and Bicol rivers are among the largest and longest rivers of the country. Luzon is also the most populous of the Philippine islands, for with its total population of nearly 13 million persons, it contains approximately 47 percent of the total Philippine population. On Luzon there are twenty-four of the fifty-five political provinces into which the republic is divided. Its population is the most highly urbanized, for on the island are located three of the seven principal cities of the Philippines, and fifteen of the twenty-nine cities with urban populations greater than 50,000 persons. It is the site of the national capital, Quezon City, and the location of Manila, the only truly metropolitan center of the islands. Economically Luzon is the most highly developed island and the leading agricultural island, alone producing over 59 percent of the nation's rice, as well as being a large producer of corn, coconuts, and sugarcane. Luzon has a very large porportion of the roads and vehicle registrations, and the island has the only real rail system, which serves the Central Plain and southeastern Luzon through Manila. In Luzon a much larger proportion of the population than in the rest of the nation is employed in industrial activities, and there is a greater diversity of major industries centered on the island.

At the same time, Luzon is one of the most diversified of the Philippine islands. Its topography includes both the archipelago's largest lowlands and its highest mountain ranges. The Central Plain of Luzon is the Philippine counterpart to the American Midwest, albeit on a much reduced scale. The broad, fertile Cagayan Valley in the north is a pioneer area of considerable agricultural productivity and potential. The Bicol Plain in southeastern Luzon, and hundreds of smaller coastal and river lowlands, provide considerable land well-suited for the plow. Active and quiescent volcanoes vie with massive older uplands for domination of the relief. Climatically, Luzon contains some of the wettest areas in the Philippines—Baguio for example, with an annual precipitation of 176 inches—and at the same time, the archipelago's driest station is at Agunetan in the Cagayan Valley with only 35 inches annually. Luzon soils are extremely diverse, ranging from the fertile alluvium of the Cagayan Valley to the volcanically derived soils of southwestern Luzon; furthermore, there are soils developed from older and harder igneous materials and from the more common sedimentary rocks, such as limestone, shale, and sandstone.

Although a major segment of the Filipino population lives on Luzon, the differences in population numbers and densities vary considerably from one area to another. The Manila area, the Central Plain, and Ilocos coast are among the more densely settled areas, whereas northeastern Luzon, the Sierra

Madre Mountains, and much of the east coast are inaccessible and virtually uninhabited. Five major Philippine dialects are spoken in different sections of Luzon, as well as at least ten of the most important minor dialects. Although Luzon is highly developed economically, as measured by Philippine standards, it also contains some of the least developed areas. The agricultural landscape is shared by such contrasting techniques as highly mechanized forms of agriculture, on some of the rice and sugarcane plantations of the Central Plain, the magnificent terraced rice fields of the Igorots and Ifugao in the mountains of northern Luzon, the small subsistence rice farms on the lowlands, and the forest clearings of the shifting agriculturists in the mountain lands.

Spain actually contributed toward an intensification of the island's regional diversity through the unevenness of its long historical contacts with Luzon. Luzon always claimed the strongest of the Spanish interests; however, these interests were not always uniformly applied over the entire island. The Spanish were concerned mainly with the port of Manila and the lowlands immediately to the north and south. They were also well acquainted with the Ilocos coast because of early contacts. The peninsulas of southeastern Luzon were also well-known to the Spanish, for with their deeply embayed character, the Bicol lands were easily accessible to approach from the sea. The Central Plain was not accorded such favorable status at first, however, and until the eighteenth and nineteenth centuries there was little organized settlement in the present-day provinces of Tarlac and Nueva Ecija. Neither was the Cagayan Valley a center of early Spanish development, except at the extreme southern end of the valley where tobacco farms flourished under the Spanish tobacco monopoly. Most of the highland areas were simply ignored, for the lack of accessible resources and the sparse populations did not claim the interests of many Spanish explorers and colonizers.

It is obvious in an island with as diverse a geographical setting as is found on Luzon that it would be impossible to develop any meaningful discussions on topics applicable to the entire island. Therefore, and for purposes of convenience, the island of Luzon is subdivided into eight major, reasonably homogeneous regions, plus the metropolitan Manila complex. These regions are: the Cagayan Valley, Ilocos coast, and North Luzon Highlands in the north, the Central Plain, Bataan-Zambales Peninsula, and southwestern Luzon volcanic area in the center, and the southeastern Luzon peninsulas. A narrow strip of mountains and coastal lowlands in eastern Luzon and the urban complex of metropolitan Manila complete the major regions of Luzon.

The Cagayan Valley: Northeast Luzon

The Cagayan Valley region occupies the northeastern part of the island of Luzon and consists, in the main, of the valleys of the Rio Grande de Cagayan, and its major tributaries, together with the narrow strip of coastal lowlands which accompanies the northern coast of Luzon westward from Cape Engaño to the boundary between the provinces of Cagayan and Ilocos Norte. The region includes all of the lands west of the Sierra Madre Mountains and east of the Cordillera Central in the provinces of Cagayan and Isabela, as well as valley portions of Nueva Vizcaya Province and Mountain Province. Thus constituted, the Cagayan Valley region is basically a physiographic region consisting of a broad lowland area covered by deep alluvium and bounded on all sides, except to the north, by moderately high and continuous mountain ranges (fig. 45). The region contains a total area of approximately 5,500 square miles.

THE PHYSICAL SETTING

Along its eastern margins the Cagayan Valley is bordered by the northern sections of the virtually unexplored Eastern Cordillera of Luzon, or Sierra Madre Mountains. These highlands are extremely rugged with peak elevations in excess of 6,000 feet, and there are no roads leading into or through them. The Sierra Madres descend precipitously along their eastern flanks into the deep waters of the Pacific Ocean, leaving no room for the development of coastal lowlands. On their western slopes, however, the highlands descend gradually, merging with the broad lowlands of the Cagayan Valley. The southern end of the valley is closed off from the Central Plain of Luzon by the Caraballo Mountains, a maturely dissected upland area with maximum elevations ranging between the 5,000- and 6,000-foot contour. The western borders of the valley are formed by the massive Cordillera Central system of northern Luzon. Several peaks within this latter highland complex reach almost to the 10,000-foot contour. The Cordillera Central rises abruptly from the valley floor and presents a continuous barrier to east–west travel, except where rivers break through in deep canyons. The Cordillera Central gradually loses elevation toward the north, although its termination along the north coast is usually in steep bluffs, leaving here and there only a narrow belt of coastal lowlands.

All of the drainage of the Cagayan Valley region is toward the north. The Cagayan is the master stream. Rising in the Sierra Madre Mountains near the southern end of the valley, the Cagayan flows in a meandering path almost due north, emptying into the waters of Babuyan Channel at the city of

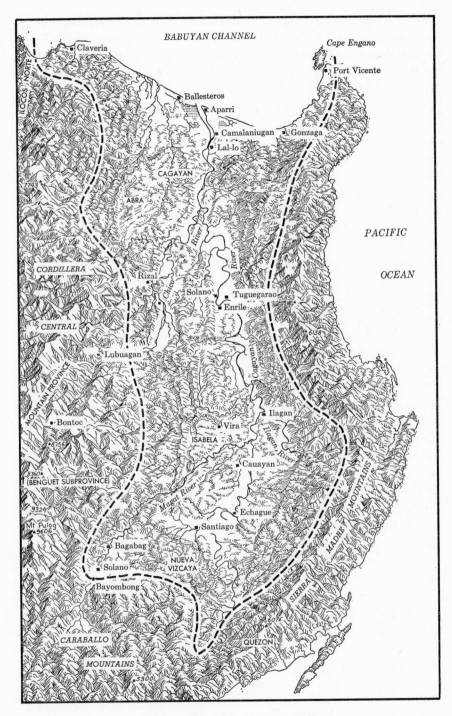

Fig. 45. Physiography of the Cagayan Valley region.

Aparri. Along its almost 275-mile valley course the Cagayan picks up numerous tributaries, some of them of major proportions, and its discharge volume is greater than that of any other Philippine river. The largest of the tributaries of the Cagayan is the Chico River that has its headwaters to the west near Bontoc in Mountain Province. The Chico descends from the Cordillera Central to the floor of the Cagayan by way of a steep, narrow gorge, and after paralleling the course of the Cagayan for several miles, finally enters the main stream approximately 30 miles above the mouth of the latter. The second major tributary of the Cagayan is the Magat River. The Magat heads in Benguet Subprovince in southern Mountain Province, and flowing northeasterly, finally joins the Cagayan near the city of Ilagan. The only large stream that enters the valley from the east is the Ilagan River, which also joins the Cagayan near Ilagan. Thus, there is a definite one-sided character to the drainage of the Cagayan, that is, most of the tributaries enter the main stream from the cordillera lands to the west, a factor that gives to the valley basin an asymmetrical profile. Most of the alluvial plain lies to the west of the main river channel.

In addition to its physiographic regionality, the Cagayan Valley region also constitutes a rather distinct climatic region and exhibits a considerable degree of climatic homogeneity throughout. The valley is never fully exposed to the broad sweep of moisture-bearing air masses because it is closed off by highlands to the east, west, and south. The amounts of precipitation received at various valley stations are considerably less than those encountered in coastal sections of the neighboring Ilocos provinces, along the exposed Pacific coast, or in the bordering highland areas. Somewhat higher rainfall amounts occur along the narrow coastal lowlands in the north where there is a greater exposure to northeastern air movements; however, most of the valley stations receive annual rainfalls that range from 60 to 80 inches. The precipitation is so distributed that the months from December to May normally are quite dry. Depending upon location and exposure, precipitation amounts during these dry months may decrease to less than one inch monthly. The drought season is not without blessings, however, for it provides a drier period for harvesting and curing of certain crops. The remaining months of the year are relatively humid and wet.

Valley temperatures, although still very much tropical, show greater diurnal and seasonal ranges than do those encountered in other parts of the Philippines. The greater temperature ranges are produced, in part, by the interior position of the valley, in part, by its location in the higher latitudes.

Typhoons are especially frequent in northern Luzon, but in the Cagayan Valley their effects are minimized because of the protection afforded by the surrounding upland barriers. The principal effect of the typhoons upon valley weather is usually a rather significant increase in precipitation.

The soil resources of the Cagayan Valley region are of tremendous significance to the region and to the country as a whole. In general, the soils of the valley are of sedimentary origin, formed principally from deposition by the rivers. The entire valley floor is covered in depths up to 9,000–11,000 feet with accumulations of alluvium. As much of the valley is subject to annual inundations from the flooding rivers, soil fertility is maintained at a relatively high level. The soils of the valley floor are mainly sandy loams. They are quite deep, generally 3 feet or more, easily cultivated, and in good physical condition. Small areas of heavier soils are encountered in several places; they are usually found in low depressions where flood waters accumulate easily and stand long, thus allowing the fine particles of clay to settle on the surface.[7]

Certainly there is no greater resource present in the Cagayan Valley than the fertile soil base, and when these good soils combine with large expanses of level land and not unfavorable climatic conditions, an excellent foundation is provided for a prosperous agricultural occupance.

THE CULTURAL SETTING

In spite of its excellent agricultural base, however, the Cagayan Valley is not a densely populated area, at least when compared with demographic levels in other prime agricultural regions in the Philippines. Quite the contrary! Today the Cagayan Valley region appears as a comparatively underpopulated area (figs. 20–23). With a total 1960 population of approximately 960,000 persons, the region supported an overall density of only 175 persons per square mile of total are: a figure below the average national density of 234 and well below similar agricultural areas on the Central Plain and in many Visayan areas. Throughout the length and breadth of the valley, even in those areas in the south of long-time Spanish control and development, it is difficult to escape the overall impression that this region is still very definitely a pioneer or frontier land. Farm sizes are larger, dwellings are cruder, towns are smaller, and the buildings within them usually are finished with raw, unsurfaced board siding. The population is much more dispersed than within the neighboring regions to the west and south. A large proportion of the present population, perhaps as much as two-thirds, has come to the valley from the Ilocano provinces, and many of these have come only within recent years.[8] Not only does the valley have a relatively new population; it has a population that is quite young in age and rapidly expanding in numbers.

The slower pace of economic and demographic development in the

Cagayan region, particularly in light of the region's excellent agricultural base and relatively early contacts and control by Spanish authority, is rather difficult to account for completely. Relative isolation from the rest of Luzon has certainly been a contributing factor. Until Highway 5, the present overland connection between the Cagayan Valley and central Luzon, was constructed in 1924 the only means of communications was by poor road or trail over the Caraballo Mountains, or by the long and often stormy sea voyage between the ports of Aparri and Manila. By these early routes only the highest value cargoes, chiefly tobacco, could bear the high transportation costs. Large-scale migration to the valley was discouraging from an economic standpoint, especially since the cost of shipping any surplus productions of cash food-crops, such as rice and corn, was prohibitive. Even today, with greatly improved transportation media and a relatively dense network of highways within the valley, there is still a feeling of isolation and remoteness from the rest of Luzon.

With the exception of those resources useful to an agricultural occu-pance the Cagayan region appears to have a very limited natural-resource base, a resource base that is not presently calculated to encourage any large-scale economic development of the valley. Minerals are not present either in quantities or variety sufficient to warrant even a modest mineral industry. There are a few small deposits of iron ore in northern Cagayan Province, at Camalaniugan, which lies only 6 miles from the coast; however, their exploita-tion could only affect a small peripheral area of the valley. Occurrences of gold have been reported from time to time, but so little geological exploration has been conducted up to the present, that their commercial possibilities are still unknown. The geologic history of the region would seem to indicate strong possibilities for accumulations of petroleum, but as yet no significant commercial discoveries have been made. Only the relatively abundant and ubiquitous clays and construction minerals are present in commercial quanti-ties. At the outset any mineral development would be crippled by the lack of cheap and efficient transportation facilities and large nearby markets.

The Cagayan region does contain some rather substantial quantities of commercial timber. The forests of the region are estimated to contain several billion board feet of merchantable timber.[9] At present timber exploitation is limited by the inaccessibility of many of the forested areas and by the general lack of transportation facilities to large markets. Claveria (Cagayan), San Agustin (Isabela), and Aritao (Nueva Vizcaya) are important small sawmill towns. The potential timber-cut could support a much larger forest industry, and possibly justify improvement of the existing transportation system by extending the central Luzon rail network into the valley, a plan now under serious consideration.

Early Spanish explorers and missionaries found the Cagayan Valley relatively well populated. The indigenous population consisted of Ibanags, Gaddangs, and other peoples of Indonesian stock who were estimated to number approximately 97,000.[10] The Ibanags had originally settled along the Babuyan Channel coast and by the late sixteenth century were occupying the lower half of the valley. Gaddangs, Itavis, Yogods, and Isnegs were found along the middle and upper Cagayan and Magat rivers.[11] Nearly a dozen cabecera settlements were established and areas of land were divided into encomiendas. The principal station was at Nueva Segovia, the present Lal-lo, which was the capital of the valley and the bishopric. As long as population pressures in other parts of Luzon did not reach serious proportions, however, there was no desire on the part of the Filipinos to colonize the valley. The journey was arduous and the Filipino then was a somewhat reluctant colonizer of inland locations. Even the inauguration of commercial tobacco production in the valley under the Spanish monopoly system failed to attract any large number of permanent settlers, although numerous Ilocanos migrated then, encouraged by government loans and transportation subsidies. For various reasons this reluctance to migrate to the Cagayan Valley is still evident today, albeit to a lesser degree.

Communications and transportation facilities, both within the valley and outward to adjacent areas, were quite inadequate even in 1960. None of the intraregional or interregional highways are hard-surfaced. The major national highways are gravel-surfaced, whereas most of the secondary roads are merely dirt tracks and passable only during dry weather. The major transportation artery serving internal and external regional needs is Highway 5. This highway connects Manila and the Central Plain with the Cagayan Valley by way of the 3,000-foot Dalton (Balete) Pass through the Caraballo Mountains. The present highway parallels the old Spanish trail that was constructed in 1768. It enters the southern end of the Magat Valley in Nueva Vizcaya and runs northward, roughly paralleling the courses of the Magat and the Cagayan rivers. Most of the more important urban centers in the region are served by this highway. Highway 5 is graveled throughout its 200-mile length in the valley from south of Bayombong to Aparri, and all of the river crossings are permanently bridged. At Aparri the highway terminates at the junction with Highway 3, which has entered the region from the west, coming by way of the Ilocos coast around the northwestern corner of Luzon. Highway 3 continues eastward past Aparri, terminating at Port

Vicente near Cape Engaño. Additional ingress to the valley can be gained from Mountain Province over very poor roads. Highway 4 connects Bontoc with Bagabag, and Highway 6 runs from Lubuagan to Enrile and Tuguegarao, following the valley of the Chico. Areas in the valley located only short distances from these main arterials, or away from the rivers, have very poor road connections. The lack of a good regional highway network has seriously retarded the settlement of the Cagayan region.

Unfortunately, the rivers of the Cagayan region do not alleviate transportation problems materially. Most of them are not navigable. The Cagayan River is navigable for seagoing vessels only to Camalaniugan; but craft having a draft under 6 feet can ascend to Lal-lo. Light barges can ascend the Cagayan about 40 miles, but they cannot go as far as the provincial capital of Tuguegarao, except during periods of high water. Small craft, such as the native *bancas,* use the Cagayan and its major tributaries frequently; however, bulk commodity shipments by river are not possible. The development of deepwater ports along the north coast of Luzon has been severely restricted owing to the unprotected character of much of the coastline; the coastal waters are relatively shallow, and the coast lies fully exposed to winds from the north and northeast. The only significant port installation along the entire northern coast is at Aparri, and its use is considered unsafe during much of the year.

The economy of the Cagayan region is oriented almost solely toward the agricultural sector. The agriculture of the region consists basically of the cultivation of various crop associations combining rice, corn, and tobacco. All three crops are produced in quantities well above regional needs, and large surpluses of each are available for sale outside the region.

As is true in other areas of initial or pioneer settlement in the Philippines, a major emphasis is placed upon the cultivation of corn in the Cagayan Valley. The cultivation of corn requires a minimum of labor and results in relatively high per acre returns. Corn cultivation also fits in with the light precipitation of the valley. Because of its relatively low moisture requirement it does well under the Cagayan Valley climate. Corn yields surpass average Philippine corn yields by more than 50 percent. The corn farms are unusually large, especially when compared with farm sizes in other regions of the Philippines, and most farms are worked by the owners. Within the valley the farm tenancy rate is less than 35 percent; the national rate is 65 percent. There is also considerable land that is not now used for any crop into which corn cultivation could expand.

The heart of the region's corn production lies at the southern or upper end of the valley in the province of Isabela. Here corn is grown in association with cigar tobaccos (fig. 46), usually appearing as the first crop, to be followed by tobacco in the off-season months of September or October through May. The local supply of farm labor is not sufficient during the main corn planting and harvesting seasons, and large numbers of seasonal laborers migrate to the valley, coming mainly from areas in central Luzon and the Ilocos coast. The large surpluses of corn characteristic of valley farms result from the larger farm units, the higher yields obtained, and a relatively sparse population. Each year approximately 40,000 tons of corn are produced which are beyond local requirements. Generally these surpluses are shipped to the populous central Luzon area southward by truck or by water transport through the port of Aparri.

Although the Cagayan Valley region is especially noteworthy for its large corn production, producing approximately 11 percent of the total Philippine corn crop, the amount of land which is devoted to rice, and the production from this rice area, greatly exceeds that of corn. Whereas only 6 percent of the national rice crop is produced in the Cagayan region, the volume of rice production (by weight) exceeds corn by almost 50 percent.

Rice generally requires greater amounts of moisture than does corn, and the lighter rainfall of the valley is not especially favorable for rice cultivation. Until recently, however, little of the rice had been grown under irrigation in the valley. Most of the rice lands are concentrated close to river courses so that the fields can take advantage of the greater moisture present there and the occasional natural inundations by the flooding rivers. More than one-third of a million acres within the region are devoted to rice cultivation, and average yields are approximately 10 percent higher than those obtained at the national level. The rice acreage is equally divided between the provinces of Cagayan and Isabela, with some small additional areas found in valley sections of Nueva Vizcaya and Mountain Province.

During the past decade, a very large irrigation project has been under construction along the Magat River under the Irrigation Division of the Bureau of Public Works. Located in the municipality of Santiago in Isabela Province, this project will benefit some 58,000 acres. Two other irrigation projects are under construction in the valley under the national Five-Year Development Programs. The larger of the two is located along the Abulug River in northern Cagayan Province. The Abulug Project will irrigate approximately 40,000 acres, and additionally, will serve flood-control purposes. The last of the major government-sponsored irrigation projects irrigates 5,000 acres along the Mallig River in Isabela. Altogether, nearly 100,000 acres will be brought under irrigation in the Cagayan Valley.

The valley's production of rice also greatly exceeds local requirements.

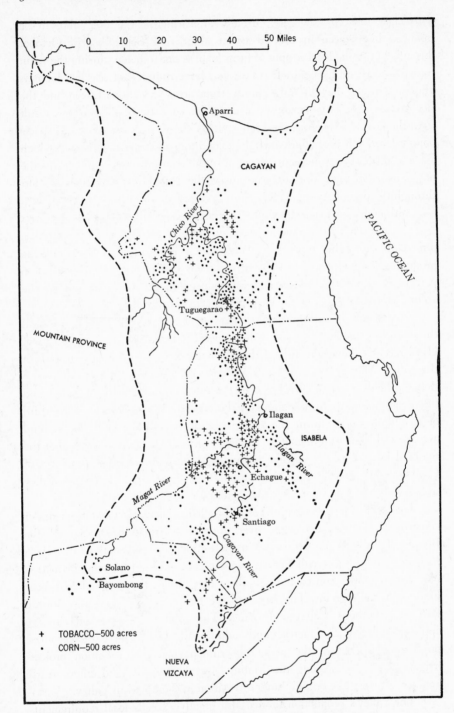

Fig. 46. Corn (maize) and tobacco in the Cagayan Valley region, 1960.

The annual surpluses, amounting to approximately 70,000 tons, find their way mainly to Manila and central Luzon, and even as far as the Visayan area.

Cigar tobaccos and the Cagayan Valley have been linked with one another since the early days of the Spanish occupance. Immediately after the declaration of a state tobacco monopoly by the Spanish authorities in 1781, it was found that the Cagayan Valley was the most favorable Philippine locale for the cultivation of cigar-wrapper and filler tobaccos. The area devoted to tobacco cultivation expanded rapidly, but production was placed under the strictest of governmental supervision and quality control. One-half of the total Philippine tobacco acreage was located in the Cagayan Valley during the monopoly period, and the Cagayan tobaccos, and the cigars produced from them, became world famous. Even with the advent of American administration at the beginning of the twentieth century the quality of Cagayan cigars was recognized through the promulgation of *Administrative Order no. 35,* which was worded as follows: [12]

> To be classed as standard, cigars must be manufactured under sanitary conditions from good to clean, selected tobacco, properly cured and seasoned, of a crop which has been harvested at least six months, *exclusively the product of the provinces of Cagayan, Isabela, and Nueva Vizcaya.*

During the twentieth century, however, world smokers gradually changed their smoking tobacco preferences from cigars to cigarettes. The light, aromatic cigarette filler tobaccos that were increasingly preferred did not do well under Cagayan Valley conditions. Whereas there has been a tremendous increase in tobacco consumption in the Philippines, particularly since 1945, the consequent increases in tobacco lands have been in other areas more favorable for cigarette tobaccos, for example, the Ilocos region, and not in the Cagayan region. The Cagayan region, nevertheless, retains a position of considerable significance in the Philippine tobacco industry, and tobacco continues to provide the region with its most important cash crop, although the amount of land devoted to tobacco cultivation has remained almost stationary at levels reached nearly fifty years ago.

The principal tobacco soil of the Cagayan Valley is a deep, friable, sandy loam, with a good physical structure. The main tobacco fields are located adjacent to the Cagayan River where they can benefit from annual rejuvenation of soil fertility through flooding river waters. The short dry season of the valley is ideal for harvesting and curing operations. Tobacco yields are high and an unusually excellent cigar tobacco is produced. Most of the tobacco is produced on lands used to grow a crop of corn during the main growing season.

None of the final manufacturing of cigars is performed within the region. The farmers harvest, dry, and cure their tobacco themselves. The tobacco is then brought by truck to central baling sites, which are usually located in the larger towns. Eventually the cured and baled tobacco is shipped to Manila where most of the large cigar factories are located. Isabela, with approximately 35,000 acres devoted to tobacco, is the principal tobacco province of the Philippines. The Cagayan region cultivates approximately 43,000 acres of tobacco, and from this land is produced approximately 11,000 tons of tobacco annually, an amount equivalent to 55 percent of the total Philippine cigar-tobacco production.

The three major crops of corn, rice, and tobacco are supplemented by substantial productions of minor foodcrops, including eggplants, tomatoes, bananas, and various other fruits and vegetables.

The agricultural economy of the Cagayan region is noticeably deficient in supplying protein foodstuffs. Fishing is relatively insignificant, except along the north coast and in certain of the rivers. There has been only slight development of a livestock industry, although many of the unused grasslands could support relatively large numbers of cattle.

With its pioneer orientation the population of the Cagayan region is distinctly rural in character and outlook. The tendency toward increasing urbanization evident in other parts of the Philippines does not appear as a particularly strong force in the valley, and urbanization has not yet proceeded to the point where any one city functions as the regional trade center or exhibits mature urbanism. Instead, most of the region's trade and commerce is conducted in numerous small urban centers or market towns. Three provincial capital cities are located within the region—Tuguegarao, Ilagan, and Bayombong—and they constitute the most important concentrations of urban populations and services. Commercial centers of lesser importance, usually dominant over the immediately surrounding agricultural area and frequently functioning as transportation centers also, form a second hierarchy of cities. Aparri, Solano, Claveria, and Santiago belong to this second group. In addition, there are some fifteen smaller centers, all agricultural trading points, which have more than local importance.

Spanish cabecera settlements and visita chapels in barrio centers numbered almost a dozen in the Cagayan Valley and along the north coast. Only three of these—Tuguegarao, Camalaniugan, and Claveria—have matured into modern urban centers, which is slightly abnormal in view of the results in other parts of the Philippines. Initial Spanish settlement activity was oriented toward the distribution of the pre-Spanish population. During the middle and later Spanish period, interest in tobacco production centered on the Cagayan Valley, and locational shifts of towns and population occurred in response to the selection of the best tobacco-growing lands. This produced a series of new town sites as points of labor residence and marketing functions. The Spanish monopoly system, the isolation of the Cagayan Valley during Spanish times, and the presence of vacant lands nearer to the older west and central Luzon centers of population pressure resulted in the slow growth of population in the Cagayan Valley as a whole. The wide distribution of good tobacco land spread out the population rather thinly and produced a number of new small towns rather than concentrating populations around the old cabecera settlements in large towns and thickly settled barrios. Even in the twentieth century this pattern remained operative through 1948, and it is only in the rather recent period that change has begun to manifest itself. Since 1948 the Cagayan Valley has become one of the significant zones of in-migration, but a very considerable majority of the population is spreading out in rural patterns rather than concentrating in the towns.

The largest town in the Cagayan Valley is Tuguegarao, since 1841 the capital of Cagayan Province. Located along the Cagayan River near the Cagayan-Isabela provincial boundary, the city serves as the principal commercial center for the southern half of Cagayan Province and for a few of the more northern settlements of Isabela. The city is situated on the inside, or eastern bank, of one of the larger meanders of the Cagayan River. Ferries provide contact with places located west of the river. Unfortunately, the river at Tuguegarao is not navigable for other than small native craft, although barges can ascend to the town during high-water stages. Tuguegarao competes with Aparri for the trade of Cagayan Province. The valley's land transportation network places Tuguegarao closer to producing areas and markets in the southern part of the valley, and to the Manila area, partially compensating for its lack of deepwater port facilities. Truck and bus service from Tuguegarao to points throughout the valley and to Manila is frequent and regular. An extension of the Manila-North Railroad has been proposed from time to time, although it is difficult to see the economic justification for its construction. If built, it is proposed that this rail line will terminate at Tuguegarao. Solano, Enrile, and Peñablanca are small satellite communities located within Tuguegarao's trade area.

Tuguegarao carries the pioneer atmosphere so apparent in the pattern of valley occupance into its streets and buildings. The busy, unsurfaced city streets are lined with stores, shops, and houses whose exteriors are completed with rough and generally unpainted board siding. The population of Tuguegarao in 1960 was 43,000, 10,000 of whom lived in the poblacion, and its population is expanding rapidly.

Aparri, the second city in size in the Cagayan region, functions as the principal port, and indeed, for all purposes the only port in the Cagayan Valley region. The establishment of the Spanish provincial capital of Nueva Segovia (Lal-lo) some 8 miles upriver for protection against attack from the sea called for the development of an outport at the river mouth. Aparri grew at the expense of the capital, however, and now Lal-lo is only a small municipality. The port of Aparri was opened to foreign commerce in the late nineteenth century. The city is situated along the eastern bank and just inside the mouth of the Cagayan River. The port and harbor are afforded by the lower course of the river, although in order to enter the harbor a river bar must be negotiated which has a controlling depth of 15 to 18 feet at high tide. Even this anchorage is considered unsafe during storms for much of the year, and Aparri's port functions are quite ephemeral. There is relatively infrequent steamship connection with Manila, and only occasionally do foreign vessels call at Aparri to load logs and lumber. Many of these vessels stand off the river mouth and lighter their cargoes over the river bar. Aparri is also important as the major trade center for the northern coastal areas of Luzon from the municipality of Claveria eastward to Gonzaga. A ferry at Camalan-iugan, 6 miles upriver, provides the only road link with the lands west of the river. Aparri is an important fishing center, and is especially noted for its large fish-paste, or bagoong, industry. In 1960 Aparri had a population of 33,000, 13,000 of whom lived in the poblacion.

Ilagan, the capital city of Isabela Province, is located near the junctures of the Cagayan, Magat, and Ilagan rivers. Much of the trade originating from the upper valleys of these three river systems funnels through the city. The name of Ilagan has long been associated with the Philippine cigar-tobacco industry, actually since the earliest days of the Spanish tobacco monopoly. The city has served, and to a lesser degree continues to serve, as the financial and warehousing center for the cigar-tobacco industry, a role it shares with the town of Echague to the south where the famous "Compania General de Tabacas Filipinas (Tabacalera)" has its headquarters. Ilagan is also an important agricultural trading center for the surrounding rice and corn farmers. The municipality of Ilagan had a population of 48,000 persons in 1960; however, the city proper (poblacion) contained less than 2,000.

Bayombong and Solano, on the Magat River at the southern end of the valley, are twin towns located 4 miles apart. Bayombong is the smaller of the two and serves as the provincial capital of Nueva Vizcaya Province. With its numerous hotels and restaurants it also serves as a midway stop on the long bus journey from the Central Plain of Luzon to points in the northern part of the Cagayan Valley. Bayombong had a poblacion population of approximately 8,300 persons in 1960. Solano is much the more important of the two towns commercially. The town already is the principal commercial center for most of the Magat Valley, and its trade area is expanding into parts of neighboring Mountain Province. The poblacion of Solano had a population of approximately 12,000 in 1960, and its growth continues to be very rapid.

Among the more important of the lesser trade centers of the region are Claveria, Gonzaga, Ballesteros, Tuao, Rizal, and Camalaniugan in Cagayan Province; Santiago, Cauayan, Echague, and Vira in Isabela Province; and Jones in Nueva Vizcaya. All of these small urban centers have populations around 5,000. Their main function is to serve as trade centers and market towns for the immediately surrounding areas. Gonzaga, Ballesteros, Echague, and Vira are solely agricultural trading centers. Tuao and Rizal dominate the trade of the Chico River Valley. Claveria has a rather poor port, but with several sawmills located nearby it serves as the shipping point for locally produced lumber. Camalaniugan, located at the head of the navigation on the Cagayan, is a small river port and ferry terminus. The new national airport, which serves much of the southern valley, is located at Cauayan. Santiago is a rapidly expanding commercial center for a southern sector of the valley. The small settlement of Jones, named for the American anthropologist killed nearby, is a new town in the newly opened lands on the upper reaches of the Cagayan River.

The Cagayan region in the early 1950's constituted one of the more empty sectors of the Philippines, and it caught on as one of the regions to which population surpluses were attracted. Population grew rather rapidly during the 1950's as a notable volume of in-migrants arrived from the Ilocos coastal zone and from Pangasinan. This growth doubtless will continue at least during the 1960's. As an agricultural region still not heavily or fully occupied, reserve agricultural land and rural attractions continue to draw the in-migrants out across the rural landscape. The region can continue to produce an agricultural surplus in each of its primary products for a considerable period of time. Simple agricultural processing and market whole-saling, of both outbound regional surpluses and inbound manufactures, represent the primary functions for the scattering of small market towns and somewhat larger primary urban centers. Thus the region is one in which the tradition of rural residence continues, and the patterns of urbanism are those of the recent agricultural frontier now expanding its patterns of primary production. As in-migration continues to occupy the still-vacant lands population will increase at a rate greater than the national rate, the variety of agricultural production will increase, the total agricultural product-surplus may grow still larger, the patterns of urbanism and industrial processing will tend toward greater variety, complexity, and maturity, and the region will play a more significant role in the national economy than has been the case in the past. For the present, one answer to the Philippine problem of pressure on the land can still be: Go north, young man, go north.

The Coast of the Ilocos: Northwest Luzon

The Ilocos coast region is located in the northwestern corner of the island of Luzon and occupies a lengthy, but relatively narrow coastal section extending from Lingayen Gulf northward to beyond Cape Bojeador (fig. 47). The core area of the region consists of a narrow belt of discontinuous coastal lowlands intermittently interspersed by mountain spurs that descend directly to the coast from the hill and mountain lands in the interior. The region extends inland, or eastward, until the higher slopes of the Cordillera Central of Luzon are encountered. The coastal lowlands, the lower western foothill sections of the cordillera, and the river valleys that extend back into the upland, most notably the valleys of the Abra and Laoag rivers, are included within the region. Thus constituted, the Ilocos coast region includes all of the areas of the provinces of Ilocos Norte, Ilocos Sur, and La Union, together with sections of the Abra River Valley in Abra Province. The region represents a total area of approximately 3,600 square miles.

THE PHYSICAL SETTING

In spite of its somewhat diverse physiography, with a mosaic of mountains, hills, and plains areas, the Ilocos coast comprises a region with a considerable degree of geographical homogeneity, both in physical and in cultural environments. The majority of the people living in the region are known as Ilocanos, a well-recognized Filipino cultural, linguistic, and ethnic group. The Ilocano is particularly noted for his enterprise and industry, traits at least partially stimulated by the restrictions of the physical environment of his homeland. Although the overall regional physiographic base offers considerable variety, all of the human occupance focuses on the narrow coastal lowlands, or on the adjacent lower slopes of the foothills, and the mountainous interior remains more or less a demographic void. This does not mean to imply that the higher mountain lands are not without significance to human existence, for their presence exerts a profound influence upon life in the river valleys and coastal lowland areas.

The coastal lowlands generally lie parallel to the coast and extend discontinuously in a north–south direction for a distance of almost 200 miles. These lowlands vary considerably in width. Where the Abra and Laoag rivers

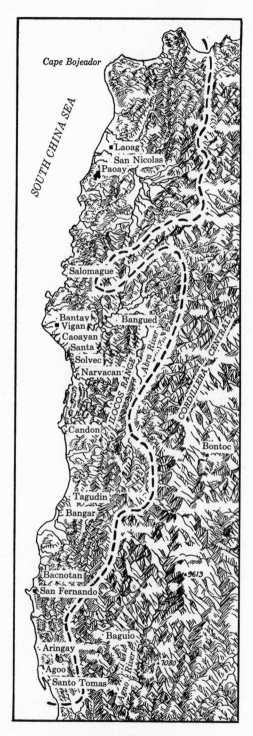

Fig. 47. Physiography of the Ilocos
coast region.

break through the mountain barriers and reach the coast, the lowlands reach their greatest width of approximately 25 miles. In a few sections they are only a few hundred feet in width. Structurally, the coastal lowlands are generally of two types: (1) those lowlands that have originated as true coastal plains, and are usually recognizable by the presence of coralline sediments, sands, and marine terraces, or (2) those lowlands that have been built up at the base of the uplands from accumulations of alluvial materials brought down by the numerous mountain streams. Generally the streams that originate in the Cordillera Central and Ilocos Range are short, rapidly flowing, and seasonally varied in flow. Usually they are overburdened with sediments stripped from the steep upland slopes and are quick to deposit alluvium at breaks in the stream gradient. There is little evidence of true floodplain development, except along short stretches of the Abra and Laoag rivers. Instead, the hundreds of short streams have built up a low, gently sloping, piedmont alluvial plain. The excessive rainfall of the region during certain seasons, however, is not conducive to the continued existence of these piedmont deposits, and in their present eroded form they are scarcely recognizable as such. The valleys of the larger rivers, namely the Abra and the Laoag, present a different landform scene. The Abra is one of the larger and longer rivers on Luzon. It rises high in the Cordillera Central in northern Benguet, and for its first 70 miles flows northward, parallel to the coast, but separated from it by the low Ilocos Range. After its junction with the Tineg and other westward-flowing rivers, the Abra breaks through the Ilocos Mountains and reaches the South China Sea near the town of Vigan. Along its lower 40-mile course the Abra has created a relatively broad floodplain. The Laoag River rises in the mountains near the Ilocos Norte–Mountain Province boundary and after a short, steep descent it is joined by several tributaries. Below this confluence point, which is approximately 20 miles above its mouth, the river has formed a large, frequently marshy, floodplain. The Laoag reaches the sea near the town of Laoag. Neither of these two rivers is navigable for any craft larger than canoes.

Unfortunately, the Cordillera Central is composed of intermediate to mafic plutonic basement-complex rocks, and the sediments washed down from them onto the coastal lowlands are of only moderate fertility at best. The most widespread lowland soil is a mildly acidic clay or clay loam with a high degree of water retention. The streams that descend from the highlands are sufficiently numerous and large during the rainy season that plentiful supplies of water are then available for irrigation purposes. The Ilocos coast region has one of the highest ratios of irrigated land to total cultivated land of

any region in the Philippines. Approximately 28 percent of the total cultivated land of the region is under some form of artificial water control, at least
during part of the year. Each of the provinces has important irrigation
systems, but those in Ilocos Norte are noteworthy, especially along the Laoag
and Vintar rivers.

The Ilocos coast lies exposed to the full sweep of the summer or
southwestern monsoon coming off the South China Sea. The massive North
Luzon Highlands shield the coast from northern and northeastern air
masses. Thus, the traditional monsoon climate with excessively rainy
summers and droughty winters is fully developed throughout the region.
Everywhere precipitation amounts are high, usually exceeding 100 inches
annually. Only in a few areas, which are sheltered by topographic barriers, do
annual precipitations fall below this amount. All areas in the region experience precipitations that are highly seasonal, and at most stations approximately 90 percent of the annual precipitation is concentrated into the
six-month period between May and October. The strong seasonal character of
the precipitation necessitates artificial water control if crops are to be cultivated during the remainder of the year. The seasonal character of the
precipitation, and the duration and severity of the drought, increase toward
the north and are particularly strong in Ilocos Norte.

Today very little remains of the original tropical monsoon forest vegetation that once clothed the hill and mountain lands of the Ilocos region.
Caingineros, the shifting agriculturists, and sedentary farmers pushing out
from the overcrowded lowlands, have ruthlessly slashed the forests, either for
complete removal so that the land could be cultivated, or for the scarce timber
supplies. Unfortunately, on the hill lands that were not permanently cultivated, the monsoon forest has not been able to regenerate itself; instead it has
been replaced either by poor stands of second-growth molave or dipterocarp
forests, locally termed *parangs,* or by the difficult-to-eradicate cogonal grasslands. Frequently the removal of the original forest vegetation has left the
steeply sloping lands exposed to erosion, and the heavy precipitation of the
region, through the action of the numerous short, swift streams, has accelerated the removal of much of the topsoil cover of the uplands. The evidences
of excessive soil depletion, however, are not confined to the uplands, for the
debris removed from the higher slopes has piled up on the fields of the
lowlands below. Large expanses of gravelly stream wash have ruined, or
removed from cultivation, much of the arable lands in the coastal lowlands.
Areas not made uncultivable by gravel wash often show the effects of soil
erosion; the soils of Ilocos Sur and La Union are among the most severely

eroded soils in the Philippines, and those of Abra and Ilocos Norte are not far behind them. For the region as a whole, approximately 60 percent of the total area is suffering from the effects of gravel wash and soil erosion.[13]

In short, the Ilocos coast region is an area that offers limited agricultural possibilities, and the present large population represents nearly the maximum agricultural population the region can support at present levels of living with present agricultural techniques. Not only does there appear to be little suitable land remaining for expansion of agricultural area, except in parts of the more lightly settled Abra Valley, but at the same time much of the land that is now being cropped is being seriously depleted of its soil resource, or actually going out of cultivation owing to stream-wash deposition. It is not too difficult to comprehend why the Ilocano is so very familiar as a colonizer in other more favorable and less crowded regions of the Philippines. Ilocanos have been emigrating during the past century in ever-increasing numbers. Today they are particularly evident as in-migrants or migratory workers in the Cagayan Valley, in Pangasinan Province and along the Zambales coast in Luzon, and on the island of Mindanao; the Ilocanos are also among the principal Filipino ethnic groups overseas in Hawaii and in the western United States.

THE CULTURAL SETTING

The Ilocos coastal region boasts one of the most homogeneous ethnolinguistic populations of any Philippine region. Ilocanos make up between 93 and 99 percent of the population of the three coastal provinces, falling to approximately 75 percent in the peripheral province of Abra.

The physical environment of the Ilocos coast has played an important role in shaping the character of the Ilocano. Steep slopes, thin soils, strongly seasonal precipitation, and limited arable land have required maximum labors for survival. The Ilocano is well-known, both in the Philippines and abroad, for his willingness to work and his work capacity. He has supplied most of the Filipino labor force in the Hawaiian sugarcane fields.[14] Many members of his cultural group hold positions of high responsibility in the government of the Philippines. An overcrowded homeland has encouraged out-migration into other areas where his presence is quickly evidenced by his hard work and attendant economic successes.

More than one million persons live within the Ilocos coast region (fig. 20). All of the provinces in the region, except Abra, have population densities well above the national average. Whereas the average population density for the Philippines is 234 persons per square mile of total area, the Ilocos region supports 282 persons on each square mile of area. La Union is the most densely populated of the four provinces, with an average density of 508 persons per square mile, a density figure that exceeds the national average by more than twofold. Population densities in Ilocos Sur exceed the Philippine national average by approximately 50 percent, and the Ilocos Norte density is approximately equal to the density elsewhere in the country. Only mountainous Abra, with its relatively sparse population concentrated along the narrow floodplain of the Abra River, falls below the national average. Limited in the amount of arable land, the population of the Ilocos coast region exerts considerable, and in some respects dangerously high pressure upon the cultivated lands. Physiological densities for the region as a whole are slightly less than 2,000 persons per square mile of cultivated land, a figure about double the national figure. Ilocos Sur and La Union have especially high physiological densities, 2,335 and 1,780 persons, respectively.

The Ilocos coast has long been one of the more densely populated regions of the Philippines. Juan de Salcedo, the first Spaniard to explore along the Ilocos coast in 1572, reported the area to be thickly populated. By 1591, the Ilocos coastal section had been organized as the province of Ilocos, and perhaps overly enthusiastically, was described thus: "the whole narrow coast facing the China Sea from the extreme north of Luzon to the Gulf of Lingayen, yielded 17,130 tributes, including 'El Abra de Bigan (Vigan)', which would give us a population of 68,520 souls." [15] The early Spanish occupance, however, apparently ushered in a period of relatively slight population growth, or maybe even an actual decline, during the one and one-half centuries following these initial contacts. In the latter half of the eighteenth century the population of the region began to increase rapidly, partially in response to the increased economic opportunities in tobacco and textiles. This trend continued into the latter part of the nineteenth century. In more recent years emigration has siphoned off much of the excess population, and since 1903 the regional population increase has fallen considerably behind the national rate (figs. 20, 24, 48). The 12-year intercensal period, 1948–1960, saw the population of the Ilocos region increase by only 22 percent, whereas that of the Philippines had increased by 41 percent in the same period.

Because of its large population and limited agricultural potential the Ilocos coast has developed into one of the larger food-deficit areas in the Philippines. Whereas the regional production of corn is essentially equal to demand, it is estimated that the three provinces of La Union, Ilocos Norte, and Ilocos Sur have an annual rice deficiency of over 73,000 metric tons of palay, or nearly 50 percent of their total rice requirements.[16] The small surpluses of palay that are produced in Abra are shipped to the coastal provinces; however, the bulk of the regional rice deficiency must be made up

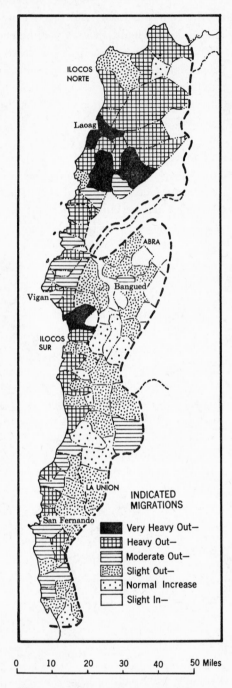

Fig. 48. Indicated net migrations of the Ilocos coast region, 1903–1960.

by shipments from the surplus rice provinces of the Cagayan Valley and the Central Plain. Shipments of surplus rice from Cagayan Province meet a large part of the deficiencies of Ilocos Norte, and deficiencies in La Union, Ilocos Sur, and the area as far north as southern Ilocos Norte Province, are generally met by shipments from Pangasinan.

Since the region cannot supply itself with essential foodstuffs, there has been pressure within the region to meet the interregional trade balance. Several areas within the Ilocos region have developed an intensive agriculture centered around the cultivation of certain cash crops, but agriculture alone cannot balance the deficit. There is seasonal migration of the relatively abundant labor force of the region to labor-deficit areas such as the Cagayan Valley; some labor goes into manufacturing and industrial occupations in different areas; and a homeward flow of funds occurs among Ilocanos who have emigrated.

Rice is the principal crop throughout the Ilocos region and in 1960 it was grown on a total of approximately 60 percent of the cultivated area, or 260,000 acres. More than one-third of the total rice crop is grown under some form of irrigation, for the Ilocano has had to turn to water control in order to insure as large and dependable crops of rice as possible. The control of water not only assures a more dependable crop, but it also permits the cultivation of longer-maturing and higher-yielding varieties of rice. Generally, the irrigation systems of the Ilocos region lack large water storage capacities, and with few exceptions, only one crop of lowland rice is attempted each year. Many of the irrigation installations are quite old, operate as cooperatives, and are well maintained. Only 7 percent of the rice lands are used to produce a second crop of rice. Even with this heavy dependence upon irrigation, the yields of rice obtained in the region are well below national averages, undoubtedly reflecting the poorer edaphic environment and generally lower land qualities, for example, steeply sloping and excessively eroded fields.

Because the summer or southwestern rains work their way northward through the Philippines and reach Ilocos Norte somewhat later and in lesser quantities than in areas farther to the south, the need for irrigation is greater in the more northern areas. Approximately two-thirds of the lowland rice area of Ilocos Norte is under irrigation, particularly in the areas along the lower courses of the Laoag, Vintar, Bacarra, and Pasuquin rivers. Ilocos Sur irrigates approximately one-third of the lowland rice lands, and these are concentrated mainly along the Santa Maria, Buaya, and Chico rivers. La Union irrigates about one-quarter of its rice crop, almost all of which is in the large 9,100-acre Amburayan River Project in the municipalities of Luna, Balaoan, and Sudipen in the northern part of the province.

It appears that without the expenditure of considerable sums of money the highly seasonal flows of the rivers of the Ilocos region cannot be effectively impounded so that a second crop of rice can be cultivated universally. Technically, the problem is not insurmountable; however, it would seem that the funds could be put to better use in other areas in the Philippines where the resultant returns in increased yields and production would be more economically justifiable. It also appears that areas of possible expansion of rice cultivation within all of the provinces of the region, except in Abra, are quite limited, and even in this latter province the mountainous topography imposes certain economic limitations.

The inability of the Ilocos region to produce sufficient rice is not unique in the Philippines; another example is the central Visayan area. Many of the other deficiency areas have turned to the cultivation of corn in order to supplement food supplies, and to a limited degree the Ilocos region has found a partial solution to its food problems in the cultivation of this less water-demanding grain crop. The amount of land available to corn, however, is relatively scarce; and since the Ilocanos continue to prefer rice to corn, those capable of producing the higher-yielding rice do so, and the corn crop generally is relegated to the hillsides and to the lowlands with poorer soils. Extremely low yields of corn are the result.

The cultivation of corn and rice is supplemented by substantial productions of sweet potatoes, beans, cassava, sugarcane, and various other fruits and vegetables. Coconut palms line the shorelines, especially occupying the sandier soils that are too infertile or dry for other crops. The coconut palm is used mainly as a source of vegetable oil, but the region produces quantities sufficient to meet local consumption only. The lower foothills and adjacent lower mountain country provide excellent environments for the cultivation of various tree fruits, for with an increase or decrease of elevation, an almost perfect range of temperature conditions can be found in these uplands. Bananas, mangoes, papayas, and pomelos are the leading fruits, and small surpluses, particularly in La Union, are available for sale in other provinces.

Tobacco is the leading commercial crop in the Ilocos region, and the region ranks as one of the principal tobacco-producing areas of the Philippines. Although cigar and native tobaccos have been cultivated in the region since shortly after the introduction of the tobacco plant into the Philippines by the Spanish, the Ilocos production of these types of tobacco has always been overshadowed by the much larger production from the Cagayan Valley. The present strong emphasis on cigarette tobacco, and the relatively large area devoted to its cultivation in the region, have come about in very recent times, actually since political independence was achieved in 1946. During the 1930's and 1940's the world's tobacco tastes gradually shifted from cigar tobaccos to the light, aromatic cigarette tobaccos, and a similar preference was acquired by the Filipinos. Most of the cigarette tobaccos and manufactured cigarettes had been imported from the United States, but with Philippine independence the continued import of cigarettes constituted a very considerable drain upon the foreign-exchange currencies available. A policy of controlled importation, coupled with price support for locally grown Virginia tobacco, was inaugurated. After lengthy investigation it was found that the Ilocos region could grow the light, Virginia-leaf tobaccos essential for cigarette manufacture. At the present time over 80 percent of the cigarette tobaccos produced in the Philippines comes from the Ilocos region, with over one-half of the national crop coming from the province of La Union alone. The region also continues to produce approximately 10 percent of the Philippine cigar tobaccos.

The introduction of Virginia-tobacco production in the Ilocos region has contributed some rather profound socioeconomic changes. The farmers have readily accepted this new crop, largely because of its excellent income potential, and at the same time, it has filled the gap between the rice harvest and planting seasons. The average family income has increased nearly fivefold since the introduction of Virginia-tobacco production. Furthermore, the additional labor demands in the tobacco fields have reduced the large seasonal migrations of farmhands. It is extremely unlikely, however, that Virginia-tobacco production would be financially successful were it not for the economic sheltering of the import controls.[17] The Ilocos region produced approximately 13,000 metric tons of Virginia leaf annually. Most of the larger cigarette factories are located in Manila, although a number of small cigarette companies have factories within the region. By their choice of location these smaller local concerns are able to take advantage of local supply situations, and at the same time, utilize the large local labor supply. Most of the region's cigarette factories are located in the municipality of Santa Catalina, Ilocos Sur (11 factories), with lesser concentrations at Laoag, Ilocos Norte, and Aringay, La Union. The funds earned from the sale of tobacco and tobacco products permit the Ilocanos to purchase food products grown in other regions and thereby correct the food deficiency of the region.

A large sector of the nonagricultural labor force, and large numbers of agricultural workers during the off-season, find employment in the important local textile industry. The Ilocos coast has long been a center for a significant weaving industry based upon native textiles. Gradually the generally inferior native fibers have been replaced by better fibers, and most of the industry now uses imported cotton. The weaving of cloth from cotton or native yarns, locally referred to as "Abel Iloko cloth," is generally a household or cottage industry. Blankets, Baguio cloth, luncheon sets, and mosquito and fish netting are specialty textile products of the region, particularly in the province of Ilocos Sur, and their manufacture provides employment for thousands of Ilocanos. In 1952 the National Development Corporation, a federal government corporation, established a large modern cotton spinning and weaving mill at Narvacan, Ilocos Sur. This 17,000-spindle factory employs several hundred workers and is the second largest textile mill in the Philippines.[18]

The South China Sea provides two important economic resources for the Ilocos region: fish and salt. Fishing is second only to agriculture in its economic importance. The open and unprotected character of much of the Ilocos coast precludes fishing operations at any great distance from the shore; thus, most of the fishing operations are conducted from small boats in waters close inshore, or in river estuaries. Several fishponds located along the coast supplement the fish catch. Laoag is the center of the Ilocos fishing industry. In general, fish production is sufficient to satisfy regional demands, but not large enough to permit outside shipments.

The six-month period of intense drought prevailing in the region from November or December through May is highly favorable for the recovery of salt from the evaporation of sea water. The most important areas of salt evaporation beds are located near the mouth of the Abra River and in the municipality of Pasuquin (Ilocos Norte), with smaller centers at Narvacan (Ilocos Sur) and Santo Tomas (La Union). Within the region much of the salt is recovered by means of the so-called Pangasinan method. Beach sands impregnated with up to 10 percent salt concentrations are leached, concentrated, and the resultant brine cooked until a relatively fine-grain crystal salt results. The production of salt by solar evaporation is big business, particularly in Ilocos Sur, and overall salt production exceeds the region's needs. Large quantities of salt are shipped to other areas in the Philippines where it finds its principal market as a fish preservative. Altogether, Ilocos salt represents 2 percent of the total salt production of the Philippines and over 3 percent of the total value of the product.

In spite of its eccentric location in the far northwestern corner of the island of Luzon, the transportation network of the Ilocos coast region is reasonably well integrated into the island's transportation system. By Philippine standards the transportation facilities within the Ilocos region are quite adequate, at least in the more densely populated areas along the coast.

The major transportation artery serving the region is the north–south route, Highway 3, which enters southern La Union from Manila and the

Central Plain, and after paralleling the entire length of the coast for over 200 miles, exits around northwestern Luzon and into the Cagayan Valley. All of the important urban centers of the region except those in Abra Province lie along, or close by, this major north–south highway. Highway 3 is concrete-surfaced throughout its length in the two southern provinces of La Union and Ilocos Sur, and here it is one of the finest highways in all of the Philippines.

Five national highways lead at right angles back from the coast toward the Cordillera Central and Mountain Province. Two hard-surfaced, all-weather roads, Highways 9 and 11, connect La Union with the highland resort city of Baguio in Mountain Province. Highway 4 links Tagudin with Bontoc. Highway 6 leaves the coast near Narvacan, passes through the Abra River Valley near Bangued, and terminates at Lubuagan; and Highway 2 connects Laoag with Kabugao. The latter three highways are gravel-surfaced for the most part, and service is frequently interrupted, particularly during the rainy season.

Bulk interregional transportation demands are provided for by the Manila-North Railroad, which enters the region from the south and terminates at Bacnotan, La Union, where a large government-constructed cement plant is located. Large numbers of passengers traveling from Manila to Baguio use the railroad, transferring from the train at Damortis for the bus trip to the highland resort center.

Owing to the presence of a good land-transportation network, the Ilocos region has not developed its water-transport facilities to the degree found in most other Philippine regions. That there is no great need for water transport is fortunate, for the Ilocos coast generally lacks good natural harbors. Most of the larger cities are served by small outports, if they are provided with port facilities at all. The most important port for the region is Poro Point, the outport for the city of San Fernando, located a few miles to the southwest. Foreign ships load and discharge at Poro Point, and a little interisland trade, consisting mainly of incoming coal, passes through the port. Lesser port installations are located at the national ports of Gaang Bay and Salomague, serving Laoag, and at Solvec, which serves Vigan.

The population of the Ilocos coastal region is a more urbanized population than that found in most other parts of the Philippines, probably owing to a greater density of population and a lesser emphasis upon agriculture. This greater degree of urbanization in the Ilocos region, however, does not imply a wealth of large cities, for only Laoag in Ilocos Norte could rank as a major urban center. Rather, there are large numbers of small towns, not exclusively agricultural market towns, but towns performing several urban functions.

Each of these larger centers has a population of between 5,000 and 10,000 persons. Approximately one-third of the population of the region is found in such centers.

Laoag, with a 1960 population of 50,000 persons, 25,000 of whom resided in the poblacion, serves as the capital of Ilocos Norte and is the largest city in northern Luzon. The city is situated along the northern bank of the nonnavigable Laoag River and begins at a point about 4 miles above the river mouth. Laoag is one of the older cities in the Philippines and was occupied by Juan de Salcedo in 1572. It serves as the major trade center for the province of Ilocos Norte and is equipped with warehouses, retail and whole-sale outlets, and several small industries. The immediate hinterland of Laoag produces large quantities of corn, rice, and aromatic cigarette filler-tobacco; the tobacco is processed in several small cigarette factories located within the city. Overland transportation facilities are good toward the east, north, and south. A good road connects Laoag with Bago where an excellent airfield is located. In good weather, ships can stand off the mouth of the river to discharge cargoes; but when the southwestern monsoon blows, service is provided through the more protected Port Currimao or Salomague Harbor.

Vigan is the capital city of Ilocos Sur. Originally named Fernandina, Vigan was founded by Vezaris in 1575 as an outpost for the Spanish defense against Japanese pirate incursions. It is the See of the Catholic Ecclesiastical Province (Archdiocese) and Territory of Nueva Segovia, which include most of northern Luzon north of Tarlac. Vigan is located along the small Mestizo River, which flows across the Abra Delta a few miles north of the main-stream. It is a town of considerable commercial importance, commanding much of the trade of the productive Abra Valley to the east. Several small textile and pottery establishments are located in the city. Pandan, 3 miles to the southeast, is the main fair-weather outport for Vigan. In 1960 the poblacion of Vigan contained approximately 10,000 persons.

San Fernando is the capital of La Union and serves as a major commercial center of far greater significance than its small population would seem to indicate. The city is located on one of the few indentations along the Ilocos coast. San Fernando is the headquarters of a Customs Service District that embraces all of northern Luzon, and its outport, Poro, which is located on Poro Point approximately 3 miles west of the city, is a Philippine port of entry. Through Poro passes much of the supplies for the rich mining districts in neighboring Mountain Province, and in turn, all of the copper concentrates and part of the gold ores produced in the highlands are shipped overseas through Poro. At the port are several large bulk-storage petroleum facilities. San Fernando is a major terminal on the railway line from Manila, and until the line was continued beyond San Fernando to Bacnotan in 1955, it served as the northern rail terminus. The 1960 population of San Fernando was 38,000 persons, of which only 4,400 lived in the poblacion.

Bangued is the capital of Abra Province. In spite of an early beginning as a seat of Spanish influence, Bangued has not increased its population markedly, owing largely to the continued small population and limited productivity of its hinterland. The city is located on the floodplain of the Abra south of the river. It is the principal commercial and market center for the agricultural areas in the valley. A good highway links Bangued with the Ilocos coastal highway system south of Vigan. In 1960 the population of the poblacion of Bangued was 7,600 persons.

Several towns of smaller size are important as minor textile centers. These centers, with their 1960 poblacion populations, include Narvacan (2,900), Caoayan (2,000), Santa (1,300), Paoay (3,200), Bangar (2,200), and Bantay (2,900). They manufacture Baguio cloth, blankets, and other finished and semifinished textile products. Adjacent to Narvacan is the National Development Corporation's large cotton-spinning and weaving mill. A small quantity of the cotton is grown locally, but the majority is imported, mainly from the United States. Caoayan is also important for its surrounding salt beds, as is Narvacan. Agoo (6,500) and Santa Catalina (1,000), small towns in the larger tobacco-producing areas, have important cigar and cigarette factories. Other towns of greater than local significance include Santo Tomas (1,200), with its fabrication of various bamboo products and pottery and salt production; San Nicolas (11,000); Candon (4,200), a sugar-milling town; and Bacnotan (1,100). At Bacnotan, which was an important agricultural town, a government-financed cement plant was established in 1955.

Steep slopes, short swift streams, and narrow coastal lowlands make up the Ilocos landscape. The Ilocano, faced with a lack of arable land after the middle of the nineteenth century and only a small amount of land that can be irrigated, has chosen to seek his livelihood in various nonagricultural pursuits, or his attentions have been focused outside the region. Because of intense population pressures in his homeland the Ilocano has become one of the prime sources of Filipino migrants who continue to supply the economic deficit of the home-resident population by the steady remission of savings. It is the continued home relations of Ilocano residents outside the region that helps to "balance the budget" and support a relatively dense population in a region with climatic, soil, and other environmental limitations. Fishing, salt-making, and textiles play relatively important roles in the economy of the region, providing the funds to purchase sufficient amounts of food, mainly rice, from other areas in the Philippines.

The Ilocos coast shows a high degree of regional cohesiveness and maturity. One has the distinct feeling that after a long absence there would be few observable changes in the landscape.

The North Luzon Highlands

The highland country of central northern Luzon is the largest single block of high and mountainous landscape in the Philippines. Roughly 40 miles wide and 200 miles long in greatest dimensions, an irregular area of just over 6,000 square miles makes up a regional entity that can be termed mountainous in every sense (fig. 49). Essentially a physiographic region, the other elements of regionalism are less sharply drawn, but in general, there is a large amount of correspondence in historical, economic, and cultural patterns that combine to make the North Luzon Highlands one of the most distinctive regional units of the Philippines. The name Cordillera Central is sometimes applied to the whole region, and in colloquial reference, the region sometimes is simply referred to as Mountain Province.

THE PHYSICAL SETTING

The North Luzon Highlands contain three separate range systems placed *en echelon* without intervening lowlands. On the west and north is the Malayan Range system, which extends southward from the north coast of Luzon. Centrally placed is the Central Range system, of lesser overall length but more massive build. On the east is the shortest of the three systems, the Polis Range system, which contains the highest elevations. The roughest and most abrupt highland fronts are on the south and west, where the Malayan Range system stands loftily above the narrow west coast of Luzon and the north end of the Central Plain, with maximum elevations approaching 6,000 feet. The Central Range system reaches elevations of 8,800 feet in massive rounded blocks rather than in individual peaked mountains. The Polis Range system on the east contains the highest elevation on Luzon in Mount Pulog, 9,612 feet, but the Polis uplands gradually descend toward the Cagayan Valley in steep-sloped gradients rather than standing above as strongly cliffed mountain fronts. The whole highland region has its greatest heights toward the south, and the skyline-trend drops northward toward the north coast of Luzon. The Caraballo Mountains, trending northwest–southeast, are not properly a part of the North Luzon Highlands, although their northwestern terminal units abut upon the southern ramparts of the highlands to close off the Central Plain of Luzon on the north. River systems have cut deep entrants into the highlands; gorges, narrow canyons, and deep V-shaped valleys fringe the

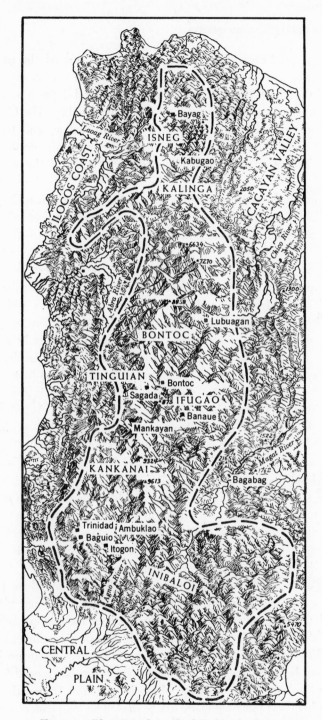

Fig. 49. Physiography of the North Luzon Highlands.

region; and all streams have steep gradients until out on the surrounding lowlands. The Agno River drains much of the southern sector into Lingayen Gulf, but the Magat River also heads in the south and drains a portion of the southern highland northeastward into the Cagayan Valley. The Chico drains much of the northeast into the lower Cagayan Valley, and the Abulug (Apayao) River drainage basin serves the north, emptying into the Babuyan Channel. The Laoag and Abra rivers transport much of the water of the northwest and west, with the Amburayan River tapping the southwestern section; and all three streams empty into the South China Sea. Other shorter streams have smaller drainage basins sandwiched between the primary streams, and their headwaters lie mostly in the margins of the highland country.

The highland region contains a mixture of basement-complex rocks widely exposed in the mountain cores. Metamorphics are distributed along zones of strain, fracture, and intrusion; and a variety of sedimentaries, younger intrusives, and volcanic extrusives are located on crests, margins, and flanks of the main mountain blocks. Streams are numerous in this humid landscape, and heavy floods keep primary channels scoured deeply, but none of the interrange sectors has been reduced to broad lowland form. Tributary headwater streams sometimes pitch into primary channels from hanging valleys, either as falls, rough rapids, or oversteepened races. Within the heart of the highland several streams have sections of more gentle gradients than are found lower on their courses, but there are no broad, filled valleys and there are very few localities having extensive level surfaces. Occasional hard local baselevels have permitted the filling of small areas by alluvial materials. Old river terraces, fragmented benches, and block-shoulders at varying positions on mountain flanks give breaks in long steep slopes. Rock slides are frequent along steep fronts, slip-off masses of rock occasionally collapse after weathering or undercutting, and gravity movements pile debris in canyon bottoms; all these processes make road maintenance difficult.

Viewed as a lowlander might see the higher uplands, there is nothing but mountains, and there are almost no areas suitable for agriculture. The highlander, on the other hand, sees many areas of lesser slope such as high benches, shoulders, soft-contoured crestlands, and medium slopes, which are usable. Within the canyons there are gravel-filled areas at stream junctions, near-bottom benches, and old talus slopes which can be cropped by shifting cultivation or used in the building of terrace systems. Around the flanks of the main highland there are many usable sites. The long eastern slope of the Polis Range system, toward the Cagayan Valley, has foothill zones of fair utility. Toward the northern end of the main highlands in the Apayao district, where elevations are lower in general, there are many hill slopes and valley margins suitable for cultivation. Although the highlands form a rough and mountainous region of strong relief and steep slopes, the landscape surface does not present a total aspect of hard rock surfaces and sheer mountain walls.

As a generalization, soils are thin, skeletal in development, and patchy in occurrence. There are many areas of hard-rock surface and zones thinly covered with semiweathered rubble. Benches and river terraces tend to be gravelly to sandy. Areas long covered with vegetation have deeper mantles of weathered materials; there are zones of volcanic extrusives with relatively unconsolidated surface materials. There are a few such regions as the Trinidad Valley, north of Baguio, in which local alluvial filling has produced surfaces of gentler gradients with soil cover relatively well developed. Located at 4,800 feet elevation, the Trinidad Valley is but about 1½ miles wide by 3 miles long, but in the highlands it is a valuable agricultural area. For the terrace-builder there is soil material to be had by gathering in small lots from stream bottoms, shoulders, rock crevices, and benches. This is the region of famous terrace development in which the historical building of agricultural surfaces has turned whole valleys or mountain slopes into highly controlled agricultural landscapes. On such terrace systems, soils are artificial and created by human labor; old terrace systems show the developmental effects of the processes of soil formation. In the lower country and the foothill margins soil covers become thicker and less skeletal. Shifting cultivation normally has involved infrequent cropping of precise sites, with long regeneration cycles, so extreme damage has been negligible. Around some of the old population centers, however, shifting cultivation on lands complementary to the terrace systems has involved only short regeneration cycles, with a considerable effect in altering both soils and vegetation.

The natural situation of the highlands, uninhabited, would indicate a forest cover for wild vegetation. Human occupation of the North Luzon Highlands, however, is of long duration, and the vegetation cover in the contemporary period is a very mixed one. The vertical range of the highlands, and the varied exposures of local regions, result in a wide range of wild-growth systems and of vegetation patterns, almost all of which have been modified by the long historical occupance of the highland country. The lower zones on the western, northern, and eastern flanks are naturally areas of dry monsoon forests, owing to their seasonal dry periods. Above about 3,000 feet the Benguet pine is at home in extensive, open, and relatively pure stands of forest, and above about 7,000 feet the moss forests of mixed species become common. Viewed today, there are extensive areas of grass cover, numerous parklands, areas of immature secondary forests of mixed species patterns, zones of secondary bamboo-and-thicket jungle (chiefly at relatively low elevations on the eastern and northern flanks), strips of dry deciduous forest, middle-upland coniferous forests, and the highland moss forests. In localities where some land is currently being utilized in shifting cultivation (fig. 50), there is marked variety by mosaic patterns ranging from weed-and-tree seedling plots to patches of mature forest about ready for clearing. Timber cutting in the modern period has stripped off large areas of the Benguet pine for use in and around the gold and copper mines. The highland wild vegetation cover does not yield so rich an appropriative harvest of food products as can be had in the lowland forest areas.

Climatically, the North Luzon Highlands differ from almost all of the rest of the archipelago by virtue of elevation, and they resemble the medium-elevation tropical highlands in general. Temperature regimes are lower and more comfortable for all, as attested by the development of Baguio (elevation 5,000 feet) as a modern summer political capital and as a summer resort for the lowlander. Baguio has an annual average temperature of 64.2° F., which is 15–17 degrees cooler than the surrounding lowland country, and the loftier highlands are, of course, cooler still. During the winter months of November through February, Filipino lowlanders find the highlands very cold at night, and wonder at the scanty clothing of the nonacculturated native resident, whereas many non-Filipinos from mid-latitude homelands find the temperatures of the highland country delightful at all times of the year. With a wide range in elevations and exposures there is local variety in temperature regimes between the foothills and the high mountain areas, and frosts are not uncommon at higher elevations.

Most of the higher sections of the highlands fall into the per-humid climatic pattern of the Thornthwaite classification, with precipitation totals ranging from 70 to 200 inches per year. There are local situations and regions that suffer rain-shadow effects at some season of the year, and the northwestern margins tend to be less humid in winter and the south to be very wet in summer. The lower flanks of the highlands, on all sides, have short-to-long dry seasons. Summer seasons often tend to be more cloudy than the winter periods, particularly in the southern sector. Within the upper sector of the southern highlands the overabundance of precipitation is somewhat of a problem. Particularly when a strong typhoon passes across northern Luzon, extremely heavy downpours may occur, resulting in every stream becoming a torrent. Such occurrences create problems for some of the rice terracers, who then must guard against heavy flooding of their field systems. On the other hand, seasonal scarcity of water, through an unusually prolonged dry spell,

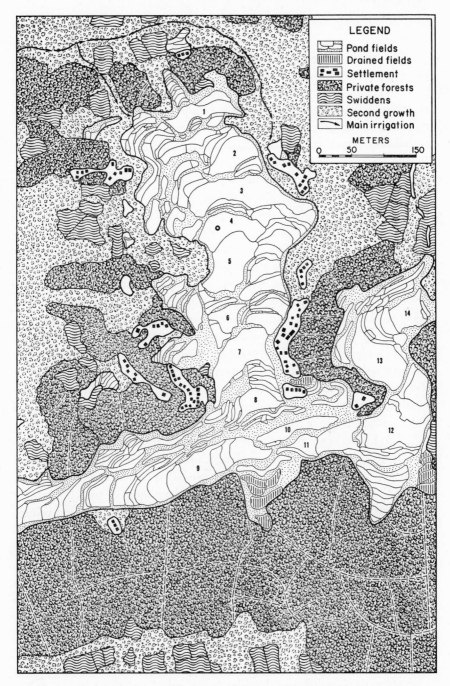

Fig. 50. Land use and field patterns in Banaue, Mountain Province, 1964.

may cause shortage of water for the maintenance of flow on wet-field systems growing rice.

One agricultural potential of the highland climatic regime remains to be properly exploited. Not all mid-latitude crops will thrive under the equable, cool temperature regimes and humid precipitation regimes, but many of the vegetables will do very well.[19] A growing Filipino appetite for a wide range of mid-latitude vegetables can be satisfied in large part by exploiting this particular climatic situation. Although a few vegetables have been grown near Baguio for some decades, it is only recently that effective development of vegetable growing has come about, and the pattern can be developed to a far greater extent than has been done so far.

Although the cropland resources of the highlands are not marked, there is a strong range of resources in minerals and in timber. The North Luzon Highlands contain valuable resources of gold and copper, plus a few minor minerals occurring in combination with these two, such as lead, zinc, chromite, and silver. Of these, silver is the only one of present economic significance. The Baguio gold district, in the south, is a productive one far from being worked out at present, and the Lepanto copper-ore bodies, north of Baguio, contain sizable reserves of medium-grade ores. Other potential sources of both minerals have not been well surveyed. Much of the old forest cover has been reduced to mixed second-growth or to noncommercial woodland, but there remains a considerable volume of timber scattered throughout the highlands which can be utilized without endangering watershed control, and timber cutting is one of the highland economic pursuits.

The hydroelectric potential of the highlands represents another environmental resource, the development of which has just begun. The development of the double-unit Ambuklao-Binga multiple-purpose dams and power plants, northeast of Baguio, are the first of what may be a series of such projects for flood control and power development around the highlands. A huge volume of water, derived chiefly from summer precipitation, drains out of the highlands, with consequent floods in the surrounding lowlands. The first power was produced at Ambuklao in 1956. By 1963 two of the seven potential sites were producing 175,000 kilowatts. The total Ambuklao-Binga project, when completed, will produce 420,000 kilowatts. All presently produced power enters the Luzon Grid and is consumed around Manila.

THE CULTURAL SETTING

Embedded in the literatures and vocabularies dealing with the peoples and cultures of the North Luzon Highlands are such descriptive terms as *pagan, non-Christian, tribal, headhunter, Stone Age, mountaineer, terrace-building*

proto-Malay, and *Igorot,* as well as a few less meaningful terms such as *wild,*
savage, barbaric, aboriginal, primitive, uncivilized, and *semicivilized.* This
regional population fell outside the normal threefold Spanish classification
"moros, negrillos, and indios" because it could not easily be civilized as were
the other indios. Here was the largest single block of peoples remaining
infieles (heathen wild people to the Spanish, and therefore, a fourth grouping), and as they occupied an environment quite different from the lowlands,
a special aura of differentness became attached to them.[20] Anthropologists
early seemed to find basic subracial differences among the highlanders and
between the highlanders and the lowlanders. Ethnographic studies elaborated
many groupings based upon supposed racial characteristics and upon particular culture complexes. Attempts to fit the variations into classified patterns
resulted in a large series of ethnocultural names for groupings, and at one
point, well over a dozen ethnic regionalities seemed valid. Popular reference
adopted the term "Igorot" for the whole population, in an ethnic but
all-inclusive sense, although the term properly is only the Tagalog word for
"mountain-dwelling" or "mountaineer."

More recently the separate racial origins have become suspect, the major
groupings have been reduced by careful linguistic-cultural studies to six or
seven, and an organically constructed account of the occupance of the
highlands is beginning to take shape. There remain many puzzles and
questions as to the sequences of development prior to, and during, the
Spanish occupation of the Islands. Anthropology has produced a large literature that often tends to discuss distributions, agricultural economics, and
cultural patterns in a somewhat static sense, in that the areas and peoples are
considered culturally stable for purposes of analysis, that is, changing variables had to be ignored while analyzing the constants. The nature of the
constants, and the nature of the variables, have become increasingly open to
question among anthropologists.

Meanwhile, culture change was taking place at a rapid rate during the
decades of the American period. The peoples of the highlands are undergoing
processes of assimilation into the whole Filipino population. For example,
only 28 percent of the population tabulated by the 1960 census of Mountain
Province admitted to being pagan in religion, whereas 55 percent claimed
some form of the Catholic religion and 16 percent claimed to be Protestant.
Some 19 percent of the total population claimed Ilocano as their mother
tongue, and obviously, many of the Christians are Ilocano in-migrants now
permanently resident in the highlands. This, however, may well be only a
pattern typical of the whole historical process of occupance of the highlands.
The process is not equal in rate among all regional subgroups. In the 1960

census enumeration only 5 percent of the 16,000 residents of Bontoc municipality (the heart of the Bontoc culture region) admitted to paganism, and 42 percent of the population over 10 years of age claimed to be literate. None of the 3,740 residents of Bayag municipality (Apayao culture area) admitted to paganism in 1960, and 62 percent claimed literacy. But in Sagada municipality (within the Bontoc culture area) 57 percent of the 11,548 people claimed paganism, although 62 percent claimed literacy; and in Banaue municipality (the heart of the Ifugao culture region) 67 percent of the 17,877 inhabitants admitted to paganism, and only 25 percent claimed to be literate.[21] Comparable data for the 1903 census are not available, for all population not claiming to be Catholic were considered wild Igorot, and therefore, pagan and illiterate. The 1903 census does indicate that very few Ilocano were then resident in the highlands as compared to the significant number present in 1960 (see appendix tables 9–13 under Mountain Province).

During early Spanish times processes of cultural change proceeded rapidly on the lowlands, with many of those who resisted change moving out of range of Spanish contact; in north Luzon this probably meant moving into the protective high-country margins where possible. As lowlanders became Christianized the resisting elements of a former culture group became set apart into what later became recognizable as an apparent, discrete culture group. For example, the Tinguians, formerly identified as a linguistic-culture group of the northern, western flanks of the highlands, may have been Ilocano who declined to become Christian and who, thereby, preserved much of the old culture during the period in which the Christianized Ilocano took on a new segment of culture and dropped much of the old. Even language is involved in such change and Tinguian (Tinggian) today is still a minor dialect of a few thousand people of Abra (chiefly) and Mountain Province. Around the fringes of the North Luzon Highlands this process perhaps occurred in several situations.[22]

This chapter is not concerned primarily with the comparative ethnic, linguistic, or sociopolitical makeup of the North Luzon Highlands, but it cannot escape the implications of processes of historical settlement, cultural development, and the patterns of interpretation of those phenomena. The margins of the highlands offered numerous river valley–canyon approaches to the highlands for the lowlanders, either as whole groups, or as individuals, families, bands, and segments of former culture groups. The processes of access may have been migration in the formal sense, slow drift away from steady pressures, or inching along in one direction over a landscape in patterns of normal usage through time. The migrational movements into the highlands are very old and long-continued, but it is clear that the Spanish period was a time of accentuated regional movement. Since it occurred almost all around the highlands, there resulted the differential regional separation of lowlanders from highlanders. Each group moving into the highlands preserved some of its group culture patterns; the highlands, therefore, became a region of great cultural diversity. The struggles for position among the newer in-migrants, and between the newcomers and the prior occupants, involved the control of usable localities, the control over water sources among the wet-rice growers, and the establishment of territoriality patterns. These struggles normally involved varieties of tribal warfare and sociolegal institutions out of which emerged the lowland concept that all highlanders were militant headhunters and warlike peoples.

At the end of the Spanish period there came a relaxing of political, religious, and economic pressures upon the peoples of the highlands as American controls sought new means of arranging the governance of the region. These new means set up new processes of change because of their very differences from Spanish patterns. At present the processes of change are incomplete and partial; some decades will be required to affect the mature reshaping of highland regional and unit cultures to the end that distinctive regional patterns will remain which are, at the same time, essentially Filipino patterns.

Accepting the broad circumstances of the American period, it is clear that the following seven regionalisms can be loosely described, although this becomes somewhat an oversimplification that fails to include several minority groups as yet little studied.[23] Six of these seven are properly parts of the larger highland regionalism.

1) Along the southern, western Malayan Range front and eastward into the southern Central Range, and in the higher northwestern sections of the Caraballo Mountains, is the region of the Inibaloi (Benguet Igorot, Benjuet, Nabaloi, Ibaloi, and other names). These people are chiefly resident in dispersed settlements or small hamlets, and they have been in the past chiefly cultivators of root crops. Taro and yams appear to be the oldest, but the sweet potato (camote) had risen to status as the chief crop early in the Spanish period. In the nineteenth century they were learning to build earth-walled terraces on which to grow wet rice in the winter and camotes in the summer. Perhaps they derived from the peoples of the northern Central Plain of Luzon, having followed the southern river valleys northward for river gold and for refuge. The several groups do not form one single culture group, but the regional variations within the zone are not marked. It was within this sector that Baguio was chosen as a hill station in 1903, and the nearer Inibaloi

have become quite highly modernized in many ways. The 1960 census tabulated 63,000 Inibaloi-speakers, of whom 56,000 resided in Mountain Province.

2) Along the western flanks of the Malayan Range, northward of the Inibaloi, but reaching eastward also, is the home area of the Kankanai (Igorot, Lepanto, Lepanto Igorot, Northern Kankanai, Southern Kankanai, Kankany, Kataugnan, and various other local names). Village dwellers in the lofty highlands, they were growers of root crops for a long period, but have been building terraces and increasingly growing wet-field rice since the late eighteenth century. Differentiated into several local groups by variable trait complexes, their essential unity and origins are not clear, but they may well be derived from repeated movements off the west coast lowlands. Copper mining and gold panning, and trading routes to the western lowland, are old phenomena. The 1960 census tabulated 71,000 Kankanai-speakers, of whom 59,000 were in Mountain Province and the rest located in Ilocos Sur and La Union provinces in the foothill country.

3) In the middle northwest, in the upper Abra River drainage basin, have been rural scatterings of peoples labeled Tinguian. Chiefly mobile and rural, shifting cultivators of the hill country margins, these groups never attained a sufficiently large population or territorial control to achieve regional unity. Their hillward movements were perhaps pre-Spanish, and there was further movement during Spanish times, but late Christian movement in the same direction is submerging the Tinguian as a culture group. The 1960 census tabulated only 6,300 Tinguian (Tinggian)-speakers, almost all of whom were located in Abra Province, indicating a foothill zone of residence rather than a highland location.

4) In the far northwest and north, in the northern, lower-mountain country, and among several drainage basins are scattered several related groups of peoples who occupied the mountain region without ever achieving a territorial stability or a united culture pattern. Known chiefly as the Isneg (Apayao, Apayaw, Itneg, and other names), these people lived either in dispersed, rural dwellings or in small hamlets and practiced shifting cultivation with dry rice as their crop. Those who were farthest interior worked along the median slopes, the lower slopes, and into the stream valleys, with their residential bases seldom far from a stream course, but many of these peoples are still lowland residents. Many crops are grown as complements, and there are local variations in the agricultural economies according to the local ecological situation. Collectively, several thousand persons are to be grouped here in the highland sectors of several drainage basins leading northward toward the coast. Not clearly related to either the Ilocano country

or to the Cagayan Valley, perhaps these folk moved upstream along the rivers leading out of the northwest corner of Luzon. The 1960 census tabulated 33,000 Isneg-speakers, of whom 11,800 were within Mountain Province, and 18,600 in Abra, with small numbers in each of Ilocos Norte and Cagayan provinces.[24]

5) Right across the highlands, from the western crests to the eastern lower flanks, south of the Isneg zone, is the home of the Kalinga (Calinga, Catalungan, Kalibugan, and other names). Separable into several subregional and subcultural groupings, the basic economies vary according to the ecological environments, the duration of their occupance, and perhaps, their ultimate origins. These patterns range from rural dispersion of homesteads to village dwelling, and from mobile shifting cultivation to the construction and cultivation of excellent wet-field rice terraces. With an old basic economy of root cropping, there is evidence of the evolution of dry-field rice cultivation, and the gradual evolution of the terrace and wet-field systems. The Kalinga show relationships to both the Isneg to the north and to the Ibanag of the Cagayan Valley, but local regionalisms of several kinds remain clear among them. Perhaps the Chico River line was their approach into the higher country. The 1960 census tabulated 46,600 Kalinga-speakers, of whom 44,500 resided in Mountain Province.

6) East of the Central Range, and in the valleys around the Polis Range, toward the south, live the Ifugao (Ifugaw, Mayayaw, and other local names). They occupy steep-relief landscapes in which the most impressive of all the terrace systems have been elaborated. The Ifugao are perhaps old residents of the highland margins, although they have moved steadily upward into the higher country. Perhaps their origins lie in the lower hill country to the southeast. They are village dwellers who depend chiefly on wet-field rice crops, but who also practice shifting cultivation on slope fields for cropping camotes. The 1960 census tabulated 75,000 Ifugao-speakers, of whom 72,000 resided in Mountain Province; the remainder were in the foothill zones in the southeast just outside the political province.

7) Somewhat centrally located, but with a range that stretches westward onto the Malayan Range flanks, is the Bontoc country (Bontoc, Bontoc Igorot, Bontok, and other regional names incorporating the word "Bontoc"). The Bontoc are one of the most numerous of the regional groups. Dwelling chiefly in compact villages, the Bontoc build good to excellent stone-walled terraces, grow wet-field rice as a primary crop, but also employ shifting cultivation for camotes, yams, and other root crops. Camotes are grown on terraces as a summer crop in the modern period, but the Bontoc grow little upland, dry-field rice. There is considerable variation both culturally and in

the economy of the Bontoc from east to west across their range. The 1960 census tabulated 78,000 Bontoc-speakers, with all but a thin scattering resident in the home area in Mountain Province.

Although there was no distinct regionalism, there were certain zones formerly occupied by the Negrito peoples of this part of Luzon. During Spanish times Negrito were reported from all the foothill margins of the North Luzon Highlands. Since 1900 the Negrito population has been much reduced, although today there still are small bands of them to be found in the northern margins of the highlands, and in a few other locations.

The above regionalization has not dealt with the factual elements of culture as the ethnologist marshalls them, except for the patterns of language, residence, and agricultural economy. Social structure, political organization, patterns of dress, religious practice, and customs and mores are important in the differentiation of these upland cultures. Linguistic studies of relationships, and change, between the highland groups and the surrounding lowlands are by no means complete. The broad bases for regionalisms, however, are relatively clear within the highlands, and between the highlands and the surrounding lowlands. The latter contrasts will, of course, decline steadily. Already Ilocano, as a language and as an indicator of a cultural pattern, is the mother tongue of more highlanders than speak any of the local languages; and the numbers of Tagalog, Pangasinan, Pampangan, and Ibanag (Cagayan Valley) speakers are rising steadily, along with the use of English. In 1960, 153,000 persons, just over one-third of the population, could speak English, and some 80,000, or almost one-fifth, could speak Tagalog. The changing religious patterns have been suggested, and changes in dress, housing, and social custom will grow steadily as the Philippinization of the North Luzon Highlands proceeds.

Terrace building and water control, as a reputed "eighth wonder of the world," is a distinctive cultural phenomenon of the North Luzon Highlands. Terracing, as done at Banaue in the Ifugao region, consists of building stone dry-walls (without mortar) along the slope and on contour. (In fig. 50 elevation decreases more than 300 feet between fields 1 and 14.) The walls are given a slight batter (inward lean at the top), and often exceed 20 feet in height, being topped by sluices for water drainage. Earth materials fill each unit to a level just below the top of the wall. By staggering the field units in overlapping manner on different levels, a whole valley slope may be terraced toward the top of such a manner as to resemble a sculptured system. The field units may be as narrow as 8 feet and up to nearly 100 yards in length on steep slopes, though they commonly are somewhat wider and not so long. Water is introduced either at the top of a terrace series, or as a complementary supply, at some intermediate point. Through sluices in each field unit the water moves by gravity downward across each terrace level until it empties into a stream channel in the valley bottom. Water control consists of careful adjustment of the initial volume and its distribution to all field units in a terraced series. Water control must be able to bring in at high-level points the needed volume at any time during the growing season, but such control must also be able to divert excess water at any point at any time.

Whereas the Ifugao build terrace walls of stone with a slight batter, the Bontoc build stone walls with almost no batter, the Kalinga use a stone basewall with upper walls of earth given a high batter, and the Inibaloi build rather crude earth walls with a high batter. Northern Kalinga and the Isneg areas exhibit little high-quality terracing, and the terrace series consists of a few levels only. Tremendous labor goes into construction of the walls, gathering the earth fill and maintaining the soundness of terrace walls, but it is the skill of water control making for good soil maintenance and field productivity that expresses the true engineering ability of the terracers.

Spectacular as a few individual valleys are as sculptured mosaics, admiration has enlarged the areal extent of wet-field terrace systems in the North Luzon Highlands. Precise data is scanty, and the proper elements were not tabulated in regular census-taking. The 1960 census listed 53,470 farms in all of Mountain Province, encompassing 186,000 acres of actual cropped land. Listed as "irrigated" were 36,450 farms possessing 63,000 acres actually under irrigation, of which 57,000 acres were planted in first-crop wet-field rice during the census crop year. Yields of about 1,200 pounds per acre in 1960 were slightly above the national average, but upland rice yields in the province averaged only about 830 pounds per acre. Regardless of inadequate data, the conclusion is sound that there is far less land under terrace-and-water control than has often been inferred; but the system remains spectacular even if the whole of the highland is not extensively terraced.

The standard data take no cognizance of the physical nature of crop fields, and there is no sure way of determining the total acreage of terraced fields. In 1960 camotes ranked second to rice in the amount of land devoted to cultivation, a total of 36,000 acres. There were also several thousand acres of corn, cabbages, potatoes, beans, bananas, and coffee trees. Underreporting may be suspected, either purposeful or owing to lack of accurate survey data upon farmlands on rugged terrain. Underreporting of caingin cultivation on slope fields is very likely, as official policy seeks to abolish it. Estimates by well-informed sources have suggested a total of 60,000 acres for the total of terraced lands, but this total must be considered no more than an educated guess.

In addition to areas of cropped terraced lands, every culture group in the highlands carries on a complementary program of shifting cultivation varying in scale both among different localities and among the several groups. The Isneg are chiefly shifting cultivators, whereas the Bontoc now practice less shifting cultivation than they do terraced permanent-field cropping. Lands cropped by shifting cultivation often lie among the terraced sectors or surrounding them, but in some situations the temporary fields lie at varying distances from terraced zones. Figure 50 shows a considerable area of land actually under cropping by shifting cultivation, as well as a significant area of land in some stage of vegetative regeneration preparatory to future cropping; however, as this figure is restricted in area to permit a detailed presentation of terracing, it does not effectively present the area distribution of shifting cultivation in the local region.

THE ECONOMIC PATTERNS

The agricultural economy of the North Luzon Highlands can be characterized as dominated by subsistence patterns somewhat more completely than that of any other major region in the Islands. There are at present just the beginnings of modern commercial agriculture, though it is likely that these patterns will increase rather rapidly in the future production of certain crops. Two cropping systems have been employed by all the peoples of the highlands, shifting cultivation and permanent-field cropping, with the latter growing steadily in significance through time. Each ethnic group has employed both in some order of importance: the modern Isneg still are chiefly shifting rice-cultivators who grow only a small portion of their crops in kitchen gardens or permanent fields, whereas the Bontoc perhaps do as little shifting cultivation as any group, with a larger share of their cropping being done on terraced fields. The kitchen garden and the terraced field have been the sites of permanent-field cropping, and to the extent that any group has employed either, its importance has been larger or smaller.

At the early base of the cropping systems was the employment of the taros, a few of the yams, some of the fruits, and a very few vegetables; gathering of wild products and the hunting of animals formed a complementary phase. The antiquity of wet-field terracing and the employment of rice as a crop are open to some doubt, although the common interpretation is that both are very old in the highlands. In any case, rice has increased in importance in the cropping systems over time, and it may well be that more rice is grown in the highlands today than ever in the past. Soon after its introduction to the Islands by the Spanish the sweet potato replaced in importance the taros and the few yams grown in the highlands, and the sweet potato has been the staple food crop of many of the local regions and ethnic groups in the post-Spanish period. Corn quickly spread throughout the highlands, but its ranking importance remains rather low except in the western foothill country; the recent increase of corn-growing in the Cagayan Valley is slowly spreading it into the foothill margins there too. Bananas and coconuts, nearly ubiquitous in the lowlands, are grown in only a few favored localities in the highlands; many other fruits widely disseminated on the lowlands are of lesser importance in the high country.

Rice and camotes are the two basic staple food crops of the highlands. Traditionally, wet-field rice had been a winter crop and the camote a summer crop when one or the other is the crop staple; traditionally, also, some ethnic groups have depended more upon one than upon the other. The nature of the climatic regime, particularly in the southern highlands with the most humid and most cloudy period in the summer, might seem to account for this seasonal reversal of wet-field rice growing, but there is more to it than that. Conflicting seasonal demands for labor, the sacredness of the rice crop, and other complicating factors are involved, and the variable adoption and ranking importance of each crop at any given time period (since the historical record began in Spanish times) to any given ethnic group remains one of the puzzles of highland economic history. The double cropping of wet-field rice is rather new in the highlands, and a number of changes have taken place in recent decades. On balance, in recent decades rice outranks the camote in value of crop, in acreage planted, and in order of preference among the whole population.

The North Luzon Highlands had, for the most part, fed itself; however, there have been deficiencies in certain agricultural products that are not grown there in adequate volume to meet the demand. Betelnut, for example, has long been a trade product carried into the highlands on all trade routes. Cattle and pigs have been moved as a trade product into the highlands where they are utilized in ceremonial feasts. Cotton and various types of cloth have long been imported, although the scanty clothing of the highlanders required only small amounts of cloth in the past. In the contemporary period a taste for many varieties of food products is expanding importation of food commodities not grown in the highlands. During the era of the Spanish tobacco monopoly, highland-grown tobacco frequently was smuggled down into the surrounding lowlands for illicit sale into the commercial market. In the modern period tobacco is grown on perhaps one farm in ten, for local home use or barter trading only, but the region no longer supplies its consumption volume.

In the past the highlands produced no agricultural surpluses worth trading to the lowlands. In the more modern period the rise of mid-latitude vegetable growing in the highlands is producing a valuable regional export product whose future development could be rather large. Such mid-latitude vegetables as cabbage, onion, celery, tomato, white potato, and many others are now flowing in steadily increasing volumes from the highlands. Begun in the Trinidad Valley near Baguio for the summer-resort trade, this commercial cropping system is spreading outside the local area.

In the whole of the highlands there is not much reserve land that can easily be put into agriculture of a productive kind, and with a growing population, it is an open question how much longer the region can continue to feed its inhabitants. Although some terracing has been done in recent decades, terracing is increasingly costly. Slope fields previously utilized in shifting cultivation became eroded and go out of productive use. Per acre yields of rice are not notably high in the highlands, but camote yields are above the national average. Whether agricultural production within the highlands can keep pace with increasing demand remains to be seen. The conversion of some lands formerly planted in food crops for home use to commercial vegetable production may well prove financially productive and more than pay for the import of food deficits.

The forest resources of the highlands are significant in value but represent a special situation; there is the problem of the growing demand for watershed protection of the surrounding lowlands which inhibits the exploitation of timber resources, and there are the more costly problems of transporting timber out of the highlands. Around the flanks of the highlands there are some dipterocarp forests, but the chief resource lies in the mid-mountain forests consisting chiefly of the Benguet pine. Some 20 percent of the highlands carries commercial forest growth, chiefly of these pine forests. Growing more openly, the volume of timber per acre is less than for lowland forests. In the past, cutting for economic use has been chiefly for mine timbering and building construction within the highlands. Official government policy is to keep the highland timber in the highlands, and the region does cut sufficient amounts for its own regional use. In the early 1960's there were fifteen sawmills distributed throughout the highlands.

The mining industry producing gold and copper is an old one in the highlands. Alluvial gold panned from streams formed an early trade commodity employed in the barter for goods in the lowland, and such gold may have stimulated much of the settlement of the highlands. Copper mining is at least pre-Spanish in age. In neither product, however, did the population carry on sufficiently advanced mining, or hold sufficient stocks of the metal, that the Spanish could easily develop a larger mining industry or reap a rich harvest by seizure. Late Spanish efforts at mining both gold and copper were unproductive. Therefore, highland mining is a twentieth-century development, and the total resources of the region are not well-known. In practical terms, gold mining is confined to the southern highlands where several companies are working lode deposits in the region just east of Baguio. In the earlier years the Baguio gold mines produced a large share of the Philippine gold output. Marginal low-grade reserve ores have rendered production more costly, and general high costs of mining gold have restricted the expansion of mining operations. The Baguio mines provide appreciable employment and continue to be significant to regional economy. Copper mining at Mankayan, north of Baguio, works a large body of medium-grade ore containing by-product silver and gold; the copper concentrates are trucked down to Poro, on the southern Ilocos coast, for overseas shipment. The recent rise of copper mining in other parts of the Islands reduces the relative importance of the Mankayan copper mines, but the mines continue to employ a goodly number of miners and make a contribution to regional economy. As the ore body is large, copper mining can continue at Mankayan for a long period. Undeveloped mineral resources elsewhere in the highlands will, in time, provide further contributions to the regional economy.

In modern terms, the highlands are not well provided with transportation facilities. Mountain Province stands well below the national average in road density. One airport at Baguio gives easy access to and from Manila. Traditionally, the separate ethnic regions within the highlands had little contact with one another, except for militant raiding, and the main lines of contact were with the surrounding lowlands. Today a half-dozen lines allow access from different lowland situations, but the mountain roads were costly to build, are difficult to maintain, and do not provide for heavy-volume traffic flows. Several approaches lead into the southern highlands from the southern Ilocos coast or from the Central Plain, and with their cross connections, give the Baguio region a reasonably adequate regional road system. Mining development and the Ambuklao dam and power project have helped develop this local regional pattern. Two roads from the west coast, farther north, lead into the highlands, but no road so far gives access to the northern highland sector, and only two roads approach from the Cagayan Valley. Within the central northern highland a few short roads lead off the single north–south main route. High relief and difficult country will long inhibit the development of a really good pattern of road transport in the highlands, but several routes are under construction, and in time, a reasonably good road pattern will crisscross the highlands.

In the past the peoples of the highlands carried on relatively little trade and commerce, so market towns, trade centers, transport centers, wholesale centers, and similar facilities have been lacking in the region. Silent barter often served between enemies, and the items traded internally often did not require extensive facilities. Economic exchange certainly was not lacking, but the chief markets, and the market sites, lay in the surrounding lowlands, and highlanders took their gold, corn, deerskins, beeswax, fibers, and other items down from the highlands to trading points adjacent to their home sectors. There they engaged in barter trade for cloth, ceramic wares, beads and jewelry, salt, metal products, iron for tools, cattle and pigs, and other wares.[25] There was little centering of intrahighland movement of exchange because of hostile relations between groups, and because economically the highland was not one region but a zone of subregions, each unit of which was tributary to a lowland region.

In the modern period it is only slowly that stores, shops, restaurants, hotels, warehouses, transport terminals, and related facilities have accumulated in any of the "towns" of the highlands, except for Baguio. Baguio, by virtue of its capital status and the many seasonal visitors to its summer resort, has developed since 1900 a significant pattern of most of the physical facilities and services that go with the normal functioning of commerce and interregional movement of people and goods. Its closest connections are with Manila, from whence comes its resort traffic and to which flows most of the special mid-latitude vegetable produce of the local region. Judged as a Philippine trade center Baguio is both small and eccentric in location in its highland region, but intraregional unity and trade flow is barely developing, and most of the subregions maintain the old connections with the adjacent lowland regions. These connections are now being facilitated by the evolving road system.

In evolving the modern political structure of Mountain Province, which was organized in 1908, there was partial recognition of the ethnolinguistic structure of the highlands.[26] The Apayao, Kalinga, and Ifugao zones became subprovincial districts, but Bontoc and Benguet (Inibaloi) districts divide the Kankanai region between them. Subdistrict and municipality administrative centers were chosen partly on accessibility and partly on the basis of locality centering and size of villages. As the Ifugao, Bontoc, and Kankanai formerly had large villages, both the poblaciones and the barrios show higher populations. Although the Inibaloi formerly showed greater tendency toward dispersal, modern influences have increased many of the settlements in the Baguio hinterland, and the only settlements over about 4,000 are in the Baguio region. Itogon, with a poblacion population of 7,400 in 1960, and Trinidad with 3,300 are considered most nearly urban entities. Elsewhere, poblacion populations still represent village concentrations of the traditional variety, and there are a good many of them that range in the 2,000–3,000 size pattern.[27] The Apayao zone shows lighter populations, fewer municipalities, and smaller villages than do the areas farther south. Western Bontoc and the Ifugao districts have heavier regional populations, so there are more municipalities with smaller areas and large villages. In the modern period the mine centers show large residential settlements. Baguio is now a chartered city of some territorial size, with a total population just over 50,000, of whom 27,000 resided in the city proper in 1960.

The 1903 census reported about 200,000 people in north Luzon as Igorot, although the political boundaries differed from those of what later came to be Mountain Province. The 1960 census reported the provincial population at 435,839. About 110,000 nonhighland-language speakers were tabulated as resident in the province in 1960, and about 320,000 speakers of the six highland languages.[28] In 1903 there were extremely few lowlanders resident in the highlands; since then there has been an active in-migration pattern in which Ilocanos from the western lowlands have been the chief migrants. The native population has increased only moderately during the first half of the twentieth century, at a rate lower than the national rate.

TEN

~~~~~ *The Core Region:*
Central and Southern Luzon

The Zambales-Bataan Hill Country

The Zambales-Bataan region occupies the westernmost part of the island of Luzon. The region consists, in the main, of a low, rugged mountain range, the Zambales Mountains or Western Cordillera. These highlands extend for more than 150 miles from Cape Bolinao southward into Bataan Peninsula and reach maximum elevations of over 6,000 feet in their central region (fig. 51). The Zambales Mountains lie between the broad Central Plain of Luzon and the South China Sea and rather effectively block moisture-bearing air masses, removing considerable quantities of moisture that might otherwise reach the Central Plain. Numerous short, rapidly flowing streams have their sources in these well-watered mountains, and the small floodplains and deltas they have created along the South China Sea coast constitute the only level, arable lands in the region. Generally the mountains are heavily forested and very difficult of access. Thus delimited, the Zambales-Bataan region includes all of the areas of the provinces of Bataan and Zambales, together with mountainous sections of northwestern Pangasinan, western Tarlac, and western Pampanga. The total land area of the region is approximately 2,900 square miles, upon which live slightly more than 500,000 persons.

Unlike many other areas on Luzon, particularly in the adjacent region of the Central Plain to the east, the Zambales-Bataan region is relatively sparsely

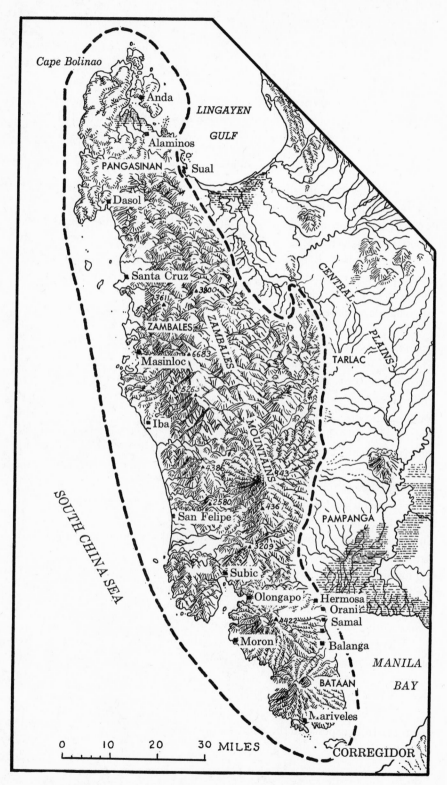

Fig. 51. Physiography of the Zambales-Bataan region.

settled. The average density of population is only 175 persons for each square mile of total area. Nevertheless, in light of the limited expanses of arable land, the physiological population pressures are relatively high: 1,900 and 1,500 persons per square mile of cultivated land in Zambales and Bataan, respectively, and somewhat lower in northwestern Pangasinan. Relatively dense populations are found in the northwestern section of the region near Lingayan Gulf, along the eastern shores of Bataan Peninsula facing Manila Bay, and in a few places along the western littoral (fig. 21). The interior mountainous sections are sparsely occupied by shifting agriculturists.

Agriculture is the dominant economic activity throughout the region although in certain areas fishing, forestry, and mining assume considerable importance. In spite of its nearness to Manila and the populous Central Plain, the Zambales-Bataan region participates only marginally in interregional trade and commerce. Limited arable land, relatively sparse populations, and poor communications are contributing factors to the lack of regional economic development.

THE PHYSICAL SETTING

The Zambales Mountains, which furnish the region with its distinctive topographic character, are part of the basic structural framework of the Philippine Archipelago. Extensions of these mountains appear far to the south on the islands of Mindoro and Palawan. In places the main mountain mass of andesites and diorites is surmounted by recent volcanic cones, the more prominent of which are mounts Pinatubo, Dome, Lanat, Natib, and Bataan. The mountain slopes are steep and deeply ravined with numerous canyons, whereas the summits consist of high peaks and rugged ridges. Hill spurs frequently extend from the main mountains westward toward the sea, terminating in cliffed headlands. There are many short rivers, draining in all directions, usually flowing in steep-sided, winding mountain ravines. A narrow, discontinuous band of coastal plain parallels the west coast, broadening toward the interior where there are small floodplains. In the north, where the Zambales Mountains begin to disappear beneath the waters of Lingayen Gulf, there are more extensive lowlands. There are small lowlands near the border with Pampanga and at Olongapo and Subic on the west coast.

Dense stands of dipterocarp forests clothe the summits and steeper slopes of the highlands, and extensive areas of cogon grasses, usually indicating the presence of caingineros, cover most of the lower slopes. The lowland areas that are well drained are completely devoted to cultivation.

The entire west coast of central Luzon, and particularly the Zambales coast, lies fully exposed to the moist southwestern monsoon air masses during

A water buffalo, known in the Philippines as a carabao, relaxing in his favorite location, a waterhole. Scattered throughout the cultivated landscape are sufficient waterholes, ponds, and streams to keep these important draft animals in good condition. Photographed by W. L. Thomas, Jr., in Ilocos Norte, northwest Luzon.

The Filipino farmer often "commutes" from village or town to his cropland on his saddled carabao, carrying all needed equipment. The plow and lunch basket are on the near side, and behind the rider is a nipa-palm rain cape. Photographed by W. L. Thomas, Jr., in Ilocos Norte, northwest Luzon.

Rice fields are plowed when wet so that the soil may be worked to an almost colloidal state preparatory to transplanting rice seedlings. Photographed on the coastal plain of Ilocos Sur, northwest Luzon.

Water buffalo trampling a rice field instead of plowing it. An old technique, trampling is sometimes done when men are scarce but animals numerous. Photographed in Camarines Norte, Bicol Peninsula, southeast Luzon.

Harrowing rice fields after plowing is both a means of breaking up mud lumps and of leveling the field. The harrow is of wood, with a single row of teeth set in the bottom crossbar. Photographed in Laguna, on the Laguna de Bay coastal plain, central Luzon.

Well-developed rice seedlings about six weeks old are pulled from the seed bed and bunched for transplanting into nearby fields. Several bundles at a time are carried on a shoulder pole and delivered to a planting crew. Photographed by W. L. Thomas, Jr., in Ilocos Norte, northwest Luzon.

Newly transplanted seedlings in small-unit fields have a pale color. Beyond the rice fields are coconuts on grass-covered slopes, with a small patch of corn just below the trees at the upper left. Photographed on western Negros Island, Visayas.

Crew at work transplanting rice. Men and women work together, sometimes as hired labor, sometimes in owner cooperation. On the bund at the far right is a musician, with umbrella and mandolin, who plays speed-up contests at intervals, and entertains the planting crew all day. The large planting crew accompanied by a musician is a Laguna regional practice. Photographed on the Laguna de Bay coastal plain, Laguna Province, central Luzon.

Rice fields a few weeks after transplanting turn dark green as growth begins. Rice is new in this locality, which has recently acquired a new water supply provided by a pump and canal system engineered and financed by the Irrigation Service Unit, a national government bureau. Continuous coconut plantings occupy the rolling foothill zone. Photographed near Claver, eastern Surigao Province, northeast Mindanao.

Harvesting crew at work in a rice field in which serious lodging has occurred. This is an all-woman crew working as hired labor. Photographed in Ilocos Sur, northwest Luzon. The coconut, bananas, sugarcane (below the tall tree, right center), and bamboo are typical homestead plantings.

Threshing rice by trampling it through a bamboo screen on a temporary scaffold erected above a threshing floor. When a good breeze is blowing this method achieves a first winnowing as part of the threshing operation. Photographed on western Negros Island, Visayas.

Large straw piles that accumulate around a threshing floor are saved for feeding animals. The straw will be carefully stacked and capped by a thatching layer peaked at the center of the pile. A stack of unthreshed rice is at the left. Photographed in Laguna Province, central Luzon.

This view overlooks fields of half-grown sugarcane on a large holding. In the background coconuts are maturing to the point of driving out the cane crop. The home of a sector field manager lies in the left foreground, and in the distance are the outlying foothills of the Central Cordillera of Negros. Photographed in the Bais area of southeastern Negros Island, Visayas.

Sugarcane plantings run up the footslopes and even over the tops of low, rounded cinder cones on the western flanks of the Central Cordillera. Every vestige of forest has been cleared from the western foothill zone. Photographed east of La Carlota, northwestern Negros Island, Visayas.

Cane en route to a sugar central on a narrow-gauge railway provided by the sugar central. Cane is trimmed of its leaves and loaded about five tons to a car. Portable tracks are laid into fields from main lines. Photographed on western Negros Island, Visayas.

The marshalling yard and part of the mill of the Victorias Milling Company sugar central. More than 125 miles of main-line track services 47,000 acres of cane land during the ten-month milling season. Photographed at Victorias, northwestern Negros, Visayas.

A former Japanese plantation with young abaca planting about eight months old in the foreground and older, producing plantings in the background. This land was confiscated after World War II and parceled out in small holdings to farmers who replaced the abaca with corn and other crops. Photographed west of Davao City, southeast Mindanao, in 1948.

Abaca-stripping machines of the Hagotan variety, powered by electricity, turn out many times the quantity of clean fiber that can be produced by hand-stripping procedures. The Hagotan stripper produces fiber from the full length of the plant stalk. Units of cleaned fiber at the left will be hung in the sun to dry. Photographed in the Davao abaca district, southeast Mindanao.

Two loads of cleaned abaca fiber being carried out of interior southern Negros highland to be marketed in Dumaguete. This volume, a little less than two hundred pounds, represents a family yield from almost a year of cultivation by hand labor. Photographed in the southeastern Negros Island hill country, Visayas.

Abaca being inspected as it dries and bleaches in the sun. As the fiber dries it will be sorted according to quality and tied into bunches. Photographed in southern Davao, southeast Mindanao.

Modern commercial plantings of coconuts are widely spaced in even rows; a ground cover is maintained, but heavy undergrowth is not permitted, facilitating annual cultivation of the soil, easier picking, and volume transport of the periodic coconut harvest. The lines across the picture are rural electric, telephone, and telegraph wires along the main line of the Manila-South Railroad. Photographed near San Pablo, Laguna, south central Luzon, in a locality where coconut plantings cover all available land for miles around.

The native system of planting coconut trees produced thick jungle-like patches in which undergrowth often became heavy and trees were allowed to grow at all angles. Photographed in Camarines Norte, southeast Luzon.

Trays of copra drying beside the road show several stages of this process, the whitest portions being those that were laid out most recently. Some of this may end up classified as "Cebu sun-dried No. 1" copra. The kilometer post is 118 north of Cebu City. Photographed near Medellin, northwest Cebu, Visayas.

In a barrio setting, this house with walls of nipa-palm thatch and a roof of galvanized iron displays window decorations for a fiesta celebration. The roof has a wide overhang, and the sliding windows may remain open most of the year, with window plants in pots half filling the openings. The stairway is at the left, masked by the shrub, and all living quarters are on the upper level. Photographed in Malabon barrio, Binan, Laguna, central Luzon.

Upper-class older housing within a block of a municipio plaza has cement and wrought-iron fencing and plentiful tree plantings on large lots. The two houses at left are wooden construction in the upper story and are set on cement pilings. The nearer house has a nipa-palm thatch roof, with galvanized iron ridge line covers, and its sliding windows are closed. The second house has a galvanized iron roof, and its windows are open. Photographed in Binan, Laguna, central Luzon.

A timber house under construction, with nipa-palm thatching still unfinished on the roof. The walls will be filled in with nipa-thatch panels applied to a studding framework. Setting the house high off the ground on wood piles permits the use of the ground floor for storage. Photographed in Roxas City, northern Panay Island, Visayas.

A timber and bamboo house in a traditional Ilocano style, in which the bamboo is used in the round to fill wall panels. The roof is of galvanized iron. The fence is of World War II aircraft landing mats of sheet steel. Photographed near San Fernando, La Union, northwest Luzon.

Older town housing in the Spanish style, with doorways opening on the street, and second floor overhangs. Photographed in Vigan, Ilocos Sur, northwest Luzon.

Bontoc houses are of a distinctive pattern and shape, with high peaked roofs and low, overhanging eaves. Photographed near Sabangan, Bontoc subdistrict, Mountain Province, northern Luzon.

This plank house with a thatch roof is set on a log raft to facilitate floating during the high-water season. The river, at mid-low water in this scene and six feet below the level of the terrace, has often risen ten feet over the terrace on which the house now rests. Most pioneer housing in this region has been built in the "floating house" manner. Photographed along the upper-central Agusan River, south of Talacogon, Agusan, northern Mindanao.

Upper-class urban housing of a style common to Manila prior to World War II, built of brick and cement, with glass windows, tile roof, and wrought-iron grillwork. Photographed on Taft Avenue, Manila, central Luzon.

Upper-class urban housing in the style popular in the postwar period in Manila. Modern structures such as this are air conditioned; windows admit light but are seldom opened. Such housing has yard landscaping of native plants, in the American manner, and the living quarters are on the ground floor. Photographed in the Forbes Park residential quarter of Manila, central Luzon.

Cement block, stuctural cement, and stucco finishes, with paint and fully modern inside finishes in the American manner are increasingly popular with urbanized upper classes. Photographed in Manila, central Luzon.

Small ships built in the United States for military service during World War II still make up much of the Philippine interisland fleet, carrying both freight and passengers. This small vessel can carry a few hundred tons of cargo, a large interport passenger list, and makes regular trips on scheduled runs throughout the archipelago.

The dock at Zamboanga is built in the shape of a T with the cross parallel to the shore. Large ships may tie up on the outside of the T; launches and small craft dock at the main section inside. The launches and passenger craft on right are chiefly commuting boats operating to Basilan Island. Zamboanga is a busy interisland entrepôt serving the whole Zamboanga Peninsula and the Sulu Archipelago.

The Cebu City docks often are piled high with lumber, corn, and drums of petroleum to satisfy the chronic deficits within the island. The corn comes chiefly from southern Mindanao.

Air view of the ore-loading facilities at Masinloc, on the central Zambales coast of north central Luzon. This is a private dock provided with conveyer-belt loading of the refractory chrome ore mined nearby. The dock is protected from the southwest monsoon by San Salvador Island offshore (1.6 square miles). The coastal highway cuts arcoss the photo, and the road to the mines runs inland.

Fishing outriggers use the beach rather than the dock at the municipal port of Siain, on the north coast of the Tayabas Peninsula, southeast Luzon. The simple dock is typical of many of those at the small municipal ports.

Dumaguete is classified as an official port of entry and is open to foreign shipping. Its single |-shaped dock can handle several interisland ships at a time, as seen here, or two large ships, and is a regular port of call for many interisland shipping lines. The Cuernos de Negros, almost always cloud-capped, rises high behind the city of Dumaguete on the southeast corner of Negros Island.

The dugout canoe is still widely used on the small streams, rivers, and calmer bays throughout the Philippines for ferrying and for local transport. Here a ferryman returns over a small stream after taking a passenger across. Photographed in Laguna, central Luzon.

Local water traffic is heavy and almost constant around many of the main island shores dotted with small offshore islands, and the irregular coastal view is a common one throughout the archipelago. Photographed looking southeastward along the coast of Panay Island from Estancia near the northeast corner of Panay, Visayas.

The little island of Bayas lies about a third of a mile offshore from Estancia, northeast Panay Island, Visayas. It is less than half a square mile in area, but has a resident population of about 1,200. The tiny islet to the right is planted in coconut.

A coastal barrio near Dumaguete fronts right on the seashore, a site pattern very common throughout the Islands. A solid planting of coconut palms and fruit trees reaches inland. Photographed on southeast Negros Island, Visayas.

Long sandy beaches lined by coconut trees and other littoral vegetation are not quite ubiquitous, but they are a common occurrence in this island world. Photographed on eastern Panay Island, Visayas.

Many a village situation, as a sitio or a barrio, occupies a protected cove behind a small headland. Here a wide beach is exposed to the open ocean during the northeast monsoon blowing onto the coast from the distant right, but the lee position is protected both by the headland and the coconut planting. Photographed on the north coast of the Tayabas Peninsula, southeast Luzon.

Fishing boats at the shore and fish traps in the shallow waters offshore are common sights on hundreds of islands. The southern part of Siquijor Island lies in the left background, twelve miles away. Photographed south of Dumaguete, southeastern Negros Island, Visayas.

Air view along the central west coast of Ilocos Norte, northwest Luzon. A belt of active dunes, a half-mile wide in places, lines this coastal section. Roads, settlements, and orchard plantings follow the crests of the old stabilized dunes, the intervening swales being planted to wet-field rice. Photograph by W. L. Thomas, Jr.

The barrio of Balasinon, Sulop municipality, occupies a small spit accessible only by foot on the landward side; the lagoon filled with wet marsh is being turned into fish-ponds. On the far shore are barrios belonging to Malalag municipality. Seaward from this coast are many fish traps at the ends of long bamboo screening fences built to direct fish toward the traps. Balasinon had a 1960 population of 231 persons. The barrio primary school is among the coconut trees at the left. Photographed on the coast of Davao Gulf, south of Davao City, southeast Mindanao.

A close view of a fish trap built fairly near the shore. Shaped like an arrowhead, the shaft portion forms a diverting screen to fish moving along the coast, and the projecting wings direct the fish to the trap located at the extreme point of the arrowhead. Fish traps normally are built of bamboo matting supported on wood posts, and are serviced from small boats. Photographed in Zamboanga, southwest Mindanao.

A community well and pump of the type now being provided in rural areas under a government program to improve domestic water supplies. The well is dug to a relatively great depth to tap an aquifer not contaminated by surface water. In regions with extended dry seasons rural supplies of potable water often are scarce. Photographed in Mahayahay barrio, Hagonoy municipality, southern Davao, southeast Mindanao.

The catching of rainwater for domestic water supply is common in many parts of the Philippines in which a dry season occurs. Here a relatively well-to-do householder maintains two storage tanks that catch the drainage from most of the roof. The contours of the roof are arranged to enhance catchment. Photographed in Padada poblacion, southern Davao, southeast Mindanao.

A large bamboo, with the interior nodal filaments removed, forms the traditional water tube for transporting and storing fresh water. Augmenting the traditional tubes by a modern metal can, these three girls are about to tap a spring for fresh water that will be carried about three hundred yards to the rural homestead. Photographed in the upland interior of southern Negros Island, Vasayas.

The *caleza* is the traditional town-and-market taxi throughout the Philippines. Here the two-wheeled carts are lined up outside a municipal market awaiting the completion of morning shopping. The small horses are locally bred descendants of stock introduced by the Spanish in the eighteenth century. Photographed in Binan, Laguna, central Luzon.

The jeepney is the modern town-and-market taxi in a great many towns throughout the Philippines. A converted wartime army jeep, the jeepney serves as a taxi, a small bus, or a small cargo-handler with lower fares than those charged by larger vehicles. Here a line of jeepneys has replaced the traditional caleza line. Photographed in Davao City, Davao, southeast Mindanao.

The traffic is heavy during the morning marketing period in most municipal markets in towns throughout the Philippines. Market baskets, rain hats (or sunshades), and a variety of native and American costumes are quite normal. Photographed in Binan, Laguna, central Luzon.

A textile stall at a municipal market displays dresses for girls, jackets and skirts (on the table), and yardage material (hanging in the rear). American styles have become increasingly popular since World War II. Photographed in Binan, Laguna, central Luzon.

The retail fresh-vegetable stall displays small volumes of a variety of items. Behind the vendor, to the left, are garlic and eggplant, and to her right is a tray of Chinese cabbage hearts. In the foreground, from left to right, are packaged units of a leafy green vegetable, cucumbers, choyote and green onions (in the tray at the vendor's knees), large and small tomatoes, a pile of young edible reeds, a short stalk of sugarcane, two sections of bitter cucumber (in the bamboo tray), and at the far right, a few betel nuts, some chile peppers, and two bamboo blossom buds. Photographed in Dumaguete, southeastern Negros Island, Visayas.

Kitchenware throughout the Philippines displays interesting combinations of utensils in native, Chinese, and American patterns, in galvanized iron, enamel, pressed aluminum, cast aluminum, tin, bamboo, and wood. Photographed in Binan, Laguna, central Luzon.

Morning in the new market under construction on the edge of town at Mambusao, interior Capiz Province, northern Panay Island, Visayas. A new unit is being erected at the left. The site of the old market, just off the town plaza, had become inadequate and was being utilized for a new municipal building.

A cross section of shops on a street in the central business sector of a Philippine town on a rainy day. At the far left is part of a confectionary–soft drink parlor. The Botica Nueva is a prescription pharmacy and drug store. In the center is a beauty parlor. Behind the male pedestrian is a men's clothing store, and at the far right is a bamboo products store. Photographed in San Pablo, Laguna, central Luzon.

The terms *bulaklak* and *sari-sari* stand for "variety" in Tagalog retail terminology and are in general use throughout the Philippines today. The store at the left is in a poblacion of a fairly new town. It carries kerosene (in the two drums at the left), a supply of tinned foods, and small stocks of dry rice and corn, salt, sugar, candy, confections, cigarettes, and soft drinks. Regionally such stores will also stock local items in common demand. Note the "bridge" over the drain, formed by several coconut-palm trunks. Photographed in Hagonoy, Davao Province, southeast Mindanao.

In 1948 the main business thoroughfare of a Philippine city showed both the persistence of the caleza and the presence of the jeepney as taxi transport. This scene, looking north on the primary business street of Iloilo, southeast Panay Island, shows the customary two- to four-story buildings and the covered arcade-sidewalk characteristic of the city but seldom found in the towns and villages.

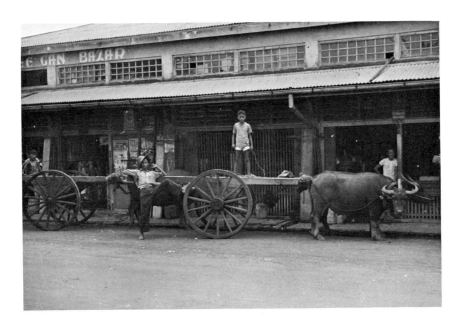

The two-wheeled buffalo cart, built with a heavy flatbed, is a common form of freight transport throughout the Philippines. Photographed in Tabaco, Albay Province, southeast Luzon.

The old and the new often form sharp contrasts in the Philippine scene. This modern service station with fluorescent lights, clean rest room, and service rack faces directly on the plaza, flanked by a cafe — both of which are situated on land rented from the Roman Catholic church, whose massive seventeenth-century bell tower rises at the left. The caleza at the left is one of about 1,000 still affording taxi srvice in a town of about 25,000, whereas the bus seen loading at the right provides transportation to surrounding towns. Photographed by W. L. Thomas, Jr., in Laoag City, Ilocos Norte Province, northwest Luzon, 1962.

A passenger bus may also provide freight service. Here a bus is loading fresh fruits destined for the Manila metropolitan markets. The chief items of cargo are bananas, papaya, pineapple, sugarcane, and jackfruit (on the ground at the right of the pile). Photographed near Tagaytay in the Lake Taal upland, Cavite Province, central Luzon.

The anatomy of the "country bus" is clearly shown in this photo of a Laguna-Tayabas Bus Company vehicle. The wooden body is built on a truck chassis. Each row of seats is entered from the right, and extra short-haul passengers may stand on the lower running board. The ticket-taker works along the running board. At the rear is a cargo section. This company maintains a scheduled set of runs from Manila southward throughout Laguna and Batangas provinces, to Lucena on Tayabas Gulf, and to Mauban and Atimonan on the east coast of central Luzon.

The national highway in southern Negros Island threads for miles through almost solid plantings of coconut palms. Settlement patterns have responded by lining the roads with dispersed homesteads for miles. This subnormal national highway is a two-lane road, surfaced with gravel and coral fragments. Photographed south of Dumaguete southeast Negros Island, Visayas.

The highway town is a relatively new type of settlement in the Philippines, responding to the needs of modern automotive transport. This is a view of the junction of a national highway with a regional service road on the outskirts of Santa Fe, Nueva Vizcaya Province, central northern Luzon. This highway is the main land artery between Manila and the Cagayan Valley in northeast Luzon. Trucks and buses make stops at Santa Fe for repairs, gasoline, food, and lodging before crossing Dalton Pass, which takes them out of the Central Plain into the Cagayan Valley.

Bridge problems are among the most troublesome and costly aspects of Philippine land transportation. Here a bus has unloaded its passengers before crossing a temporary bridge. The permanent bridge had been washed out during a previous flood. At the right were the approaches used in fording the river at low water, after the flood season, until the temporary replacement bridge was constructed. No provisions existed for construction of a permanent bridge more than a year after the washout. Photographed near Duenas in east central Panay Island, Visayas.

The log pond and sawmill at Fabrica, northern Negros. A rail line brings logs from forests more than twenty miles away in the uplands of the Central Cordillera, where cutting is currently undertaken at about 2,000 feet elevation. Most of the cutover forest has been taken over by smallholder settlers. Deep water downstream, at the right, permits barge-loading of both interisland and export shipping of saw lumber.

A small sawmill recently established in a new concession just north of Mount Canlaoan, central northern Negros Island, Visayas. Elevation is about 1,800 feet. The mill has a diesel power plant, with one large and two small saws. No cutting has been done in the forest visible in the photograph other than site clearing, but cutting is beginning off to the left.

Logs on the beach at partial low tide awaiting export shipment to Japan. When the shipment is ready to load, logs will be floated and towed into shallow water, loosely bound into a raft, and then towed to a ship anchored offshore. A total of about 400,000 board feet of timber, about half of which is shown in this view, is scattered along a mile of beach. The forest concession lies inland three to five miles in rough hill country, and along the narrow coastal fringe is a thin line of smallholder settlement almost solidly planted to coconut. Photographed in Lanuza Bay, Surigao Province, on the east coast of northeast Mindanao.

This shop in Binan, Laguna, central Luzon, builds bus bodies on truck chassis. This is an important activity for many of the towns of Laguna and Cavite provinces.

Peeled and scraped sections of rattan drying in the sun. Rattan extraction is an important source of cash income in rural areas near forest margins where heavy cutting and shifting cultivation have not reduced forest quality, particularly in the southern sector of the archipelago. Photographed in northern Agusan Province, northeast Mindanao.

An abandoned muscovado mill now stands amid rice fields. The crude boiling of sugar-cane syrup into various forms of brown sugar is a traditional industry in the Philippines which has now been replaced by the more efficient milling of sugar in modern plants (centrals) producing white sugars. Photographed on northern Negros Island, Visayas.

Overlooking the width of the Trinidad Valley, Mountain Province, northern Luzon, from the east. The main highway between Baguio and Bontoc crosses the valley. The floor of the valley lies at about 4,600 feet elevation and experiences temperatures averaging 15° F. lower than those on the adjacent lowlands. This valley has become in recent years the "salad bowl" center of an important mid-latitude vegetable production, now regularly supplying the Manila metropolitan market with cabbage, cauliflower, lettuce, celery, stringbeans, onions, radishes, tomatoes, and strawberries.

Both men and women workers are picking strawberries in the Trinidad Valley for shipment to the Manila market. The trees in the background are chiefly Baguio pines. Photographed in Mountain Province, northern Luzon.

The New Quezon barrio primary school, Hagonoy municipality, Davao Province, southeast Mindanao, serves about a hundred children through the fourth grade. The four single women teachers board with barrio families. Landscaping the yard was a barrio project. The barrio was only recently settled, and this represents a pioneer school having minimal facilities.

The Roman Catholic church of San Augustin, inside the Intramuros in Manila, is one of the most sacred of Philippine churches. Built in 1599–1606, it has withstood every heavy earthquake and suffered the loss of only one section during all the bombing throughout World War II. Photographed in 1948, before rebuilding of the Intramuros began.

The Roman Catholic church of Vigan, Ilocos Sur, northwest Luzon, represents one pattern of the traditional Spanish style of architecture.

The new Roman Catholic church at Victorias, northwest Negroes Island, Visayas, is modern in all elements of its architecture and materials.

A new Roman Catholic church on the compound of the church secondary school in Cagayan de Oro, Misamis Oriental, northern Mindanao, represents the new trend in church architecture.

The Municipal Hall of Laoag, Ilocos Norte, northwest Luzon, was built in 1903 in the traditional Spanish architectural style.

The center of Romblon poblacion, the capital of Romblon Province, on Romblon Island, in the Visayas, has but a small plaza, seen to the left. Government buildings stand across the plaza, and commercial buildings are on the right. Note the coconut plantings covering the hill in the background.

The Municipal Hall of Digos, Davao Province, southeast Mindanao, is a modest structure befitting a pioneer community. A small park planting surrounds the building, but the open space representing the traditional plaza remains undeveloped.

The provincial capitol building of Cotabato Province, southwest Mindanao, as it appeared in 1948, constructed in a combination of the Moorish and Moslem Malay styles. This building now is the Cotabato Municipal Hall, as the provincial capital was moved to Sultan sa Barongis. A well-landscaped park occupies the traditional location of the town plaza.

A cockpit is a fairly common public building around older Philippine towns. Although the architecture is usually rather unimposing, the average cockpit can accommodate a considerable gathering of persons interested in the sport. Photographed in Binan, Laguna, central Luzon.

A so-called Moro Tower or fortified watch post remaining in the landscape as a reminder of the Moslem raids on Filipino Christians throughout the western Visayan Islands during the seventeenth–nineteenth centuries. Normally erected near a town and on a site providing a good view of coastal waters, the towers were strongly built but were essentially watchtowers from which warnings of raids could be given the townsfolk. Photographed near Boljoon, southern east coast of Cebu Island.

The Legaspi Cross, housed in a protective building on Plaza Street, in Cebu City, Cebu Island, Visayas, commemorates the landing of Miguel Lopez de Legaspi at Cebu, where he made the first permanent Spanish settlement in 1565.

One of the most common landscape views throughout the Philippines from central Luzon southward is the field of rice with widely spaced young coconut palms planted as the future permanent crop plant. The difference in tree sizes indicates the continued planting of a few trees each year. Rice is the current cash crop, and rice intercropping will continue until the trees become large enough to shade out the rice, by which time coconut harvests will have replaced rice harvests. In the central background are some old coconut trees and other fruit trees surrounding a homestead. The rice is upland (dry field) rice. The grassy background slopes were probably cleared and planted for a few years by shifting cultivators. Photographed north of Sipocot, northern Camarines Sur, southeast Luzon.

Dispersed homesteads on thin stony coral soils west of Lazi on southern Siquijor Island, Visayas. Without sources of water for irrigation, farming here is often rather unproductive, and a combination of shifting cultivation and dry-farmland rotation is practiced. Current cropland is not visible, and the visible lands were not in crop.

East of Lazi, Siquijor Island, Visayas, the soils lie more thickly over the coral subsoil and country rock. Here dry-field rice yields well, complemented by a mixed cropping combination of corn and mungo beans as field crops, and bananas, coconut palms, mango trees, and an occasional kapok tree as field-margin or scattered plantings. Bananas and coconut palms do not yield well in these dry soils, but mangoes and kapok do well. At the extreme right is an interplanting of young maguey plants, a receding crop generally, but here a concession to dry soils.

Lines of banana plantings separate farmsteads in this newly settled landscape, where farms average about ten to twelve acres. The litter of a previous crop of corn remains in the foreground field, which is now planted in beans; the distant field is in corn. Photographed in New Quezon barrio, Hagonoy municipality, Davao Province, southeast Mindanao.

A planting of manioc (cassava) occupies the lower hill slope below the homestead on the crest of the hill amid the bananas and fruit trees, with a dry rice field to the right. Manioc is often planted throughout the Visayas and Mindanao as an insurance crop, to be fed to the pigs if the rice yield is good, to be eaten if the rice crop is poor. Photographed in central Panay Island, Visayas.

Hand-harvesting of ramie plants for fiber. Up to six cuttings per year may be made from established plantings. Ramie has not become a popular crop because of the difficulty in stripping and cleaning the fiber, but it is one of the strongest known plant fibers. Photographed at the outskirts of Davao City, Davao Province, southeast Mindanao.

In this intensively cultivated small-farm holding there are grown a large number of vegetables and fruits for the commercial fresh-food markets of Manila. Bananas, avocados, santols, pineapples, coffee, taro, and several green vegetables are mixed together in a near-jungle planting that is producing some salable item every month of the year. The bare tree is madre de cacao or kakawate (*Gliricidia sepium*) grown both as a commercial flowering tree and as firewood. Photographed in the Lake Taal upland near Mendez-Nunez, Cavite Province, central Luzon.

A planting of kapok trees with the pods beginning to ripen during the annual period of defoliation. These are young to half-mature trees, harvest beginning at about six years and continuing for some decades. Kapok fiber is still in domestic use in the Philippines as stuffing for pillows, cushions, and mattresses; it also finds a limited export market as a farm cash crop. Photographed in Matanao municipality, central Davao Province, southeast Mindanao.

Original forest cover was totally removed from this sector of western Davao Province, southeastern Mindanao, about 1948. Development of a wet-field rice irrigation cooperative began in 1950, and by 1965 some 5,000 acres were irrigated on farms averaging twelve acres. Scars of original land-clearing activities are still visible through patterns of the present field systems. A main irrigation canal runs through the photograph from top to bottom.

View across a small pocket embayment of the coastal plain in northern Ilocos Norte Province, northwest Luzon. Here all possible farmland has long been in use, and outward migration to Mindanao is normal. A street barrio lies along the road in the left center. The foothills of the Cordillera Central are becoming increasingly denuded through clearing of brushwood for domestic fuel. Photograph by W. L. Thomas, Jr.

A typical scene in a logged-over forest area is the caingin or shifting-cultivation patch. Young rice covers the ground in the center; sweet potatoes have just been planted in the immediate foreground (looking down the slope) and on the steep slope across the creek in the upper right. At the extreme right center is the sleeping and crop-watching shelter of the pioneer farmer. The planter may develop the site into a permanent farm in time, or he may move on to another locality. Photographed in the lower Agusan River Valley, Agusan Province, northern Mindanao.

Switchbacks on the Kenyon Canyon road, Highway 11, between Rosario on the Pangasinan lowland and Baguio in the highlands, northern Luzon. In the twenty-seven miles the highway climbs almost 5,000 feet. Three telegraph lines in the upper right take a long sweep down the mountainside.

Newly settled pioneer sector of western Matanao municipality, Davao Province, southeast Mindanao. This is foothill country of considerable local relief, and clearing of forest is still variably incomplete. A dry-season jeep road, locally built by cooperative effort, follows the high ground in the center of the photograph, but no government-built road yet services the locality. Most of the cleared land is planted in corn, as a cash crop and a home-food crop; but several plantings of coconut have been made.

The west-flank outlier of the Malayan Range of the
Cordillera Central, northwest Luzon, is deeply dissected,
rough mountain country, but the pressure on land in
the Ilocano region has pushed shifting cultivation and
fuel-cutting onto extremely rough and steep slopes.
Elevations in this air view range from about 400 to
about 2,600 feet, looking southwest, from near Nueva
Era municipality, Ilocos Norte Province. Photograph by
W. L. Thomas, Jr.

This Bontoc village is situated on the lower stream terrace, and the crop fields occupy the higher terraced ground on both sides of the stream, with steep fields above and across the stream cropped by shifting cultivation. The foreground fields are cropped in sweet potatoes, and the terraces across the stream are chiefly in rice. Photographed southeast of Bontoc town, Mountain Province, northern Luzon.

The deltaic mouth of a tributary stream has been carefully terraced to utilize the water supply from the tributary. A canal leads from a nearby tributary into the canal in the center, thus augmenting the supply of water during periods of drought; a distributary carries water to downstream terraces. Most of the fields are being cropped in rice, but there are a few scattered terraces in sweet potatoes. Photographed southeast of Bontoc town, Mountain Province, northern Luzon.

A section of the famous Banaue terraces (not the standard view) in the Ifugao region of Mountain Province, northern Luzon, north of Banaue village.

On a very steep slope below the road-cut a set of three new stone-walled terraces are in the final stages of construction in the lower right corner. The lowest terrace carries a pile of topsoil not yet leveled or settled. The middle terrace has been roughly leveled and holds a sheet of water which will settle the terrace fill; the retaining wall of the upper terrace is still not complete, and its field surface is not yet cleaned of rock debris. A workman is standing near the backwall of the upper terrace, to the left center of the upper run of terrace wall. Topsoil is gathered from all available sources along and below the actively degrading steep slopes. Photographed near Sabangan, southern Bontoc region, Mountain Province, northern Luzon.

The near-perfect symmetry of Mount Mayon showing its steam cap is unmatched by any other Philippine volcano. Grooves on its upper slopes and color patterns on its lower slopes are the marks of relatively recent volcanic action. A cloud layer is just beginning to form at middle elevation. Photographed near the outskirts of Legaspi City, Albay Province, southeast Luzon.

Air view of the eastern section of Laoag City, looking south over the Laoag River. A grid pattern is rather casually arranged. The city is densely built, and most houses front directly on the streets. In the lower sector are recently constructed units that required more space than was available inside the city; these include a convent, the provincial hospital, the city power plant, the Philippine Constabulary, and an elementary school. A distributary irrigation canal winds across the lower part of the photograph, along the edge of the cropland. Photographed by W. L. Thomas, Jr., in southern Ilocos Norte Province, northwest Luzon.

Air view of Batac, Ilocos Norte Province, northwest Luzon. About 3,000 people live within the five barrios making up the town proper, the solid tree-covered sector; to the left are adjacent outlying barrios. The town of Paoay lies up the road in the upper right corner. Within Batac the plaza is surrounded by the largest buildings in town — church, school, municipal hall, and the market. Fruit and shade trees hide most of the houses. Rice fields surround the town, and bamboo thickets and trees occupy the crests of old beach ridges toward the ocean (at top of photo), which lies seven miles from Batac. Photograph by W. L. Thomas, Jr.

South Harbor and the Port Area of Manila, central Luzon. The sector within the break-water running across the upper part of the photograph is the international port. The Pasig River mouth is at the upper right, and beyond the river mouth lies the interisland port. Roxas Boulevard (formerly Dewey Boulevard) runs diagonally across the photo-graph. The Manila Hotel lies at the lower left, and the Luneta is just included in the lower corner. To the right of Roxas Boulevard lies one flank of the old walled city, the Intramuros, with part of its wall and defensive bastions still visible. Warehouses, for the most part, have replaced the former residences and public building that were heavily damaged in the Intramuros during World War II.

Cebu City, on Cebu Island, is the second-ranking port of the Philippines, and the largest city outside the cluster within the Manila metropolitan area. The original plaza and old Spanish fort are located in the lower cluster of trees near the point at the left; port facilities are scattered across the waterfront. International shipping normally uses the piers and associated wharfage. The older settlement was grouped inland from the plaza, but Cebu has been spreading both laterally and inland, with marked expansion since World War II. At the top of the photograph rise the rather steep slopes of the hill country of central Cebu.

the summer and fall months. During their dominance there is considerable precipitation. Except for a few sheltered areas, annual precipitation averages 100 to 150 inches everywhere. In the opposite season under eastern and northeastern air flows, there is a period of pronounced drought. Less than 10 per cent of the annual precipitation falls from November through April. Three, four, and even five consecutive months may receive monthly precipitation of less than one inch.

THE CULTURAL SETTING

The coasts of Zambales and Bataan were visited by Juan de Salcedo in 1572, and this zone was one of the first areas on Luzon to be brought under Spanish control. In 1572 the province of Zambales was established in the area extending from the shores of Lingayen Gulf to Subic Bay; and northeastern Bataan Peninsula was incorporated as part of Pampanga Province. The strategic position of southern Bataan, guarding the entrance to Manila Bay, resulted in the creation of the separate *corregimiento* of Mariveles in the south. Bataan was not established as a separate province until 1754. Zambales continued to retain its large area until 1903 when the northern part was annexed to Pangasinan. The towns of Masinloc, Iba, Santa Cruz, and Mariveles (formerly Kamaya) were founded in the late sixteenth and early seventeenth centuries and are among the oldest towns in the Philippines. There was little, however, to hold the interests of the Spanish in the Zambales-Bataan area. Bataan has been peopled largely by Tagalogs, although numerous Pampangans lived in the northeast, and small-scale migrations by both groups continued throughout the Spanish period. Zambales, on the other hand, remained populated largely by tribal groups, called Zambals, until well into the nineteenth century when a steady stream of migrants from the Ilocos region began to arrive. By the beginning of the twentieth century, Ilocanos were the most numerous ethnolinguistic group in Zambales.

The attention of the world was focused on Bataan Peninsula early in World War II when American and Filipino military forces made their final withdrawal into the peninsula in early 1942. The sanguinary fighting that ensued resulted in the depopulation of the peninsula and adjacent sections of southern Zambales. Since 1945, population has increased fairly rapidly, largely because of increased activity in the agricultural, forestry, and mining sectors of the regional economy.

Agriculture is the dominant economic activity in the region, and rice is the most important cultivated crop. Normally the region produces rice sufficient to meet internal consumption, with a small surplus that is shipped to Manila. Lowland rice, usually grown without the benefits of artificial irrigation, is the principal crop. Yields exceed national averages by a considerable margin owing, in large part, to the inherent fertility of many of the soils and to the sharply monsoonal character of the precipitation that supplies enormous quantities of water during the long and dependable growing season. The majority of the rice lands are concentrated in the north in the municipalities of Pangasinan Province. Smaller areas of rice are scattered through coastal areas of Zambales and Bataan, particularly in the municipalities of Santa Cruz, Hermosa, and Botolan. Rice is practically the only grain cultivated in the region, for the heavy rainfall is not favorable for the growth of corn.

Prior to 1942, sugarcane was of considerable importance, ranking second only to rice in both Bataan and Zambales; however, the sugar mills were totally destroyed during the war and have not been rehabilitated. Sweet potatoes, beans, cassava, yams, and taro supply complementary foods, and small quantities of bananas, mangoes, and pineapple are shipped to Manila. A few coconuts are raised along the Zambales coast, mainly for their oil. In general, regional agriculture is, in the 1960's, more strongly oriented toward self-sufficiency than formerly was the case.

Farming in the Zambales-Bataan region, as in most Philippine areas, involves the use of a shallow plow and harrow pulled by a carabao. Labor requirements are large and individual productivity is quite low. Absentee ownership and land tenancy, although lower than the national average in Zambales and Pangasinan, are seriously high in Bataan probably because its proximity to Manila reflects the urban investment in farmland in areas surrounding the city. Approximately 60 percent of the potential arable land of the region is under cultivation; an area representing approximately 30 percent of the total area of the region. Reserves of marginal upland are sufficient to support a much greater population than at present, under pressure. Large sections of the uplands are occupied by caingins; their too-frequent cropping and the subsequent slow regeneration has resulted in the destruction of much valuable timber, as well as fostering and promoting soil erosion.

Utilization of the forest resources is increasing, and in the 1960's, the sawmills of the region produce approximately 8 percent of the total Philippine lumber production. Much of the region's timber is fully matured and possesses qualities not always found in Philippine woods, for example, large dimensions and unusually dense woods. The nearness of the Manila market, and the markets for timber generated by the large United States naval installation at Olongapo, places the sawmill industry of the region in an advantageous competitive position. The use of certain timbers in the large mining industry located within the region also supplies a considerable market. Most of the sawmill capacity is concentrated in the forest lands of northern Zambales Province where the timber is somewhat more accessible. Much of the timber on Bataan Peninsula was damaged or destroyed during the American-Filipino defense of the peninsula in 1942. Plywood, veneer, and parquet tiles are manufactured on Bataan. *Boho*, a thin-skinned variety of bamboo highly prized for *sawale* matting, baskets, and fish corrals, is relatively abundant in the forests of Zambales and Bataan.

Fishing is particularly important in the economy of eastern Bataan, and in all coastal areas fish supply important complements to farm incomes. Fishponds are expecially numerous and extensive in the flat, swampy lands around Hermosa, Samal, Abucay, Orani, and Balanga in Bataan. The fry for these fishponds come from Moron in western Bataan or from the beaches along the Zambales coast. The cultured fish find a ready market across the bay in Manila. Elsewhere, inshore fishing operations supply most of the fish catch, which is usually made by means of fish corrals. There also are large catches of crabs and shrimps. The region is more than self-sufficient in fish and fish products, and surpluses of several items are shipped to the markets of Manila.

Mining and associated mineral industries are particularly important to the economy of Zambales. At Santa Cruz there are large deposits of metallurgical-grade chrome ore which are under exploitation, and at Masinloc is located the world's largest refractory-grade chromite mine. Consolidated Mines, owners and operators of the Masinloc mine, have constructed an extensive network of roads, and maintain mill and loading facilities for their large open-pit chrome operations. These operations are based upon the world's largest known deposit of refractory chromite ore, a very necessary ingredient for refractory firebricks. Acoje is the largest metallurgical chromite producer in the Philippines, and its products are used extensively for ferrochrome alloys. The Acoje mine is located near Santa Cruz, and there are several other smaller operators in the vicinity. Both refractory and metallurgical-grade chromite ores are concentrated prior to overseas shipment.

The Zambales-Bataan region is also a large producer of salt. The salt is produced by solar evaporation of seawater in large salt beds in the north, especially at Anda, Alaminos, and Dasol in Pangasinan, and at Iba and San Felipe in Zambales. Most of the salt produced is of an inferior grade and is used primarily in fish preservation.

Only two transportation routes connect the Zambales-Bataan region with other areas on Luzon. Highway 7 enters the region through northeastern

Bataan from Pampanga Province on the Central Plain. This highway crosses the base of the peninsula through Zigzag Pass to Olongapo, then skirts along the western coast of Zambales and exits to the north around the shores of Lingayen Gulf. Between these two exits the Zambales Mountains are crossed only by trails.

Although several of the towns of the region were founded at very early dates, there has been little urban development. None of the towns has attained the status of a regional or interregional center. The mining towns of Santa Cruz and Masinloc, with populations in 1960 of 3,500 and 3,800, respectively, have grown with the development and exploitation of the large chrome-ore deposits of northern Zambales. The provincial capital cities of Balanga (Bataan) and Iba (Zambales) have similarly small populations. In addition to their administrative functions, both serve as local market centers for their adjacent agricultural areas. Mariveles and Olongapo-Subic have extraregional significance. Mariveles, located on an excellent harbor in southern Bataan immediately inside the entrance to Manila Bay, is something of an industrial center. The National Shipyard and Steel Corporation (NASSCO), the Matadore (National Slaughterhouse), and offices of the Bureau of Quarantine are located at Mariveles. The shipyard operated by NASSCO is the largest of its kind in the Philippines and is capable of dry-docking vessels of up to 10,000 gross tons. In 1960 the poblacion of Mariveles had a population of 2,300. The towns of Subic and Olongapo together serve the workers and base personnel from the large United States naval station at Port Olongapo. The poblacion of Subic contained only 600 persons in 1960, and that of Olongapo about 5,000. The town of San Felipe in southern Zambales, with a population in 1960 of 6,000, supports a fairly well-developed pottery industry based upon local clays. Elsewhere most of the larger settlements are market towns, each serving small populations and limited agricultural areas. The larger and more important of these market centers (with their 1960 poblacion populations) include: Bolinao (2,600), Alaminos (3,700), Anda (1,500), and Dasol (1,500) in Pangasinan; Botolan (2,600), San Antonio (8,700), and San Marcelino (6,800) in Zambales; and Dinalupihan (5,000), Hermosa (4,400), Orani (2,500), and Orion (7,600) in Bataan. Less than 15 percent of the regional population lives in towns with populations greater than 2,500.

The Rice Bin: The Central Plain of Luzon

The Central Plain of Luzon is the economic heartland of the Philippine nation. This region, in normal years, produces over one-third of the country's total rice crop, and thus, has justly earned the designation as the "rice granary of the Philippines." In normal crop years approximately two-fifths of the rice production of the Central Plain is above regional needs and is available for shipment to the major rice deficit areas in other parts of the country, principally to populous Rizal Province and the metropolitan Manila area. Although possessing a high degree of physiographic, climatic, and edaphic homogeneity, central Luzon is also a region in which there are great cultural contrasts. Large haciendas or estates vie with the fractionated holdings of the small farmer, or with the many tenant-operated farms. Rice monoculture reigns supreme with over 85 percent of the farms on the plain classed as rice farms. In general, a low level of agricultural productivity prevails throughout the region in spite of a fairly fertile soil base. The rapidly expanding population of the region, which resists emigration except to the Manila urban area, is exerting increasingly strong pressures upon an already crowded land.

Many elements characteristic of the present-day Filipino culture have their origins on the Central Plain. Tagalog—the national language—Pampangan, and Pangasinese are all indigenous to central Luzon. Many of the more notable Filipinos who are, or have been, active in the national political arena, and in various economic fields, have come from the region. A very large part of the urban population of metropolitan Manila has migrated from central Luzon, particularly from the provinces of Bulacan and Pampanga, which lie immediately north of the metropolitan area.

All of the five provinces of Bulacan, Nueva Ecija, Pampanga, Pangasinan, and Tarlac, or major portions of them, lie within the Central Plain region. The region includes a total area of approximately 5,900 square miles, nearly all of which is lowlands and arable. Approximately one-eighth of the population of the Philippines, some 3,165,000 persons in 1960, excluding the urban population surrounding Manila at the southern end of the plain, lives on the Central Plain.

THE PHYSICAL SETTING

The Central Plain of Luzon is the largest contiguous area of lowland in the Philippines. This lowland, occupying a large Quaternary sedimentary basin between the moderately high Zambales Mountains to the west and the Central (Eastern) Cordillera to the east, stretches north from Manila Bay for more than 100 miles to the shores of Lingayen Gulf (fig. 52). The average width of the plain is 40 miles. This almost level plains land lies only a few feet above sea level, except where a few isolated peaks rise abruptly out of the sea of alluvium. The nearly symmetrical volcanic cone of Mount Arayat in Pampanga is the highest of these peaks, reaching the striking elevation of

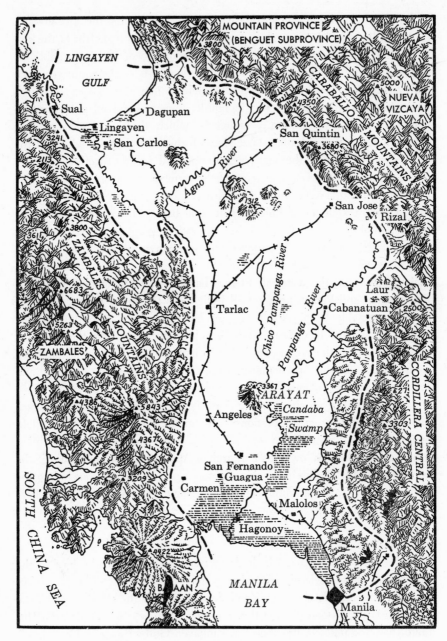

Fig. 52. Physiography of the Central Plain.

3,378 feet within a very short horizontal distance. In the northeastern part of the plain in the provinces of Tarlac and Pangasinan, Mounts Bangcay, Balungao, and Amorong extend above the 1,000-foot contour and form a low drainage divide between the waters flowing northward into Lingayen Gulf and the streams that flow southward into Manila Bay. Deposition of marine sediments in the basin has been very great, and in several places these deposits reach to depths of as much as 10,000 feet.

The drainage of central Luzon is dominated by the southward-flowing Pampanga River, which heads in the low Caraballo Mountains in the north and debouches onto the plain near the town of Rizal in northeastern Nueva Ecija. Along its course across the lowlands the Pampanga is joined by several major tributaries, including the Chico Pampanga, Lubao, and Angat rivers, and finally empties into the waters of Manila Bay through dozens of separate mouths. The Agno River, another of the major rivers of Luzon, dominates the drainage of the plain northward into Lingayen Gulf. The Agno originates in the mountains of Benguet in Mountain Province, and after flowing many miles through deep canyons where several hydroelectric projects have been constructed since 1950, finally reaches the plain near the Pangasinan–Mountain Province boundary. The Agno flows westward across the plain, then strikes north, and finally empties into Lingayen Gulf at the town of Lingayen. Where the Pampanga enters Manila Bay, and the Agno enters Lingayen Gulf, large swampy areas have been formed. Another large swamp area, the Candaba Swamp, has been formed on the low ground between the Pampanga River and the Angat immediately north of their juncture.

The deep marine and river sediments that blanket the Central Plain have weathered into fairly fertile sandy loam and clay loam soils; however, the successive generations of rice farmers have reduced much of the inherent soil fertility. Too little attention has been paid to soil conservation and management in the past. Soil erosion is not as serious a problem as is soil depletion.

The presence of the Zambales Mountains to the west and of the Eastern Cordillera to the east exert blocking effects upon moisture-bearing air masses from either the Pacific Ocean or the South China Sea, and have profound effects upon the climate of the Central Plain of Luzon. Because of its interior location, a slight continental warming effect is observable in the temperature regime on the Central Plain; however, the principal climatic modification appears in the patterns of annual precipitation amounts. Most areas within the lowland receive precipitations that are under 80 inches annually, and several areas in the central section experience less than 70 inches annually. Peripheral locales, particularly at the open ends of the lowland in the north and south and in the highlands to the east and west, receive considerably heavier precipitation.

Precipitation is strongly seasonal. All areas within the region receive at least 80 percent of their annual rainfalls within the six-month period from May through October, and this is particularly true in the north along the shores of Lingayen Gulf where over 90 percent of the annual rain occurs during this period. The months from November through April are quite dry, frequently receiving less than an inch of rain during each of three or four consecutive months. The question of the adequacy of the precipitation, and its strongly seasonal character, place a severe restriction on the agriculture of the Central Plain. At present, relatively little use is made of farmland during the dry period except in a few areas where irrigation systems have been installed.

THE CULTURAL SETTING

The Malayan-Filipino was formerly a seafaring individual, and until well into the Spanish period he chose to site his settlements in close proximity to the sea. In early days, overland journeys were slow and extremely difficult and fraught with danger. Thus, much of the Central Plain of Luzon was unoccupied and undeveloped when the Spanish arrived at Manila Bay in 1570. Only the extreme southern parts of the plain around Manila Bay supported a relatively dense population. Here significant quantities of food were produced, namely rice, which was later to be the trademark of agriculture in the region. At the close of the sixteenth century, Lower Pampanga Province, which included the present-day provinces of northeastern Bataan, Pampanga, and Bulacan, was estimated to have a population of approximately 75,000 persons.[1] This population was all concentrated within about 10 miles of the shores of Manila Bay. The peoples of the settlements of Macabebe (Pampanga) and Hagonoy (Bulacan), as well as those in Manila, attempted to resist the encroachments of the early Spaniards under Legaspi, but they were unsuccessful. In 1571, Martin de Goiti quickly pacified central Luzon, reporting the almost complete absence of population on the lands between Manila Bay and Lingayen Gulf littorals. Juan de Salcedo established control over the Lingayen Gulf shores of Pangasinan, but also found that the population generally was confined to the immediate vicinity of the gulf. The interior regions of the Central Plain in the present-day provinces of Tarlac and Nueva Ecija were at this time heavily forested, possessed virtually no indigenous population, and as a consequence, were not at first divided into encomiendas or estates.

Inevitably the Spanish authorities began the construction of roads and trails into the interior of the Central Plain, probably more to facilitate the collection of tributes or taxes than to aid in the opening of the agricultural lands, for Spanish colonial policy paid scant attention to agricultural developments. By 1800, much of the interior of central Luzon had begun to experience considerable permanent settlement; however, relatively remote and inaccessible Nueva Ecija Province remained sparsely populated for another century, and then its population was to expand only under the system of another colonial power's administration.

Nevertheless, by 1900 the broad patterns of the present-day population distribution, population densities, and land-tenure systems were beginning to emerge. The population on the plain had reached one million persons, and most of the land was occupied by some form of cultivation or other regular land use. The prevalence of widespread tenancy and absentee ownership of farmland was clearly evident. From this date onward the increases of the cultivated area would not be sufficient to match the rapidly expanding population. Virgin lands were fast disappearing, and the large sugarcane and rice estates, of which there were many, resisted the breakup and subdivision of their landholdings. Then, as now, there was no land available for purchase. The rate of land tenancy was to increase from a rate of 38 percent in 1903 to 54 percent immediately prior to the outbreak of hostilities in the Pacific. By 1948, some 60 percent of the farms on the Central Plain were being cultivated by tenant farmers. The population of the five provinces situated on the Central Plain has increased from slightly over one million persons in 1903 to nearly three and one-half million persons by 1960. Farm sizes have continued to get smaller and smaller, for out-migration, which has kept the population pressures within bounds in the Ilocos region and in the Visayan area, was not looked upon with favor by the plains people. They have preferred to remain in their familiar environments and have simply kept spreading out over the plain. When no more empty lands were left, pressures on the cultivated area grew stronger. To some extent the urban centers of central Luzon, and the Manila zone outside the region, have absorbed some of the excess population, but the strong family and social ties, the high costs of migration, and a certain amount of distrust and concern about living conditions in the new settlement areas, precluded any large-scale migrations from the Central Plain to the Cagayan Valley or to the southern islands. The average size of the cultivated land per capita in the region has continued to decrease steadily from approximately 0.9 of an acre in 1918 to less than 0.5 of an acre in 1948. Although these absolute statistical values are open to question, the downward trend in the ratio of cultivated lands to population has become increasingly evident during the last several decades.

The present-day population of the Central Plain region is somewhat unevenly distributed over the plain. The areas of greatest population concentration are found at the two ends of the valley: near Lingayen Gulf and along Manila Bay (fig. 21). The numbers of people tend to increase sharply with increasing nearness to Manila. Elsewhere the presence of swamplands places restrictions upon intensive land occupance. The average population density over the whole of the Central Plain was approximately 536 persons per square mile of total area in 1960, a figure approximately double that of the national average.

ECONOMIC ACTIVITIES

Agriculture is the dominant economic activity in the Central Plain, and rice is overwhelmingly the principal crop, both in terms of the amount of land and time devoted to its cultivation, and the returns that its cultivation provides. Sugarcane, the most important secondary crop, is but a poor second, except in certain local areas near centrifugal sugar mills where it becomes dominant. Various other crops, such as corn, peanuts, tobacco, beans, feed for livestock, and various fruits and vegetables, are produced in limited quantities throughout the region.

The importance of *palay* (the Philippine term for rice before it is milled) in the agriculture of the Central Plain cannot be overemphasized. The 1960 census classified 89 percent of all farms in the five provinces that lie on the plain as having more than one-half of their cultivated area devoted to the cultivation of palay. More than one-fifth of the rice-producing lands of the Philippines are found on the Central Plain, and from these lands comes nearly one-third of the nation's total rice production.

The division of the climatic year into two pronounced rainfall seasons—a wet season and a dry season—of approximately equal duration means that most of the rice cultivation is limited to only one crop within a single calendar year. The *palagad* crop, or second lowland rice cultivation, is attempted on approximately one-sixth of the rice lands of the region, and its cultivation usually results in substantially lower yields than those obtained from the first main-season crop.

Typically, the rice farmer of the Central Plain operates with a shallow plow and primitive harrow, and generally without the benefit of controlled irrigation waters. Some time between the middle of May and the end of June the water necessary to flood the paddies is supplied by heavy seasonal rains. The crop makes its growth during the remainder of the rainy season. Harvesting operations begin in November and December as the dry season appears. Usually there is neither sufficient moisture nor time remaining after the main harvest season to permit a second crop. The rice farmer of central Luzon endures almost complete dependence upon the six-month rainy season. This dependence could be lessened through the more widespread use of irrigation water, although even now, those areas on the plain which are provided with irrigation systems usually employ them only to supplement the rainfall during the main growing season. There are, at present, slightly more than 500,000 acres under some form of irrigation on the Central Plain; this amount is relatively insignificant when compared to the total area under rice cultivation, and yet, it is an amount that represents fully one-third of the total irrigated land of the Philippines (fig. 53).

In spite of the many physical and cultural handicaps and limitations placed upon the cultivation of rice in central Luzon, such as the inadequacies of rainfall, the small sizes of the farms, the high rates of tenancy, and the widespread use of primitive implements and farming techniques, the yields of palay obtained from the rice lands of the region are substantially higher than those obtained from most other rice areas in the Philippines. The rice yields from the Central Plain average 30 percent more than the average of the national yields. In normal years the Central Plain produces surpluses of rice which are more than sufficient to meet the demands of metropolitan Manila, and in certain very favorable years all of the rice deficiencies of the island of Luzon can be met by surplus production in this single region. Nueva Ecija and Pangasinan are the leading rice-producing provinces of the Philippines, and the other provinces of central Luzon also rank high among the archipelago's primary rice producers.

The development of irrigation systems on the Central Plain of Luzon was first undertaken during the nineteenth century. The earliest developments were initiated by the Catholic church on their large church-controlled estates. At the same time a few of the larger sugarcane haciendas in Tarlac and Pampanga provinces undertook construction of smaller projects. The Spanish colonial government did not initiate any large-scale public irrigation projects, and it was not until 1907 after the American government assumed the administration of the Philippines that construction was begun on several large-scale, publicly financed irrigation schemes. The largest and most important of these twentieth-century projects is located along the lower course of the Pampanga River. In recent years there have been several small irrigation-pump projects undertaken by the national government, each

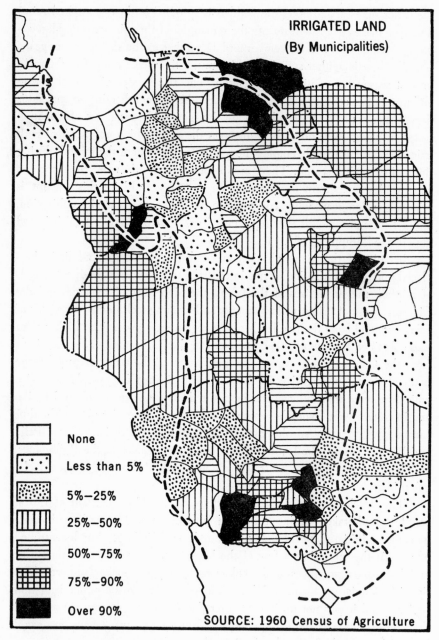

Fig. 53. Irrigated land (by municipality) on the Central Plain, 1960.

supplying the water for a few hundred to several thousand acres on the Central Plain. These have been constructed by the national government through the Irrigation Service Unit.[2] Most of the irrigated areas on the Central Plain are concentrated close to sources of water, particularly in the Cordillera Central and Caraballo Mountains in Pangasinan and Nueva Ecija provinces. Also, there are considerable areas under irrigation in southern Tarlac and along the Pampanga River and its tributaries in eastern Pampanga and western Bulacan. Since most of the present Philippine irrigation systems employ simple gravity-flow principles, the areas that can be irrigated are limited by the ability to deliver water and by the lay of the land. Practically all irrigated lands in central Luzon are used for rice or sugarcane cultivation.

Sugarcane is the leading commercial crop produced in central Luzon, and its cultivation and processing, and the systems of land tenure associated with its production, stand in sharp contrast to the practices associated with rice cultivation. The majority of the commercial production of sugarcane is concentrated on large sugar haciendas. Many central Luzon farms have small patches of sugarcane growing in their fields, but these are intended for local consumption and do not enter commercial channels. The haciendas are organized into large sugar districts, and each sugar district is organized around a sugar "central," or centrifugal sugar mill. The mills and the sugar haciendas sign long-term contracts in which the haciendas agree to supply all of their cane to the central, and the central agrees to process this cane into centrifugal sugar on a fixed percentage fee. There are five sugar districts on the Central Plain of Luzon, two each in the provinces of Tarlac and Pampanga, and one small district in Pangasinan Province. Combined, the region produces approximately 225,000 metric tons of centrifugal sugar annually, an amount that represents approximately 20 percent of the total Philippine quota sugar production.

Sugarcane is transported from haciendas to mill by railroad and truck. At the mill the cane is "ground" into centrifugal sugar, with large quantities of molasses produced as an important by-product. The Manila Railroad provides facilities both for the hauling of much of the cane from fields to mill, and for the transportation of the processed sugar and molasses from the mills to shipping points at Guagua, in Pampanga, or to Manila from where the final products are shipped overseas.

Within each of the sugar districts sugarcane is the dominant crop, almost completely excluding other crops. Because the commercial cultivation of sugarcane is concentrated on large landholdings, and because these large landholdings require large seasonal labor forces, there is a very large number of landless farmers resident in the sugarcane areas and a very serious unemployment situation during the off-season. Tenant farming is very prevalent in the sugarcane areas with the tenancy rate approaching 100 percent in many areas. The combination of the high tenancy rates in the sugarcane areas, and the small sizes of the farms and high tenancy rates in the rice areas, has created serious sociological problems in the Central Plain of Luzon. Much of the support for the dissident Hukbalahap movement in the decade following World War II came from discontented tenants in the central Luzon area.

In contrast to virtually all other regions in the Philippines, the Central Plain is relatively well supplied with an adequate land-transportation system, at least when measured by Philippine standards, a further testament to the region's importance to the national economy. The nearly 300 miles of main-line and spurline track of the Manila-North Railroad which traverse the plain provide connections with Manila and points south, and with Lingayen Gulf and the southern Ilocos region. Many of the more important cities of the region, for example, San Fernando, Tarlac, and Dagupan, lie along the mainline, whereas spurlines furnish connection with others, such as San Quintin, San Jose, Clark Air Force Base, Cabanatuan, and Carmen. The railroad is especially important in the movements of sugarcane and sugar, which together make up more than 80 percent of the railroad's freight revenues. Two paved, all-weather, national highways run north–south through the plain, providing good intra- and interregional road connections. Highway 5 parallels the eastern side of the plain and leads on into the Cagayan Valley; and Highway 3 skirts along the western edge of the lowland as far as Lingayen Gulf and then leads on into the Ilocos coast area and Mountain Province. There are numerous east–west highways and feeder roads that facilitate road transportation into virtually every barrio on the plain. Highways and roads are heavily used by buses, trucks, and passenger cars, and passenger and freight transportaion on the Central Plain is both rapid and frequent.

Estuarine and foreshore areas surrounding Lingayen Gulf and Manila Bay, and the brackish-water swamplands north of Manila Bay along the lower courses of the Santa Cruz, Lambangan, Hagonoy, Pampanga, Guagua, and Pasay rivers, are the sites of an extensive fishpond culture. The tidal marshes of Manila Bay north of Manila in Bulacan and Pampanga provinces support the largest area of fishpond-culture development in the Philippines. Altogether there are nearly 100,000 acres, or some one-third of the total Philippine fishpond area, devoted to fishponds in the Central Plain region.[3] The small fry, which are caught along sandy coasts and near river mouths in various parts of the archipelago, are brought to Manila by rail, truck, and airplane. These fry are first placed in nurseries, 100,000 to 200,000 fry to the acre, where they are raised to fingerling size. From the nurseries the fingerlings are transferred to rearing ponds where, in from three to six months, they attain commercial size. The fish, known as milkfish, can then be marketed as the market dictates, thereby insuring a constant supply of fish regardless of fishing conditions in the regular fishing grounds. The very large commercial fishpond culture in the areas north of Manila Bay has developed largely because suitable lands lay close to the large markets of metropolitan Manila. Not only does the Manila Bay area lead the nation in the size of its fishpond development, but the area suitable for expansion of fishponds is greater than that already utilized in Pampanga and Bulacan provinces.

Mining and mineral industries do not play a very important role in the economy of central Luzon. The only mineral industry that makes any important contribution to the economy of the region is the cement industry. There are three large cement plants located on the Central Plain close to the Manila markets, two in central Bulacan and one in the adjacent province of Rizal. To a great extent these cement plants utilize raw materials available locally— local limestones, shales, and silicas—and require only gypsum and fuel oil from outside the region. Formerly central Luzon was a more important mineral area. The earliest known commercial deposits of iron ore in the Philippines lay in eastern Bulacan Province near the cordillera lands. These deposits have been worked, desultorily, for centuries, but the deposits are not large enough to base a modern iron and steel industry. The Central Plain has received considerable attention from petroleum exploration interests, but as yet these efforts to locate commercial deposits of petroleum have not been successful.

Sugar centrals, with their associated distillery activities, the several cement plants, a few sawmills near the forests in Nueva Ecija, and numerous small-scale handicraft establishments make up the industrial and manufacturing sector of the central Luzon economy. Apalit (Pampanga), San Carlos and Calasiao (Pangasinan), and Laur (Nueva Ecija), small municipalities of the Central Plain, are particularly important as centers of localization of certain handicraft industries. Apalit has several establishments that manufacture and fabricate bolo knives and pottery items, and hats, mats, and handbags from buri palm fibers. San Carlos is a center for a large local pottery industry and for the fabrication of articles from bamboo. Calasiao manufactures bolo knives and calasiao hats, a peculiar hat traditionally manufactured in Calasiao from buri palm fibers. Laur manufactures numerous products from bamboo. Actually, home handicrafts or cottage industries are neither very important nor is their manufacture very widespread in the Central Plain. This poor development of home handicrafts may be a reflection of the better distribution means and methods in the region and the closeness of the large factories of Manila which can mass-produce many of the items.

Unfortunately, the net result of the tremendous seasonal fluctuations of demands for farm labor, coupled with the absence of subsidiary or supplementary incomes from nonagricultural pursuits, has created a very serious unemployment, or underemployment, problem in central Luzon. Dissidence and a disenchantment with the status quo have periodically erupted in active violence, and much of the strength of movements against central authority, such as the Hukbalahap movement, have received succor from the peoples of central Luzon.

The settlement scene in the Central Plain region is one of literally hundreds of small agricultural villages, each providing residential facilities for the farmers and farm laborers of the surrounding agricultural lands. Also each village serves as a marketplace for produce from its local agricultural area. Because of recent political unrest within the region, and increasingly greater pressures of population on available agricultural land, the population in many parts of central Luzon is somewhat more highly urbanized than that in most areas in the Philippines. Approximately 10 percent of the populations of the Central Plain lives in municipality poblaciones that have populations of more than 2,500. Furthermore, an additional 15 percent of the people live in barrios with populations greater than 2,500 persons.[4] Nueva Ecija, with its more recent settlement and with a considerable amount of political unrest throughout the surrounding countryside in the recent past which has tended to concentrate the population in the larger and more secure settlements, shows the greatest degree of urbanization—40 percent urbanized in Nueva Ecija versus 25 percent for the region as a whole. Tarlac also has a larger proportion of urban residents, chiefly because of the relatively large size of the city of Tarlac and its suburbs when compared to the total population of the province.

The proximity and relative accessibility of the chief Philippine city of Manila has precluded the development of any large and dominant regional center in the Central Plain. Furthermore, since the region lacks an adequate first-class port, Manila has assumed an important position with respect to interregional and international commerce. Tarlac and Cabanatuan are the leading cities of central Luzon and major trade centers. Tarlac is the capital of Tarlac Province. It is one of the larger cities of central Luzon. The city is particularly important as a transportation center, for not only is it an important point on the Manila-North Railroad, but it also is located at the juncture of Highway 3 which connects with the Lingayen Gulf cities. A large sugar central is located in the suburban community of San Miguel. The 1960 urban population of Tarlac was approximately 31,000 persons.

The chartered city of Cabanatuan is the capital of Nueva Ecija Province. This large city also functions as the principal commercial center not only for the province of Nueva Ecija, but for the entire eastern side of the Central Plain. The surrounding lands are devoted to the production of rice almost exclusively. The urban population of the city of Cabanatuan proper in 1960 was approximately 40,000; however, within the chartered city limits, which include considerable rural lands, there were over 70,000 persons. Cabanatuan serves as an important transportation center, the terminus of a rail spurline, and the gateway to Dalton (Balete) Pass and the Cagayan Valley via Highway 5. Numerous transvalley roads into Pangasinan and to the east coast towns on Baler Bay and Dingalan Bay in Quezon Province originate at Cabanatuan.

The chartered city of Dagupan is the principal commercial city on Lingayen Gulf. It is one of the oldest cities of central Luzon and was founded by the Augustine fathers in 1590. Dagupan is situated on the Dagupan River approximately two miles above the shallow river mouth and serves as a minor port for small, shallow-draft vessels. The immediate hinterland of Dagupan produces substantial quantities of fish, solar-evaporated salt, rice and fruit. The 1960 urban population of the city proper was approximately 15,000, and within the chartered city limits lived some 63,000 persons.

Angeles, Pampanga, is a bustling army town of comparatively recent origin. Angeles has grown with the expansion of the facilities and personnel of the large United States Clark Air Force Base nearby. The city functions mainly as the shopping and recreational center for personnel and dependents of the base, and in its suburbs there are several large "off-base" housing developments. The 1960 urban population of Angeles was approximately 22,000 persons.

Among the lesser cities of the Central Plain of Luzon, with their 1960 poblacion populations, are: the other provincial capital cities of San Fernando, Pampanga (3,200); Malolos, Bulacan (3,000); and Lingayen, Pangasinan (8,200); the sugar central towns of Panigui (6,500), Bamban (4,300), and Floridablancà (3,000); and several minor port cities. The small port of Sual (1,700) on Lingayen Gulf was one of the first ports opened to foreign shipping in the Philippines when it was established in 1855, but the railroad and highways have captured its trade hinterland and nature has silted its harbor. The river ports of Hagonoy (2,000) and Guagua, (6,000) 9 and 12 miles, respectively, upriver from Manila Bay, are accessible for small, light-draft vessels, and considerable quantities of sugar and molasses pass through their facilities.

The Heartland: Metropolitan Manila

Manila is the principal city and only true metropolitan center of the Republic of the Philippines, and the city can be numbered among the truly great cities of southeast Asia. La Pérouse, the famous French navigator of the eighteenth century, once described Manila as occupying the finest commercial site of any city in the world.[5] As the single most important economic area of the Philippines, as well as the nation's capital in fact if not legally, Manila forms a distinct regional entity apart from the Central Plain of Luzon upon which it lies, and as such warrants separate regional status.

Manila presents a soft blending of the cultures of the Occident and the Orient, and is by far the most populous and urbanized center in the Philippines. The population of its metropolitan area exceeds the next most populous center, Cebu City, by almost tenfold. Within the fourteen districts, covering an area of 14.3 square miles, which make up the city proper, live over one million persons, and an additional 1,000,000 to 1,500,000 people reside in the surrounding suburban fringes in the adjacent province of Rizal. Manila is the nation's economic, cultural, educational, industrial, and governmental center. Most of the alien European and Chinese population of the country lives in the city. Through the portals of its busy harbor lies the gateway to the world, and its port facilities handle a large share of the Philippine international and domestic commerce. It is the home of the various overseas business firms, numerous banks, and other financial institutions, including the Manila Stock Exchange; the headquarters of the Philippine press and radio; and the seat of the Catholic church hierarchy. It is as dominant in the life of its country as the cities of Bangkok and Saigon are in theirs, *the one principal city*.

THE SITE OF MANILA

The selection of the site of Manila as the future economic center and administrative capital for the Philippines was not without good justification. It did not just happen to grow. A location in the innermost or eastern reaches of commodious Manila Bay, some 30 miles from the constricted bay entrance, and at the mouth of the Pasig River, provides excellent protected anchorage for ships, but not very good conditions for the development of a port. The city lies on a narrow strip of level, low ground situated between the bay to the west, the high Eastern Cordillera of Luzon to the east, and Laguna de Bay to the southeast (fig. 54). This narrow lowland provides a land corridor between the two most important agricultural regions on Luzon—the Central Plain of Luzon to the north and the volcanic lowlands of southwestern Luzon. The mountains to the east, and the mountains of Bataan Peninsula which guard the northern entrance to the bay to the west, give the eastern shores of Manila Bay a considerable degree of protection from the weather elements. A similarly protected site along the northern shores of the bay could not have avoided the low marshy and swampy grounds that accompany the delta lands

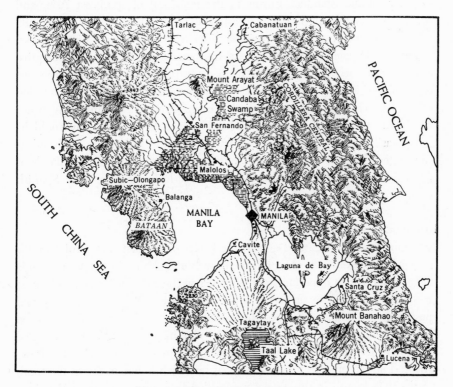

Fig. 54. The situation of Manila.

of the southward-flowing Pampanga River and its several distributaries. A location along the southern shores would have lain along a steep escarpment or on low marshy ground, and furthermore, would have been exposed to the high surf that frequently sweeps southward across the open bay.

Although the slow-moving waters of the Pasig River bisected the city and presented some difficulties to transportation, its presence also facilitated defense, and at the same time, provided a source of domestic water and freshwater fish. Marginal wharfage was afforded by the lower course of the river. The Pasig provided an easy access route into the interior, especially to the large inland water body Laguna de Bay and the productive lands that surrounded it. In earlier years the river also could be, and was, the site for a very large floating population that lived on barges and rafts on the river.

STRATEGIC ASPECTS OF THE SITE

There were several strategic considerations involved in the selection of the site for Manila, and their satisfaction made its growth inevitable. First, the closeness of the island of Luzon to the mainland of southeast Asia, and particularly to the south China coast, and the splendid harbor of Manila which was already receiving periodic visits from numerous Chinese junks, reinforced the commercial position of the port with respect to the lucrative oriental trade. Second, the city lay at the crossroads of the two most important economic regions of Luzon, and thus became the natural transportation center for overland connections with Luzon, as well as maintaining water contacts to the rest of the archipelago. The fact that Manila Bay could be rather easily defended because of its virtually landlocked nature, with only a constricted entrance divided and dominated by the small channel islands of Corregidor and Caballo, was a factor not overlooked by the early Spanish conquistadores.

HISTORICAL DEVELOPMENT

Captain Miguel Lopez de Legaspi, the leader of the first successful Spanish colonizing expedition to the Philippines, while exploring in the Visayan area heard reports of an important trading center in the Manila Bay area. The area was described to him as fertile and abundantly supplied with food, and possessing an estimated 80,000 Moros in its environs.[6] In 1570 he dispatched his chief lieutenant, Martin de Goiti, who upon his arrival found and captured the two fortified Moro settlements lying at the mouth of the Pasig River. The settlement of Maynila, ruled by Rajah Soliman, lay to the south of the river mouth in the district now called Intramuros. North of the river, in the present-day districts of San Nicolas and Binondo, was the "Kingdom of Tondo," ruled by Rajah Lakandola. The following year Legaspi brought up his entire expedition and started building the future capital of the colony on the sites of these two settlements. He inaugurated the construction of some 150 wooden buildings that would house his soldiers, laid out the city with a government house, church, and monastery, and reconstructed and improved upon the fortifications. It was well that he paid close attention to the fortifications, for in subsequent years there were repeated attempts by Chinese, Dutch, and British forces aimed toward the capture of the city. Limahong, a Chinese pirate with a force of some 3,000 followers, was repulsed only at the very gates of Manila in 1574. The Dutch were successful in establishing several small settlements along the northern shores of Manila Bay during the seventeenth century, and they were not driven away until their naval forces were defeated in 1624, and again in 1635, while in Philippine waters. British armed forces under Admiral Samuel Cornish and General William Draper occupied Manila from 1762 to 1764 as a subsidiary operation to the Seven Years' War.

Spanish authorities removed Manila from the provincial political structure of the archipelago in 1574, and since that time it has served as the national capital. (Quezon City, a suburb of Greater Manila, was designated as the future capital in 1948, but most of the offices of the national government remain in Manila.) Successive Spanish governors-general enlarged and improved upon Legaspi's plan, and many of Europe's foremost military architects helped plan its fortifications. Until 1830, however, when the port of Manila was opened to foreign shipping, the city remained an exclusive domain of Spanish influence, the home port for the famed Manila galleons that plied between Manila and Acapulco from 1593 to 1815, and center of Spanish and Catholic power in the Far East. By the end of the Spanish era, the population of Manila had reached approximately 200,000 persons.

United States military forces occupied Manila after only token resistance by the Spanish in May, 1898. The new American administration quickly infused new life to the city, in contrast to the long period of status quo or actual decline under an increasingly disinterested Spanish rule. They inaugurated municipal electric and gas service, improved sanitation through the installation of sewage and drainage systems, and insured a safe and dependable source of domestic water. The port and harbor were improved through construction of breakwaters, dredging, and the establishment of navigational aids. The eminent Chicago landscape architect Daniel H. Burnham was invited to visit the Philippines, and he prepared a formal "city plan" that provided for an orderly growth of the capital city. Parks, major radial thoroughfares, a government office center, and a comprehensive development plan were instituted. Much of present-day Manila reflects this comprehensive Burnham Plan, though the full plan never was executed.

Manila was almost totally destroyed during World War II. An estimated 80 percent of the city was razed during the liberation battles. The new Manila, now largely rebuilt, stands in testament to the advantages inherent in its strategic and natural site.

THE CITY OF MANILA

Politically and administratively, the city of Manila is divided into fourteen municipal districts. Seven of the districts lie north of the Pasig River, and six lie to the south. The Port Area, the fourteenth district, is split by the river.

Although the Pasig River is spanned by some nine bridges, there is still a considerable amount of congestion at the various river crossings, especially during periods of heavy traffic flows. Each of the fourteen districts has its own distinctive character and urban functions, and usually centers around a city-owned public market and one or more large churches. The central

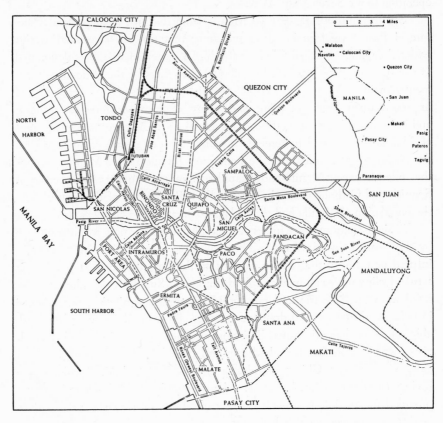

Fig. 55. Districts, major streets, and suburban areas of Manila.

business district, if there is a true central place (for businesses are widely dispersed throughout the city and its suburbs), includes the districts of Binondo, Quiapo, and San Nicolas (fig. 55). Within these three districts, all of which are situated along the north bank of the Pasig River, are located warehouses, banks, offices of various business firms, shipping companies and insurance firms, retail stores, and theaters. The heart of the business section is the short Escolta, the "Fifth Avenue" of Manila. Along the Escolta are located many fashionable shops and department stores that display almost every item of imported and Philippine origin. Juan Luna Street, with its many tall, modern buildings, is the center of Philippine banking. Rizal Avenue, including its extension into the Santa Cruz District, is lined with crowded shops, theaters, hotels, restaurants, schools, and business offices. In the early morning hours each major bridge and major thoroughfare pours forth its heavy traffic into the narrow and crowded streets of "downtown" Manila. Although primarily commercial in nature, the districts of Binondo, Quiapo, and San Nicolas, with a combined area of only 0.9 square miles, housed a resident population of 73,000 in 1960, including over 23,000 alien Chinese.

The Tondo district occupies all of northwestern Manila. Tondo is a district primarily of crowded low-income residences and small shops; many of the latter are Chinese-owned. It is extremely densely populated; its average residential population of more than 150,000 persons per square mile, rivals that of any city in the world. The railroad from the north enters Tondo, terminating operations on the Central Luzon Plain at the railyards of Tutuban Station. The busy docks of Manila's North Harbor, catering exclusively to domestic shipping, lie within Tondo.

The central business district is gradually expanding into what were formerly the mainly residential districts of San Miguel, Santa Cruz, and Sampaloc. These incursions are particularly evident as narrow strips of commercial developments along the main thoroughfares of Rizal, Santa Mesa, Quezon, España, and Aviles. Higher education is centered in Sampaloc where many of the outstanding universities of the Philippines are located, including Arellano, Far Eastern, National, Manila, Santo Thomas, and the University of the East. The Dominican-sponsored University of Santo Tomas, founded in 1611, is the oldest university in the Philippines. Near the Pasig River along Aviles Street in Santa Mesa are several large industrial companies, several of the national bureau offices, and Malacañang Palace, which was built in 1863 to house the Spanish governors-general, but now is the official residence of the President of the Philippines. Approximately 400,000 people still reside in the nearly 5 square miles included within these three districts.

The Ermita and Malate districts lie south of the Pasig. Both districts are strongly westernized with many fine hotels, restaurants, nightclubs, and apartment buildings, and with several modern specialty shops and retail stores catering to the well-to-do and the tourist. Most of the national and municipal government office buildings, and many of the foreign legations, are located in Ermita. Dewey (Roxas) Boulevard, broad and tree-lined, skirts the seawall along the eastern shores of Manila Bay and passes through Ermita and

Malate. Strung out along this section of Manila's waterfront are such fashionable addresses as the Manila Hotel, Army-Navy Club, the modernistic American Embassy, Hotel Filipinas, and the Manila Yacht Club. Taft Avenue, which parallels Dewey Boulevard further inland, is a sort of "federal way," for along much of its length it is bordered by government office buildings, including the city hall, the legislative building, and the Bureaus of Finance, Agricultural and Natural Resources, Fisheries, and Science.

After World War II much of the historic Intramuros district lay in the ruins of Manila's liberation. It was in Intramuros that a die-hard core of Japanese defenders made their final stand and destruction was virtually complete. Of the many historic churches and Spanish government buildings that once lined the narrow streets behind the walls, only the ancient St. Augustine Church was left standing in a condition for rehabilitation. Today the old 20-foot-thick stone walls, which once enclosed most of the official Spanish quarter of Manila, now surround a largely unplanned development of quonset huts, warehouses, shipping offices, Lyceum and Letran colleges, and many shacks. In 1960, 13,000 persons resided in Intramuros. The busy streets of Dewey Boulevard extension (A. Bonifacio), Padre Burgos, Taft Avenue, and Aduana encircle Intramuros. The historic core of Manila, however, has been lost forever.

The Paco, Santa Ana, and Pandacan districts, which are located along the southwestern periphery of Manila, are mainly middle-class residential areas. Several very fine and expensive housing areas have been developed in the Santa Ana district, particularly in the areas adjacent to the country club. The Manila-South Railroad passes through these three districts before crossing the Pasig.

Commercial Manila focuses upon the Port Area district. The port of Manila consists of two separate types of facilities—an international port for foreign commerce, the Port Area, and an interisland port for domestic commerce in Tondo. South of the mouth of the Pasig River is South Harbor where deepwater facilities are provided for foreign shipping. A low breakwater encloses the 2-square-mile harbor, leaving a 700-foot-wide channel for access. The four commercial piers, Piers 5, 7, 9, and 13, provide simultaneous berthing space for fourteen large vessels. The entire South Port district, including the Customs building and several bonded warehouses and sheds, is enclosed by barriers. Since Manila is an important port of call for many steamship lines that operate to the Orient from the United States and Europe, the port frequently is quite congested, and vessels must either lie at anchor in the harbor awaiting their turn or discharge their cargoes to lighters tied alongside. Unfortunately, South Harbor does not have belt-line rail facilities, and cargoes must be transported to and from the piers by trucks or river barges, called "cascos."

In addition to its port functions, the Port Area houses several industrial concerns, particularly those that must depend upon foreign sources for their raw materials. Automobile and truck assembly, industrial machinery and engineering works, drydocks, cigarette factories, knitting mills, and pharmaceuticals are located in the Port Area.

North Harbor, which extends along the bay north of the mouth of the Pasig, is given over exclusively to domestic shipping. Hundreds of vessels reach out from North Harbor connecting all ports in the Philippine archipelago, distributing products of manufacture and import, and bringing to Manila cargoes of food and raw materials. Inbound and outbound passenger traffic is very heavy. Seven piers are available for the interisland vessels. Although there is a complete lack of shore-based equipment for handling cargo, North Harbor is served directly by tracks of the Manila-North Railroad. A few of the larger interisland shipping companies have warehouse facilities within the North Port district.

Limited marginal wharfage for interisland vessels, and particularly for barges and lighters, is available along the lower course of the Pasig River. Low water at the river mouth, and the numerous bridges further upstream, restrict the number and size of vessels that can be accommodated along the river.

Surrounding Manila to the north, east, and south are seven major suburban communities in Rizal Province which, with the city, comprise the official Greater Manila metropolitan area (table 5). All seven of these subur-

Table 5   POPULATION AND AREA OF METROPOLITAN MANILA

Political unit	1960 population	Area (in sq. mi.)	Density per sq. mi.
Manila	1,138,611	14.29	79,679
Quezon City	397,990	60.46	6,583
Pasay City	132,673	5.71	23,235
Caloocan	145,523	32.92	4,421
Makati	114,540	6.60	17,355
Mandaluyong	71,619	6.49	11,035
Parañaque	61,898	7.53	8,220
San Juan	56,861	5.85	9,720
Metropolitan Manila	2,119,715	139.84	15,158

SOURCE: "Manila's Metropolitan Problem," *Philippine Journal of Public Administration*, 5 (1961), and *1960 Census of Population*.

ban cities and towns lie within a distance of 3 miles from the center of the city of Manila. Eight smaller communities lie at somewhat greater distance, and although not part of the metropolitan area administratively, can be considered as included within the region. Most of the suburban communities occupy hilly ground. In general, they are rapidly developing residential areas with growing numbers of commercial and industrial establishments. Each suburb is self-contained, with a small shopping center, and administered as a separate political unit. The growth of suburban Manila has been a relatively recent phenomenon, largely since independence. Much of the suburban growth has been due to the small area of the city, which has long completely occupied its 14 square miles. Also the high costs of industrial sites within the city proper have forced many companies to move into the suburbs, especially those industries that require large factory sites, such as textiles, paper and pulp, and tire and rubber factories. Several of the satellite communities have grown at annual rates of more than 10 percent in the years since 1948, for example, Quezon City, Mandaluyong, and Makati (table 6).

Table 6 AVERAGE ANNUAL RATE OF POPULATION GROWTH FOR METROPOLITAN MANILA AND FOR THE PHILIPPINES, 1903–1960

Area	*1903–1918*	*1918–1939*	*1939–1948*	*1948–1960*
Metropolitan Manila	2.58	4.33	5.02	4.01
Manila	1.65	3.99	4.80	1.38
Quezon City	n.a.	20.10	11.01	12.13
Pasay City	6.51	5.46	5.06	3.60
Caloocan	7.90	3.40	4.15	8.50
San Juan	10.70	6.90	5.15	5.37
Mandaluyong	n.a.	15.55	3.84	10.23
Makati	9.70	4.92	1.94	9.40
Parañaque	7.50	0.23	3.37	6.93
Philippines	1.92	2.22	1.90	3.22

SOURCE: "Manila's Metropolitan Problem," *Philippine Journal of Public Administration* 5 (1961), 96.

Suburban Manila, including all fifteen communities, reported a total population of approximately 1,400,000 in 1960. Most of the suburban towns and cities function as "dormitory towns," housing workers who commute to Manila for employment. Adjacent to northeast Manila is Quezon City, the largest of Manila's suburbs and the second largest chartered city in the Philippines. Originally conceived by former President Quezon as a place to house factory workers and laborers, it has far outstripped this modest goal. Quezon City was granted its charter in 1939. In 1948, the city was selected as the future capital of the Philippines, although few of the governmental offices have been located there as yet. The University of the Philippines and Ateneo de Manila are located in Quezon City, and several large housing projects, financed by insurance companies, have been constructed in recent years. The long, major thoroughfares of Quezon Boulevard and Epifanio de los Santos, the circumferential bypass around Manila, are almost solid lines of offices, small shops, and other commercial establishments. Pasay City adjoins Manila to the south. Pasay has long been densely populated and highly commercialized and has experienced a much smaller growth rate in recent years than the other suburban communities. The busy Manila International Airport, and the even busier domestic terminal, are located on the outskirts of Pasay City. Caloocan, chartered as a city in 1963, Malabon, Navotas, Obando, and Polo to the north are growing centers of industrialization and manufacturing. Chemicals, plastics, cigarettes, automobile and truck assembling, fabricated steel products, pharmaceuticals, and cosmetics are a few of the industries located in the northern suburbs. Navotas, and to a lesser extent Malabon, are important commercial fishing centers for Manila. Approximately one-half of the total Philippine commercial fish catch is landed at Navotas. Malabon and Navotas produce bagoong and other fish preparations. Marikina, San Juan, Mandaluyong, and Pasig are growing industrial and residential communities located east of Manila. Makati, Pateros, Parañaque, and Las Piñas lie to the south. Makati is a particularly important community, for along its segment of the circumferential highway a very large manufacturing center has developed. Here most of the firms are national or foreign, and the buildings and factories are very modern in design. Las Piñas is a major center of salt production.

Manila provides many specialized central services for the entire nation. Over its piers and wharves passes fully 85 percent of all Philippine imports, and approximately 20 percent of the export products move to Manila for eventual shipment overseas. In addition, Manila is the principal regional center for the northern half of the Philippines, and the major trading center for its population and a large immediate hinterland. Unlike the suburban growth around American metropolises, housewives will travel by bus for hours in the early morning to shop for foodstuffs in the Manila markets. Nearly one-third of all industrial establishments in the Philippines are concentrated in metropolitan Manila. The major industries of the Manila area include iron and steel, plywood and veneer, cement, tanneries, fertilizer, pulp and paper, and textiles. Although the number of industries established in Manila's suburbs since 1955 has surpassed those in the city, the city remains the chief source and place of employment for the nation. Most of the industries in the Manila area are located either on or near tidewater, or along the outskirts of the city, particularly on sites adjacent to Highway 54, the recently completed circumferential highway that bypasses Manila to the east.

Manila ranks high as a center of higher education, and as such it attracts thousands of young people to its universities and colleges. Fourteen of the 24 Philippine universities are located in Manila and Rizal, and 79 percent of all Philippine university students attend Manila's universities. There are 71 institutions of higher education located in Manila, and 40 additionally in Rizal. In 1958 there was a total of 397,000 students attending classes in Manila proper.

Manila is the most cosmopolitan and westernized city of the Philippines, and its population reflects its close cultural and economic ties with the rest of the world. Although Filipinos form the dominant racial group in the Greater Manila area (96 percent), there were sizable numbers of Chinese (90,000), Americans (5,600), and others (3,900) living and doing business in Manila in 1960. Approximately one-half of the alien Chinese population of the Philippines resides in the Manila area. (See appendix table 9, under Manila and Rizal, for linguistic indications of the way in which Filipinos from all parts of the Islands are represented in the urban population of the Manila metropolitan area.)

Manila is not a city of skyscrapers and tall buildings in the traditional western sense, for the deep, unstable alluvium that underlies the city will not permit their easy construction. Instead, Manila sprawls. Distances are great and traffic confusing. More than one-half of the private automobiles registered in the Philippines are in the Manila area. Buses, taxicabs, and converted wartime jeeps, called jitneys or jeepneys, vie with horse-drawn buggies. It is a city of great contrasts. Modern, multistoried and air-conditioned buildings often lie adjacent to the poorest of shacks. Various sections of the city are reminiscent of the various periods through which the city has developed: Spanish, American, Japanese, Commonwealth, and Republic. Tondo is Chinese; Intramuros and San Miguel have considerable Spanish flavor; Malate and Ermita are American; Quezon City and the newer residential areas to the south are modern Filipino; and the Port Area belongs to the world. And above all, Manila is the glittering mecca of cultural and economic life for the whole Philippine nation.

The Country of the Lake and the Crater: Southwest Luzon

Southwestern Luzon is a transition region lying between central northern Luzon and the middle sector of the Philippine Archipelago, southeastern

Luzon and the Visayas. In important physical aspects part of it shares the character of the Central Plain, lying to the north, but a history of vulcanism gives it strong physical features generally lacking in the Central Plain. Climatically it lies on the southwestern margins of the typhoon belt, but it shares the climatic character of the western coasts of Luzon. Agriculturally, coconut begins to replace rice as the dominant crop, as compared to the Central Plain, and the region has developed a diversified commercial agriculture oriented toward the Manila urban and international trade markets. Southwestern Luzon is almost purely Tagalog country, and to some extent, is the heart of the Tagalog zone, and yet it is a region in which Spanish, Chinese, and American influences are deeply planted. The region came thoroughly under Spanish political control; yet is one of the regions in which the independence-from-Spain movement was strongest late in the nineteenth century. Although landscapes, land-use systems, people, and culture history show relationships to both the Central Plain and the areas to the south, southwestern Luzon has evolved regionalism sufficient to set it apart. A total area of about 2,800 square miles is included in the region, wholly including the provinces of Batangas, Cavite, and Laguna, the western arm of Quezon Province, and the parts of Rizal Province lying adjacent to Laguna de Bay and Manila Bay. Physically, Manila lies just within the southwestern region, although it is not so included. Excluding the population of metropolitan Manila, the population of the southwest Luzon region exceeded two million by 1960.

THE PHYSICAL SETTING

The physical forms providing the landscapes of southwestern Luzon are of two different varieties, the alluvial lowlands and the volcanic uplands. The downwarped sedimentary basin that extends southward from Lingayen Gulf through the Central Plain extends southward into Tayabas Bay (fig. 56). Manila Bay represents an unfilled portion of the lowland, and Laguna de Bay presents a southern, low-lying sector that has been turned into a lake by a slight upward flexure extending southwesterly between the lake basin and Manila Bay. On the west side of Laguna de Bay the southern Central Plain shades into the margins of the lake lowland without noticeable change in the alluvial forms. North and northeast of the Laguna de Bay, however, a rather hilly tract borders the lake margins, the result of the flexure that created the lake. Owing to the flexure, the Laguna occupies the southern floor of the basin, which is only poorly drained by the Pasig River. The area of Laguna de Bay is normally stated at 356 square miles, but it is surrounded by low-lying lake plains that may be inundated during seasons of heavy rainfall.

The lake basin receives the flow of numerous small river systems that slowly are extending their sediment-fills into the lake.

East and northeast of the lake basin the marginal hill lands of the Eastern Cordillera run spurs out into the lowlands, so that the lake is bordered only by very narrow stretches of plain. Northward from the lake basin, along the western fringe of the Eastern Cordillera, extend a string of small volcanoes and rolling uplands covered with tuffs and ash.

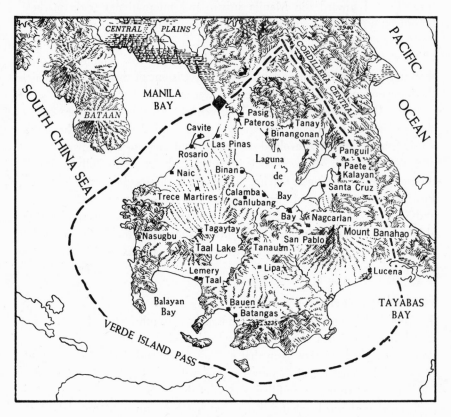

Fig. 56. Physiography of southwest Luzon.

Southward from the lake stand larger volcanoes, such as Maquiling, Malepunyo, Macolod, San Cristobol, Banahao, and Banahao de Lucban, ranging upward to the 7,177-foot crest of Mount Banahao. The peaks do not form a continuous chain, but with their associated ejecta of tuffs, ashes, and cinders, they have constructed a southern closure to the lowland which creates a minor drainage divide. Southward of this divide several streams have only short runs into Tayabas Bay. The slopes of the volcanoes themselves are steep and variably etched into rough surfaces, but there are wide gaps between the peaks, and the tuff-covered uplands are only rolling to moderately hilly.

To the southwest and west the volcanic landscape is more complete, and its forms occupy the whole of the Batangas-Cavite sector south of Manila Bay. Toward the west coast, north–south, stands a series of volcanic peaks dominated by Pico de Loro, Nasugbu, and San Pedrino.

Inland from this series are other scattered volcanic peaks of fair height and bulk, such as Batulao at 2,694 feet, northwest of Lake Taal, Carilao, to the west, and numerous others to the south, with Mount Panay standing above the Calumpan Peninsula with a crest of 1,620 feet. Below the volcanic peaks there are spread out rolling to rough hilly lands, high rolling plains, and smoother piedmont plains to compose an irregular landscape. The whole of the sector is surfaced by ashes, cinders, and tuffs that are but lightly consolidated. A great many small drainage systems share this volcanic landscape, and on the higher surfaces and steeper slopes, the streams often have incised ravines and barrancas into the surface.

The whole of the western sector is dominated by the great caldera of Taal, now containing a lake and a small volcano.[7] The old crater margins measure about 12 miles east–west by 15 miles north–south. The outer flanks of the huge old volcano rise gently on all approaches to the cliffed crests overlooking Lake Taal, which now occupies the caldera. The highest point remaining on the flanks of the blown-apart volcano is Mount Macolod, 3,107 feet, on the southeast quadrant, but the whole north quadrant stands close to 2,000 feet and from Tagaytay Ridge presents an outstanding spectacle. On the southwest the caldera has been broadly breached, and through the gap flows the Pansipit River, draining Lake Taal into Balayan Bay at Lemery, so that the surface elevation of the lake today is but slightly above sea level.

Sectors of the west coast drop abruptly into the sea without accompanying coastal plains, but much of the coast of southwestern Luzon is fringed by marine terraces set only slightly above sea level and by long volcanic footslopes that gently drop toward Manila Bay, on the north, and on the southwest and south toward Balayan, Batangas, and Tayabas bays. During heavy rainy seasons these coastal fringes may be wet and flooded by drainage from the uplands.

In only two areas do old sedimentary rocks outcrop in the region of southwestern Luzon. The arched flexure north of the Laguna de Bay has exposures of marine limestones, and marine limestones form a slightly exposed basement along the west coast of Batangas. Elsewhere the surface is composed of volcanic materials and recent sedimentary deposits derived almost entirely from volcanic sources.

The soils of much of southwestern Luzon are above average in quality and ease of cultivation, being formed either of alluvial lake-plain deposits or weathered volcanic tuffs, ashes, and mixed ejecta. Locally some sectors are rather high in cinder content or alluvially sorted sandy material, and suffer seasonal edaphic drought. The Lipa series of soils, weathered from tuffs, is the most widely distributed series, providing an above-average soil covering much of the rolling upland zone. The lower lake plains and the lower coastal plains have soils of somewhat heavier textures, forming good wet-field rice lands.

At an early date the southwestern region possessed a heavy forest cover except in areas of quite recent volcanic activity; however, southwestern Luzon has long been occupied by crop cultivators, and the forest cover has been much reduced.[8] Spanish influence extended the agricultural landscape, and the only region that has maintained a forest cover of commercial significance is the eastern section of Laguna Province, along the lower slopes of the Eastern Cordillera. A large share of the region is in farms today, although there are some areas of grassland and jungle thickets not currently occupied. High on the flanks of several volcanoes there are still patches of heavy forest, and any unoccupied spot becomes quickly overgrown with native or introduced plant species. The region supplies considerable firewood and some small saw-timber but is not a region of rich forest resources. Eastern Laguna does still possess commercial forests, although to date the chief exploitation of these has been for the softwoods that can be carved into wooden shoes and related handicraft products.

Southwestern Luzon is not a region of significant mineral resources, and there is little mineral production from within the region. The coastal flats are utilized for the solar production of salt as the most significant mineral product of the area, and the Binangonan cement plant uses local limestone.

Southwestern Luzon is not a region possessing significant power resources in a hydroelectric potential. The western flanks of the Eastern Cordillera, bounding the region on the east, do possess a number of medium-to-small potential sites for eventual development. To date only one of these has been utilized; the Caliraya Project northeast of the Laguna de Bay was started in 1939, although power delivery was delayed until 1950. A total of 36,000 kilowatts is developed, the power being transmitted to the Manila consumer region.

Climatically, southwestern Luzon belongs in the zone sharing the summer rainy season derived from the southwest monsoon. Ranging from the early thundershowers of late May into the declining monsoon rains of October, the summers are wet and humid. The dry season in some years begins in

November, extending through April, although it is not so severe as that in some other regions. March, April, and May, usually hot, dry, and quite uncomfortable, are referred to by Manila residents as the "hot season," and are thoroughly disliked as the most disagreeable period of the year. Locally, regional patterns show considerable variation in detailed periodicities of season. Precipitation sequences vary rather markedly also, from annual totals of around 70 inches just west of the Laguna de Bay, to well over 100 inches in some west coast situations and along the foothills of the Eastern Cordillera. Tagaytay Ridge, at 2,000 feet, is somewhat cooler than Manila and enjoys some traffic as a hill station, but it is not high enough to provide markedly lower temperatures. There are high volcanic peaks with cool crest temperatures, but none provide situations for the establishment of hill stations. The region lies toward the southwestern margins of the main typhoon belt, and does not suffer the frequency or severity of storms found in areas to the north or east; however, typhoons regularly sweep across Luzon within storm range of the region, and there is annual damage from high winds and flood freshets. Manila, in this respect, is badly located on the low divide between Laguna de Bay and Manila Bay, so typhoons, which produce heavy falls of rain within the drainage basin of the Laguna, may produce floods on the Pasig River. These augment volumes of local rainwater drainage to the end that about one flood a year immobilizes Manila from periods of one to five days.

THE CULTURAL SETTING

Southwestern Luzon was a relatively heavily populated region when the Spanish came to Manila in the 1570's. In addition to the often-noted settlements on Manila Bay around the mouth of the Pasig River, there were points of settlement scattered clear around the shores of the Laguna de Bay. Cavite, inside the entrance to Manila Bay, was an old point of settlement. The present towns of Lemery and Taal, at the mouth of the Pansipit River draining Lake Taal, are near the center of what was a well-settled coastal fringe, and settlements were located around the southern shores of Lake Taal itself. The head of Batangas Bay, where modern Batangas City is located, was lined by settlements, as was the head of Tayabas Bay, near the present site of the city of Lucena. Chiefly, these were littoral settlements, the home bases for rather mobile populations who probably grew some crops in the near hinterlands and who fished the lake and shore waters. Both Laguna de Bay and Lake Taal were accessible by water from the saltwater coastal zones, via the Pasig and Pansipit rivers. Early Spanish references are to local regional chiefs and to what appear to have been local territorial political structures.

As Manila became the primary center of Spanish operations, Spanish political officers and the priesthood spread out around the Laguna de Bay, into the nearer hill country, and into coastal Batangas. They founded several formal towns and established cabecera churches and visita chapel circuits; Spanish civil and religious controls were organized to include as much of the local population as possible. By the middle of the seventeenth century there were about thirty-five such Spanish cultural centers outside Manila, in what is here delimited as southwestern Luzon. The three groups—Franciscan, Augustinian, and Jesuit—were represented within the region as a whole. Many of the present towns date their beginnings from the town-cabecera church establishment; it is likely that most of them actually represented pre-Spanish zones of settlement, although the precise new sites normally were sufficiently inland to be on nonfloodable situations. The Hispanization of this sector of the Tagalog country, therefore, began at an early point with a relatively dense network of stations of influence. Only the western coastal fringe and the south coast between the present cities of Batangas and Lucena were not affected; although much of the deeper hinterland also was then not touched by Spanish activity, that hinterland seems to have been very lightly populated. There were no interior population concentrations in the form of warlike pagans who resisted Spanish control.

As with the Tagalogs of the Central Plain, the elaboration of the Spanish network of control in southwestern Luzon proceeded rather smoothly, with a minimal amount of early rebellion. Although rebellion was to raise its head here strongly in the nineteenth century, southwestern Luzon settled into a relatively peaceful program of development along Spanish-planned lines during the seventeenth and eighteenth centuries.[9] Beyond the towns the religious orders early established cattle ranches in the Batangas hill country, and many of the early encomienda grants were in Cavite and Laguna. Laguna de Bay settlements were assigned the duty of providing food rations for the Manila area during certain months of the year, but little of the rest of the region provided sufficient surpluses that could be drawn upon for the Manila markets, except for the Batangas cattle ranches.

Although all of the peoples from Tayabas Bay northward into the central part of the Central Plain are labeled Tagalog, there were early distinctions of a more local nature. Coastal Pampanga, Cavite, Manila–Laguna de Bay, and coastal Batangas represented separate local orientations of culture groups within a larger regionalism. The Spanish recognized such regional distinctions, and to an extent, they maintained such. The Laguna de Bay shores formed the core of a political administrative area at an early date, although its northern towns have since been made part of modern Rizal Province, and its southerly margins have fluctuated steadily. Batangas had been made, at first, a part of an administrative region that included several islands lying to the south, but it became a Luzon province on its own in time, although its boundaries against Laguna long fluctuated. Cavite remained a military commandancia to the end of the Spanish era, but this largely resulted from the slow settlement of the rural area and the presence of the naval station and shipbuilding yard established at Cavite town by the Spanish. As Rizal Province matured, and as Quezon Province took shape, the northern margins of the Laguna province were included in Rizal and the coastal section of Tayabas Bay was placed in Quezon (then Tayabas) Province for administrative purposes, although both regions belonged to southwestern Luzon in other respects.

Population growth in early Spanish times in southwestern Luzon appears to have been neither rapid nor general, but this is an uncertainty. The Laguna de Bay shorelands had been the most heavily populated in the first decades of the Spanish period, and in the 1590's the whole region perhaps held a population not far from 85,000, excluding Manila. By 1800 the total settled population was reported at about 150,000, excluding Manila, and Batangas was forging ahead, whereas Cavite and Laguna were gaining but little. Zuñiga made it plain, however, that around 1800 the hinterland country between Manila Bay, the Laguna de Bay, and the Batangas south coast was the refuge of outlaws and such other elements as opposed Spanish rule, Christianity, labor drafts, and regular taxation.[10] Therefore, it is possible that population was actually growing, but that a share of the increase was moving into the hinterland hill country out of contact with, and control by, and Spanish.

The 1903 population of the region stood at about 635,000, and by 1960 the total had risen to approximately 2.1 million; both figures exclude the metropolitan area of Manila. It is clear that a process of spreading toward the hinterland has taken place. In Batangas of the 1960's, the south coast east of Batangas City, and the rougher hill country west of Lake Taal, are still areas of only few settlements. The same result has been achieved in Cavite and around the Laguna de Bay. The hilly north and east shores of the Laguna show less hinterland movement, but on the south and west there has been marked growth in inland localities. Some of the towns founded by the Spanish have remained quite small, whereas others have matured into sizable cities. Bay, on the south coast of the Laguna de Bay, a Franciscan cabecera church station in 1655, held a poblacion population of only 1,227 in 1960; and Panguil poblacion, on the eastern arm of the Laguna, held only 952 people in 1960. Santa Cruz, on the southeast corner of the Laguna, by virtue of becoming the provincial capital of Laguna Province, had grown to a poblacion total of 5,248 in 1960. On the other hand, San Pablo, an inland cabecera church site on a route to the southeast sectors of Luzon, has become a modern road-and-rail transport center, regional marketing center, and minor manufacturing community. Now a chartered city, its population totaled 70,680 in 1960, of whom approximately 30,000 resided in the urban center. Similar figures can be presented for other sections of the region.

The old cabecera church towns close to Manila have, of course, become dormitory towns in part, with large resident populations that commute daily to Manila. Thus, southern Rizal towns and several Cavite towns, founded as cabecera church towns, have grown markedly as appendages of the metropolitan Manila region, and the process is beginning to affect some northern Laguna towns. The Batangas towns, however, lie too distant from Manila for this process of dormitory urbanization to affect them in the same way.

In that Tagalogs do not take well to moving long distances from their home areas to new frontiers, most of the population increases in recent decades have remained within the region. Most barrio, poblacion, town, and city populations, therefore, are growing rather rapidly at the present time, and the settlement process is filling in the smaller reserve areas within the region. It will not be long before the agricultural landscapes of southwestern Luzon become maturely developed and pressures for expanding the agricultural economy become serious.

THE ECONOMIC PATTERNS

Southwestern Luzon today is primarily an agricultural region. Lacking mineral resources and having cut off most of its forests in the development of farm landscapes, agricultural activities involve the largest share of the population. A location adjacent to the Manila metropolitan region does mean that an increasing share of the population finds employment somewhere within the urban complex, and as previously noted, an increasing number of nearer towns are becoming dormitory settlements tributary to Manila. As the development of industrial organizations expands outward from Manila, an increasing variety of manufacturing and agricultural-processing activities are locating in the near-urban zone surrounding Manila on the east, south, and southwest. The trend is toward greater participation in secondary economic activities; this trend is relatively recent, however, and agriculture still is dominant throughout the region (fig. 57).

Within the region there are about 125,000 farms containing about 747,000 acres of cropped land, involving about 40 percent of the total land area of the region. Rice and fruits other than bananas are grown on about two-thirds of all farms; bananas show up on about half of the farms; coconut is also grown on about one farm in two; and corn is produced on about one farm in four. About half of the farms can be classified as rice farms, about 15 percent as coconut farms, and about 10 percent as farms engaged in mixed farming. Almost 40 percent of the farms may be labeled "irrigated," but this is a region in which late-Spanish small-scale irrigation projects were developed. Owner and part-owner farms amount to about 40 percent of all farms. Farms

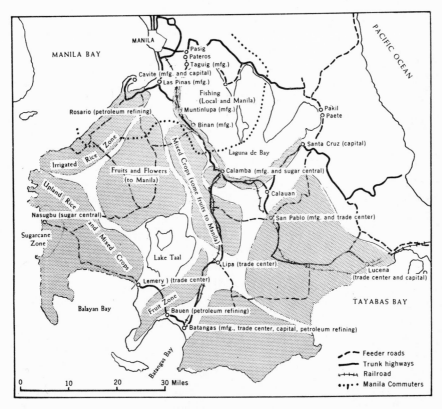

Fig. 57. Transportation and major economic areas of southwestern Luzon.

in the region are small; most are under 10 acres, and many are under 3 acres. Although there is still considerable subsistence farming, the internal urban and the nearby Manila market areas attract a very significant share of the total crop yield, and the region today must be designated as a commercial agricultural area. An increasing number of landowning families have members now engaged in urban commercial, professional, or industrial occupations, so they no longer can work their own farms. This trend has led to an increase in tenancy ratios statistically, but it does not signify a pattern of absentee landlords owning large holdings worked by whole villages of tenants, as is still to be found in the Central Plain.

Within these broad generalizations there are significant variations in subregional patterns which show most clearly in the contrast between northwest Cavite and the southeast Laguna-Quezon border tract. Whereas rice and coconut are widely grown as the basic cropping combination, rice is dominant in upland Batangas and the lower to middle elevations in Cavite, and coconut becomes dominant southward and southeastward from the Laguna de Bay. A great many Batangas farms at higher elevations grow upland rice with other crops serving as minor complements. From just north of San Pablo, Laguna, and on to the south and east, coconut becomes so dominant as to produce a monocrop landscape. Southwest Laguna is a commercial sugarcane producer, with a sugar central at Canlubang, northwest of Calamba; the northwest coast of Batangas repeats this pattern, with cane lands surrounding the sugar central at Nasugbu. Throughout the middle elevations of Batangas, mixed farms and fruit farms are common, with a wide range of fruits represented; on these farms rice, corn, and coconut are complementary crops. The chief fruit-growing zone lies along the middle southeastern slopes of the old Taal Volcano from Lipa southwestward into the hilly Calumpan Peninsula, and in the hilly region south of Batangas City. In some localities the plantings assume the aspect of an orchard land-scape. Near the northeast Cavite urban fringe of Manila, and also at higher elevations on the upper flanks of old Taal Volcano in southern Cavite, coconuts and a wide range of fruits show up in major proportions, with rice, corn, and commercial vegetables serving as complementary crops.

Prior to the late nineteenth century, coffee was rather widely grown in the Batangas-Cavite hill country, and abaca was almost everywhere cultivated as a minor crop. Epidemic disease killed off much of the coffee by the turn of the century, and disease and low per-acre returns reduced the importance of abaca. Today coffee plantings, associated with some cacao plantings, are again increasing in the Batangas hill zones, and are beginning to increase in Cavite, but abaca today is to be found only in token plantings anywhere in the region. The former importance of tobacco plantings appears to have been reduced, and today only token plantings are present. Batangas was formerly noted for its cattle ranches, producing a large number of meat cattle and many of the domestically raised horses. As part of a trend toward a mixed commercial agriculture, Batangas still raises more water buffalo, cattle, horses, pigs, and poultry than other parts of the region; but raising of livestock and poultry is becoming integrated into small-farm economy, whereas formerly the cattle and horses came off large range-pasture ranches that did not produce many crops. Both Batangas and Laguna have developed duck-raising; the meat goes into the general poultry trade, and the eggs go into the Manila market for balut.

There are other variations in detail within the broad regional pattern of agriculture. Kapok is quite commonly grown in small plantings in Batangas, but only an occasional tree is to be found in Cavite or Laguna. Oranges and tangerines (mandarin oranges) are widely cultivated in small holdings in Batangas but are rare in Cavite and Laguna; the lanzon, on the other hand, is a common fruit in eastern Laguna-Quezon but rare in Cavite-Batangas. Upland Cavite produces a considerable volume of fresh pineapples for the Manila market, but the plant is uncommon elsewhere. Upland Cavite also has recently begun to develop commercial flower-raising for the Manila markets, whereas this activity is minor in Batangas and Laguna, although it is increasing in southern Rizal areas east of Manila.

Many of these variations in cropping patterns are of fairly old standing, and they represent trends that have continued with the more complete development of the agricultural landscape toward its maximum extent in the several regions. Some of the trends, however, are reflections of the changing commercial market demands and the favorable returns to be derived from newer cropping patterns more closely in tune with those market demands. It is to be expected that further changes in cropping combinations and agricultural land-use will take place, following changing market demands in the towns of the region and in the Manila metropolitan region.

Perhaps the majority of the pre-Spanish settlements in southwestern Luzon were situated with a regard for the local fishing waters. Fishing, to a certain number of inhabitants in all these settlements, is still a significant enterprise that adds to the regional economy. The Laguna de Bay and Manila Bay are good fishing waters the year around, but the coastal waters off Batangas do not form a major year-round fishing area. Most of the towns around the Laguna de Bay, near Cavite on Manila Bay, and on the southwest Batangas coast house a population concerned with the fishing industries, either in catching or in processing. Manila and nearby shore settlements, of course, today provide the largest fishing fleets and comprise the largest market. Fresh fish are available in all the lake and coastal towns, and also in some of the interior towns on good transport lines. Most of the Laguna de Bay catch is consumed locally or moves to the Manila market as fresh fish. The Cavite towns process a large volume of smoked fish. The Batangas towns salt some seasonally surplus fish but also process a share of the catch into bagoong and sinaeng for shipment outside the coastal area. There are only a few fishponds in operation around the coasts of southwestern Luzon, at

Cavite and Batangas, for not much of the coastal fringe is well adapted to ponds, but the southern end of the Laguna de Bay could support a considerable area of such ponds.

The whole of the southwestern Luzon region had about 2.4 percent of the national industrial labor force in 1960. A part of this force is located in the sector close to the Manila metropolitan area, but the larger part of it is scattered over the region as a whole. Some of the secondary economic activities carried on in southwestern Luzon relate closely to the agricultural economy, and some derive from traditional economic activities, but others are unrelated to internal regional factors and are reflections of the location of the region adjacent to the national industrial-commercial center of Manila. Such agricultural processing as rice milling, sugar refining, and coconut processing are located in towns and cities adjacent to production areas. Rice milling correlates fairly well with the rice-growing regional patterns; sugar central locations determine, quite directly, the location of commercial cane growing; and significant coconut-processing plants are located in the primary coconut-growing regions. The rice mills are generally small and numerous, and are located in municipality centers for the most part. Sugar centrals are located at Canlubang in southwest Laguna and at Nasugbu in western Batangas. Home processing of coconut into copra is to be found in areas with relatively small production, but in southeastern Laguna-Quezon, San Pablo City is a major processor of copra and desiccated coconut, and Lucena also has sizable processing plants. Smaller processing centers are located in other towns in the area. There is little other significant agricultural processing carried on which is of more than local traditional economic importance. The processing of rice into various semiconfectionary forms, such as *pinipig* or *putong*, is widespread, but normally such activities are not considered as manufacturing.

Throughout the older towns and cities of Laguna and Batangas, and in the city of Cavite, handicraft manufactures hold a traditional place. Textile manufacture, from abaca, banana, pineapple, and palm fibers, formerly supplied a variety of textiles for many purposes. The modern replacement of this native textile volume by imported yarns, fabrics, and garments led to a decline in basic processing of traditional textiles. During the replacement process, however, local operations shifted to the further processing of imported textiles and to the making of garments. In almost every town tailors and dressmakers are active. Some operators have extended their activities to the manufacture of garments for sale in local markets, but such activities rarely get statistically enumerated. The leathers replaced wood and textile footwear in the same way. In both Laguna and Batangas there are numbers of towns in which apparel manufacture has increased to a level that is included in statistical reporting. Near Manila, but outside the economic area tabulated as Greater Manila, such towns as Las Piñas, Taguig, Pateros, and Pasig, in Rizal Province, engage in apparel or shoe manufacture. Calamba and San Pablo, in Laguna Province, manufacture clothing, and Biñan manufactures shoes. In Batangas Province, Lipa, Batangas City, and Lemery are such centers. Lipa is growing into an apparel-manufacturing center of regional importance, and its products can be found in many of the shops and markets throughout the whole region. In Cavite Province, only Cavite City engages in very much of such activity beyond the handicraft level.

In several of the Laguna towns around the Laguna de Bay, such as Biñan on the west and Kalayan, Paete, and Pakil on the east, the traditional Tagalog wooden *bakya* footwear are manufactured. This activity is still a home handicraft, despite the rise of plastics and enamel paints as elements in "shoe styling," but it provides a living for a considerable number of families. Furniture manufacturing is assuming specialized character and becoming an urban industrial operation, and clay products, soaps, and locally used chemicals are now being produced in many towns. The furniture factory at the Muntinlupa Penitentiary in Rizal is the largest furniture factory in the Philippines. The manufacture of transport equipment is somewhat more specialized, but in such transport centers as Biñan, San Pablo, Batangas City, and Cavite City, in which transportation companies have located, the manufacture of bodies for taxis, buses, and trucks is important. Several of the urban-fringe towns of southern Rizal also have such industrial operations.

Along the shores of Manila Bay, both east and west of Cavite City, and at a number of points on the southwest Batangas shores, the manufacture of salt by solar evaporation is a localized activity, primarily to produce salt utilized in curing fish. The cement plant at Binangonan, in southern Rizal, is located for a large regional market, but it does use local limestone that outcrops in the hills north of the Laguna de Bay.

Industrial operations not internally motivated involve petroleum refining and related by-product chemical manufacture. Three petroleum refineries are located in southwestern Luzon, at Bauen and Batangas City in Batangas Province, and at Rosario in Cavite Province, just west of Cavite City. Locations on deepwater port sites, with positions close to Manila and central to national distribution routes, were the orienting factors, but these activities do add a higher level of operations to regional industry than any of the internally motivated activities.

From its location near Manila it is to be expected that southwestern Luzon, as a region, will increase steadily in the level and volume of its manufacturing and industrial operations. A coastal situation, good internal transportation facilities, and the availability of a growing industrial labor force will be factors in such growth patterns. Although no large mineral or power resources are available locally, the location of the region close to Manila will provide much of the stimulus necessary to such growth.

Two factors worked together to provide southwestern Luzon with excellent transportation facilities in relation to general Philippine conditions. Late-Spanish road building began the development of a well-distributed system, as a historical factor. The position of southwestern Luzon adjacent to Manila, the political and economic heart of the archipelago, has ensured that good transport facilities lead through the region to other parts of southern Luzon. The continued expansion and development of the old Spanish system provides all parts of the region except northwest Batangas with a rather close-order network of good highways that, in quality, are among the best in the country. Traffic by road is heavy out of Manila southward, and truck and bus routes fan out to Cavite provincial areas and to southward and eastward points. A main truck line extends southward along the west side of the Laguna de Bay to branch out into Batangas on the west, and southern Laguna and Quezon on the southeast. The main southern line of the Manila Railroad system roughly parallels this truck highway into southern Laguna, enroute to the Bicol Peninsula. Large numbers of transport companies, running both buses and trucks, operate frequent services to all parts of the region, and through-services destined for the east coast and southeastern Luzon pass through the heart of the region.

Such transport facilities provide the region with multiple services that bring all areas within close contact with Manila, both in terms of communications and for the handling of commodities. Local surpluses of regional products have easy access to a major consuming market. All products available in Manila may flow easily to all parts of the region. Cavite, Batangas, Lemery, Calamba, San Pablo, Lucena, and Santa Cruz are all major regional transportation centers. Many of the land-transport facilities serving the region operate out of fringe-point bases in southern and eastern Manila, but some of them operate out of terminal locations, such as Batangas and San Pablo. Cavite, for the province of Cavite, and Biñan, for the western part of Laguna, are intermediate points at which are located bus and truck systems that provide added facilities to and from Manila.

As a consequence of the transport pattern and the adjacent location of Manila, the region of southwestern Luzon has neither a major interregional nor an intraregional trade center. Manila is not only the national trade center, but it functions as the major wholesale trade center of southwestern Luzon. Only Lucena, in the southwestern corner of the region, has any status as a general regional center, and a part of its trade hinterland lies outside southwestern Luzon as delimited in this study. Lucena is a regional wholesale distributing point for the southern coastal region, a center for agricultural processing, particularly for coconut products, a rail and road transport center, and the provincial capital of Quezon Province. In 1960 its charter area included 49,000 people, of whom about 30,000 resided in the urban zone.

The three cities of San Pablo, in Laguna, and Lipa and Batangas, in Batangas Province, are sufficiently important to rank as secondary trade centers, but each is overshadowed by Manila in almost all except purely local functions. San Pablo is a major center for the processing of coconut products of all varieties, a center for apparel and shoe manufacturing, a center for numerous service activities, and a major road center and rail shipping point. Its charter area, in 1960, included a population of 70,680, of whom about 30,000 resided in the urban area. Lipa was an old Spanish military headquarters and formerly was an important center of handicraft manufacturing, particularly for the textile and clothing industries. It is a chartered city with a population, in 1960, of 69,000, of whom about 15,000 lived in the truly urban sector. Lipa is a regional center of the apparel-manufacturing industry, does some agricultural processing, and is a local market center. Batangas is a national port, a fishing port, a petroleum-refining center, and the provincial capital of Batangas Province. As such it is an important trade center for much of the southwestern coastal region. About 18,000 people lived in the urban center in 1960.

Cavite is the largest city within the region, barring Greater Manila, with a 1960 population of 55,000. As the old Spanish naval base, Cavite remains a Philippine and United States naval base and shipyard today, although other bases have been developed and Cavite is no longer so significant as it was in the past. Cavite formerly engaged in a good deal of handicraft manufacturing, but apart from the naval-base operations, its chief economic operations today concern the manufacture of transport equipment. Cavite was once the residence of many Spanish families, and the compact site is rather tightly built. Today Cavite is a residential dormitory settlement tributary to Manila, a fishing port, a military base, and the provincial capital of Cavite Province.

Significant lesser towns in the region are chiefly rather old settlements that either were Spanish cabecera church centers or have long served as municipios in the administration of a local region. In southern Rizal, east of Manila, a number of these towns recently have begun to grow rapidly as they become involved in the eastward expansion of the Manila metropolitan area. Pateros, Taguig, Pasig, Cainta, Taytay, and Antipolo are such old rural agricultural towns now being filled up by dormitory residents, small service businesses, light manufacturing, and a few larger branch establishments. In several of them the poblacion remains small, for it is the open rural spaces that are now being settled. Antipolo is at about the 1960 eastward limit of the urban sprawl, but the process is continuing. Binangonan, on the western side of the peninsular projection into the Laguna de Bay, is a local regional trade center with a poblacion population of 7,000; it is the chief market center for Talim Island in the Laguna, and is the site of a cement plant. Tanay on the northeastern shore of the Laguna is a regional trade and transport center for eastern Rizal, and had a 1960 poblacion population of 11,000.

In Cavite Province the towns have chiefly been small until recently, except for Cavite City, but many of the eastern ones have been growing rather rapidly in the recent period as residential communities for families occupied in Manila. Naic, on the coast west of Cavite City, had a 1960 urban-core population of about 6,500, is a market center for the western part of the province, and does rice milling for the coastal rice-growing region. Tagaytay, on the northern flank of old Mount Taal, is a chartered city, but perhaps the most rural of all the Philippine chartered cities, for it is chiefly notable as a slightly cool upland picnic and resort site with a beautiful view. Market gardens growing products for the Manila market are more obvious in Tagaytay than the urbanism. Trece Martires recently became a chartered city (May, 1954), but its total population in 1960 was only 4,422, and its barrio serving as a poblacion held only 516 people; the legal maneuvers for chartering a city are not accompanied by significant population requirements.

In Laguna there are a considerable number of fairly sizable towns, all old cabecera church sites of towns that early achieved municipio status. Biñan, in the northwest part of Laguna, was not one of the earliest cabecera sites, but it was an early encomienda and its church and town site date from the early eighteenth century. Biñan, in 1960, had an urban population of about 13,000. A shoe-manufacturing center, a rice-milling center, and a residential town for many people employed in Manila, Biñan also is the terminal for several bus and truck lines. Calamba, with a 1960 population of about 15,000 in its urban core, is a rail and road junction, a rice-milling center, a sugar central, and a general marketing and trade center for southern Laguna and eastern Batangas. Its trading functions include servicing the population of the nearby Canlubang sugar central. Santa Cruz is the provincial capital of Laguna Province, located on the southeast corner of the Laguna de Bay. It is a minor regional trade center with a 1960 poblacion population of just over 5,500. Nagcarlan, south of Santa Cruz in the inland plain, is a minor agricultural-processing center and local trade center with a 1960 poblacion population of 8,200. There are a number of other Laguna municipio towns, with poblacion populations between 4,000 and 7,000, whose residential patterns reflect Spanish influence in that people reside in the towns and on farmlands around the towns. Although these towns are urban in some respects, they resemble villages in other respects.

In Batangas Province, in addition to Lipa and Batangas City, the Lemery and Taal pair of municipio towns, situated on opposite banks of the Pansipit River, represent very old residential sites. Lemery had a 1960 poblacion population of 8,800, and Taal had a total of 5,000 in the poblacion; the pair form an almost continuous residential zone, and constitute a fishing center, an agricultural-processing center, and a transport break-point and regional terminal. Nasugbu, on the west coast, is a national port, a sugar-central location, and a regional trade center, with a 1960 poblacion population of 8,500. In northern, upland Batangas, Tanauan is a regional marketing and trade-transport center for the eastern hill-country sector of the Mount Taal upland; it had a 1960 population of 7,100 in its poblacion.

Bicolandia: Southeast Luzon

The several peninsulas that form the southeastern extremity of Luzon, together with the adjacent larger island of Catanduanes and numerous smaller islands, make up the very distinctive subregion of the island called the Bicol region, or Bicolandia. Within this Bicol region there is a very considerable degree of geographic homogeneity. Culturally, the four southeastern provinces of the main island, and the larger islands of Catanduanes, Masbate, Burias, and Ticao, are inhabited primarily by peoples belonging to a Philippine cultural-linguistic group referred to as "Bikol." The Sibuyan Sea islands of Masbate, Burias, and Ticao, however, possess physical and agricultural landscapes that differ rather markedly from those characteristic of the Luzon peninsula, and largely for this reason, these latter islands are excluded from the Bicol region. Thus delimited, the Bicol region includes all of the five provinces of Albay, Sorsogon, Catanduanes, and the two Camarines, and represents a total area of approximately 5,400 square miles.

THE PHYSICAL SETTING

Structurally, the southeastern peninsulas of Luzon, and also the island of Catanduanes, lie along and upon the eastern edge of the main Luzon Platform. Their main structure is provided by the Samar Arch, which, broken by the trough occupied by strategic San Bernardino Strait between Sorsogon Peninsula and the island of Samar, continues southward into the eastern Visayan Islands. The whole southeastern extremity of Luzon is almost severed from the main mass of Luzon to the north by the deep embayments of Ragay Gulf (Catabangan Bay) and Calauag Bay. At this point only the narrow, 8-mile wide Tayabas Isthmus provides a land connection, and even then, the Viñas River almost cuts through this tenuous link.

The Bicol Peninsula has a very irregular form with several very deep and extensive coastal embayments, large subpeninsulas, and a very lengthy coastline (fig. 58). The smaller peninsulas of Camarines, in the north, and Caramoan and Sorsogon, in the south, are separated from one another by the extensive water bodies of San Miguel and Sorsogon bays and Lagonoy and Albay gulfs, all of which penetrate far into the main landmass. Much of the irregular form of southeastern Luzon is imparted to it by the underlying structure of the Samar Arch with its two upturned flanks and intervening longitudinal low zone. The Ragay Hills, a low, 1,000-foot-high range of uplands, is formed by the westernmost flank of the arch. These hills lie along the coast abutting Ragay Gulf. The present form of the Ragay Hills is the result of deep dissection of the uplifted sedimentary rocks, which consist mainly of silts, limestones, and marls. The erosion process has been greatly accelerated because the hills have been generally denuded of their original dense forests. Today their slopes are covered with grass or with noncommercial, second-growth forests. The Ragay Hills are neither sufficiently high nor continuous to impose much of a barrier to east–west travel.

The main highland area of southeastern Luzon is provided by the eastern flank of the Samar Arch along which there has been, and still is, considerable vulcanism. The presence of this eastern structural arch is evidenced by a series of high volcanic cones, among them Mounts Labo (3,092 feet), Malinao (5,079 feet), Isarog (6,182 feet), Mayon (7,943 feet), and Bulusan (5,115 feet). These separated volcanic forms give the Bicol region a very distinctive topographic character, for it is seldom that at least one of them is not in sight. The volcanos reach their culmination in the beautifully symmetrical, and still active, cone of Mount Mayon, which, rising from the shores of Albay Gulf, stands watch over the city of Legaspi.

A nonvolcanic arm of the eastern highland system breaks off from the main range at Mount Labo in Camarines Norte. This subrange consists of a low, rugged hill land that trends almost due east, forming the Caramoan Peninsula, and beyond Maqueda Channel, supplies the main form of the island of Catanduanes.

The small islands of San Miguel, Cagraray, Batan, and Rapu-Rapu lie to the east of Luzon and form the northern rim of Albay Gulf and the eastern edge of Tabaco Bay. These islands represent a low monoclinal continuation of the eastern structural arch into the waters of Lagonoy Gulf. Most of the land surface of the two northern islands of San Miguel and Cagraray is low-lying and covered with basalts, tuffs, and sandstone, whereas the higher island of Rapu-Rapu has exposed basement-complex rocks in its interior, consisting mainly of serpentines. Rapu-Rapu and Batan have small commercial deposits of coal and copper.

The 550-square-mile island of Catanduanes has a dissected upland inte-

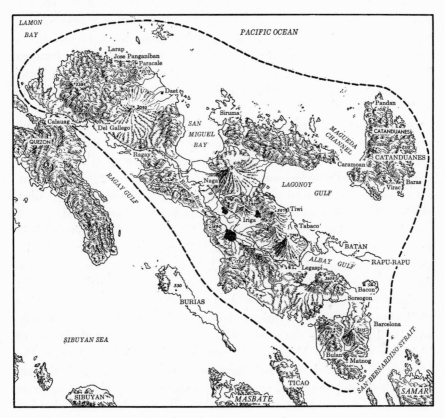

Fig. 58. Physiography of the southeastern Luzon.

rior composed of basement-complex materials, mainly serpentines and schists. A narrow strip of lowland parallels the coast, reaching its greatest width along the south coast around Cabugao Bay and the provincial capital of Virac. Elevations remain below 2,000 feet. The coast of Catanduanes is quite regular, lacking in good harbors, and coral-fringed except in the west.

The largest area of contiguous lowlands in the Bicol region is the long structural trough that extends from the southern shores of San Miguel Bay approximately 60 miles southward to Albay Gulf. Drainage of this lowland generally is toward San Miguel Bay. A low topographic divide, located near the town of Camalig in Albay Province, approximately 6 miles west of Legaspi, separates the northward drainage that is dominated by the Bicol River from that which drains southward across the small plain around Legaspi and into Albay Gulf. This large lowland area is called the Bicol Plain. There are two relatively large lakes, Lakes Bato and Baao, which occupy a central position on this Bicol Plain. Virtually all of the plain is arable, and most of the farmland is devoted to the cultivation of lowland rice. Smaller, but still important lowlands are found along the Labo and Basud rivers, west and north of the city of Daet, and on the Lagonoy Plain between Mount Isarog and Lagonoy Gulf. The Tabaco-Legaspi Plain and the Sorsogon Plain, the latter north and east of Sorsogon Bay, are other areas of small lowlands in the south.

A measure of the usability of the lands of the Bicol region for agricultural purposes is indicated by the fact that fully 68 percent of the total area of the region is classed as arable, and approximixately 90 percent of this potential farmland is actually under some form of utilization at present.[11] The percentage of arable lands to total area is especially high in the provinces of Albay and Sorsogon. Catanduanes has the smallest proportion of arable land.

All of the Bicol region is well-watered, for everywhere precipitation is in excess of 80 inches annually. The northern Camarines and Caramoan peninsulas, northeastern littorals of Albay and Sorsogon, and the island of Catanduanes receive precipitations in excess of 120 inches annually. Baras, in southeastern Catanduanes, has the dubious distinction of being the rainiest Philippine weather station, with 215 inches of rain annually. The least moist areas are located along the shores of Ragay Gulf, in the lee of the eastern highlands and Ragay Hills, and in certain sheltered interior locales. The exposure of most of the peninsula to moisture-bearing air masses, both from the northeast and southwest, prevents the occurrence of prolonged or severe droughts. February, March, and April and usually the driest months, but few stations in the region record precipitations less that 4 inches monthly. Generally most western exposures and interior locations tend to experience maximum precipitation in the period from June to October, whereas eastern and northern exposures receive their heaviest rainfalls during the period from October to January. In general, the rainfall is sufficient to keep the soils moist throughout the year.

Typhoons are an especially frequent and destructive menace in the Bicol region. The months of September, October, and November experience the more destructive of these violent tropical storms. Forty percent of the storms carrying high-velocity winds in the Philippines pass through southeastern

Luzon. Often the abaca and rice crops, as well as most other field crops, experience considerable wind damage during the passage of these typhoons, and coastal and overseas shipping usually avoid the Pacific coast ports during the chief typhoon season.

Much of the original luxurious forest vegetation of the Bicol area has been cleared away, and now most of these lands are under cultivation. In Camarines Norte, on the Caramoan Peninsula, and on the island of Catan-duanes, however, there remain considerable stands of virgin tropical rain forest. The standing timber resources of the Bicol region are sufficient to base approximately 7 percent of the Philippine sawmill capacity, and reserves amounting to approximately 9 billion board feet of accessible timber are sufficient for a modest forest industry for many years to come. Considerable quantities of logs and lumber are cut from the Bicol forests and moved to markets in the Manila area or exported directly. Little commercial forest growth remains in the provinces of Albay and Sorsogon, and the lands not actually under cultivation are largely in cogon grasses in these two provinces.

The interesting and valuable abaca plant, the source for the production of Manila hemp, perhaps is indigenous to the natural vegetation association of the Bicol region; however, abaca is now grown extensively on small holdings throughout much of the eastern Philippines.

THE CULTURAL SETTING

The essentially homogeneous character of much of the cultural environment of the Bicol area appears to supply an even stronger regional unifying factor than does the possession of somewhat similar regional physical landscapes. The Bikol dialect, a common Spanish background, similar political aspira-tions, and agricultural crops and land-use patterns show considerable homoge-neity throughout the Bicol area, and yet these are quite different from other areas on Luzon.

The strongest regional tie, which manifests itself in a host of associated cultural traits, is supplied by the sharing of a relatively similar Philippine dialect throughout the region. To be sure, the Bikol dialect gradually loses out to the Tagalog dialect in northern Camarines Norte, generally north of the city of Daet, and numerous elements of the Waray-Waray dialect of the Samareños are encountered in southern Sorsogon. Nevertheless, the group of dialects usually referred to as Bikol are dominant in all of the Bicol prov-inces.[12] Bikol is the mother tongue of 93 percent of the population of southeastern Luzon. The average Bikol-speaking Filipino also clearly iden-tifies himself very much as a Bicolano, that is, one who speaks Bikol and lives in the Bicol region, and there is an almost conscious psychology in the linguistic identification. Since Filipino loyalties generally stem from the family and town outward, it may very well be that the residents of Bicolandia identify themselves as much as Bicolanos as Filipino nationals. Be this as it may, there is a strong ethnolinguistic basis to the identification and delineation of the Bicol region.

Spain was in early contact with the Bicol region. The very important San Bernardino Strait, which gave Manila a shorter access to the Pacific Ocean, could be guarded and controlled from the southern shores of Sorsogon Peninsula. Furthermore, at an early date an important segment of the Spanish shipbuilding industry was concentrated in southeastern Luzon. Several of the famed Manila galleons were built in Sorsogon and in the Camarines during the seventeenth century, including the vessels "Nuestra Señora de Guadalupe" and "Angel de la Guardia." Spanish forces had first explored the Bicol region in 1569, and returned in 1573 to establish the towns of Libon in Albay and Naga in Camarines Sur. Soon the area along the lower course of the Bicol River became a particularly important area of heavy Spanish influence. The shrine-church of Nuestra Señora de Peñafrancia, the patroness saint for all of Bicolandia, was constructed at this time along the Bicol River in Naga City. For a long time the bishopric of Nueva Caceres (Naga) included Camarines Norte, Camarines Sur, Albay, Ticao, Masbate, Catanduanes, and Tayabas (Quezon). In 1800 this district represented 200,000 persons.

All of the central characteristics that tend to unify the peoples of the Bicol area into a distinct cultural region are further reinforced by the comparative geographic isolation enjoyed by the region. Transportation between the Bicol and the rest of Luzon has always been difficult, except by water, a factor that further facilitated the development and growth of a distinctive indigenous and relatively homogeneous cultural environment within the region. Even today, the only easy land connection with the rest of Luzon is by an all-day rail trip.

The Bicol region is one of the more populous regions in the Philippines with a population of slightly more than two million. Population densities, both crude and physiological, approximate those for the archipelago as a whole. Most Bicolanos are agricultural village-dwellers living close to the lands they cultivate. The most densely populated area is the Bicol Plain, including the Legaspi-Tabaco Lowland, where some 8 percent of the area of the region supports something over 40 percent of the population (fig. 21). Other thickly settled areas include the plains adjacent to Lagonoy Gulf and around Sorsogon Bay, various small coastal lowlands along San Bernardino Strait, and the southern lowland area of Catanduanes.

Although there are few large cities in southeastern Luzon, over 17 percent of the people live in settlements with populations of 2,500 or more. Naga and Legaspi are the major urban centers. Naga, the capital of Camarines Sur Province, is the principal metropolis of the Bicol area. It is the major trade center and market town for the rich agricultural area of the Bicol Plain. The city is strung out along the Bicol River, which is navigable to the city for vessels drawing up to 9 feet. Naga is one of the oldest Spanish settlements in the Philippines and was founded in 1573 as the city of Nueva Caceres. It was, and still is, an important center of Spanish influence. It is a major stop on the Manila-South Railroad, and important highways radiate out in all directions. There are several educational institutions located here, and the city's cultural influence is felt far out into the surrounding area. In 1960 the poblacion of the city of Naga had a population of 13,000 persons, with 55,000 residing within its chartered limits.

Legaspi is the capital city of the province of Albay. Located along the western shores of Albay Gulf, Legaspi serves as the primary port and port of entry for southeastern Luzon. Its eccentric location does not permit the city to exert as strong an influence upon the commercial life of the Bicol region as does Naga, and it contents itself with a trade area that contains the Legaspi-Tabaco area and the offshore islands in Albay Gulf. Nevertheless, large quantities of abaca, abaca products, and copra move overseas through the port of Legaspi. The port also serves as a crossroads for interisland vessels from Manila and the Visayan area, and major petroleum depot facilities are maintained. Legaspi is the terminus of the Manila-South Railroad, and good all-weather roads link it with all important points in the Bicol area. Besides its administrative and commercial functions, the city supports a large abaca handicraft industry. The grass-covered rocky headlands that jut out into the gulf immediately south of the city, coupled with the bright-red tile roofs of many of the downtown buildings, give a sort of Spanish mediterranean color to the city. Mount Mayon lies immediately to the north, and its volcanic ejecta is exposed along the beach as black sands. International shipping is serviced through the flimsiest of temporary bamboo piers, for the deep waters lie close inshore, and the frequency and severity of typhoons operate against more permanent facilities. Legaspi, now separated from its suburb of Daraga, had an urban population of 22,000 in 1960 with 60,000 people under the chartered city limits.

A second hierarchy of towns includes Iriga, Daet, Bulan, Nabua, Sorsogon, Tabaco, and Ligao. Each of these towns had a population in 1960 between 10,000 and 25,000. Bulan, Sorsogon, and Tabaco are primarily small ports. Tabaco is a Philippine port of entry (administratively, in conjunction with the port of Legaspi) through which abaca and copra are exported. Tabaco serves as the mainland trading center for Catanduanes Island, and regular launch service is maintained with the towns of Pandan and Virac on Catanduanes. Mount Mayon, rising abruptly back of the town, lends to Tabaco one of the most picturesque settings in the Philippines. Bulan is the largest town in Sorsogon Province. Unfortunately its port and harbor are inadequate, and the small quantities of abaca and copra that are shipped must be lightered to vessels lying offshore. Fishing, and trade with the surrounding agricultural lands, are the mainstays of the Bulan economy. Sorsogon is also the capital of its province. Daet, the capital of Camarines Norte, is the principal commercial center of the province; it is served by its outport of Mercedes. Iriga, Nabua, and Ligao are major trading centers on the Bicol Plain.

Among the towns of lesser importance are the two mining communities of Paracale and Jose Panganiban in Camarines Norte. Important abaca and clay handicraft industries are located in the small Albay towns of Malilipot, Oas, and Tiwi.

The economy of the Bicol area can be simply described as consisting basically of a subsistence-oriented agriculture, with overtones of commercial agriculture (fig. 59). Rice is far and away the dominant food crop; however, only in certain more favorable years are there small surpluses of this grain available for sale outside the region. Generally, the chronic rice deficits of the provinces of Sorsogon and Camarines Norte are such as to absorb the expected overproduction from the other Bicol provinces. Most of the region's rice cultivation centers in the two provinces of Camarines Sur and Albay, which together produce approximately 80 percent of the rice crop from about equal proportions of the total rice acreage. Most of the rice is of the lowland, wet variety and is grown extensively on the heavy clay soils of the Bicol Plain. Double-cropping is common and occurs on about one-fifth of the rice lands, particularly in the provinces of Albay and Sorsogon. The raising of two rice crops is facilitated by the installation of irrigation systems, which are rather widespread except in relatively undeveloped Catanduanes. Several irrigation-pump units have been installed in the Bicol area in recent years. The area devoted to rice within the region, excluding Sorsogon Province, has doubled in all of the provinces in the years since World War II, and production has managed to keep pace with the expanding population. Rice yields generally have remained well above the national averages.

Considerable land also has been planted to various varieties of upland or dry rice. The Sipocot River area, lying northwest of the mouth of the Bicol River, has nearly one-half of its total rice lands in upland varieties, and

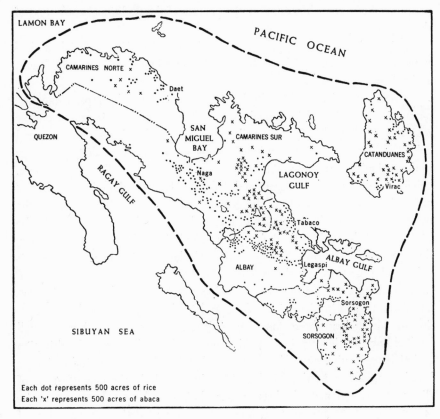

Fig. 59. Rice and abaca in southeastern Luzon, 1960.

elsewhere sloping lands unsuited to field inundations are planted to upland rice varieties.

Maize ranks second to rice as a food crop within the region, with approximately one-third of the region's total acreage. Maize has provided a very adaptable crop with which to bring into use arable lands with soils or topography not suited for rice cultivation. The area planted to maize has expanded severalfold in the last decade. In Camarines Norte and Sorsogon in the years between 1955 and 1959, the area planted to corn increased by more than 300 percent. The increase in corn production has been even more spectacular.[13] Camarines Sur and Albay are the leading provinces in corn acreage and production, as they are with rice; however, because of the generally poor character of the soils and large area of steeply sloping lands in Sorsogon, the maize acreage in that province is almost double the rice area. Overall corn production is sufficient to meet internal regional requirements, partly because needs are modest, as the peoples of the Bicol area are not accustomed to a corn dietary as are the peoples of the traditional corn areas of the Visayas.

Regional food-grain supplies are supplemented with substantial productions of several fruits and vegetables, including camotes, cassava, taro, beans, and onions.

Coconuts and abaca are the leading commercial cash crops. Generally, coconuts are cultivated in coastal locations, whereas abaca is grown on the relatively fertile volcanic loam soils near and on the slopes of the several volcanoes of the eastern uplands. Coconuts supply many products necessary to the region's internal economy, and also provide for a small export of copra, chiefly from the ports of Legaspi and Tabaco. Abaca, on the other hand, is of major significance, not only to the economy of the region, but to that of the nation. Approximately one-fourth of the total acreage devoted to abaca in the Philippines is located in the Bicol area, particularly in the provinces of Albay, Sorsogon, and Camarines Sur. A particularly large region in which abaca is cultivated almost exclusively extends from Mount Isarog to Mount Mayon. Smaller abaca areas are found on the slopes of Mount Bulusan in Sorsogon and Mount Labo in Camarines Norte and in the central uplands of Catanduanes. Throughout the region, abaca cultivation is usually confined to small landholdings. Little attention is paid to proper plant selection, and cultivation and yields are quite low. A large array of handicraft or cottage industries are based upon abaca in the Bicol region; these include the manufacture of slippers, rugs and mats, baskets, nets, webbing, and rope. Large quantities of both raw abaca and abaca handicrafts are exported through the ports of Legaspi and Tabaco.

Minerals have played a relatively important role in the economy of the Bicol area, and some two dozen companies are now active, or have been active in the immediate past, in mining operations. A strongly mineralized area in northern Camarines Norte constitutes one of the major mineral districts of the Philippines, and a secondary district lies along Lagonoy Gulf and on Rapu-Rapu Island. A wide variety of minerals is present, including commercial deposits of gold, copper, iron ore, chromite, manganese, silver, lead, and coal. The reported presence of gold at Paracale first brought the attention of the Spanish authorities to the northern Camarines area. The other minerals have been developed under the subsequent American administration. The immediate target for Spanish gold exploitation was the auriferous gravels in many Paracale streams and rivers. Subsequent American operations utilized huge dredges and later concentrated on primary lode deposits. Small amounts of gold continue to trickle out of the Paracale area; however, the collapse of a main tunnel of the major gold-producer in 1952 and the tragic loss of 56 miners, the greatest mine disaster in Philippine history, brought a halt to large-scale gold-mining operations. Small gold-mining operations continue in Paracale and the adjacent municipality of Jose Panganiban. The Paracale area also produces small amounts of copper, silver, and lead.

Today the principal mineral of the Camarines Norte area is a high-grade hematite iron ore. Although there are several mines producing iron ore near the town of Jose Panganiban, the largest producer is that of the Philippine Iron Mines at Larap. The mining of iron ore was first attempted in 1918, but it was not until 1934 that large quantities of ore were produced regularly for shipment to Japan. The Japanese authorities continued to mine small amounts during World War II. Since rehabilitation, production has ranged between one and two million tons of 58 percent iron-content hematite ore. The Larap mines are both shaft and open-pit operations and are located only a short distance from the coast. The deposit of iron ore at Larap is the principal source of commercial-grade iron ore in the Philippines; however, the entire production is shipped to Japan at present. Larap is a large company-owned town, complete with company hospital and commissary. Small quantities of ore supplied from small independent producers nearby are purchased by Philippine Iron Mines and mixed with company ores. The ore is then railroaded to the company wharf on nearby Calambayanga Island.

The secondary mineral zone centers on Rapu-Rapu Island. Pyrites from Rapu-Rapu are shipped to the government fertilizer plant at Maria Cristina Falls in northern Mindanao, and small quantities of a good-grade bituminous coal are desultorily mined. Tigaon and Lagonoy on Lagonoy Gulf are sites of small deposits of chromite and manganese ores.

Mining and operations attendant upon mineral production employ several thousand workers in southeastern Luzon. The northern Bicol area perhaps ranks second in importance only to Mountain Province in the Philippine mineral industry. Although present proven reserves appear rather modest, it can be assumed with a reasonable amount of assurance that new ore deposits and larger reserves will appear with increased exploration of the two Bicol mineral zones.

Fishing, logging, and sawmilling round out the basic economy of the Bicol region. Ragay Gulf, San Miguel Bay, and Lagonoy Gulf, all located within or adjacent to southeastern Luzon, are among the more important Philippine commercial fishing grounds. San Miguel Bay is a particularly important fishing ground during the southwestern monsoon. In addition, most coastal areas in southeastern Luzon are endowed with rich fish resources. Many residents of the coast participate in part-time fishing to supplement their agricultural incomes. Fishing attains extraregional commercial stature within the municipalities of Mercedes, Ragay, Calabanga, and Legaspi where many of the larger commercial fishing vessels are based. Many of the barrios in the municipalities of Calabanga (Balongay, Punta Calabanga, Sabang), Timambac (Bagacoy, Buenavista), Cabusao (Castillo, Barceloneta), and Siruma in Camarines Sur are solely dependent upon fishing. Shrimp, crabs, croakers, and sea catfish are especially abundant. Most of the fish-catch is consumed fresh. Several commercial fishponds have been established since World War II, particularly in Sorsogon and Camarines Sur. Supplies of fish are sufficiently large to meet regional fish consumption.

Forest industries have long played an important role in the Bicol economy. The abundant rains and volcanically derived soils have produced a forest resource that is large and of excellent quality. Several of the more exotic true Philippine hardwoods are native to the Bicol rain forests. At present there are some thirty sawmills, with a rated capacity of 230,000 board feet of lumber daily, in operation. The virgin forests of the northern part of the Bicol area are the site for most of the sawmills. Basud, Jose Panganiban, Tandoc, Sipocot, and Del Gallego are major lumber towns. Considerable quantities of lumber are shipped to Manila or exported, in log form, to Japan. Firewood and rattans are important minor forest products. Tandoc, in Camarines Sur, is the site of a large plywood and veneer plant. Under proper management the forest resources of the Bicol should continue to play an important role in the regional economy.

Until the present decade southeastern Luzon has been very poorly provided with interregional transportation facilities; however, within the region itself there has been a reasonably adequate network of roads that are well developed and well maintained by Philippine standards, and connect most of the more important towns. Highway 1, hard-surfaced and all-weather throughout, is the major artery of communications. The highway runs the entire length of the peninsula, terminating in the south at Matnog on the shores of San Bernardino Strait. Daet, Naga, the length of the Bicol Plain, Legaspi, and Sorsogon all lie on this route, and from each of these centers a network of minor roads radiates into the surrounding countryside. Buses, trucks, and cars are quite numerous on the southeastern Luzon highways, providing an inexpensive, frequent, and rapid transportation system. Recently a large section of Highway 1 in northern Camarines has been completed through to the Tayabas Isthmus, connecting into the main highway system at Luzon. The island of Catanduanes has, on the other hand, only the bare framework of a land-transportation system.

The coastal area adjacent to Ragay Gulf, and the northern Camarines and Caramoan peninsulas, have no roads. Small coastal vessels are employed to serve those areas lying near the coast, and the more populous offshore islands, including Catanduanes, are linked to the main island by relatively frequent sailings of these vessels. Most of the larger ports in the Bicol area have regular service by interisland vessels from Manila or the Visayan area.

Daet, Naga, Legaspi, Jose Panganiban, Bulan, and Virac lie on scheduled routes of the Philippine Air Lines, and thus, are connected with Manila and the rest of the archipelago.

The Manila-South Railroad enters the Bicol region from southwestern Luzon along the northeastern shores of Ragay Gulf. After reaching the latitude of Naga City the rail line cuts inland to Naga, then traverses the length of the Bicol Plain, and terminates at Legaspi. A branch line that formerly went on to Tabaco has been abandoned owing to insufficient traffic. The Manila-South Railroad is an important mover of freight, particularly large quantities of petroleum products from the Manila area. Until very recently the railroad provided the only land link between southeastern Luzon and the rest of the island. From 1921 to 1938 the rail system connected the Bicol rail system with southwestern Luzon facilities by way of a ferry between Pamplona, Camarines Sur, and Aloneros, Quezon, across the head of Ragay Gulf.

The Far Coast: The Eastern Luzon Littoral

The eastern Luzon region fronts on the open waters of the Pacific Ocean north of the Bicol Peninsula. This picturesque, but sterile, eastern rampart of Luzon extends from Cape Engaño in the northeastern corner of the island southward for over 360 miles, through Tayabas Isthmus, and into Bondoc Peninsula (fig. 60). The region consists of several small, scattered coastal lowlands and a rugged, inaccessible highland interior composed of the Eastern Cordillera of Luzon and the northern extension, which is known as the Sierra Madre Range. The cordillera lands descend abruptly on the east, leaving little room for the development of coastal plains. Furthermore, the many short, swift-flowing streams have been unable to build deltas out into the deep waters that lie close inshore. The eastern coast of Luzon lacks good harbors. All of the region is exposed to the full effects of the moist air masses and raging storms of the western Pacific Ocean. Everywhere the rainfall is abundant and constant.

Heavily forested, windswept, excessively moist, and relatively inaccessible, eastern Luzon has not offered a particularly hospitable environment for human occupance, and only the very great population pressures on the Central Plain of Luzon have succeeded in pushing settlers into this eastern

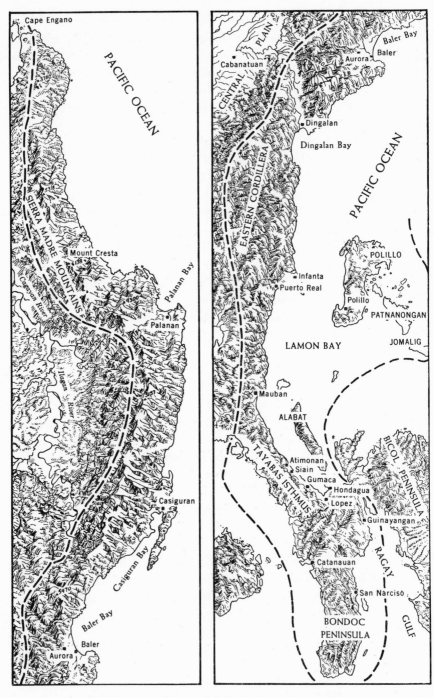

Fig. 60. Physiography of eastern Luzon.

littoral. Even today, agriculture is of only minor significance along the east coast, except for some rather large areas devoted to coconuts in the south, and most of the regional economy is tied to forest exploitation, particularly in the north. The majority of the settlers (89 percent) speak Tagalog, the dominant dialect of central Luzon. Crude population densities are very low, except in the more accessible Tayabas Isthmus, and vast stretches along the coast are virtually uninhabited.

The eastern Luzon region consists of the cordillera lands and coastal lowlands of the eastern sections of Cagayan and Isabela provinces, as well as those of the Central Plain provinces, and most of the areas of the province of Quezon, excepting a small section in southwestern Luzon north and west of the city of Lucena. The offshore islands, including Polillo, Patnanongan, Jomalig, and Alabat, also are included within the region. Altogether, the eastern Luzon region includes a land area of approximately 5,600 square miles.

Although seemingly fitting the category of a "region of convenience," that is to say, one by which a large and inconvenient area can be collectively discarded, the eastern Luzon area nevertheless does possess a certain degree of regional homogeneity and lends itself to several valid regional generalizations.

THE PHYSICAL ENVIRONMENT

The Sierra Madre Range, and its continuation southward as the Eastern Cordillera, provide the common physiographic frame upon which the regional delimitation rests. This continuous and lofty highland system closely parallels the eastern shores of Luzon. The eastern slopes form a bold and almost inaccessible shoreline that is exposed to the full force of the northeast trade winds and the nearly continuous waves and heavy surf that belie the name Pacific. For over 200 miles from Cape Engaño southward to Dingalan Bay, the bold, rocky coastline is a steep, timbered wilderness that rises sharply from bare cliffs and is backed by a massive mountain system. Only five small municipalities, with a combined population of 30,000 persons, are located along this section of the coast. Few bays indent the northern coastline, and heavy surf continually crashes against the rocky shores. The only areas of lowland are located at the heads of Palanan, Casiguran, and Baler bays.

South of Dingalan, the mountains stand somewhat farther back from the shoreline, and a coastal plain begins to develop; however, until Lamon Bay is reached much of the southern coast remains exposed to the open reaches of the Pacific Ocean, except in the lee of Polillo Island. Farther south the main ridge of the Eastern Cordillera plunges under some young sediments and forms the narrow Tayabas Isthmus, and finally, the Bondoc Peninsula.

Narrow, discontinuous plains accompany the coasts of Bondoc, and low, wooded hills form the upland interiors.

Several relatively large islands lie off the eastern coasts of Luzon. The largest of these islands is Polillo with an area of 233 square miles, followed in size by Alabat (73 square miles), Patnanongan (33 square miles), and Jomalig (20 square miles). These offshore islands lie upon a shallow submarine platform, and extensive coral reefs, mangrove forests, and shoal waters surround all but Alabat. Because of its proximity to the relatively populous Tayabas coast, the island of Alabat supports a fairly dense population, but the more inaccessible islands of the Polillo group are very sparsely populated.

Most of eastern Luzon lies fully exposed to northeastern air flows. Exposed locations receive annual precipitations well in excess of 100 inches. Generally the period from October through March sees the heaviest rains, but the other months are certainly not dry. Only the more sheltered Bondoc Peninsula, lying partially in the lee of the Camarines Peninsula of southeastern Luzon, experiences moderate rains and an actual dry season lasting from one to three months. Typhoons are a constant hazard in eastern Luzon. Those typhoons that approach from east or southeast of the islands of Leyte and Samar and cross the archipelago north of Manila are particularly dangerous, for their paths are directly through eastern Luzon. The typhoons that pass to the south of Manila are no less to be reckoned with, for they bring strong northeast to southeast winds and heavy rains. Although typhoons can form at any time, they are most prevalent along the east coast in the period from September to December.

THE CULTURAL ENVIRONMENT

Approximately 415,000 people live in the eastern Luzon region, the great majority of whom live in the south (fig. 21). The rolling lands of Tayabas Isthmus are the most densely populated and contain approximately 40 percent of the population of the region on less than 10 percent of the total land area. Here, in the south, the density of settlement reaches 650 persons per square mile of total land area. Elsewhere, population densities are less than 100 persons to each square mile, often a great many less. Owing to the lack of arable land, however, physiological densities approximate those for the nation as a whole. Towns are few and far between, except in Tayabas, and each town serves a rather large area as its hinterland.

The population of eastern Luzon has been increasing at rates in excess of those for the nation since World War II. Three separate streams of recent migrants have been directed toward the region. From the Central Plain, particularly the provinces of Pangasinan and Nueva Ecija, immigrants have moved into the Baler area. Migrants from Batangas, Laguna, and Manila have moved into the central coastal section, and large numbers of Bicol and Marinduque peoples have entered the southern municipalities of the Tayabas Isthmus and Bondoc Peninsula. Most of the good agricultural land has already passed into private ownership. Seen from the air, many hill-country clearings mark the infiltration of caingineros on the less steep and somewhat sheltered slopes in the central sector, from Dingalan Bay to the Tayabas Isthmus.

Few urban centers have arisen in eastern Luzon and none has assumed the function of a true regional center. Lucena, the capital and largest city of Quezon Province, lies outside the region. Almost all settlements in eastern Luzon are located on the coast and function primarily as ports for a very restricted trade hinterland, restricted, that is, in population, not in area. The largest towns have populations between 5,000 and 10,000.

Gumaca is the largest town of the region. It is an important fishing town with many commercial vessels operating in Lamon Bay. Large quantities of copra are produced nearby. Gumaca has a small port, road connections with the rest of Luzon, and is served by the Manila-South Railroad. Gumaca's poblacion contained a population of approximately 9,100 in 1960. Atimonan is the most important commercial town in the region. Although neither a port nor a rail point, much of the trade of Tayabas funnels through the town. Its outport of Siain, six miles to the south, is located on the railroad. In 1960 the population of Atimonan was 8,400. Lopez with a 1960 population of 7,200, is the most important trading center for the southern Tayabas area. Hondagua, a small barrio of Lopez, is an active port and railroad station. At Hondagua ocean tankers can discharge to the several fuel oil tanks maintained by the Manila Railroad. Logs and firewood from Polillo and Casiguran are brought to Hondagua for transshipment by rail to Manila. A large sawmill is located at Calauag. Catanauan, Aurora, San Narciso, and Guinayangan are small settlements on the Bondoc Peninsula.

Palanan, Casiguran, Baler, Infanta, and Mauban are the more important towns along the central and northern parts of the east coast. Palanan is a small isolated settlement in eastern Isabela Province. Here the surrounding floodplain supplies subsistence-level agriculture, and occasionally logs are shipped to supplement the economy. Casiguran is located on the large Casiguran Bay, the entrance to which is guarded by the ruins of an old Spanish fortress. Logging and sawmilling are important here. In Baler, the largest town in the north, the rich delta lands of the San Luis and Aguang rivers are cultivated to rice; copra, lumbering, and mat-making are important industries. Baler is served by its outport, Port Aurora. Farther south, Infanta serves a limited agricultural hinterland. Copra and lumber move through the outport of Puerto Real. Mauban is primarily a fishing port. The towns along the central coast of eastern Luzon have been growing rather rapidly in recent years with the completion of highway connections with central Luzon.

Eastern Luzon is poorly provided with transportation facilities. The many small ports of the region have never generated much traffic, although even today many of the small communities must still rely solely upon shipping for all their outside contacts. The lack of protected harbors and the omnipresent typhoons along the east coast have precluded any major port developments. The mainline of the Manila-South Railroad provided the first overland connections with the Tayabas area, and to many of the larger urban centers the railroad is their economic lifeline. Siain, Gumaca, Lopez, Hondagua, and Calauag are the main rail stations for the region.

Highways have been slow to enter eastern Luzon, owing in part to difficulties of construction, and in part to the lack of potential traffic. Luzon's Highway 1 approximately parallels the railroad, although it has been put through to the Bicol area only in very recent times. A feeder route now leads into northern Bondoc, terminating at San Narciso on Ragay Gulf. Tortuous roads wind across the Eastern Cordillera from Cabanatuan in the Central Plain to the east coast towns of Baler and Dingalan, and Mauban and Infanta are connected with the southwestern Luzon highway network. An isolation imposed by the lack of transportation facilities continues to restrict the economic development of eastern Luzon.

The eastern Luzon region does not raise enough food crops to supply regional demands. The region is, in general, a rice-deficit area; yet it does not have the large areas devoted to alternate grains, such as maize, which is widely cultivated in other areas in the Philippines where rice deficiencies are chronic. Quezon Province supplies only three-fourths of its rice requirements; the remainder comes from the Central Plain. The main rice-producing lands are located in the municipalities of Lopez and Baler, with secondary concentrations in Infanta and Atimonan. The cultivation of upland or dry rice is extremely widespread, and nearly one-third of the rice-producing lands are devoted to this lower yielding variety. Upland rice is of particular importance on the Bondoc Peninsula where its acreage greatly exceeds that of the lowland wet crop. The lack of suitable soils and the intense competition from the coconut palm preclude extensive rice cultivation in Tayabas. Maize is of little significance.

The concentration upon coconut palms, particularly in the Tayabas area, almost amounts to a monocrop economy. Quezon Province is the leading coconut-producing province in the Philippines, not only in the amount of land devoted to coconut cultivation and the resultant product of nuts, but also in production of copra. Nearly one-quarter of a million acres are planted to coconut palm within the region, an acreage almost double that of rice. Approximately one-half of this acreage lies in the seven municipalities of the Tayabas Isthmus. Quezon Province produces approximately 15 percent of Philippine copra.

Between rains the highways of the region are covered with the white coconut meat drying in the hot sun. The somewhat rancid, sweet smell of copra hangs in the air. Trucks are busy carrying copra to the shipping points. The little wharves at the ports of Siain, Catanauan, Mauban, and Hondagua are piled with 100-kilogram (220 pounds) sacks of copra awaiting shipment overseas. Most of the coconuts are produced from small holdings; however, it is difficult to discern where one plot starts and another ends because the band of coconut palms is continuous along the shores. The economic prosperity of the southern sector of the region rises and falls according to the fluctuations in demand and price of copra.

Eastern Luzon as a whole is not a rich region nor is it one that is particularly well endowed with resources for the future. The rocky shores that fringe much of the northern coasts make access extremely difficult, and commercial development has been discouraged. North of Tayabas the only arable lands are restricted to small deltaic areas. Tayabas, with its coconut palms, is an exception in that its agriculture is profitable and commercially oriented. Elsewhere the marginal lands of eastern Luzon have been settled largely because of the heavy population pressures of the neighboring regions to the west.

ELEVEN

~~~~ The Islands of the Sunda Shelf

Mindoro, Palawan, the islands of the Calamianes group, and the smaller adjacent islands represent an ancient land surface. All lie on the very stable Sunda Platform or Sunda Shelf, the same land surface that underlies Malaya and Borneo. This Philippine macroregion is considered neither part of Luzon nor the Visayas. Structurally, botanically, zoologically, and in many respects, ethnically, these islands belong more with the Indonesian island of Borneo than with the Philippines. For several obvious reasons, not the least of which is the factor of geographic isolation, the Philippine Sunda Shelf islands have not participated in the economic development or demographic growth of the Philippines, at least until the past two or three decades. These Sunda islands form two Philippine regions—Mindoro and Palawan.

The Northern Shelf: Mindoro and Islets

The island of Mindoro in many ways would appear to have been a demographic void, failing to attract large numbers of permanent settlers in spite of its location adjacent to the crowded lands of Luzon and its position astride one of the main interisland shipping routes of the Philippines. Ten-mile-wide Verde Island Passage, for a half-century busy with ships plying between Manila and the southern islands, is all that separates Mindoro from the densely populated Luzon province of Batangas. This unpopulated condition was most notable in pre-Spanish and Spanish times, as only a small population was resident on the island in 1900. Mountainous, densely forested, and malarial, Mindoro supported only a scattering of lowlanders around its periphery in 1900 while then providing a refuge for numerous simpler tribal group-cultures in its relatively inaccessible mountainous interior. Subsistence agriculture was the general practice, and there have been few overtones of any progressive commercial development until very recently. The few logging, lumbering, and related extractive industries, with a minor production of sugarcane and solar-evaporated salt, were all that relieved the basic orientation of the economy toward simple agriculture. Only a few miles of roads provided advanced intraregional contact, and the ports were merely open roadsteads. It seemed that the development of Philippine culture and economy had passed Mindoro by.

The regional anomaly has remained, but in actual fact Mindoro recently has begun to grow rapidly in percentage terms, and in the most recent intercensal period the Mindoran population has increased at a higher rate than any region except the Manila urban zone and the southern Mindanao provinces. The island started with a very small base population in 1900, so the total still is not very large when compared with other large islands; but Mindoro no longer is being bypassed in the same way as formerly. Of course, there still is a frontier aspect to Mindoran life which will not disappear for some time, and the future may not hold great promise for the island as the home of a large agricultural-commercial population. Potential mineral exploitation may not involve a large population.

The island of Mindoro contains a high, rough, and largely unexplored mountainous interior that trends generally north northwest–south southeast (fig. 61). This interior upland appears to be composed of two major highland systems, with several isolated mountain outliers scattered along the north coast of the island. Mount Halcon forms the core for the northern of the two highland systems, and at an elevation of 8,481 feet it is the highest point on the island, and among the higher peaks in the Philippines. In south central Mindoro is Mount Baco, only slightly less lofty than Mount Halcon at 8,160 feet, which forms the core for the second of the interior upland areas. Each of these mountains provides an upland core around which are arranged extensive areas of elevated country. Mounts Calavite (4,990 feet) and Abra de Ilog (5,682 feet) stand as sentinels along the north coast of the island. Virtually unexplored by contemporary, economically minded, Christian Filipinos the interior of Mindoro is densely forested and accessible only by a network of rough mountain trails, which instead of paralleling ridges or valleys, persists across the grain of the topography. The western and eastern coasts of

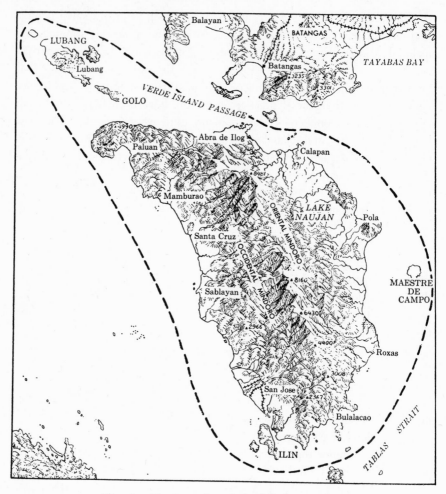

Fig. 61. Physiography of the Mindoro region.

Mindoro are bordered by strips of lowlands—lowlands that are extremely narrow along the west coast but reach back to maximum widths of 12 to 15 miles in the northeast.

Upland interiors are encountered on all of the smaller islands of the region. The 8-square-mile island of Ambil reaches to an elevation of 2,477 feet. The only extensive area of lowland on any of the smaller islands is located in northern Lubang.

The highland areas of Mindoro are composed of the basement-complex rock materials, including granites, diorites, gabbros, peridotites, serpentines, and schists. Slow to weather, even under the moist tropical climate, these basement rocks have developed a topography of steep, serrated ridges and deep, steep-sided stream valleys. Extended periods of inundation in the geologic past clothed the lowland areas, and parts of the southeastern Mindoro uplands, with thick mantles of limestone materials that frequently outcrop in precipitous bluffs along the coasts. Mindoro, together with Palawan and the Calamianes group, is considered to be a part of the very stable ancient Sundaland Platform, and there is little evidence of recent vulcanism throughout the region. Here and there are small deposits of coal, gold, gypsum, mica, hematite, and various minor minerals; however, only the deposits of coal, which outcrop near the town of Bulalacao in southeastern Mindoro, appear to offer commercial possibilities.

Eastern and western Mindoro exhibit considerable contrast in rainfall, the only weather element showing significant areal variation, except for the temperature modification with altitude. Western Mindoro participates in the full benefits of "summer" monsoonal circulation, receiving very heavy annual precipitations of 100 inches or more, which occur mainly during the period from June through September. With airstream reversal, however, four to five months of severe drought are felt in the west. Northern and eastern Mindoro, on the other hand, receive less annual precipitation, 80–100 inches; however, most of this is concentrated in the "autumn" and "winter" months during the dominance of northeastern air movements. Furthermore, the latter areas do not experience any pronounced dry periods. Except for certain sheltered intermontane locations, the mountain lands of interior Mindoro are extremely well-watered with annual rains that total 120–150 inches or more. Typhoons are a menace at all seasons, although Mindoro is marginally located to the south and west of the main tracks of these violent tropical storms.

Tropical rain forests cover much of interior and northwestern Mindoro. Some of these forests may be of virgin growth, but much of the cover is young-to-mature second-growth forest variably cropped in shifting cultivation by tribal groups. These dense forests, although composed mainly of members of the Dipterocarpaceae family, also show evidence of close botanical affiliations with the natural vegetation of Palawan and northeastern Borneo, indicating the presence of a land connection that extended toward the southwest in relatively recent geologic times. Apitong, guijo, molave, tangile, and yakal are among the more common commercial timber species, and much of the Philippine supply of dao, kalantas, malugai, and narra now comes from Mindoro. Extensive cogonal grasslands, interspersed with stands of still-young and scrubby secondary forest growth, cover the western slopes of the central cordillera and extend well back into the headwaters of the major westward-flowing streams, the work of many generations of caingineros. Mangrove forests accompany the coasts of Mindoro in the south and southwest.

The combination of topography, climate, soils, and natural vegetation in the Mindoro region, although not necessarily favoring an intensive agricultural occupance, nevertheless certainly did not preclude an agriculturally based population greater than was present in the past. It would appear that the sparsity of population on Mindoro cannot be explained simply in terms of limitations imposed by the physical environment.

THE CULTURAL SETTING

The present population of the Mindoro region is relatively small in total numbers and relatively well dispersed around the peripheries of the main islands, with greater densities on the smaller islands. Somewhat greater concentrations of population are found along the east coast lowlands of Mindoro, extending in a narrow band from the capital city of Calapan in the northeast southward to the municipality of Mansalay, a distance of nearly 70 miles (figs. 21, 22). At San Jose in southwestern Mindoro there is a small area of relatively dense agricultural population, and fairly large numbers of people occupy northern Lubang. On the other hand, northern, western, and southern coastal areas on the main island support extremely light populations. A total of approximately 313,000 persons lived in the region in 1960, which gave an average density of only 80 persons per square mile of total area. As only 10 percent of the land area of the region was under active cultivation at that time, however, population densities on the cultivated lands were approximately 550 persons per square mile. Both of the above man-land ratios are well below Philippine averages and serve to indicate further that Mindoro is one of the more relatively empty regions of the Philippines.

When Legaspi's lieutenants first sailed around Mindoro in 1570, they estimated the population of the island at three to four thousand; a figure that estimates taken in 1591, and thereafter, were to bear out. Even as late as 1850 the island of Mindoro was reported to have a population of only 35,000. Early Spanish chronicles are replete with accounts of numerous raids upon Mindoro by the Moro seafarers from the south, and there can be little doubt that the early population of the island was held down by the frequency and severity of these raids. These depredations were not fully contained until the middle of the nineteenth century. The two Christian towns of Pinamalayan and Mansalay in southeastern Mindoro were actually abandoned in the face of Moro raids in the seventeenth and eighteenth centuries, and for several years the Mindoro towns of Mamburao and Balete served as advance Moro strongholds from which raids were launched against the adjacent Christian settlements.

Another important partial explanation for the lack of population lay in the widespread prevalence of malaria. Even today Mindoro is one of the more serious malarial areas in the Philippines.[1] The low-lying, poorly drained areas along the east coast, and the heavily timbered and excessively moist interior uplands have been breeding areas for the anopheles mosquitoes that transmit the disease.

The present lowland population of Mindoro is largely composed of migrant Tagalog, Ilocano, and Visayan ethnic stocks, though Tagalogs are the most numerous by far. The Tagalogs continue to migrate to the relatively empty areas on Mindoro from well-populated areas in central Luzon, particularly nearby Batangas Province. The Ilocanos are settling chiefly in the western sector, and people from the island of Panay are locating in southern Mindoro. Immigrants have come chiefly as agriculturists. Since the 1948 census enumeration the population of Mindoro has increased at a rate nearly double the national average. The peoples who occupy the interior of the island are pagan tribal culture groups, known collectively as Mangyans. The Mangyans are forest-dwelling shifting agriculturists for the most part, and they normally complement their food supplies by hunting and gathering. They number approximately 20,000, and culturally form relict ethnic groups having minimal social or economic contacts with the Christian peoples of the lowlands.[2]

Most of the population of the Mindoro region lives in small agricultural villages scattered along the coasts. Calapan, the capital of the province of Oriental Mindoro, had a poblacion population of approximately 4,000 in 1960. It is the leading commercial center for the region and maintains regular ship connections with Manila, Batangas, Boac, Romblon, and the small ports of northern Mindoro. Copra shippers, and the several sawmills in the surrounding area, use the port of Calapan as their shipping point, and several small woodworking establishments contribute to the town's economic base. Calapan is situated near the northern margin of the eastern coastal plain, and is linked by road with Puerto Galera, 25 miles to the west, and with Mansalay, which lies on the southeast coast more than 75 miles to the south. Bansud, Pinamalayan, Bongabong, and Mansalay are important small-trade centers and market towns in eastern Mindoro, supporting small agricultural populations in their hinterlands. Each has a small port, and in 1960 each had a population numbering between 2,500 and 6,000. San Jose, with its 1960 poblacion population of about 4,000, is the leading commercial settlement in Occidental Mindoro, although it is not the provincial administrative center. Situated on the extensive floodplain of the Bugsanga River in southwestern Mindoro, San Jose is the center of the region's only commercial sugarcane district, and the town functions largely in the service of this sugar industry. A network of narrow-gauge railways leads to the fields, brings large quantities of cane to the mill, and further transports the resultant sugar and molasses to a small wharf on Caminawit Point, from where it is shipped overseas. San Jose maintains regular ship connections with Manila and also is served by commercial aircraft. Mamburao, recently made the capital of the new province of Occidental Mindoro, is only beginning to assume the morphological and cultural characteristics that normally accompany a provincial capital. At present it is a relatively minor port and an important center for small sailboat construction. In 1960 the poblacion of Mamburao had a population of 2,500. Paluan and Abra de Ilog are small ports and centers of lesser commercial importance in northern Mindoro, with 1960 populations of 2,400 and 1,100, respectively. Port Tilic and Lubang are the leading towns of the Lubang Islands. Lumber, copra, rattan, and rice are the main products shipped in small quantities from the several small-trade centers of the region.

The agricultural occupance of Mindoro is dominated by the cultivation of a single crop of lowland rice each year. Well over 50 percent of the cultivated lands on the eastern plain are devoted to lowland rice cultivation. Upland rice is extensively cultivated by the dominant pagan peoples of the interior and by pioneer settlers in the hill-country margins. The yields obtained from the lowland rice lands are surprisingly high when measured by archipelago-wide standards, in spite of the fact that virtually none of the crop is grown under controlled irrigation. The soils of the area, however, are relatively fertile, and much of the rice is being cultivated on lands that have only recently been brought under cultivation. The acreage devoted to rice cultivation, and the total rice production, in the region have been increasing rapidly and steadily during the past two decades, and today the Mindoro region produces rice in quantities well above regional needs, so that modest surpluses are shipped to Manila, southwestern Luzon, and to the nearby islands of the Romblon group.

Corn is of little regional significance except in the vicinity of San Jose where nearly one-half of the corn acreage of the region is located. The relatively minor role that corn plays in the agricultural economy of Mindoro appears to be a reflection of the general disinterest in corn as a food grain on the part of most Tagalogs. Hiligaynon-Bisayan-speaking peoples from Panay, with their long tradition of corn cultivation, are the principal settlers in San Jose, thereby accounting for the larger acreage there. Other food crops that supplement the two grains include sweet potatoes, yams, taro, cassava, beans, bananas, and various other fruits and vegetables.

Coconuts and sugarcane provide the region with its principal cash crops. Coconut palms are found in most coastal areas; however, their commercial cultivation is concentrated mainly in eastern Mindoro in the municipalities of Pinamalayan and Pola. Sugarcane, on the other hand, is produced commercially only in San Jose municipality. The Philippine Milling Company operates a sugar central at San Jose, and some 4,000 to 5,000 acres on the surrounding floodplain are devoted to the production of sugarcane for the overseas export market.

From old Spanish records it appears that placer gold played an important role in earlier economic occupance of the island. Indeed, the very name "Mindoro" indicates "gold mine." At present the gold deposits are not being worked, nor for that matter, are any of the other commercial metal deposits. The only important mineral industry currently active is the large solar salt-bed zone located near San Jose in western Mindoro. The annual production of approximately 50,000 metric tons of solar-evaporated salt, an amount representing nearly 30 percent of total Philippine salt production, is intended for industrial uses in the Manila area.

The forests of Mindoro have proved rather attractive to modern logging and lumbering interests, particularly the forests of northern Mindoro which lie close to tidewater and the markets in the urban centers of central Luzon. Approximately 4 percent of the total Philippine sawmill capacity is located within the region, and some 40 to 50 million board feet of timber are cut annually. Logs and lumber are shipped either to Manila or directly overseas.

The Southern Shelf: Palawan and Its Island Clusters

Lying to the southwest and west of the main group of Philippine islands and pointing, as it were, like an arrow toward the northeastern corner of the Indonesian island of Borneo, is the long, narrow island of Palawan. An assemblage of over 1,000 smaller islands and islets surrounds Palawan. The Palawan region provides the bridgelike transition zone between Moslem-dominated cultures of northeastern Borneo and Indonesia and the basically Christian-oriented traditions of the Philippines. In addition to its mixed cultural heritages the Palawan area also provides a meeting ground for both Bornean and Philippine floral and faunal associations. A generally rugged topography, with little present development either of coastal or river lowlands, and a relatively meager and infertile soil base, impose rather serious limitations upon any sedentary agricultural occupance of Palawan. Sparsely settled, largely undeveloped economically, with a rather poor resource endowment, and separated from the rest of the Philippine Archipelago by broad expanses of open waters, the Palawan region supports a relatively low-level subsistence economy with minor overtones of commercial forest and mineral extractive economies. Slightly more than 15 percent of the region's land surface is under active cultivation.

Lengthy coastlines front both the South China Sea and the Sulu Sea. Separated by the deep structural trench of Mindoro Strait from the other main Philippine islands, and by Balabac Strait from Borneo, the Palawan area warrants a separate regional status by virtue of its geographical isolation and geologically transitional character. The Palawan region coincides with the political boundaries of the province of Palawan. It consists of the large main island of Palawan, the fifth largest Philippine island, which alone represents nearly 80 percent of the region's land area; the larger secondary islands of Busuanga, Culion, Dumaran, and Balabac; and some 1,164 other named and unnamed islands and islets (fig. 62). The region includes a total land area of nearly 5,700 square miles.

THE PHYSICAL SETTING

Palawan and the smaller islands of the Calamianes and Balabac groups, which lie to the northeast and southwest, respectively, represent the summits of a submarine ridge system, one that takes its origin in the highly complex mountain core of north central Mindoro, and after stretching to the southwest for over 500 miles, finally terminates in the highlands of the Crocker Range of northeastern Borneo. The northeast–southwest trend of the island of Palawan and its major island festoons maintains a remarkably straight align- · ment and clearly outlines the edge of the ancient Sundaland land platform. Although the interior uplands of the main island are not particularly lofty, they are extremely rugged, with a topography that often is sharpened by widespread development of mature karst topography. Mount Mantalingajan, in the south, at an elevation of 6,839 feet, is the highest point on the island of Palawan, although the spectacular Cleopatra Needle (5,199 feet) north of Honda Bay well merits its descriptive nom de guerre. The inshore waters of the South China Sea off the northwestern coast of Palawan are quite shallow and strewn with coral obstructions. This coast is extremely dangerous to approach by sea and generally is avoided by all shipping. The eastern coastline facing the Sulu Sea, on the other hand, has deep waters close inshore, and there are several excellent landlocked harbors, particularly at Puerto Princesa. Coral materials are very widespread throughout the region and occur as thick mantles of surface rock in narrow coastal belts along the southern, southeastern, and southwestern shores of Palawan and on the southern islands of Balabac and Bugsuk. In the north the waters of Taytay Bay, and the waters surrounding the Cuyo Islands, are fouled by reef corals. Where the baselevel of erosion is lower than the present erosion surface, as in

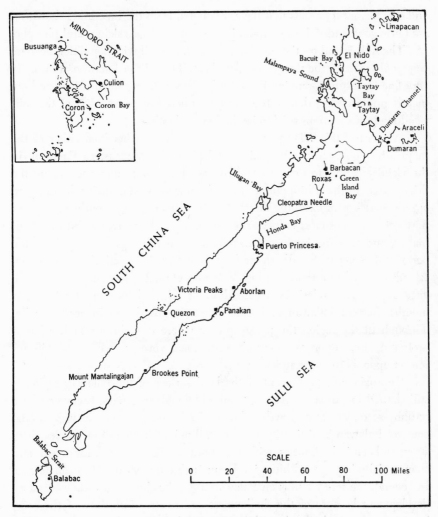

Fig. 62. The Palawan region.

foothill sections of the central highlands on Palawan, there is considerable solution work by water in the soluble coralline limestones. In general the interior uplands are composed of basement-complex materials, mainly quartzites, schists, and serpentines. The Calamianes Islands appear to be composed basically of quartzite materials. On the island of Busuanga thin lenses of relatively high-grade manganese ores are found within the twisted layers of quartzite.

The soils that have weathered from the metamorphosed upland core materials normally are infertile and consist of thin residual clays, sandy clays, and clay loams.[3] The soils that have weathered from the limestones, however, are fairly good and rich in more basic elements such as calcium and phosphorus. The soils found on the limited areas of recent alluvial deposition also are commonly more fertile than those elsewhere. The soils of Palawan are usually very fine in texture—ranging from sandy clays to fine-grained clays—and are mainly primary soils, that is, they have weathered in place. Most of the soils in all kinds of situations tend to be shallow in depth.

No part of the Palawan region gets the full benefits from either of the major Philippine airstreams, and several places in southeastern Palawan, in the vicinity of Puerto Princesa and Brookes Point, are numbered among the drier areas of the Philippines. The alignment of the major landmasses, approximately parallel to the direction of movement of the southwestern and northeastern monsoons, reduces the possibilities of orographic lifting of air masses, and therefore, reduces precipitation and prolongs and heightens the periods of drought. Northern and western Palawan and the Calamianes Islands receive more than 100 inches of rain annually; however, they experience a period of relatively severe drought which lasts from two to four months. Eastern Palawan and Balabac receive barely 70 inches annually. Throughout the region the presence of a severe drought season has had a profound effect upon the natural vegetational cover as well as significant impact upon all forms of agriculture.

Approximately 70 percent of the land surface of the Palawan region is still clothed in primary forests, and an additional 17 percent is covered by a scrubby secondary tree growth. The species composition of the vegetational cover of Palawan is distinctive for the Philippines in that most species show stronger botanical affinities with the Bornean flora. The widespread and commercially important Philippine lauan is absent from the Palawan forests. In general, the forest stands on Palawan are quite thin with little understory development because of the shallowness and relative infertility of the soils; however, many of the hardest Philippine woods are found on Palawan. Akle, almaciga, apitong, bitanghol, dao, ipil, and mancono are among the more important commercial species; more than 80 percent of the Philippine supply of ipil, a very important construction wood, originates within the region. Cogon and talahib grasses occur over extensive areas. Marshes and mangrove forests line many coasts, especially in northwestern Palawan.

THE CULTURAL SETTING

The earliest Spanish contacts with the Palawan area were quite unproductive, and indeed, continued to be so almost until the end of the Spanish period. Here, as in the Sulu Archipelago and in parts of Mindanao, Catholic

Spain came in direct contact with a militant Islamic culture that was just gaining a strong foothold. Actually the Moslems had begun to trickle into Palawan only during the late fourteenth and early fifteenth centuries. Ruled by the powerful Sultan of Borneo, the Palawan Moslems resisted encroachment by the forces of Spain, at first limiting the gains of the latter to the more northern Calamianes and Cuyo Islands. By 1591, only a single Spanish encomienda, based in the Calamianes, had been established with an area embracing 2,500 tributes and representing a total population of approximately 10,000 persons.

Augustinian, and later Recollect, fathers began to establish villages, towns and churches early in the seventeenth century. The cabecera towns of Cuyo, Alutaya, and Taytay on Palawan were established by 1622, and small settlements at Barbacan, Aborlan, Ypolete, Dumaran, Linapacan, Culion, and Busuanga quickly followed. By the middle of the seventeenth century the Spanish controlled the Calamianes and Cuyo groups and parts of northern Palawan, which they called Paragua. These territories were organized into the province of Calamianes; however, disease and native hostility forced abandonment of many settlements, particularly those that lay farthest south. In fact, the strong fortress of Taytay was hard-pressed to repel an attack by some 3,000 Moros in 1735.

Spain, very desirous of controlling the Palawan area in order to control the piractical raids by Moslem seafarers sweeping up through the Sulu Sea, particularly those from Mindanao and Sulu, continued to make strong attempts at control. In the middle of the eighteenth century the Sultan of Borneo finally ceded the remainder of Palawan and the island of Balabac to Spanish authority, and the Spanish were gradually able to extend a nominal political influence over the entire region. In 1858 the two provinces of Castilla and Asturias were created in the Palawan area, with the islands of Balabac and Bugsuk constituted as a separate politico-military district. All units were finally combined into the present province of Palawan in 1905 under the American administration. Balabac served briefly as a prison for political prisoners during the uprisings connected with events before and during the termination of Spanish authority in the late nineteenth century.

In the light of its relatively poor agricultural base, it is not surprising that the Palawan region is rather sparsely settled. The average crude population-density figure of 29 persons to each square mile of total area in 1960 was far below even that of the relatively lightly settled areas on Mindanao. Physiological population densities, however, remain near the archipelago-wide averages, largely because of the small area under cultivation.

The very small proportion of land that is actually under crop cultivation—15 percent of the total area of the region—does not indicate any serious agricultural land-tenure problems. A very large proportion of the cultivable land not under cultivation at present can be brought under cultivation and is available for homesteading. The Palaweños often combine agriculture with fishing activities. Since the conclusion of World War II the empty lands on the island of Palawan have become the target for relatively large numbers of migrants, particularly from central Luzon and from the western Visayan area. The main island has received the bulk of these new settlers, especially along the more hospitable east coast in the municipalities of Aborlan, Brookes Point, and Puerto Princesa. The smaller islands of Agutaya, Cagayancillo, Coron, and Cuyo, already densely settled for a number of years, have maintained relatively stable populations, and in some instances have actually shown a population decline. Physiological densities exceed 2,500 persons per square mile of cultivated land in the municipality of Culion, although these figures are inflated and misleading because of the presence of the Culion Reservation, one of the world's largest leper (Hansen's disease) colonies.

Virtually all settlement in the region is peripheral, and interior locations are either devoid of population or support only scattered primitive caingin cultivators and a few mineral and forest concessionaires. The Christian element of the population, which in addition to the indigenous Christian Kuyonons, Kalamians, and Agutayans includes substantial numbers of Tagalog and Visayan migrants, has settled mainly along the east coast of Palawan, north of Brookes Point, and in the northern islands. There are 13,000 Moslems who occupy the areas close to Borneo—Balabac and the southern shores of the main island of Palawan. Bataks, Ke-Nay, and Tagbanua pagan groups occupy the interior lands and constitute approximately 12 percent of the total population of the region. Thus the Palawan area, with a total population of approximately 160,000 persons, is the meeting ground of three very diverse cultures, although the Christian element now is dominant and very much in ascendancy.

The population of the region is not highly urbanized, and no major regional center has developed. Puerto Princesa, the provincial capital and principal commercial center, is the largest town in the region with a 1960 population in its poblacion of approximately 7,500 persons. Situated on a narrow arm of land at the entrance to its nearly landlocked harbor, Puerto Princesa completely dominates the trade of the east coast of Palawan. Frequently scheduled ship service is maintained with Manila, and less frequent sailings connect the provincial capital with Balabac, Bugsuk, Cuyo, the Calamianes Islands, and the small east coast ports of Brookes Point, Malcampo, and Araceli. Small shipments of rice, copra, livestock, and lumber for the Manila market originate at Puerto Princesa, and the port receives, in return, rather large quantities of manufactured goods and rice at certain seasons. The only integrated road system in the entire region extends along the east coast from Aborlan to just beyond Honda Bay and focuses on the capital city. Brookes Point, Aborlan, Taytay, Cuyo, and Culion are small towns with trade areas of somewhat more than local significance.

As in virtually all other Philippine regions, agriculture is the dominant economic activity in the Palawan area. The agriculture of Palawan is not technologically advanced. Forms of caingin agriculture are widely practiced and perhaps best characterize the basic regional occupance pattern. Only within the past two decades, largely under the impact of Luzon and Visayan migrants, have the shifting-agriculture practices of the Moslems and pagans been challenged. Grass-covered clearings occur over an area many times larger than the present cultivated area and bear mute testament to the widespread efforts of the caingineros. Sedentary agriculture on the main island is confined to scattered coastal locations, usually along the river valleys or at the mouths of the numerous short rivers. Most of the permanent agricultural land of the region lies in the municipalities of Puerto Princesa and Brookes Point. Coconuts and rice are the leading crops, both in terms of acreage devoted to their cultivation and the value of the product. Upland rice is dominant everywhere, but the lowland crop is restricted by soil and rainfall conditions to a few small areas, mainly in the municipalities of Busuanga, Coron, Aborlan, and Puerto Princesa. Yields from the upland rice fields are quite high, primarily because much of the farming is on newly opened lands. More than one-fourth of the cropland of the region lies in the single municipality of Brookes Point. Small areas of sugarcane, cassava corn, camote, and various fruits and vegetables complete the basically subsistence agricultural crop pattern.

Coconuts are the sole commercial crop, with most of the coconut area concentrated along the east coast in the municipality of Puerto Princesa. A considerable quantity of copra is exported, and large numbers of coconuts are converted to coconut oil for home use within the region.

Mining, forest industries, and fishing are economic activities of extraregional significance conducted within the Palawan region. The recovery of manganese, mercury, chromite, and silica sands makes a significant contribution to the region's and nation's economic base. The principal manganese deposits of the Philippines are located in eastern, central, and northwestern Busuanga Island in the Calamianes group. This manganese ore is unusually high-grade, and unlike the other manganese ores in the Philippines, requires no beneficiation prior to shipment. The several mines on Busuanga customarily produce approximately 80 percent of Philippine manganese production. Overseas vessels are loaded by means of lighters or from small company-owned piers on the island. Reserves of manganese are undoubtedly large; however, Philippine manganese production suffers from the relatively low-grade characteristics of much of the ore when compared to the major manganese producers of the world. All of the Philippines' modest production of mercury comes from deposits of cinnabar ore at Tagburos, a barrio of Puerto Princesa. Small quantities of metallurgical-grade chromite are also produced in Puerto Princesa. The relatively pure silica sands at Del Pilar on Green Island Bay, Palawan, provide the raw materials for an important glass-manufacturing industry in Manila, and over 36,000 metric tons of these sands are mined annually. Although the contribution of the various mineral industries within the Palawan region is still relatively small, mining has been increasing in recent years, and as the geology of the Palawan area becomes more perfectly known their contribution should increase substantially.

Slightly more than 1 percent of the Philippine sawmill capacity is located within the region; however, the high quality of the timber-cut and the large volume of the resource still present in the region are of considerable significance. In general, the timbers secured from the Palawan forests are extremely hard and durable and excellent woods for furniture and cabinet stock. The individual sawmills within the region are of small capacity, and most of them are located either near Puerto Princesa or in the extreme southern part of the main island. Timber reserves are large and stand at approximately 19 billion board feet, an amount equivalent to about 7 percent of the total Philippine timber resource. Several important minor forest products are secured from the forests of Palawan, including the Sica variety of rattan vine, and manila copal, the exude from the almaciga tree.

Approximately one-sixth of the total Philippine commercial fish-catch comes from the waters adjacent to Palawan, particularly from the very productive fishing grounds of Bacuit, Coron, Green Island, and Taytay bays, Malampaya Sound, and Cuyo and Dumaran channels. Many fishing vessels based in Manila, as well as those based at Palawn, participate in the rich Sulu Sea fishing area. Almost two-thirds of Manila's fish supplies come from the waters surrounding Palawan. Round scad, caesio, mackerel, sardines, and anchovy are the principal species caught. Within the Palawan region, large-scale commercial fishing operations are based in the municipalities of Coron, Araceli, Taytay, and Puerto Princesa; these names have become almost synonomous with Philippine commercial fishing. Although some drying, salting, and canning of fish is accomplished in the region, most of the fish-catch is iced on board the larger fishing vessels and marketed in the

Manila area as fresh fish. A large proportion of the region's labor force, numbering in the thousands, is employed in the fishing industry, and several entire barrios in northern Palawan and in the Cuyo and Calamianes islands are solely fishing communities. Because many of the latter small islands are so strongly oriented toward fishing as their principal economic way of life, one should not view the heavy physiological densities of population on these small islands with any great alarm. The fish-resource base is excellent, and providing destructive techniques such as fish poisoning and dynamiting do not ruin the present fishing grounds, the commercial- and subsistence-fishing economy of the Palawan region should continue to flourish.

TWELVE

~~~~~ The Central Philippines: The Visayan Islands

Introduction to the Central Philippines

The group of islands located near the center of the Philippine Archipelago is referred to as the Visayan Islands, or Visayas (Bisayas), and generally includes the larger islands of Samar, Leyte, Negros, Panay, Cebu, Bohol, and Masbate, together with the smaller islands of Tablas, Romblon, Sibuyan, Ticao, Burias, Siquijor, and numerous smaller adjacent islands and islets.[1] These islands, lying between the two largest Philippine islands of Luzon and Mindanao, are grouped around the Philippine mediterranean sea, the Visayan Sea. Together they represent a land area of approximately 24,300 square miles, or 21 percent of the land surface of the Philippines. In general, lowlands are few and small, and are usually confined to narrow coastal strips on the larger islands. There are, however, three relatively large lowlands: the Iloilo Plain, Leyte Valley, and the broad plains of northern and western Negros. The Visayan Islands are densely populated, and all but three of the fourteen Visayan provinces have population densities above the national average. Approximately 30 percent of the Filipino population lives in the Visayan area, and the resultant land pressures have created conditions encouraging large-scale emigration. In

444

addition to occupying a position of dominance in their home islands, peoples of the Visayan ethnolinguistic stock presently constitute the major cultural-linguistic group in all of the provinces of Mindanao except Lanao del Sur and Cotabato.[2]

The Visayan Islands constitute one of the major geographic units of the Philippines; one in which considerable homogeneity exists by virtue of location, proximity to each other, geology, climatology, history, and ethnolinguistic characteristics. The Visayan Islands, focusing inward upon the central Visayan Sea, are separated from the other major islands of the Philippines by the relatively broad and deep water bodies of the Sulu, Sibuyan, and Mindanao seas and the Tablas, Burias, and Ticao straits. The open Pacific Ocean forms the eastern boundaries, and all approaches to the region from the Pacific must funnel through the narrow waters of two strategic straits, San Bernardino and Surigao straits. The open exposure of the western Visayas across the Sulu Sea facilitates approach from Borneo, Palawan, and the Sulu Archipelago, a factor not overlooked by the southern Moro raiders from the sixteenth into the nineteenth centuries.

The narrow stretches of water which separate the various member islands of the Visayas have for centuries borne much of the water commerce of the Philippines. The important regional trade centers of Cebu and Iloilo, and to a lesser extent Capiz, (Roxas City), Bacolod, and Dumaguete, have grown and continue to flourish in the service of the Visayas and neighboring Mindanao Island; at present the ports of Cebu and Iloilo rank second and third among Philippine ports in the volume of their domestic and overseas trade.

The physical environments of the various islands of the Visayan group are quite similar. A Visayan subtype of climate is typical to all but the peripheral areas. Described as a "modified monsoonal climate," the Visayan climatic year is characterized by a short, but pronounced, dry season occurring during the first two or three months of the year, and only a moderate rainy season that occurs in the late summer and early fall months. Annual rainfall usually averages 50–80 inches. The rainfall of much of the Visayas, which is quite low by tropical standards, is limited by the sheltering effect of the mediterranean position of the Visayas. Furthermore, the interior position of many of the Visayan islands, particularly Romblon, Masbate, Cebu, Negros, and Bohol, has given rise to summer temperatures that are perceptibly warmer than elsewhere in the archipelago, for there is a certain degree of continental warming. Of course, those areas that are more fully exposed to moist air masses arriving directly in the area after traversing the Sulu Sea or the western Pacific Ocean experience climatic conditions more normal to their latitude and tropical climate, that is, they usually receive very heavy precipitations in season.

Each of the Visayan islands possesses several geologic conditions that are rather closely related to conditions on others in the Visayan group and are quite different from those on Luzon, Mindanao, and Palawan-Mindoro. Grouped around the Visayan Sea, the Visayan Islands rest upon a submarine platform, the Visayan Shelf or Visayan Block.[3] All of the islands have more or less elevated uplands in their interiors and all are aligned along one of the two major Philippine structural trendlines that come together in the island of Masbate. The inference of close geologic conditions within the Visayas is not meant to imply that the Philippines is not a geologically homogeneous archipelago; however, structural relationships are especially close within the islands of the Visayan group.

Visayan cultural homogeneity is equally strong. The name "Visayas" actually stems from the ancient tribal name of the people who inhabit the islands and are called Visayans or Bisayans. There is a strong likelihood that the name "Visayan" is in some way related to the Javanese Sri Vijayan Empire, which grew to dominance in the late seventh century, and enduring for six centuries, held a part of the Philippines in its political sway.[4] The Visayan Islands can be delimited culturally on the basis of the dominance of the various Visayan dialects (fig. 25). The Visayan cultural-linguistic group embraces several distinct, but related dialects, and counts nearly twelve million members among its speakers. The four major Visayan tongues include Waray-Waray (spoken in Samar and northeastern Leyte), Cebuano (Cebu, Bohol, eastern Negros, southwestern Leyte, and southeastern Masbate), Hiligaynon (Panay, except for the northwestern corner, Romblon, western Negros, and southwestern Masbate), and Aklanon (northwestern Panay). Many of the Visayan-speaking people have migrated to other areas of the Philippines and overseas to Guam, Hawaii, and the Pacific coast of continental United States; nevertheless more than eight million still reside in their home Visayan islands.

Visayan people occupy their home islands in great density, ranging from a lowest crude density figure of 167 persons in Samar to 678 persons per square mile in the crowded province of Cebu. The average population density in the Visayan Islands as a whole is 52 percent greater than for the nation. The early imposition of Spanish control undoubtedly contributed to an early and more stable population growth. Even though Moro raids continued in the western Visayas until the nineteenth century, their frequency and severity were restricted by the presence of the military forces of Spain. The Visayan area today remains one of the more Hispanicized areas in the archipelago.

Magellan and Legaspi set up headquarters at Cebu, and the Spanish capital was transferred from Cebu to Manila only when the Visayas proved unable to supply adequate provisions. Many of the Visayan sugarcane haciendas are still owned by old Spanish families.

Considerable diversity does exist within the Visayan area, however, and these differences lead to the fourfold regional subdivision: the northern, eastern, central, and western Visayan regions.

The Islands of the Sibuyan Sea

The islands of Marinduque, Masbate, Burias, Ticao, and the several small islands that comprise the Romblon group occupy a transitional position between the large main island of Luzon and the islands of the central Visayan group. Although many of the structures that provide the physiographic framework for the island of Luzon are continued in these transitional islands, they also exhibit many of the structural elements that are encountered to the south in the larger Visayan islands of Cebu, Negros, Samar, Leyte, and Panay. Thus, in addition to their transitional geographical location, the Sibuyan Sea islands form a physiographic bridge between two major Philippine areas. The transitional nature of the islands is further heightened by the presence of both Luzon and Visayan cultural items such as dialects, food preferences, crops, and cropping systems. All of these smaller islands lie within, or immediately adjacent to, the Sibuyan Sea, the large interisland water body situated south of Luzon and east of the island of Mindoro. The various islands and island groups do not appear to be related to one another closely in a structural sense. Neither do they appear to share a common bond with the structures of the Sibuyan Sea basin. All of the islands, however, do share in the resources of this sea, and all use the sea as their main artery of communications. The use of the sea for fishing is of tremendous economic importance, and the large fish-catch is of considerable national significance. Because of their common economic bonds, these islands are referred to collectively as the Sibuyan Sea region.

The Sibuyan Sea region includes all of the area of the three provinces of Masbate, Marinduque, and Romblon, and represents a total land area of approximately 2,450 square miles. In 1960 a population of approximately 582,000 persons lived within the region.

THE PHYSICAL SETTING

The physiographic landscapes of the various islands of the Sibuyan Sea area have resulted from the action of several kinds of structural controls, all mainly mountain building (fig. 63). The Sibuyan Sea itself occupies a deep basin, an extension of the Manila Low Zone that forms the Central Plain of Luzon farther to the north and the Iloilo Plain of Panay to the south. Between the islands of the Romblon group and the island of Panay the waters are deeper than 3,000 feet, and similar depths are encountered between Tablas Island and Mindoro and between Sibuyan Island and the Bondoc Peninsula of southeastern Luzon. The oval-shaped island of Marinduque appears to be

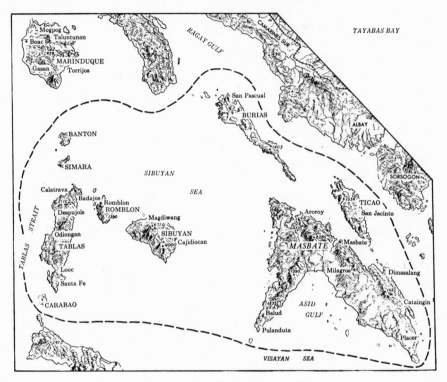

Fig. 63. Physiography of the Sibuyan Sea region.

rather closely related, in a structural sense, to adjacent areas on Luzon. Romblon, Tablas, Sibuyan, and the smaller islands lying to the north and south are mounted upon a high sinuous submarine ridge. The island of Masbate, on the other hand, appears to rest, at least in part, upon the main Visayan Platform. The juncture of two of the major Philippine structural arcs gives Masbate its very unusual, inverted-V shape.

Masbate, which ranks eleventh in size among the islands of the Philippines, contains nearly two-thirds of the land area of the Sibuyan Sea region. Two relatively low, and frequently discontinuous ranges of highlands provide the basic physiographic frame of Masbate. The higher of the two is aligned northwest–southeast and forms the long southeastern peninsular arm of the island. This rugged range of highlands contains maximum elevations between 1,900 and 2,300 feet. A narrow strip of coastal lowlands accompanies the northeastern shores facing Masbate Pass, whereas the southern slopes of the highlands are bordered by broader piedmont and coastal plains. The second highland system lies to the west and is oriented north northeast–south southwest. Maximum elevations on the southwestern peninsula are slightly above the 1,000-foot contour. Relatively broad bands of coastal lowlands accompany the west coast facing the Sibuyan Sea. The two upland systems come together south of Aroroy in the highly complex Conical Peak area where the principal mining district of Masbate was located. Relatively broad lowlands lie along the shores of Asid Gulf in the south, particularly at the head of the gulf within the municipality of Milagros. Most of the land adjacent to the mountains in the interior of Masbate is rolling plateau land that generally is covered with tall stands of cogon and other wild grasses. Several bays indent the western and northeastern coasts, the more important of which are Port Barrera (Aroroy) and Masbate Bay.

The long, narrow islands of Burias and Ticao lie north and west of Masbate and are separated from the larger island by the waters of Masbate Pass. These two islands are separated from the coast of southeastern Luzon by relatively deep waters. Burias and Ticao appear to be the summits of high submarine mountains that are aligned along a major northwest–southeast Philippine structural trend. Both islands have rugged topography, Ticao less so than Burias, and very limited expanses of level land. On Burias only 10 percent of the land area is under cultivation, in spite of the fact that the island has been occupied since pre-Spanish times. On both islands the maximum elevations reach to around the 1,400-foot contour.

The small islands of the Romblon group are arranged in somewhat the same inverted-V pattern as is the island of Masbate. The westernmost arm is composed of a chain of small islands, including the islands of Banton, Simara, Tablas, and Carabao, whereas the islands of Romblon and Sibuyan are aligned toward the southeast. All of the Romblon islands contain very mountainous topography. Tablas, with an area of 265 square miles, is the largest of the group, whereas Sibuyan, with an area of 173 square miles, is the most mountainous. Tablas is a long, tilted block with the high edge lying along the east coast. Sibuyan, on the other hand, is composed of several volcanic mountain masses that reach their highest point on the summit of Mount Guitinguitin at more than 6,700 feet. The topography of the remaining Romblon islands is that of typical submarine mountain summits.

The structure of Marinduque also is that of a large, tilted block, although some volcanism is evident. The interior of the island is composed of low, heavily forested mountains that reach to elevations of 3,000 feet. A narrow coastal lowland accompanies the northern and eastern coasts.

Throughout the Sibuyan Sea region, good arable land is at a premium, and this factor has encouraged a strong economic orientation toward the sea on the part of the population.

Climate does not impose any serious limitations upon agriculture in the Sibuyan area. To be sure, most areas experience the short drought season during the first three or four months of the year which is part of the precipitation regime associated with all of the central Visayan islands. Yet, average annual precipitations are relatively high—80 to 100 inches—and during the main growing season in the late summer and fall months the rainfall is more than adequate for most Philippine crops. Typhoons, although presenting an ever-present menace to agriculture, are not as frequent as in the areas farther north and east. The Sibuyan Sea islands are too limited in area to constitute a major timber source, and most of the original forest cover has long since been cleared. Extensive grasslands cover 70 percent of the island of Masbate.[5]

THE CULTURAL SETTING

The transitional character of the Sibuyan Sea region, located between the large main island of Luzon and the Visayan area, is very evident in the culture of its people. Four of the major cultural-linguistic groups of the Philippines are represented in the region in nearly equal strengths, giving clear indication of the source regions of many of the present residents. The peoples of Marinduque speak Tagalog, the main dialect of Manila and central Luzon. The Bikol dialect of southeastern Luzon is dominant on Burias and Ticao and in parts of northern and northeastern Masbate. Visayan dialects are dominant in the south. The peoples of the Romblon Islands, and those in southwestern Masbate, speak the Hilagaynon-Bisayan dialect of Panay and western Negros, whereas the population of southeastern Masbate uses the Cebuano-Bisayan of Cebu. Many of the cultural attitudes traditional with these cultural-linguistic groups also are shared by the population of the region. The Chinese element in the population is quite strong and very evident in many commercial fields, especially in the small-town bakeries, rice and corn mills, retail stores, and in fishing, for local Filipino investment capital has been either nonexistant or reluctant to enter into these occupations.

The Sibuyan Sea was well-known to the early Spanish explorers. From their base at Cebu, Legaspi and his lieutenants made frequent excursions along the coasts of Masbate, Burias, and Ticao. Owing to their position astride the main sailing routes to Manila from the south, the islands of the Romblon group became important way-stops. During the early seventeenth century several of the large Spanish (Manila) galleons were built in ship-yards on Marinduque and Masbate. Yet, the lack of populous and productive hinterlands, and the failure of the Spanish to recognize the presence of significant mineral deposits, operated against any large-scale economic development under the Spanish administration. Two economic developments, occurring near the end of the period of Spanish control, contributed significantly to the economic potential of the area, and encouraged considerable new settlement. At this time there were the beginnings of an important cattle-ranching industry based upon the large expanses of wild grasslands on both Marinduque and Masbate. Under the American administration these two islands became the principal sources of beef cattle for the nation. At the same time, the large and relatively rich veins of gold-bearing quartz located south of Aroroy and Masbate were opened. At a somewhat later date the iron-ore deposits on Marinduque and the fine marble deposits of Romblon were to contribute to a modest mineral economy.

The lack of a good resource base upon which a productive agricultural economy could be developed, however, has kept the population of Romblon and Marinduque at relatively stable rates, and at least since the beginning of the twentieth century when relatively accurate censuses were inaugurated, the increase of population in these two provinces has been at a rate much slower than the national increase. The present densities of population on Romblon and Marinduque approximate those for the whole Philippines, and in both provinces it is apparent that the population is approaching saturation levels when compared with the limited agricultural potential. On the other hand, the population of Masbate has been expanding at a rate that is greatly in excess of the national average. Since 1900, the relatively empty grasslands on the piedmont lands of interior and southeastern Masbate have been one of the prime targets for Philippine migrations.

Most of the population of the region is distributed but a short distance from the seashore. A peripheral population is particularly characteristic of Marinduque and the Romblon Islands. Areas of denser population on Masbate are found along the northeastern coast and on the southeastern peninsula. The mountainous interiors of all islands are virtually empty of inhabitants (fig. 22).

The comparative isolation of many coastal settlements, the general absence of large, productive agricultural areas, and the ease and ubiquitous nature of water transport have discouraged the development of any major urban centers. Masbate is the largest town of the region with a 1960 poblacion population of approximately 11,000 persons. The town occupies a picturesque site on the steep bluffs along the eastern side of the Masbate Bay. For many years the town of Aroroy, 18 miles to the northwest, eclipsed Masbate in the importance of its mines. The postwar demise of mining on the island, and the steady growth of trade in copra, corn, fish, and cattle at the port of Masbate, have pushed the capital city back into its position of commercial dominance. It is the principal trading center and port for the province. Foreign vessels call occasionally to load copra, and a brisk interisland trade is maintained with Manila, Cebu, Catbalogan, and Tacloban. Masbate has road connections with settlements along Asid Gulf and the northeastern coast of the island, and its airport schedules frequent service to Manila and Legaspi. Romblon, the capital city of its province, is an important port of call for interisland vessels enroute between Manila and Cebu, Iloilo, and ports in Mindanao. Romblon also serves as the collection point for the copra produced on the several islands of Romblon Province, and considerable quantities of copra are exported from Romblon. A modest quantity of marble is produced from the quarries immediately north of the city, moving through the port of Romblon to Manila. The town clings to steep bluffs at the eastern end of the deep, protected harbor formed by the island of Romblon and the small island of Lugbon. The town of Romblon had a population of approximately 3,300 persons in 1960. Boac, the capital of Marinduque Province, is located along the southern bank of the Boac River about a mile above the river mouth. The small town of Laylay at the river mouth serves as the outport for Boac. The capital city is the hub of commerce for the island with which it is connected to all points by highway. In 1960 the population of Boac was approximately 4,000 persons. No other towns in the region had 1960 populations greater than 5,000. Balud, a small municipality in southwestern Masbate, is the center for a large and very important fish-salting industry. Cataingan, Dimasalang, Milagros, Aroroy, and Placer are larger agricultural towns on Masbate. Cattle-raising and agriculture have replaced mining in the area surrounding Aroroy. No strong regional commercial center has developed in the Sibuyan Sea region, and the cities of Manila and Cebu continue to exert a very strong force on the internal commerce of the region.

Agriculture is the dominant economic activity in the Sibuyan Sea area; however, it is not as overwhelmingly important as in many other Philippine regions. In some areas fishing and cattle ranching are of considerable importance. Rice is the principal cultivated crop except in Masbate Province where there are large acreages devoted to corn. The major rice areas are located in northern Marinduque, western Tablas, and in the municipality of Milagros in southern Masbate. Small quantities of surplus rice are shipped from these areas from time to time to Manila and Cebu. Corn, grown largely because of its ease of cultivation and relatively high yields, is of major significance in northern Masbate, particularly in the municipality of Cataingan where nearly one-half of the corn acreage of the province is concentrated. Root crops also are cultivated extensively and produced in large quantities. The area generally has achieved a condition of regional self-sufficiency in food crops.

Coconuts supply the region with its only significant cash crop. Everywhere the coasts of the islands, both large and small, are bordered by fringes of coconut palms, and coconuts are especially widespread on Marinduque, Ticao, Burias, and the islands of the Romblon group. Copra is the principal coconut product. In general, the region's copra production is concentrated at the two export ports of Romblon and Masbate, although small quantities leave the region on board interisland trading vessels destined for the ports of Manila and Cebu.

All of the provinces within the region have an important livestock industry, and ranching is especially well developed on the island of Masbate. Masbate has had a long history of a cattle industry based on breeding stock imported from India. Red Sindhi and Nellore cattle were and are the principal strains. At present there are several large cattle ranches in the grass-covered upland areas between Milagros, Masbate, and Aroroy, including a government cattle-breeding station. The livestock herds were decimated during the Japanese occupation, and the industry has had to be rebuilt completely. Marinduque and Romblon have smaller herds. The region supplies several thousand head of cattle annually to the slaughterhouses of Manila.

There are literally tens of thousands of fishermen in the Sibuyan Sea area, and every bay and estuary has its harvesters. Not only are the people able to use the waters of the Sibuyan Sea, but equally accessible are the adjacent rich fishing grounds of Ragay Gulf, Tayabas Bay, and the very rich Visayan Sea. Commercial fishing interests have concentrated at the southern tip of southwestern Masbate, especially in the municipality of Balud. Here several large, Chinese-owned fish-drying and fish-salting companies have based their operations in the small coastal barrios of Bongcanaway, Pulanduta, Calumpang, and Guinayangan—barrios whose very names mean salted fish to the rest of the Philippines. Placer, Milagros, Masbate, and Dimasalang are lesser commercial fishing centers. Various fish products are shipped to Manila and Cebu, and even as far away as northern Mindanao.

Mining has played a role of considerable importance in the Sibuyan region. During the first four decades of the twentieth century several companies were engaged in gold-mining operations near the town of Aroroy. In the beginning the ores were quite rich; however, the remaining ores are low-grade, and with rising production costs and the establishment of fixed prices for gold in the postwar period the mines have not been able to resume operations. At the height of the mining boom, several thousand workers were employed in the Aroroy area. Today the mining interests of the region have been transferred to the deposits of high-grade hematite iron ore at Taluntu-nan on Marinduque. These rich iron-ore deposits are mined through open-cut operations. The iron ore is trucked approximately 8 miles from the mines to loading facilities at Balanacan from where the ores are exported to Japan. Another mineral resource of considerable value is the large marble deposit on Romblon. This beautiful, rose-colored marble is widely used as a building stone and for monuments. All of the monuments and markers at the large United States Battlefield Monument and Cemetery south of Manila are cut from Romblon marble. Reserves of high-quality marble on Romblon and on several of the small islands nearby are quite large. Small deposits of copper and manganese, although not being worked at present, are of commercial significance.

Land-transportation facilities in the Sibuyan Sea region are insignificant. Marinduque Island has the best road system, with a 60-mile road encircling the island and connecting all of the important towns. This road, however, is hard-surfaced for about one-half its length only. On Masbate, a highway winds across the interior of the island from the capital city to Milagros on Asid Gulf, and from there back across to Aroroy. There is also a road for a short distance along the northeastern coast, south from Masbate as far as Cataingan. Tablas has a road paralleling its west coast from Looc to Cala-trava, and one part way down the east coast. Elsewhere there are only short stretches of dirt roads. Hence, water transport looms importantly in the region's communications. Boac, Gasan, and Balanacan are busy interisland ports on Marinduque. Romblon, Azagra on Sibuyan, and Looc and Odiongan on Tablas, are regular interisland ports of call. Masbate, Aroroy, Cataingan, Dimasalang, Limbuhan, Milagros, and Pulanduta have regular ship service from Manila, Cebu, and Tacloban.

All of the Sibuyan Sea region lies within the economic hinterland of the port of Manila, and to a lesser degree Cebu, and most of the region's trade is with these ports.

The Stormy East: Leyte and Samar

The eastern Visayan region forms the eastern ramparts of the central Philip-pines, closing off the Visayan Sea area from the open reaches of the western

Pacific Ocean. The region is composed of the two large islands of Leyte and Samar and clusters of small offshore islands on all sides of the larger islands (fig. 64). The eastern Visayas are separated from southeastern Luzon by narrow, strategic San Bernardino Strait, and the equally narrow Surigao Strait lies between the southernmost parts of the island of Leyte and the coast of northeastern Mindanao. Thus constituted, the region includes the political areas of the three provinces of Leyte, Southern Leyte, and Samar in their entireties. The total land area of the region is 8,400 square miles, 93 percent of which lies on the two larger main islands of Leyte and Samar.

Both Leyte and Samar are among the larger islands of the Philippines; Samar is the third largest island of the archipelago, whereas Leyte ranks eighth in size. Among the larger and more important of the numerous offshore islands are Biliran, Maripipi, Santo Niño, and Almagro, in the Samar Sea; Homonhon in Leyte Gulf; and the long, narrow island of Panaon, which lies off southern Leyte. The swift and treacherous waters of San Juanico Strait, in two places reduced to a width of barely 200 yards, is all that prevents the islands of Leyte and Samar from being one contiguous landmass.

The eastern Visayas has been a region of general neglect by the central government, in large part owing to the marginal isolation of the region from the mainstreams of Philippine commercial and cultural life. At the same time the amount of arable land on the two islands is quite limited, and the climate of much of the region is excessively moist. Typhoons continually plague the eastern coasts of the Philippines, and particularly in eastern Samar, much of the area has remained relatively lightly populated because of the ever-present danger from these storms. Many of the commercial crops cultivated elsewhere in the Philippines have found a rather discouraging environment in the eastern Visayas. Present occupance remains oriented basically toward a subsistence agricultural economy. Regional ties are quite strong, however, and are heightened by the sharing of a common Samar-Leyte (Waray-Waray) ethnolinguistic culture. Within recent times the region's cultural homogeneity has been weakened in certain of the peripheral areas by the settlement of sizable numbers of Bikol- and Cebuano-speaking migrants from neighboring provinces.

THE PHYSICAL SETTING

Although the historical and structural geological backgrounds of Leyte and Samar are quite dissimilar, the islands present somewhat similar physiographic landscapes.

Leyte, in common with most islands of the Philippines, has a rugged

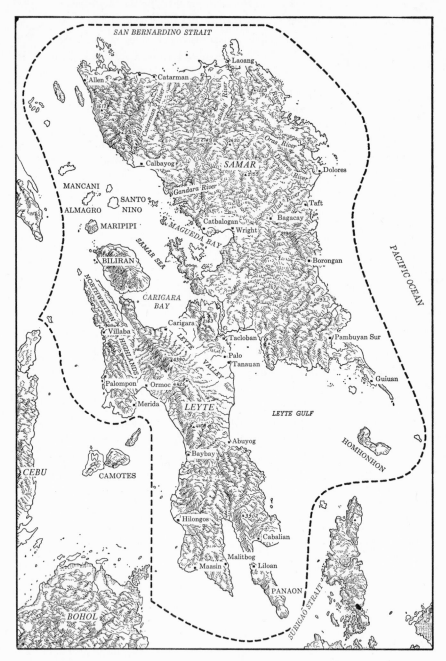

Fig. 64. Physiography of the eastern Visayas, 1960.

mountainous interior. Three clearly distinguishable mountain systems form the backbone of the island. In the island's northwestern corner are the low Northwestern Highlands, which in the south appear as the western edge of Ormoc Bay. A higher Central Cordillera, which contains the highest points on Leyte on Mount Magsanga and Mount Matagob with maximum elevations in excess of 4,400 feet, establishes the main structural trend of the island. The Central Cordillera parallels the west coast, except in the north, and reappears north of Leyte on the smaller islands of the Samar Sea; it is particularly prominent on Biliran and Maripipi. This latter highland also provides the main structure of the long, narrow southern island of Panaon. The low Northeastern Highlands front along San Juanico Strait. All three of Leyte's highland systems evidence past histories of considerable vulcanism.

The central upland core of Samar, in contrast to the highland systems on Leyte, is formed from a broad, maturely dissected plateau surface with local relief on the order of 700 to 1,000 feet. Into this plateau surface the numerous streams have cut sharply incised valleys, and on the whole, the present topographic landscape is one of low, extremely rugged hill lands. For the most part, the upland interiors of both islands are relatively sparsely settled and form the living area for a few caingineros only.

Generally, lowlands are not extensive in the eastern Visayan region and are usually confined to peripheral locations, or they may occur as small alluvial plains and deltas that frequently accompany the large rivers. The largest contiguous lowland area is Leyte Valley, located in northeastern Leyte between the Northeastern Highlands and the Central Cordillera. Formerly a shallow arm of the sea, this extensive plain has been filled deeply with alluvium in relatively recent geologic times. A complex system of short rivers drains from the Central Cordillera and flows sluggishly across the lowlands, reaching the sea either at Carigara Bay or Leyte Gulf. The second largest lowland area on Leyte is Ormoc Valley, which is located along the western side of the island extending north from the head of Ormoc Bay. Highlands surround and shelter Ormoc Valley, except on the south. The valley is drained to the south by the Bao (Pagsangahan) River and its tributaries. Other lowland areas on Leyte are quite small and usually found along the coasts, particularly near the mouths of rivers in the west and south.

The largest area of lowlands on Samar is located along the north coast, extending up the valleys of the Catubig and Catarman rivers. Other important small lowlands on Samar are found at Calbayog and on the deltas and up the valleys of the Gandara, Oras, Dolores, Ulut, and Palapag rivers. These riverine lowlands seldom are contiguous.

Because of the small, compact size of the land areas, and the characteristic radial drainage patterns, all of the rivers of the region are short. Most of the settlements are situated either along the coast or within a short distance from it. Small native watercraft can ascend the rivers for short distances only. The coastlines of both main islands are, in places, rather deeply embayed, owing to recent land submergence. This is an encouragement to water transport, and much of the internal trade of the region is carried by coastal shipping rather than overland because of a lack of good road connections.

The climatic environment of the eastern Visayan area also exhibits a considerable degree of similarity throughout the region. In general the northern and eastern sides of both large islands, although partially sheltered from southwestern air movements, lie fully exposed to the northeastern air masses and tropical cyclonic disturbances in the low-sun period. At this season these areas receive very large amounts of precipitation. On the other hand, the western and southern sides of the islands receive only moderate quantities of rainfall during the "winter" period, since the intervening highlands provide a partial barrier to weather from the east and north. All areas within the region receive substantial rains during the period of dominance of the southwestern air movements, with the partially sheltered eastern areas receiving somewhat lesser amounts. The net effect is a relatively humid climatic condition prevailing over the entire region throughout the year, particularly along the eastern and northern coasts. Average annual precipitations are large, varying from a low of approximately 90 inches in western Leyte (Inopacan and Ormoc) to more than 160 inches in eastern Samar (Borongan). The absence of strong seasonal patterns in precipitation, that is, the lack of a pronounced drought period, allows agriculture in the eastern Visayan region to exhibit less seasonality than in most other areas in the Philippines. The steady, heavy rainfall is not entirely a blessing, however. Where impermeable soils are present, such as those found in the Leyte Valley, the excessive precipitation often creates swamp or marsh conditions, as the Allied airfield-construction personnel found to their sorrow during World War II. In Leyte Valley, where impermeable soils are present, the most serious problem facing agriculture is adequate drainage.

A distinctive feature of the climatic environment of the eastern Visayan region is the great frequency and destructiveness of typhoons. Forty percent of the storms carrying high-velocity winds in the Philippines pass through this area. This large group of storms has velocity characteristics that are, on the average, considerably higher than other storm groups. These storms may occur during any month, but they are particularly frequent and destructive during the months from October to December.[6] The strong winds and heavy rainfalls that accompany these typhoons often cause not only considerable loss of life and property but also widespread damage to field and tree crops through flooding, winds, and high seas.[7] Eastern littorals are especially susceptible to damage from these raging tropical storms, and the storms are most frequent in northeastern Samar.[8] Typhoons have actually discouraged settlement along exposed coastlines.

The forest resources of both Leyte and Samar are quite large. The estimated accessible timber reserve totals nearly 30 billion board feet on the two larger islands.[9] Most of this large timber volume is located on Samar, which is almost completely covered by rain forests, except for the small cultivated areas along the coasts and a few cogonales or grasslands in the interior. The forests on Leyte cover approximately 35 percent of the island and are found principally in the Central Cordillera and in southeastern Leyte. Yakal, narra, guijo, tangile, lauan, apitong, and molave are the principal commercial species, and the forests also contain large quantities of rattan. At present the annual timber-cut is only 18 million board feet, an amount that could be increased manyfold. Most of the region's sawmill capacity is concentrated on Leyte, particularly at the southern end of Leyte Valley near the coastal town of Abuyog. The logging and sawmill operations on Samar are located mainly along the east coast at the towns of Dolores, Taft, Borongan, and Oras.

Neither Leyte nor Samar appears to be well endowed with a large or varied mineral base; however, several minerals are present in quantities sufficient to warrant a limited mining industry. Small, scattered deposits of iron ore, copper, manganese, asphalt rock, gypsum, sulfur, and various clays are present, but only the deposits of copper and rock asphalt are under active exploitation. The principal mining center of the region lies in south central Samar where the recently opened Bagacay copper deposit is located.[10] The Bagacay deposit is located near the Wright-Taft cross-island highway and consists of several small deposits of relatively high-grade, 16–18 percent copper content, direct-shipping ores, and several million tons of 3–4 percent copper content milling ores. The milled ore is concentrated at Bagacay, and along with the direct-shipping ores, is trucked to stockpiles at Jia-an near the east coast port of Taft. At Villaba, on the northwestern coast of Leyte, there is active exploitation of a 400,000-ton deposit of a crude-oil impregnated sandstone and limestone termed rock asphalt. This material has wide use throughout the Islands for roadway, waterfront, and playground paving. A modest-sized deposit of manganese ore lies near Baybay in western Leyte, and has been worked occasionally. Prior to 1959 a small, but very rich deposit of iron ore was mined at Pambuyan Sur (General MacArthur) in southeastern Samar, but the deposits have been exhausted. Large deposits of limonite iron ore are known to exist on the islands of Manicani and Homonhon in Leyte Gulf, and there are large deposits of relatively pure sulfur on Biliran Island. Little geological exploration and reconnaissance has been conducted in the eastern Visayas, and although the known variety and quantity of the mineral resource is not impressive now, the picture could brighten considerably with new geologic information.

THE CULTURAL SETTING

The islands of the eastern Visayan region share a long common historical background. Magellan made his first Philippine landfall on Samar, landing for supplies on the small Leyte Gulf island of Homonhon on March 16, 1521. Finding little of either water or food, the expedition moved on to the small island of Limasawa at the entrance to Sogod Bay off southern Leyte, where the first Philippine-held mass was celebrated. Later the expedition based at Cebu, where Magellan met his death. The islands of Samar and Leyte were known to the early Spaniards as Ibabao and Tandaya and were organized collectively into a single political unit under the jurisdiction of Cebu. In 1735, the two islands were separated from the jurisdiction of Cebu and made a separate province with the capital at Carigara on Leyte. The two islands were split into two separate provinces in 1768, with the capital of Samar at Catbalogan, where it has remained, and with the capital of Leyte successively at Carigara, Palo, Tanauan, and since 1860 at Tacloban. In 1960 the southern part of Leyte, including sixteen municipalities, was constituted as the province of Southern Leyte with its capital at Maasin.

Leyte was one of the more populous Visayan islands, whereas Samar was quite empty at the time of such early Spanish contacts as those of the Legaspi expedition and the first Jesuit priests. For a considerable time piratical incursions along the western coasts of both islands by the southern Moros prevented any significant population increase. Father Zuñiga recorded a population on the two islands of 10,860 tributes in 1800, representing approximately 43,000 persons. This population was no greater than that enumerated in 1735.[11] However, once the Moro depredations were controlled, as they finally were during the nineteenth century, the population of the region increased at a rate at least equal to, if not in excess of, the national increase. Additional stimuli to rapid population growth during the nineteenth and twentieth centuries also were supplied by the economic sector, particularly the stimulation to economic growth generated by the opening of the port of Tacloban to world trade in 1874, and by the transfer of the Philippine administration to the American government. The latter event threw the large United States markets open to Philippine-produced sugar, copra, lumber, and abaca. In 1903 the first American census enumerated a population of 600,000 persons in the two provinces, a very rapid population growth over 1800 enumerations, even if these earlier figures are suspect. Leyte's population quickly leveled off early in the twentieth century, however, and even before World War II the island of Leyte supplied large numbers of migrants to the settlement areas on Mindanao.

In 1960 the population of the eastern Visayan region stood at slightly more than two million persons, of whom approximately 60 percent lived on Leyte. Most of the population of the region lives in small agricultural villages scattered around the peripheries of both the large and small islands (fig. 22). A location close to the sea has encouraged water communication and discouraged the development of overland transportation facilities. Furthermore, many of the farmers living in the estuarine and coastal agricultural areas supplement their incomes by part-time inshore fishing. The most populous and productive area in the region is Leyte Valley. Approximately 37 percent of the population of the provinces of Leyte lives in this valley. Smaller concentrations of population are found in the Ormoc Valley in western Leyte, on Guiuan Peninsula in southeastern Samar, and in the valleys of the Catubig, Catarman, and Gandara rivers of northern and northwestern Samar. Coastal areas of eastern Leyte and eastern and western Samar also are relatively densely settled; however, almost without exception the interior sections of the islands, with their steep slopes, dense stands of rain forests, and lack of communication, are devoid of most forms of sedentary occupance.

The absolute numbers of people and the man-land ratios on the two main islands of Leyte and Samar contrast sharply with one another. When viewed by the national yardstick the density of settlement on Samar is considerably less than the average for the nation, whereas the density of Leyte exceeds the national average by nearly 60 percent. Physiological population densities in both provinces are approximately equal to each other and to the Philippine average. A large amount of arable land on Samar which remains uncultivated holds a considerable potential. The agricultural lands on Leyte appear to have reached saturation under present crops and agricultural techniques.[12] Leyte has become one of the important out-migration islands of the Philippines, sending large numbers of migrants to Manila and Rizal Province and to the Mindanao provinces of Davao, Agusan, Surigao, Cotabato, and Zamboanga del Sur. Samar has not supplied any significant group of out-migrants. Neither Leyte nor Samar have received any large numbers of in-migrants in recent years, in spite of the relatively large reserve of as yet uncultivated farmland on Samar. The principal period of population growth on Leyte occurred between 1903 and 1918, whereas Samar experienced a larger than normal population increase during the years between 1939 and 1948. At all other census intervals in the present century the populations of Leyte and Samar have failed to increase at the national growth rate, and in fact, usually remained well behind. On Leyte 96 percent of the 1960 population was born on the island; the comparable figure for Samar was 98 percent. Some 240,000 Leyte-born persons resided off the island in 1960. Cebuano-speaking people from Cebu and Bohol have been active along Leyte's west coast for a long time, and the Cebuano dialect has become dominant in that area. Almost the entire population of Samar claims Waray-Waray as the mother tongue.

One of the principal deterrents to increased settlement and economic development of the eastern Visayan region, particularly on Samar, lies in the inadequacies of the present network of land transport. The Samar road system consists of a poor road along the west coast of the main island from Basey in the south to Catarman, a similarly poor road paralleling the east coast, and a single cross-island road between the towns of Wright and Taft. Most of the roads on Samar are inadequately ballasted, poorly maintained, and impassable in times of heavy rains because of washouts and because of the fact that many of the streams are not permanently bridged. Leyte is somewhat better served with overland facilities. Although the Allied campaigns on Leyte during World War II resulted in great destruction, they were not without their blessings. United States Army Engineers built a new road system on Leyte. The present coastal road network is essentially complete, although the quality of the highway is somewhat wanting. A single all-weather highway crosses the island between the towns of Abuyog and Baybay, and a relatively dense network of roads serves Leyte Valley; however, at present neither of the islands has a road network that can be considered adequate for its internal transport needs, and the small offshore islands are virtually roadless. Businessmen in western Leyte, for example, find it simpler and cheaper to trade with Cebu than to travel overland to the regional center of Tacloban. Regular and relatively frequent commercial air service is maintained from Tacloban, Guiuan, and Calbayog to Manila and Cebu.

A large proportion of both intra- and interisland commerce in the eastern Visayas is transported by water carriers. The largest and most modern port facilities in the region are found at Tacloban; these facilities also were considerably improved by the United States Army while Tacloban served as a major Allied logistical base during World War II. The port lies in the lee of Cataisan Point and consists of a 1,200-foot-long marginal concrete wharf with deep water alongside. Frequent interisland sailings connect Tacloban with Manila, Cebu, ports on Samar, and other ports on Leyte. Catbalogan,

Calbayog, Catarman, Laoang, and Ormoc are other busy subregional ports. Important minor port facilities are located at Allen, Borongan, and Guiuan on Samar, and at Palompon, Baybay, Hilongos, Maasin, Malitbog, Liloan, and Cabalian on Leyte. These minor ports, together with dozens of others of lesser stature, serve small local trade hinterlands and furnish important links in the overall regional transportation network.

The major economic emphasis in the eastern Visayas, as in most other Philippine regions, is upon an agricultural occupance oriented toward general regional self-sufficiency. There are, however, certain significant differences in crops and cropping systems within the region. Whereas corn and rice compete on almost equal terms as principal grain crops on Leyte, rice is by far the most important crop on Samar. Yields of both grains on the two islands are very low and are considerably below the national averages. Furthermore, the total production of each grain crop is well below regional consumption levels, and relatively large amounts of rice and some corn must be shipped in from other regions. Most of the rice-producing lands of Leyte are concentrated in the Leyte and Ormoc valleys, with smaller areas of rice cultivation found in isolated coastal lowlands in the southwest (fig. 65). The larger and more productive rice areas on Samar lie on the northern plains and follow up the floodplains of the Catubig and Catarman rivers. The rice lands of the eastern Visayas usually do not bear a second crop of rice within a single year, in spite of the general availability of water from the heavy year-round rainfall. There are no elaborate irrigation systems within the region; however, approximately 14,000 acres of lowland rice are cultivated under some form of artificial water-control in Leyte Valley. A considerable share of the rice cultivated in the region, approximately 25 percent, is of the upland or dry-rice variety. The eastern Visayan region produces slightly less than 7 percent of the Philippine rice crop and consumes slightly less than 8 percent.

In contrast with the rice lands, the corn lands usually produce two corn crops during the span of a single year, and three crops a year are not uncommon. The principal corn areas lie in extreme northern and southern Leyte. Approximately 7 percent of the total corn area is found on Leyte, and 5 percent of the total corn production of the archipelago originates there. Regional corn production is insufficient for local requirements, and local supplies must be supplemented by shipments of corn, mainly from Mindanao and Cebu.

The large production of the two basic grain foods is complemented by substantial production of sweet potatoes, cassava, taro, yams, and bananas. The root crops are especially important and extensively cultivated at times when the rice and corn lands face crop failures because of drought or the

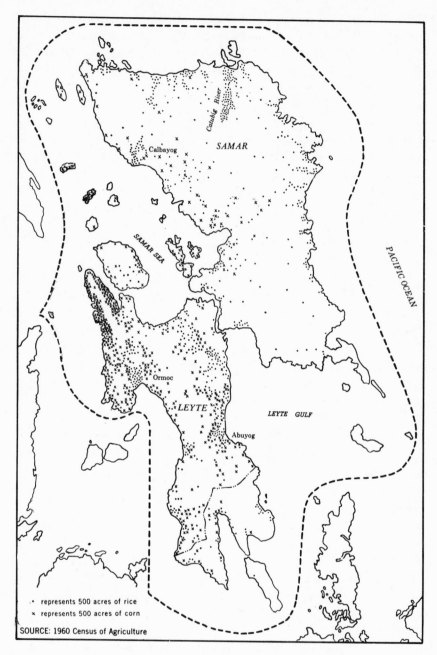

Fig. 65. Rice and corn in the eastern Visayas, 1960.

failure of seed germination. On the other hand, the areas devoted to root crops generally decline when bumper grain crops are expected.

The cultivation of commercial crops in the eastern Visayas has not received the strong emphasis it has in many other Visayan islands. Nevertheless, coconuts and abaca are rather extensively cultivated. Coconuts are the most important commercial crop, although the coconut palm is not cultivated as extensively as in the years prior to World War II, owing in part to the tremendous wartime destruction of the coconut plantations, particularly along the shores of Leyte Gulf. Although coconuts are widespread on both islands, the larger commercial plantings are found in southern and western Leyte. Tacloban is the principal point of collection and export for the copra produced along the Pacific coast, whereas most of the copra of the west and south coasts moves to the port of Cebu for eventual export. The eastern Visayan region is responsible for approximately 12 percent of the Philippine copra production.

Abaca is widely cultivated, generally on small holdings and with scant attention paid to the care of the crop. Nine percent of the abaca acreage and 19 percent of the abaca production of the Philippines originates within the region, and approximately three-fourths of it is produced on Leyte alone. Abaca-baling facilities are maintained at Tacloban, from where some hemp is shipped to Cebu prior to export. An important sector of the economic life of southern Leyte is oriented toward abaca. The small quantities of abaca produced on Samar are generally sent to Tacloban for baling, or are shipped as loose abaca to Manila.

Ormoc contains the only commercial sugarcane district in the eastern Visayas. The Ormoc Sugar District produces slightly more than 1 percent of the Philippine sugar crop; its foreign and domestic quotas total 16,000 metric tons of sugar and 6,500 metric tons of molasses. The climate of Ormoc Valley, with its lack of a clearly defined dry season, is not particularly adapted to sugarcane cultivation, and the yields obtained there are not high; however, the sugar industry is of considerable importance to the region, for it furnishes employment to a large labor force and generates considerable commerce. The sugar central is located a short distance south of the city of Ormoc, drawing its supplies of cane from a relatively extensive area of tenant-farmed sugarcane plantations nearby and from around the town of Merida, which lies across Ormoc Bay. The final sugar product and the molasses are shipped from company-owned wharfage at Panalian Point either directly overseas or to Philippine domestic markets. There are several small muscovado mills scattered through the region; each grinds cane exclusively for local consumption.

Next to agriculture, fishing is the most important occupation in the eastern Visayas, and in some locales fishing assumes a position of dominance. Maqueda Bay, Carigara Bay, Leyte Gulf, and the waters of the Samar Sea are among the richer fishing grounds in the Philippines.[13] These water bodies are especially important for their large catches of anchovies, hasa-hasa, slipmouth, herring, sardines, shrimp, and crabs. The numerous small villages located along the shores of western Samar, northern Leyte, and on the small offshore islands in the Samar Sea, are the bases for very large commercial and subsistence fishing operations. Most of the commercial fish-catch is processed in western Samar. Although large quantities of fish are salted and dried in the small fishing villages, the town of Catbalogan has developed into the principal year-round fishing center. Here the freshly caught fish can be iced for shipment to Manila or to the populous islands of Cebu and Bohol. At Guinsorongan, a short distance from Catbalogan, there is a large, modern fish-canning and fish-salting factory. Calbayog, Tacloban, Tanauan, Inopacan, and Zumarraga also are major commercial fishing ports.

Weather conditions often disrupt fishing operations, and in order to ensure a more dependable supply of fish, a number of fishponds have been established in the region. These fishponds are particularly numerous on Samar in estuarine locations along the shores of Magueda Bay. Fishponds cover an estimated 9,800 acres on Samar and 3,400 acres on Leyte, and many thousands of additional acres of marshy lands could be converted to fishponds.[14] The eastern Visayas region produces fish catches and fish products well above its regional demands.

The eastern Visayas, with its basically subsistence-oriented agricultural population, is a region of numerous small towns and agricultural or fishing villages. The only large city in the region is Tacloban. A number of the settlements have grown into notably large centers because of transportation difficulties. Three urban centers had 1960 poblacion populations in excess of 10,000; twenty had populations between 5,000 and 10,000; and 17 percent of the population of the region lived in settlements with more than 2,500 persons.

Tacloban, the capital of the province of Leyte, is the largest city in the eastern Visayas. The city is situated on San Pedro Bay near the head of Leyte Gulf, and dominates the southeastern entrance to San Juanico Strait, the narrow channel between Leyte and Samar. Tacloban functions as the premier port for both islands. Through its excellent port facilities passes much of the commerce of the region, domestic and foreign. The productive Leyte Plain, in particular, lies within Tacloban economic hinterland, as do nearby coastal sections of eastern, western, and southern Samar. The port of Tacloban was first opened to foreign commerce in 1874, and though slow to develop, it has become an important overseas shipping point for copra and lumber. The port also serves a fairly active interisland commerce, and large quantities of corn, rice, and fish arrive from other centers for local consumption within the Tacloban area. In addition to the various provincial-government functions there are numerous offices and warehouses of commercial firms, and a large bulk-petroleum depot. In 1960 the poblacion of Tacloban had a population of approximately 36,000.

Catbalogan is the principal commercial city on Samar, as well as the provincial capital. Noted particularly as an important commercial fishing center, Catbalogan also functions as the principal shipping point for incoming cargoes, and as the main distribution center for the entire island. The city is located at the head of a small bay at the mouth of the Catbalogan River. The harbor is an open roadstead. Catbalogan had an urban population of 14,000 in 1960.

Calbayog is an important religious and educational center and one of the principal copra- and abaca-shipping ports of Samar. Calbayog was established as a chartered city in 1948 with the amalgamation of the three municipalities of Calbayog, Oquendo, and Tinambacan. It serves as the principal outport for the productive northern plains of Samar with which it is connected by highway. Fishing and mat-making are the principal industries. In 1960 the urban population of Calbayog was only 6,500, although within the chartered limits, which include some 400 square miles, lived 77,000 persons.

Catarman in the largest city and the principal commercial center for the northern plains of Samar. Along with its twin port-town of Bobon it is an important abaca-shipping port; however, neither port can function except under ideal weather conditions. Catarman had a population of 8,200 in 1960, Bobon only 3,500. Laoang is another important trade center in northern Samar which dominates the trade of the rich Catubig Valley. The town is located on a small island that lies off the mouth of the Catubig River, and the harbor is a protected roadstead. In 1960 Laoang had a population of 8,500 persons. Ormoc is the most important port and commercial center in western Leyte. Frequent ship connections are maintained with Cebu. Ormoc Bay is commodious, but open to southwestern seas. Considerable quantities of copra and sugar pass through the port. Ormoc is a modern city that has replaced the war-shattered former town. The city has a 1960 population of 62,988 within its chartered city limits, although its poblacion contained only 9,300.

Other lesser urban centers (with their 1960 populations) are: Basey (6,200), Llorente (5,000), Wright (5,100), and Guiuan (5,800) on Samar, the latter being an important fishing center and former United States naval base; and Baybay (10,000), Maasin (7,300), Palompon (6,400), Dulag

(6,400), Tanauan (7,300), and Carigara (8,300) on Leyte. Maasin is the capital of the newly created province of Southern Leyte.

Cebuano Homeland: The Central Visayas

The central Visayan region lies at the geographical center of the Philippine Archipelago. This unique location positions the region midway between the two most important islands, Luzon and Mindanao, and at the same time, the region is closed off from the open expanses of the Pacific Ocean and the Sulu Sea by other Visayan islands. The central Visayan region centers upon the island of Cebu, and includes all of Siquijor, Bohol, and the islands of the Camotes group, numerous smaller offshore islands, and the eastern side of the island of Negros, including the province of Negros Oriental and the two municipalities of San Carlos and Calatrava in Negros Occidental (fig. 66). Altogether the central Visayan region represents a total land area of 5,880 square miles.

Within the central Visayas, regional homogeneity in both the physical and cultural environments is achieved to a very remarkable degree.

THE PHYSICAL SETTING

Physiographically, the islands of the central Visayas present similar landform organizations, which are due at least partially to their common geological backgrounds. Virtually everywhere, except in a few peripheral volcanic areas on Negros which are included within the central Visayas because they lie along an especially significant cultural divide, sedimentary materials are much in evidence. Calcareous-derived deposits clothe both the uplands and low areas with thick mantles of limestones and marls, in some instances overlying the basement-complex materials to depths of several thousand feet. Relief in the uplands has been generally subdued to rolling hills with maximum elevations approximating 2,000–3,000 feet. Evidences of accelerated erosion are extremely widespread, and are particularly severe on Cebu where the almost complete removal of the forests has contributed to slope erosion. Several areas of karst topography are found on Cebu and Bohol, and include numerous caverns, sinkholes, and possible "haycocks".[15] The entire region, therefore, has undergone periods of profound, relatively simultaneous inundations, allowing thick accumulations of marine sediments. Relatively level arable land is confined to narrow coastal strips usually at, or near, to the mouths of the many short, swift, and often ephemeral rivers. The major exception is interior Bohol where a low plateau landscape occurs over an extensive area surrounding the town of Carmen. Among the larger, and more

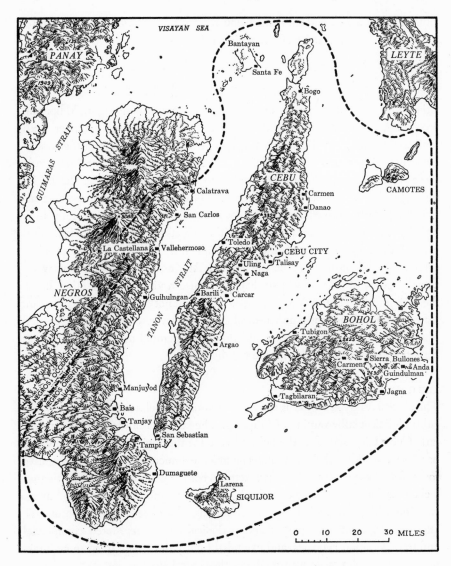

Fig. 66. Physiography of the central Visayas.

economically important, of the peripheral lowlands are those located at Bais and San Carlos on Negros, at Cebu City, Talisay, Carmen, and Barili on Cebu, and at Tagbilaran on Bohol.

Climatic and edaphic conditions also contribute considerable homogeneity to the region. Partially sheltered from the full effects of moist air masses from all directions by adjacent islands, the central Visayas receive less precipitation than do most Philippine areas. Several particularly sheltered areas in southeastern Negros and southern Cebu receive precipitations of less than 60 inches annually, and most of the region lies within the 60-inch and 80-inch isohyets. A few peripheral areas with good western exposures experience annual precipitations in excess of 80 inches. Throughout the region the months of February, March, and April are the months with the least precipitation, and these dry months may actually present real drought. Maximum precipitation occurs during the period from June through October with southwestern air flow. Typhoons are not as frequent as in areas farther north; however, neither is the region completely free from their effects. As a rule those typhoons that are most destructive to the region enter near the beginning (July) or end (November-December) of the main typhoon season. Soils most frequently derived from calcareous materials, and with generally high porosity structures, serve to heighten the effects of the dry period. This general droughty nature of the soils, with few exceptions, is a problem common to all agriculture of the region. At times, the shortage of water actually poses problems even to domestic consumption. On the other hand, the soils of the central Visayan area, although not well-suited to rice, are reasonably fertile for most agricultural crops; however, when they are cleared of their natural forest vegetation and the slopes planted to row crops, such as corn, their steeply sloping lands are rapidly eroded.

THE CULTURAL SETTING

The central Visayan region is the homeland of the Cebuano-Visayan, a major cultural-dialect subgrouping of Filipinos. The central island of Cebu, particularly Cebu City, serves as the cultural core for the region. Historically, Cebu has functioned as the cultural, economic, commercial, and administrative focus for the peoples who have settled both Bohol and eastern Negros. Cebuanos have peopled all parts of the region, and many adjacent areas, carrying with them their language, traditions, and close Cebu socioeconomic attachments. Cebu newspapers and periodicals, Cebu-registered commercial and transportation agencies, and extended family ties have served to maintain close cultural relationships through out the central Visayas.

In view of strong similarities both in the physical and cultural environments within the region, it is not surprising that cultivated landscapes have evolved which reflect these similarities.

The central Visayas is one of the most densely populated regions of the Philippines, in terms of the total number of people as well as the density of their settlement. The total number of persons living within the region was approximately 2,713,000 in 1960, a figure that represented an overall crude density of 461 persons for each square mile of total land surface. Unfortunately, all too little of the land within the region is suited to agriculture—perhaps 30 percent of Cebu, 45 percent of Bohol, and 32–33 percent of eastern Negros.[16] The population pressures upon total land actually under cultivation reach serious proportions on the island of Cebu, with 2,300 persons per square mile. A cursory glance at the population map (fig. 22) points up the extreme unevenness of the population distribution within the region. The distributional pattern is essentially peripheral, clearly reflecting the lack of agricultural lands in the interiors of the islands, except for the limited settlement in central Bohol. Most of the region's better arable lands are concentrated either on narrow coastal plains or along small riverine floodplains near the coast. Coastal settlement is further encouraged, as large numbers of the Cebuanos look toward the sea for an important source of supplementary foods. Especially dense populations are found along both coasts of central Cebu and in northeastern Negros in the municipalities of Guihulngan, Vallehermoso, and San Carlos. Parts of Bohol and interior sections of southern Negros support relatively sparse populations at the present time.

Most of the region's population is considered rural. More than 80 percent of the people of the region lived in centers of less than 2,500 persons in 1960. The city of Cebu is the only major urban center, although San Carlos, Tanjay, and Dumaguete, which have urban populations of 10,000–25,000, perform many of the functions of urban centers. Their trade areas, however, are much more restricted than that of Cebu.

The combination of a large population and a general shortage of good arable land has been largely responsible for the development of the central Visayan area into one of the most important areas of population emigration in the Philippines. The population of Bohol has virtually stood still since World War II, and growth was relatively slow even in the prewar period. Since World War II the population of Cebu has increased at a rate less than one-half the national growth rate. The present population of the northern coast of Mindanao, especially in the provinces of Misamis Occidental, Misamis Oriental, and Lanao del Norte, is predominantly central Visayan in origin. The Cebuanos also have penetrated in large numbers into the Davao region and have participated significantly in the Koronadal and Allah valley resettlement projects in Cotabato Province.[17] The strong cultural ties between these Mindanao migrants and their Visayan homeland form the basis of a very substantial volume of passenger traffic on interisland vessels, with approximately 100,000 inbound and a similar number of outbound passengers annually at the port of Cebu alone.[18] Important numbers of migrants also have left the region for Manila and Rizal Province and have even migrated overseas, principally to Hawaii, Guam, and to the West Coast of the United States.[19]

The present occupance of the central Visayan region is essentially agricultural in character; however, the agriculture within the region differs rather markedly from that found in most other areas of the Philippines. The modern orientation is toward corn as the chief subsistence crop, rather than toward the traditional rice, a crop selection that in large part is grown in response to local edaphic and climatic conditions, although cultural preferences today undoubtedly play an important, but difficult to assess, role. Generally the water requirements for corn cultivation are less than those for rice. The droughty nature of central Visayan soils encourages a major concentration upon corn; within the region is located more than 20 percent of the total harvested corn area of the Philippines, whereas only 4 percent of the Philippine rice area is harvested within the region. This large amount of land, approximately 58 percent of the total cultivated area, devoted to the growth of maize is not reflected, however, in the regional corn production. The total production of corn within the central Visayas amounts to only 15 percent of the national crop. Average yields are only 68 percent of the national average, that is, 6.7 bushels per acre as opposed to 10.0 bushels per acre.[20] The low yields now associated with the cultivation of corn in the central Visayas are, unfortunately, also accompanied by equally poor performances in other crops, and are symptomatic of a generally unfavorable natural environment, soil depletion, oversettlement of land and consequent use of marginal lands, and anachronistic tendencies on the part of the farmers. In short, although the central Visayan region is not particularly well-suited to corn cultivation, corn is one of the few grain crops that can be cultivated. The extensive cultivation of corn on Cebu and on eastern Negros virtually represents a form of "soil mining," in that not only is an erosion-promoting crop tolerated, but fully 80 percent of the land grows two crops of corn, and some even three crops of corn, within the period of one calendar year (fig. 67). Thus, the fields have little or no rest, and soils are constantly tilled and cleared, and consequently, exposed to the heavy tropical rains. Only 18.7 percent of the soils of Cebu show slight to no apparent erosion,[21] and conditions in eastern Negros and on Bohol are only slightly better. The region as a whole is not self-sufficient in corn, owing to the shortage of arable land and generally low yields, and quantities of corn grain approximating 150,000 tons annually must be shipped in, mainly from corn surplus regions in the provinces of Cotabato and Davao.[22]

In light of the preferences of many Cebuanos for corn, coupled with the physical limitations imposed by the land, the cultivation of rice plays a

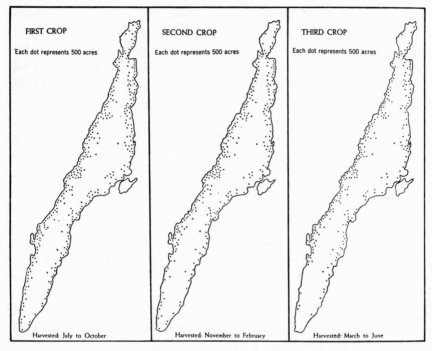

Fig. 67. Corn is grown year round on Cebu, 1960.

relatively insignificant role in the agricultural economy of the central Visayan region, except for some areas on the island of Bohol. The more important rice-producing areas are located in western, central, and northern Bohol, and in southwestern Negros Oriental. Generally, the areas devoted to rice are concentrated along the coasts on the heavy, water-retentive soils of small river floodplains and deltas. Yields of rice are well below archipelago-wide averages, and production falls considerably below even the modest regional rice demands of the region. Rice must be imported into the region in large quantities. Approximately 35,000 tons of rice arrive annually at Cebu from producing areas on the islands of Mindanao, Luzon, and Panay, and smaller quantities are unloaded at Dumaguete, Tagbilaran, and other lesser ports.

Although corn and rice are the principal food crops of the central Visayas, other so-called minor crops supply large quantities of foodstuffs. Among the secondary food crops are camotes, cassava, taro, various beans, jackfruit, papayas, bananas, and mangoes. The calcareous soils of the central Visayan area appear to be well adapted to the commercial production both of bananas and early-season mangoes, and substantial quantities of these two fruits are shipped from Cebu to markets in Manila.

The central Visayan region as a whole, and particularly the Cebu-Negros section, is an area in which the production of agricultural food crops falls far short of local demands. In spite of the general insufficiency in food production, however, extensive areas have developed within the region with their economies oriented toward commercial agriculture. Coconuts and sugarcane bulk large, both in terms of production and in the amount of land devoted to their cultivation.

The coconut palm is ubiquitous in the central Visayas, whether its intended purpose is for the production of copra, coconut oil, desiccated coconut, or tuba. These stately palms generally are found in continuous strips along most coasts, extending toward the island interiors in scattered holdings until the central mountain masses are encountered. A very significant portion of the Philippine coconut industry, quantitatively and qualitatively, is centered within the region. Coconuts cover approximately 235,000 acres, which represents approximately 9 percent of the total Philippine coconut area, and regional production amounts to 10 percent of the total national production.

Copra is the most important product of the coconut palm in the central Visayas. Not only does the region produce large quantities of copra, but the "Cebu sun-dried" copra, prepared by the simple drying of the white meat of the nut under the sun, usually on a strip of paved roadway in the somewhat droughty climate of the central Visayas, is a superior product and brings premium prices on world markets. The rancid, sweet odor of drying copra permeates almost every corner of the region. Regional copra production is mainly in the hands of the small landholders; however, marketing is generally organized by large company buyers. The city of Cebu is the copra capital of the Philippines, for to it comes, for eventual overseas shipment, most of the regional copra crop as well as much of the copra produced in northern Mindanao and in the eastern Visayas. Dumaguete and Jagna serve as secondary copra-collecting points, with direct overseas shipping facilities. Large quantities of coconuts are used locally as a source of crude coconut oil.

Commercial sugarcane cultivation is not widely distributed within the central Visayas. Instead, sugarcane production is strongly concentrated in three areas: northern Cebu at Bogo (Bogo-Medellin Milling Co.), eastern Negros at Bais (Central Azucarera de Bais), and at San Carlos (San Carlos Milling Co., Ltd.). This concentration of sugarcane cultivation has resulted from the need to centralize grinding operations in large centrifugal sugar mills. The heavily capitalized mills, in turn, require large dependable supplies of local cane; hence, the lands surrounding the mills have become sugarcane-producing lands to the exclusion of all other crops. Approximately

25,000 acres of sugarcane are located within the three sugar districts of the region. In view of the need for large and dependable supplies of cane, the farm ownership pattern is not one that would encourage small landholdings, but rather requires large plantations, called haciendas. Sugarcane farms average 38 acres, as opposed to an average of 2 acres for each corn farm. Each of the three sugar districts serves as a small agricultural region, producing cane and processing and shipping the resultant sugar and molasses from port facilities within the district. The fields within the bounds of the sugar districts stand in sharp contrast to the fields outside which are devoted to other crops. Although there is still little mechanization, the sugarcane fields receive regular fertilization, and planting stock and cultivation techniques have been carefully developed to insure maximum yields.

The bulk of the centrifugal sugar and the sugarcane by-products are not consumed within the Philippines, although small amounts are allotted the domestic markets; instead they are exported directly overseas, principally to markets in the United States, where sugar enters under a preference quota. In addition to the three areas of commercial production of sugarcane, there are numerous small sugarcane fields scattered throughout the region, totaling approximately 5,000 acres. Each of these small holdings averages less than 2 acres in size and produces sugarcane for muscovado sugar, or for chewing cane for local consumption.

Small quantities of abaca are cultivated in Bohol and eastern Negros, moving to Cebu for baling and export. A relatively significant proportion of the Philippine production of kapok and maguey are raised in Cebu. Cebu and eastern Negros produce small quantities of native tobacco also.

Fish and fish products supply the bulk of the protein in the Cebuano diet. Fishing, including the catching of crustaceans, is an important occupation within the central Visayas, not only in terms of the number of people actually engaged in fishing, but in the amount and variety of the catch. Fishing operations are conducted in all coastal areas of the region; however, commercial operations center in the waters northwest of Cebu off the small island of Daanbantayan, and off northeastern Bohol and Mactan. Approximately 5 percent of the total Philippine commercial catch, exclusive of fishpond yields, is caught in inshore and offshore operations based within the region. Among the more important species of fish caught in coastal waters of the central Visayas are herring, sardines, anchovies, and mackerel. Substantial quantities of crab and shrimp also are caught, principally in the shallow waters off Mactan. Many of the communities that lie adjacent to these and other less important fishing grounds are engaged exclusively in fishing operations, service to the fishing fleet, or in the preparation and preservation of the fish-catch. Characteristic of these communities is the omnipresence of hundreds of drying racks and brine vats and the pervading odor of the drying, salting, and fermenting fish. The part of the fish catch not consumed fresh is preserved by drying, salting, or fermentation and then transported, usually by truck or ship, to the larger urban markets within the region, or to markets as far away as northern Mindanao or Manila.

Fishing enterprises employ upwards of 20,000 persons in the region on a full-time basis, in addition to members of their families, and additional thousands of seasonal or subsistence fisherfolk. Fishing yields a multimillion dollar product annually. The culture of fishponds is not well developed in the central Visayas, owing largely to the absence of suitable foreshore lands except in Bohol, and to the richness of marine life in the surrounding coastal waters.

Too much of the land of the central Visayas has been settled too long and too densely for any significant portion to have remained in exploitable forests. Only 8 percent of Cebu and 6 percent of Bohol are in forests, and less than one-half of this forested area is classified as commercial forests. The commercial forest volume reaches only about 3,000 board feet per acre, as particular woods have been extracted. Negros Oriental, on the other hand, has 32 percent of its surface still forested, most of which is classified as commercial forest, with an average timber volume of 14,000 board feet per acre. Total accessible volume of commercial forests remaining in the three provinces of the region shows Cebu with 425 million board feet, Bohol with 68 million, and Negros Oriental with 5 billion.[23] Only in eastern Negros are there stands of commercial timber sufficient to encourage a significant forest industry. There are several small sawmills in Negros Oriental, principally at Bayawan, La Libertad, and Tanjay. Perhaps 10 percent of the lumber sawn in the region is shipped to markets in Manila, the remainder is used within the region for local needs. Veneers and plywoods are manufactured at Bayawan. Considerable timber leaves the region in log form destined for markets in Japan. Rattans and bamboos are harvested in large quantities and consumed locally or processed into basketry, matting, and furniture. Cebu City has become an important rattan furniture center, and Bohol and Dumaguete are noted for their matting and basketry industries.

The list of mineral deposits in the central Visayan region is not a long one, but the minerals that do occur are of considerable commercial importance. Coal, manganese, copper, gold, salt, and limestone for cement are actually in production, and various other minerals, including petroleum, may be present in quantities sufficient to warrant future exploitation.

The largest deposits of coal in the Philippines occur on the island of

Cebu. The major coal fields are located in the municipalities of Uling, Danao, Argao, and Toledo; the combined proven reserves on Cebu represent approximately 25 percent of the total Philippine coal reserve.[24] In general, Cebu coal is rather soft, quickly crumbling into fine particles upon aeration; however, recent techniques have been developed which now permit the coking of some Cebu coals. The production from Cebu's coal mines surpasses the combined output of all other Philippine mines, fluctuating between 75,000 and 125,000 metric tons annually. The entire production is consumed by the large cement plant at Naga. The larger coal-mining companies on Cebu employ a total labor force of approximately 1,000 workers, and the more numerous small independent operations employ an additional labor force of 2,500 workers.

Large deposits of manganese are present on the Anda Plateau in southeastern Bohol, and smaller deposits are found on the island of Siquijor. Production of manganese began on Siquijor in 1937, and during prewar years the island was a leading producer. The Siquijor deposits were exhausted, however, and are no longer the basis of any significant production. The ores from the deposits on Bohol are low-grade, but they can be beneficiated. Reserves are large, representing several million tons of ore. Production of manganese within the region has fluctuated considerably in the past, largely in response to foreign demands, but small quantities of manganese continue to move overseas, principally to Japan, through the port of Guindulman on Bohol.

Manjuyod, a small town in eastern Negros, is located in an extremely dry area with an annual precipitation of less than 50 inches. The area surrounding Manjuyod is the site of several large solar-evaporation salt beds. The opening of a copper mine at Lutopan in Toledo municipality, Cebu, in 1954 was the most significant postwar mining event in the central Visayas. The large deposits of low-grade (0.85 percent Cu) copper ore are worked by strip or open-cut methods, cyanide-concentrated at the mine site; and the resultant concentrates are shipped to Japan from the company pier at Sangi, a small barrio of Toledo. Relatively large amounts of gold are recovered as a by-product of copper-smelting. The Toledo operation is the largest copper-producer in the Philippines, employing some 1,000 men. Minerals and their exploitation constitute a relatively important sector of the regional economy in the central Visayas: reserves appear to be modest, continued operations seem assured, and future expansion possibilities are encouraging.

Manufacturing is not at present of major significance to the central Visayan economy, a fact in keeping with the essentially rural character of the occupance of the region. The limited manufacturing that does exist is oriented either toward the processing of regionally produced agricultural commodities and products of the forests and mines, or to the production of commodities intended for purely local consumption, such as handicrafts, bakeries, ceramics, and electricity generation. The city of Cebu, however, attracts considerable interregional movements of raw materials for processing or fabrication within the city.

The three large centrifugal sugar mills that operate within the region constitute the major industrial development. In addition to their final raw sugar product, these centrifugal mills produce substantial amounts of molasses. At Bais, great strides have been taken toward the development of industries auxiliary to the centrifugal mill. Alcohol from the sugar, and pulp and paper from the *bagasse* (the vegetable residue from the cane-pressing process) are being produced. A small caustic soda and chlorine plant, based upon the local salt beds at Manjuyod, operates in conjunction with the Bais pulp and paper mill. Within the central Visayas approximately 2,000 workers are employed directly in the centrifugal sugar mills; another 25,000 to 30,000 workers serve in the sugarcane fields. Thus, there are approximately 125,000 workers and their dependents whose economic livelihood rests directly with the centrifugal sugar industry. The several small muscovado mills are a relict of an earlier and more primitive sugar industry. These mills continue to produce a crude sugar product that is concentrated through boiling. Part-time, hand-to-mouth, marginal operations typify the bulk of these muscovado mills, and their numbers have decreased rapidly in recent years in the face of competition from the more efficient centrifugal operations.

Sugar quotas totaling 107,693 tons of centrifugal sugar are allotted to the three centrifugal mills within the central Visayan region, an amount representing approximately 10 percent of total Philippine sugar production.[25] All of the centrifugal sugar that is produced within the region is exported.

Of all industrial raw materials produced in or shipped to the central Visayan region none bulks more importantly, both in terms of value and quantity, than does coconut and its various products. Indeed, the central Visayas, and particularly Cebu City, are locales whose very names are almost synonymous with Philippine coconut products. The conversion of coconuts into copra is the most important manufacturing process; coconut oil, desiccated coconut, and copra cake are produced in lesser amounts. Copra is produced throughout the region wherever there are coconuts and drying ovens, or open areas where the sun can dry the white coconut meat. Whereas only 10 percent of Philippine copra production actually originates within the region, an additional 23 percent of the Philippine production is shipped to Cebu for further processing and transshipping overseas, principally from producing areas on Mindanao. A large coconut-oil factory located in Cebu City produced approximately 36 percent of total Philippine export coconut oil and 6 percent of the domestically consumed coconut oil. Incidental to the manufacture of coconut oil is the production of copra cake, the vegetable residue from the pressing process which is high in protein and valuable for cattle feed and fertilizer. Desiccated coconut is not produced within the region, although large quantities are shipped in from a factory in northern Mindanao for export through Cebu.

Although only a small area of approximately 5,000 acres is devoted to the cultivation of abaca within the central Visayas, approximately 10 percent of the Philippine abaca production is baled by the several firms located in Cebu City. The Manila hemp for these baling plants is shipped to Cebu mainly from producing areas on Leyte and Mindanao. There is no commercial manufacture of rope; however, several small home handicraft industries are involved in the manufacture of rugs, mats, and slippers from the abaca fibers, particularly on the island of Bohol.

Several hundred small corn mills are scattered throughout the region, a large share of which are under Chinese ownership. These mills most often are located in the municipality poblaciones within the corn areas and are particularly numerous in eastern Negros. Their function is to grind local corn, or corn shipped from Mindanao, into the "corn rice" important to the local dietary.

Lesser industries located within the central Visayan region include an important segment of the Philippine cosmetic, barbershop-supply, and candle industries, in Cebu City, and a sizable pottery manufacture in Dumaguete City.

Transportation facilities within the central Visayas are generally inadequate to meet the minimum demands for internal and external communications, both in terms of the quantity and quality of the transportation media. Nevertheless, transportation conditions within the region are above average when compared with national standards (appendix tables 27, 28). Most coastal areas on the larger islands are served by peripheral road networks that are occasionally hard-topped with cement or macadam, but more frequently graveled or coral-surfaced. The island interiors are seldom well-integrated into the national or provincial road networks, and often the only connection is by poor dry-season-only dirt roads or simple trails. The best road system is on the island of Cebu, which has several major cross-island roads in addition to its circumferential coastal network. On Bohol the coastal highway is supplemented by several roads leading into the interior and converging at the municipalities of Carmen and Sierra Bullones. The coast of eastern Negros is paralleled by a very inadequate highway that is primarily coral-surfaced. Ingress to the interior lands of Negros is virtually impossible except by the trans-Negros highways between Vallehermoso and La Castellaña and by a new road that is under construction between Bais and Kabankalan in Negros Occidental.

Most of the settlements located along the provincial roads are well-served by autobuses. For the most part this service is supplied by many small, independent operators with limited capitalization who are facing intense, often chaotic, competition. A few larger companies attempt some form of scheduled operations and probably account for most of the revenue. Service is frequent and inexpensive, but not always rapid or direct.

Rail facilities are completely absent within the region, except for privately owned sugar central trackage, none of which operates as public carrier. Approximately 175 miles of narrow-gauge railroad within the three sugar districts transport sugarcane from the fields to the mills and move sugar to the docks. Prior to World War II, the Philippine Railway Company operated 57 miles of mainline track between Argao and Danao along Cebu's east coast, primarily to facilitate movements of sugar, coal, and cement. The railroad facilities were badly damaged during World War II and were not rehabilitated.

Commercial airport facilities are maintained at Cebu, San Carlos, Toledo, Dumaguete, and Tagbilaran, and regular service by Philippine Air Lines connects these cities with the rest of the Philippines. The Cebu airport at Lahug is an extremely busy terminal, second only to Manila, and serves as an alternate field for international flights. Most flights between Manila and Mindanao go by way of Cebu. A new international airfield has recently been constructed across Cebu harbor on Mactan Island.

The central Visayas is supplied with a well-integrated water-transportation system. The port of Cebu ranks first among all Philippine ports in the amount of domestic shipping that enters and departs from the port, and stands second only to Manila in international ship movements (fig. 68). Dumaguete and Tagbilaran are important national ports with regularly scheduled interisland ship service. Dozens of lesser municipal ports serve inter- and intraprovincial trade. The small offshore islands of the Camotes group and Bantayan and Siquijor, have frequent water connections with the major ports. Ferry service connects Cebu with Negros at Tampi–San Sebastian and Toledo–San Carlos, and a frequent service is maintained from Cebu to Tagbilaran and Tubigon on Bohol.

Land transport generally furnishes the media for most intraprovincial transport needs, whereas interisland shipping provides for all interprovincial

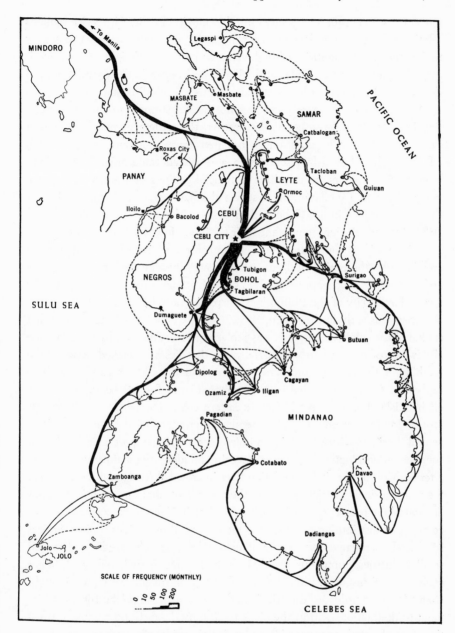

Fig. 68. Routes and frequencies of shipping services from Cebu, 1956.

movements except for a very small number moving by air. Air service remains relatively expensive and serves only a small, although growing, passenger traffic, and small quantities of high-value or perishable freight. Air service is quite frequent between Cebu and Manila and between Cebu and Cagayan de Oro on Mindanao, with several daily flights in each direction.

The central Visayan region does not have a strongly urbanized population in spite of its dense population; rather, the settlement pattern is one of numerous small villages, strongly oriented toward agriculture, and each offering only a few urban services to a restricted trade area. The region's largest urban centers are the three provincial capitals of Cebu City, Dumaguete City, and Tagbilaran, the first two also being chartered cities. A few of the larger municipios on Cebu and in eastern Negros also have populations and functions sufficient to warrant their consideration as urban centers.

Cebu City is the premier city of the central Visayas; indeed, its service area includes the entire southern half of the Philippine Archipelago. With a 1960 population of approximately 250,000 persons, the city ranks as the second largest city of the Philippines, surpassed only by Manila. Founded by the Spaniards early in their occupance (1565), Cebu was selected as the first capital of the colony. In 1571 it was replaced in this function by Manila. The city is located on the narrow alluvial plain that lies sandwiched between the foothills of the central cordillera of Cebu and the island's east coast. The harbor for Cebu is provided by the sheltered strait formed between the low offshore island of Mactan and Cebu's eastern coast. The pattern of city streets rather closely conforms to the general configuration of the shoreline. The central business district adjoins and merges with the port area. Strips of commercial developments are continued inland along the main transportation arteries. Most of the city's population lives in crowded residential sections near the main business district and along the waterfront. Better residential sections lie around the periphery, particularly to the north. Cebu serves as the principal commercial distribution point for the region and also provides similar services for densely populated northern Mindanao. Within the city are located several small industries, numerous warehouses, and many branch offices of larger commercial firms in Manila. Large quantities of freight are either brought from Manila or unloaded directly from overseas carriers at Cebu for transshipment to destinations within the city's trade hinterland. Cebu's primary function, that of a major commercial center, is very evident in its busy port. Each day twenty to thirty interisland vessels call at Cebu from ports in the Visayas, Mindanao, and from Luzon carrying cargoes for sale or transshipment at Cebu, or calling to pick up cargoes for distribution from the Cebu warehouses. Cebu is the principal Philippine port for domestic shipments of copra which are transshipped to overseas carriers there. Also from its trade area come large quantities of corn, rice, fish, and lumber for domestic use.

Cebu City is the provincial capital of Cebu Province, and as such, serves both as an administrative and a cultural center for some 1,300,000 persons. Numerous hotels, restaurants, hospitals, churches, and several educational institutions, including two universities and all of the provincial secondary schools except four, are located within the city. Cebu still retains much of the flavor of its rich Spanish heritage. The ruins of Fort San Pedro still watch over the harbor, and in both Cebu and Mactan there are relicts and symbols of Magellan's landing and death. The upper stories of the office buildings and stores project over many of the hot, dusty, narrow streets, busy with horse-drawn *calesas* and honking automobiles, trucks, and buses.

The towns of Mandawe, at the northern entrance of Cebu harbor, and Opon, opposite Cebu on Mactan Island, lie within the greater Cebu metropolitan area. Mandawe, with a 1960 population of approximately 6,000, is the site of an important small-boat-building industry. At Opon, with a population in 1960 of approximately 3,500, there are major port facilities, including three petroleum company piers and a shipyard.

Dumaguete, the capital city of Negros Oriental Province, is the second leading port in the central Visayas. In 1960 Dumaguete had a population of 35,000. The city is located on the gently sloping piedmont lands at the base of the Cuernos de Negros Mountains in southeastern Negros. Dumaguete is the only major port in Negros Oriental Province, and even it lacks protection from northeastern winds. Dumaguete serves as the principal commercial center for the province, providing major wholesaling, warehousing, and marketing facilities. The city is a regular port of call for interisland vessels from Manila, Cebu, and Mindanao, and an occasional stop for overseas vessels calling for copra cargoes. The commercial functions of Dumaguete are secondary to its educational and administrative functions, although the former are still of considerable importance. Three institutions of higher learning, which draw their student bodies from the Visayan provinces and Mindanao, are located in Dumaguete. The presence of Silliman University, with its American missionary background, has resulted in a considerable degree of Americanization. In the field of manufacturing the production of pottery is an important local industry.

Tagbilaran is the capital and principal commercial center of Bohol Province. The essentially rural character of Bohol is reflected in the small size, 1960 population approximately 7,200, of its largest city. Tagbilaran is a port city, a regular port of call for interisland vessels plying between Cebu and Mindanao; however, a passage had to be blasted through a coral reef to gain access to the port, and its maintenance requires continual dredging operations. Tagbilaran serves as Bohol's entrepôt with warehouses, distributory outlets, hospitals, schools, and various supply establishments. Bohol Island has supplied large numbers of emigrants moving as colonists and field hands to the pioneer agricultural areas on the island of Mindanao, and their arrivals and departures furnish the basis for a brisk passenger traffic through the port of Tagbilaran.

The three provincial capitals dominate the commercial and cultural activities of their respective provinces, as well as collectively dominating those of the region. Within the shadows of these administrative centers, however, several larger municipalities, the next lower order of political-administrative centers, have developed into smaller regional centers, and in some instances when their trade areas are particularly rich and populous, into rather large urban centers. This growth, which is generally evidenced by increased population, has come about because there is good access to improved transportation facilities, or some industrial activity has occurred. In eastern Negros the towns of San Carlos and Tanjay, with 1960 urban populations of 21,000 and 12,000, respectively, approach the status of small cities. San Carlos owes its initial impetus to the establishment of a large sugar central in 1912. The mill provides employment for several thousand workers. Frequent ferry service is maintained with Toledo on the opposite shores of Tañon Strait on Cebu from whence comes a large number of migrant sugarcane plantation workers. San Carlos has deepwater port facilities for interisland and overseas vessels. Tanjay, although participating to some extent in the activity of the Bais sugarcane industry located nearby, is an important agricultural market center of long standing. Smaller towns of more local importance in eastern Negros include Bais, Guihulngan, Zamboanguita, and Calatrava. Each dominates the trade of its local agricultural area. All towns on Bohol are quite small, including the capital. Among the more important market towns with 1960 populations between 2,500 and 5,000 are Calape, Guindulman, Sierra-Bullones, and Ubay. Bantayan, Bogo, Carcar, Naga, and Toledo are important lesser towns in Cebu Province. Bantayan, and its sister town of Santa Fe, are located on Bantayan Island off northwestern Cebu and are centers of an important fishing industry. Both centers have a well-established home handicraft industry with embroidery, abaca-weaving, and the manufacture of piña cloth, a home handicraft textile of considerable beauty. Toledo, the ferry gateway to Negros Island at San Carlos, is supported by a large local agricultural base and the very important copper mines a few miles inland. Naga is the initial, and still important, center of the Philippine cement industry, Carcar and Bogo are agricultural towns; in Bogo is located Cebu's only commercial sugarcane mill.

In light of the relatively large and dense population of the central Visayas, it is rather surprising that the development of urban centers has lagged. Undoubtedly, this lack of urbanization is symptomatic of the essentially rural nature of the regional occupance.

The Western Margin: Western Negros and Panay

The western Visayan region consists of a number of relatively broad expanses of river and coastal lowlands which extend well inland, and a series of rugged hill and mountain lands in the island interiors. In the east the highlands are mainly volcanic; in the west they are generally nonvolcanic. Rice occupies the majority of the cultivated lands, for the region is the second most important rice-producing area in the Philippines, exceeded only by the extensive rice-producing lands of the Central Plain of Luzon. It is, however, the extensive fields of sugarcane that give the region its distinctive character and set it apart from the other Visayan and Philippine regions. Particularly on the western lowland sector of the island of Negros, one seldom loses sight of the tall smoke stacks of the modern centrifugal sugar mills which project above the broad fields of tall sugarcane. The agricultural practices and techniques employed in the commercial cultivation of sugarcane, and hence those characteristic of much of the agriculture of the region, are not those usually associated with the traditional Philippine agriculture. Numerous farm tractors can be seen working in the cane fields, and although not observable, heavy use is made of mineral fertilizers, and field mulching is commonly practiced. An extensive network of narrow-gauge railroad tracks crisscrosses the fields, converging upon each of the region's thirteen centrifugal mills. Sugarcane is one of the most important Philippine cash crops, produced largely for the overseas United States market, and the western Visayan region is the heartland of the nation's sugar production. Beyond its impressive sugarcane production and potential, the western Visayan region has a prosperous agricultural base for many other crops, a rich marine resource in its offshore fishing grounds and extensive fishponds, sizable stands of commercial forests, and modest-sized deposits of minerals. The western Visayas is one of the richest economic regions in the Philippines, although more remote areas within the region, for example, Antique Province, have failed to share in this general prosperity.

The western Visayan region embraces all of the island of Panay, the small island of Guimaras, the western three-fifths of the large island of Negros, roughly corresponding to the province of Negros Occidental, together with a host of small islands and islets adjacent to the coasts of the larger islands. Thus constituted, the region contains a land area of approximately 7,300 square miles, or almost 7 percent of the total area of the Philippines. The physical and cultural environments of the region exhibit a considerable degree of homogeneity throughout. As defined, the western Visayan region is basically a cultural region, one that includes the main living area of the ethnolinguistic group of Visayan peoples known as the Hiligaynon-Visayans, together with nearly all of the Aklan-Visayans, a group closely associated with the Hiligaynons. Nevertheless, similar tectonic histories, similar parent-rock materials, and similar weathering and erosive agents have created remarkably similar regional landforms and physical landscapes. Furthermore, and largely because of these physical similarities, correspondingly similar patterns in crops and cropping systems have developed throughout the region.

THE PHYSICAL SETTING

The main physiographic form of Panay is set by the relatively high, rugged range of mountains that parallels the west coast of the island (fig. 69). These Western Highlands are the highest, broadest, and most rugged mountain lands on Panay. They reach their maximum elevations on the summits of Mounts Nangtud and Madiac in the north, at 6,721 and 7,150 feet, respectively. Midway along this western range, near Mount Baloy, a low range of hills branches northeastward from the main mountain mass, and terminates in a low upland area in the northeast corner of the island. The highland systems of Panay provide a convenient physiographic divider, separating the island into three distinct lowland subregions: the Iloilo Basin, the north coastal lowland, and the lowlands that accompany the western coast. The Iloilo Basin, which in turn is composed of a number of small contiguous lowlands, occupies a broad structural depression closed off to the north and west by uplands, but open to the south and southwest. The several rivers and streams that drain across the basin, particularly the Jalaud and Jaro (Iloilo) rivers, have built extensive deltas at their mouths in the southeast where they empty into the protected waters of Iloilo and Guimaras straits. The entire northern shoreline of Panay is accompanied by a band of lowlands of varying width which reach their broadest extent near the city of Roxas where the Panay River has built an extensive delta land. The coastal area that lies west of the Western Highlands consists of a series of small coastal lowlands, interspersed by rocky spurs that descend from the main mountain mass. The

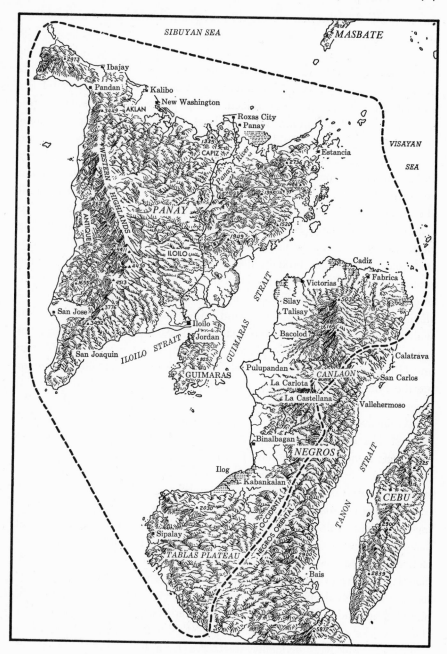

Fig. 69. Physiography of the western Visayas.

largest lowland in the west is located in the south on the delta and floodplain of the Sibalom River.

The main physiographic framework for the island of Negros is provided by a volcanic central cordillera that traverses the length of the island. This central highland reaches its maximum elevation of over 8,000 feet on the summit of the volcano Mount Canlaon. Several peaks north of Canlaon reach above the 5,000-foot contour. This highland core of Negros lies much closer to the east coast of the island. North and west of the central cordillera are broad plains that slope gently down to the coast. These plains extend in an unbroken band from the northeastern corner of Negros over 100 miles southwestward along the shores of the Visayan Sea and Guimaras Strait until they finally terminate in southwestern Negros at the Tablas Plateau. The width of the plains of Negros Occidental varies from 5 to 30 miles. The northern and central sections of the plains are composed of alluvially deposited volcanic materials brought down from the central highlands. In the south, the volcanic materials have been buried under a relatively thick mantle of marine sediments. The Tablas Plateau occupies the southwestern corner of the island and presents a rolling upland surface that is generally forested, but with some extensive areas of cogonal grasslands also. Narrow ribbons of lowland extend back into the plateau area along the courses of the Sipalay and Hinoba-an Rivers. The principal rivers of the western plains of Negros are the Himug-an in the north, the Bago in the center, and the Ilog, the longest river on Negros, in the south.

Guimaras Island lies adjacent to Panay and across Guimaras Strait from Negros. The island is composed, in large part, of coralline limestones, and coral reefs front in a continuous belt along the eastern shorelines. Guimaras resembles an uplifted coral platform with its present undulating upland surface the result of erosion subsequent to uplift.

Many of the soils of the western Visayas clearly reflect the deep weathering of the basic volcanic parent-rock materials, in situ, or their removal and deposition elsewhere through the agency of running water. Most of the soils of northern and western Negros have been weathered from recent volcanic materials that were subsequently redeposited by streams. In general, these soils are relatively deep, poorly drained, and generally quite low in nitrogen, phosphorous, and potassium. The soils of eastern Negros, north of the towns of San Carlos and Calatrava, and of the Tablas Plateau, are much older geologically and have generally weathered from limestone. The soils of Guimaras are quite similar to those of eastern Negros and also are of limestone origin. On Panay, most of the lowland soils are composed of recent alluvium. Those of the Iloilo Basin and formed from deep unconsolidated silts and clays, whereas those of the lowlands along the western and northern coasts of the island are composed of recent, fine-grained river alluvium that has been brought down from the adjacent uplands. In general, most of the soils of the region can be considered quite fertile and represent a very valuable agricultural resource. The western Visayas are reasonably well exposed to southwestern airflows and only partially sheltered from northeastern air masses. Few areas within the region receive precipitations of less than 80 inches annually, and the annual rainfall in most areas is well above 100 inches. On both large islands, areas having northern and northwestern exposures experience heavy, year-round rains, whereas more sheltered areas, such as in parts of the Iloilo basin and Tablas Plateau and in eastern Negros, receive less precipitation and precipitation that is highly seasonal. These sheltered areas experience drought periods lasting from one to four months. All areas within the region experience their season of maximum precipitation during the dominance of southwestern air masses; the drier season occurs during the months of November or December through May. The dry season generally coincides with the main harvest season of the sugarcane fields. Because of the heavy precipitation and the generally poor drainage qualities of many of the soils of western Negros, much of the sugarcane land must be artificially drained.

Dense stands of virgin tropical rain forest still clothe the slopes of the Negros cordillera lands, and forests also are found in the more inaccessible areas on the Tablas Plateau where the shifting cultivators still have not found their way. The dipterocarp forests of Negros represent some of the finest stands of commercial timber remaining in the Philippines. Much of the original forest vegetation of Panay has been removed, and only small, thinned remnants can still be found in western Panay. Excessive and wasteful forest exploitation and the indiscriminate clearing fires of the shifting cultivators have left their marks in the extensive areas of cogon grasses in central and eastern Panay and in sections of the northern Tablas Plateau. Many of the uplands that once were heavily forested now support sparse stands of secondary, noncommercial forest growth. Second-growth forests are particularly extensive in northern Negros and western Panay. Swamps and mangrove forests are restricted to a few coastal areas in northeastern Negros and eastern and northern Panay. Only the forests of Negros represent a significant resource and are intensively utilized for logs and lumber.

THE CULTURAL SETTING

The peoples of Panay and western Negros have had close cultural associations for a long time. They share a common Visayan dialect, Hiligaynon, as well as many items of common culture. Until well into the nineteenth century, the Moro depredations along the coasts of both islands created unity through adversity, and these peoples have continued to share common political and economic problems. By and large, most of the people who have settled on the plains of northern and western Negros originally came as migrants from Panay in relatively recent times; during the early years of the Spanish administration Negros appears to have been sparsely settled. Even today, there are large seasonal migrations of laborers from Panay to the sugarcane plantations and sugar mills on Negros, migrants who number in the tens of thousands. Thus, the cultural ties between the two main islands continue to be close and are constantly renewed.

Both Panay and Negros were touched by the Spaniards in the same year, 1569. Legaspi described Panay as "very populous and fertile and yielded great abundance of rice, swine, fowl, wax, and honey," [26] but the island of Negros was rather sparsely populated by Negritos. In 1569 Legaspi transferred his expedition headquarters from Cebu to Ogton, a small settlement near the present-day city of Iloilo, and Panay became an important provisioning center for later Spanish explorations and conquests. Meanwhile, on Buglas, as Negros was then known, the lack of a good harbor, the small population, and the shortage of food supplies caused the Spanish to turn their attention elsewhere.

Panay and much of Negros were administered as the single province of Iloilo until 1734 when Negros was constituted as a separate military district. Eventually the island of Panay was organized into three provinces. Capiz was the first province to be formed from Iloilo in 1716, and Antique was carved from Iloilo and elevated to provincial status in 1798. The fourth province, Aklan, was created from sections of the provinces of Capiz and Antique in 1955.

The western Visayan region continued to function basically as a supplier of foodstuffs to the rest of the archipelago, particularly with respect to rice, until the nineteenth century when the introduction and great areal expansion of commercial sugarcane cultivation occurred. However, until the beginning of the sugar industry, with its commercially oriented economy and consequent large labor demands, the population of the region increased very slowly. In 1845 the entire island of Negroes was reported to have a population of only 58,000, only 18,000 of whom lived in western and northern Negros.[27] Panay was more populous with a total population that had reached nearly 200,000 as early as 1800.[28] By the 1903 census enumeration of the Philippines, the population of the island of Negros had increased almost tenfold, reaching 570,000, and that of the province of Negros Occidental had exceeded 300,000.[29] Panay did not experience the same spectacular population increases as did Negros during the nineteenth century, for many of the migrants to Negros had come from Panay; but the population of Panay nevertheless reached 775,000 by 1903.

In 1960 the population of the western Visayan region constituted 11 percent of the total Philippine population, or slightly less than three million persons. As in most other areas in the Philippines, the majority of the people on Panay and Negros are concentrated mainly along the coasts (fig. 22). Coastal settlement is particularly dense along the shores of Guimaras Strait and the Visayan Sea; however, there are also large numbers of people living on the broad fertile lands of the Iloilo Basin and the western plains of Negros. The mountain lands remain sparsely populated, along with the more inaccessible lands on the Tablas Plateau. The Tablas, however, is entering upon an era of rapid pioneer settlement; between 1948 and 1960 the population of the three municipalities whose areas included parts of the plateau increased by 50 percent, whereas the population of the rest of the province increased by only 28 percent.

The average density of population over the region as a whole is approximately 393 persons per square mile, an average density 68 percent greater than the national average. As the proportion of total area under cultivation is much greater for the western Visayan region than for the whole of the Philippines, the ratio of population to cultivated land only slightly exceeds the national average. The strong orientation toward commercial crop production, however, particularly on Negros, has resulted in less land being available for food production, and has actually brought about a serious food deficiency in an area where such a condition need not exist. When normal interisland and international trade was halted during World War II, making it necessary to plow up much of the sugarcane land on Negros and replant the fields to food crops, a level of food sufficiency was attained. Furthermore the dominance of a commercial plantation economy has heightened problems of high land-tenancy rates and promoted widespread absentee landownership. Large numbers of landless farmers are present in the central Visayan region. Partly as a result of the tenancy conditions prevailing in the region, the western Visayas has become an area of considerable population emigration in the past several decades. Large-scale emigration has been particularly evident from Negros owing to the greater concentration upon commercial sugarcane cultivation which had led to greater dissatisfaction.

Ease of transportation and a greater emphasis upon manufacturing, viz., the numerous sugar mills, have tended to develop greater tendencies toward urbanization in parts of the western Visayas than in many other regions in the Philippines, particularly in western and northern Negros. The Office of Statistical Coordination and Standards (OSCAS), basing its definitions upon minimum residential densities, claims that 57 percent of the Negros Occidental population should be classed as urban dwellers, placing that province behind only Rizal in the degree of provincial urbanization.[30]

Concentration upon the commercial cultivation of sugarcane, and the large labor force and physical facilities necessary for the processing of cane into sugar and its various by-products, have established the basic characteristics and patterns of agriculture, transportation, and manufacturing which have come to be associated with the economy of the western Visayan region. The province of Negros Occidental alone produces some 57 percent of the total centrifugal sugar of the Philippines, and the island of Panay contributed an additional 6 percent. Altogether, some 385,000 acres within the region were in sugarcane in crop year 1962–63 (fig. 70). Thirteen of the twenty-five centrifugal sugar mills operating in the Philippines are located within the region, and ten of these are in Negros Occidental. Each sugar central lies within an established sugar district from which it draws its supplies of cane. There is a very considerable capital investment in the sugar industry of the region, for in addition to the large investments in physical plants, there is a heavy capital investment tied up in rolling stock and the more than 1,000 miles of narrow-gauge railroad tracks on Negros alone. The centrals on Panay rely upon truck transport to carry their cane and sugar to the nearest railhead of the government-owned Philippine Railroad Company.

Numerous differences exist between the various sugarcane-producing districts of the western Visayan region, climatically and edaphically. Whereas the majority of the soils of Negros are derived mainly from volcanic materials, the soils of Panay are developed principally from marine and river sediments. Similarly, whereas the lowlands of western Negros and the Iloilo Basin experience strongly monsoonal precipitation regimes, northern areas on these two islands receive heavy, year-round rains.

The majority of the cultivated lands of northern Negros, some 55 percent, is devoted to sugarcane. Since there is no period of real drought in northern Negros, the three centrals located there can operate continuously through the year, although equipment maintenance usually restricts the milling season to ten months. The long milling season permits a large yearly production of sugar from a smaller daily mill capacity. The largest sugar central in the Philippines, the Victorias Milling Company, which mills over 10 percent of the total Philippine sugar production, is located in northern Negros. The Victorias Sugar District includes approximately 59,000 acres devoted to sugarcane, and arranges individual milling contracts with over one

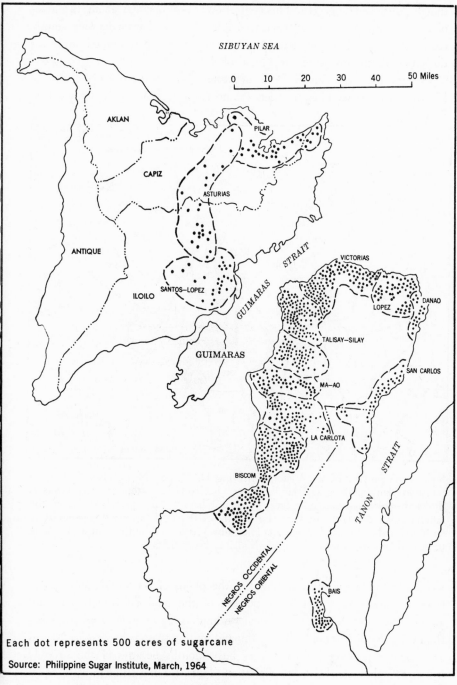

Fig. 70. Sugarcane and sugar districts in the western Visayas, 1960.

thousand growers (fig. 71). This central owns and operates about 140 miles of railroad, hundreds of rail cars, wharf facilities, and even its own transoceanic shipping. The products include centrifugal sugar, refined sugar for domestic consumption, molasses, and alcohol.

The extensive sugarcane lands of western Negros are organized into six large sugar districts. These districts extend from Saravia municipality south-

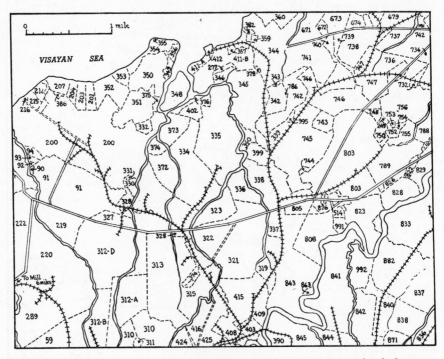

Fig. 71. A portion of the Victorias Milling District on Negros Island showing transportation facilities and landholdings (haciendas). A total of 141 farms is shown in this 18-square-mile area. (The numbers in land parcels designate the mill-hacienda contract number.) Each numbered parcel is owned separately by an individual or family *haciendero*. The railway is owned by the central. Portable track and/or unimproved dirt roads lead into every field.

ward into the municiality of Ilog. On the plains of western Negros sugarcane occupies approximately 41 percent of the total cultivated area, and approximately 40 percent of the total Philippine export sugar crop originates from these six districts. The harvesting and milling seasons in western Negros are crowded into five to seven very busy months because of the strongly monsoonal character of the precipitation. Thus, for the latter mills to equal the annual sugar production of the northern Negros mills, each mill must be larger, with a much greater daily cane mill capacity. Nearly 1,000 miles of narrow-gauge railroad tracks connect the Negros mills with their cane fields, and also lead to the several shipping points from which, in fair weather, the final sugar is lightered to overseas vessels for export.

The three sugar districts on Panay, two in Capiz Province and one in Iloilo, are neither as large nor as productive as those on Negros. The centrals in Capiz enjoy a longer milling season than does the Iloilo central. Two of the Panay mills use the facilities of the Philippine Railroad, exporting through the port of Iloilo. Central Azucarera de Pilar in Capiz utilizes barges on the Pilar River, transshipping to overseas vessels at various protected sites along the coast.

The seasonal labor requirements at the mills and in the sugarcane fields of the western Visayas are very large. Negros Island has not been able to supply sufficient labor for its sugar industry, and during periods of heavy work, large numbers of workers migrate to Negros from Iloilo Province. Approximately three-fourths of the large passenger traffic passing through the port of Iloilo is with the island of Negros, an annual traffic flow that totals nearly 160,000 passengers inbound, and a similar number outbound.

Although the uniqueness of large areas devoted to the commercial production of sugarcane establishes the distinctive character of the agriculture of the western Visayan region, from an acreage standpoint it is the rice that is the dominant regional crop. Approximately one-sixth of the rice-growing lands of the Philippines is located within the region. Most of the rice is of the wet variety, cultivated in lowland fields. Limited areas of upland dry rice are grown mainly in the rolling and hilly lands. Generally yields are slightly below the national levels. Iloilo, with its extensive lowlands, is the leading rice-producing province of the Visayas, and it is followed by the provinces of Antique and Capiz. Nearly three-fourths of the cultivated lands of Iloilo Province are given over to rice cultivation, and production far exceeds provincial requirements.

Yet, in spite of its large rice production, the western Visayan region is a net-deficit rice area. The large rice deficits of Negros Occidental, which have developed because of the strong emphasis upon commercial sugarcane cultivation, require more than the surpluses from the Iloilo Basin. The remainder of the supplies necessary to meet the Negros rice deficiency come from the Cotabato Valley in southern Mindanao. Aklan, Antique, and Capiz generally produce only enough rice to meet their internal needs, with occasional surpluses. Corn production and the patterns of surpluses and deficits are similar to those of rice.

Coconuts and coconut products do not play an important role in the agricultural economy of the western Visayas, and the few coconuts that are cultivated are confined to a narrow coastal location in the northeast and southwest. Mungo beans, sweet potatoes, cassava, taro, yams, beans, tobacco, and various fruits are produced as complementary foodstuffs in relatively large quantities.

The western Visayan region could be self-sufficient in food production with little difficulty; however, as long as commercial sugarcane cultivation is profitable, the region will continue to find it more advantageous to bring in large quantities of foodstuffs from the surrounding areas and concentrate on this highly profitable cash crop.

Much of the population of the region is engaged in nonagricultural pursuits. Fishing, logging, and sawmilling, mining, and the various activities relative to transportation and commerce are of considerable importance.

The fishing industry of the western Visayan area is of more than local significance. In many places the shorelines are lined by scores of small fishing villages, and tens of thousands of Visayans find in fishing their primary source of livelihood. Additional thousands supplement their meager farm incomes through part-time participation in fishing. Virtually every coastal village participates, to some extent, in sustenance coastal fishing. Large-scale commercial fishing is especially important along the shores adjacent to the very productive fishing grounds of the Visayan Sea, Sibuyan Sea, and Guimaras Strait; approximately one-fourth of the total Philippine commercial fish-catch is landed within the region.[31] The principal catch consists of herring, sardines, anchovies, and mackerel. Cadiz, Bacolod, Sagay, and Silay on Negros, and Iloilo, Estancia, Barotac Viejo, and Banate on Panay are major fishing centers, and large numbers of commercial fishing vessels are based at these ports. The large commercial operations insure a regular daily supply of fish to the major coastal settlements, and the region sends part of its commercial catch to Manila and central Luzon. In the larger towns of the region the majority of the fish is marketed fresh, but for the smaller interior towns the fish must be preserved. Surrounding each of the fishing villages are rack upon rack of drying fish, and the principal occupation of a village is made clearly evident from afar by the odor. Bagoong, fermented anchovy paste, is prepared in a few locales.

The regional fish-catch is supplemented by a rather extensive fishpond culture. The western Visayan area operates slightly less than one-third of the total fishpond area of the Philippines. Bays, estuaries, and low or inundated lands along the coasts support numerous productive rearing ponds. Capiz and Iloilo rank as the second and third provinces of the Philippines in the area of their fishponds; and **Negros** Occidental ranks sixth. Fishponds insure a regular flow of fish to markets within the region.

Although mining and mineral industries do not occupy a particularly important position in the economy of the western Visayan area, there are the modest beginnings of a mineral economy. Most of the mineral deposits are small, scattered, and difficult to work. Small deposits of copper, manganese, chromite, gypsum, phosphate rock, guano, and limestone are present in several places. Only copper, and to a limited extent limestone, have been developed on relatively important commercial scales, and both of these mineral developments are of relatively recent origins. A small cement plant, which mainly supplies the cement needs of the island of Panay, is located on Guimaras Island. This plant is based upon local sources of limestone and imported fuel oil. Annual production averages approximately 30,000 tons of cement.

The largest single mining operation in the region is the newly developed, open-pit Baclao copper mine in Sipalay municipality on the edge of the Tablas Plateau. These low-grade copper ores are concentrated at the mine. A molybdenum recovery mill operates in conjunction with the copper concentration process. Reserves of low-grade copper ore are relatively large. The mining company has constructed a short rail line to privately owned shipping facilities at the mouth of the Sipalay River. A small deposit of gypsum is also under development in the Sipalay area. Domestic gypsum production is significant for the Philippines, as at present, the nation's very important cement industry must import all of its requirements of gypsum. Small quantities of solar-evaporated salt are produced from several salt beds in Antique Province and at Bacolod and Escalante on Negros. The salt production is not sufficient for local regional demands. Mining activities employ 2,000–3,000 workers in the western Visayas.

The employment and income derived from the various industrial activities of the region form a rather important sector of the economy. Primary processing industries include the thirteen sugar centrals, several sawmills and logging operations, the ore concentration mill at Sipalay, hundreds of rice and corn mills, and numerous fish-processing establishments. Additional industrial developments include two large industrial textile mills, a cement plant, several furniture factories, and a well-developed home handicraft textile industry.

The relatively high degree of industrial development in the western Visayas is immediately evidenced by the sight of the many sugar mills. These heavily capitalized factories are not only engaged in the simple conversion of sugarcane to crude centrifugal sugar; but many instances, there are large alcohol distilleries associated with their operations. The larger sugar mills are usually complete with company-owned town, company-financed elementary schools, churches, doctors, hospital facilities, and a company commissary. Tens of thousands of workers are employed in the region's sugar-milling industry. In addition to the many thousands of seasonal workers, there are the large overhead administrative, maintenance, and research staffs. During the main milling season the whole sugar area takes on the bustling atmosphere of a prosperous industrial community.

Much of this is also true of the region's lumber industry. Most of the logging operations are located in Negros Occidental, and this province alone accounts for 6.5 percent of the nation's sawmilling capacity in its eighteen sawmills. The large Insular Lumber Company operations at Fabrica, Sagay, in northern Negros, is reported to be one of the largest hardwood sawmills in the tropics. Several thousand workers are employed in logging and sawmills. Most of the region's sawmills produce both for Philippine and foreign markets.

Most of the fish processing is carried on as a kind of home industry, but fish salting, drying, and processing is of extraregional significance in northern Panay and Negros, and adds to the regional income.

Industrial textiles are a rather recent addition to the industrial economy of Negros. There are two large textile factories, one located at Ma-ao and the other at Binalbagan, which are engaged in the manufacture of sacks from locally grown and imported jute fibers. The entire output of bags is used by the Negros sugar industry, and the demand has still not been satisfied. Handicraft textiles have had a long and distinguished history on Panay, particularly in and around the city of Iloilo. Piña cloth and jusi cloth are beautiful fabrics that have been woven from pineapple fibers traditionally in Iloilo. Unfortunately these cloths, as has been the case with most handwoven materials, have suffered from the competition of cheaper, machine-produced cottons, cotton prints, and synthetics, and today the traditional fabrics are produced mainly for a luxury market.

In general, the highway and road networks of the western Visayan region are well above national standards, both in terms of their total length and the generally high quality of the roads. The road network of western Negros is especially good. Everywhere the western plains are served by good, all-weather roads, and the National Highway, much of it concrete-surfaced, traverses the island's periphery from the Tablas Plateau in the south, around the northern end of the island to the Occidental-Oriental Negros provincial boundary. Most important towns of Negros Occidental are closely spaced along the road and can be reached easily from one another. The island is crossed by three roads; La Castellaña is connected with Vallehermosa, and roads will soon cross the Tablas Plateau to Bayawan and from Kabankalan to Bais. Only the small towns in more remote sections of the Tablas Plateau lack adequate road connections. The privately owned, narrow-gauge railroads of the sugar centrals, and those of the Insular Lumber Company, provide supplementary, special-purpose land transport. The coastal road system of Panay—Highways 1 and 2—is of poor quality in many sections, particularly along the west coast of the island of Antique. Interior Panay is served by Highway 3, which connects Iloilo with Roxas City in the north. The tracks of the Philippine Railroad Company parallel this latter highway. A dense network of secondary roads serves the Iloilo Basin; other areas on Panay are poorly provided with overland connections.

The coasts of Panay and Negros are not deeply embayed and there are few good natural harbors. Iloilo, a custom-staffed port open to foreign shipping, has the finest port and harbor facilities in the region. Busy interisland ports are located at Port Capiz (Roxas City), Ibajay, and New Washington in northern Panay, San Jose de Buenavista in the west, and Estancia in the northeast. Western and northern Negros are completely devoid of natural harbors. The ports of Sagay, Victorias, Mambaguid, Banago, Pontevedra, Hinigaran, and Himamaylan are merely open roadsteads located off the mouths of rivers where sugar or lumber can be transshipped from lighters in fair weather. Pulupandan is the busiest port in western Negros, serving as the terminus of regular ferry service from Iloilo. There are several good harbors in southwestern Negros, but they lie in areas not yet developed economically, for example, at Asia and Campomanes bays.

Iloilo is the premier city of the western Visayas, serving as the center for its region in much the same fashion as does Cebu for the central Visayan area. The dominant role Iloilo has played in the economy of its trade hinterland is being challenged, however, by the rapid growth of the city of Bacolod across Guimaras Strait on Negros Island. Situated at the mouth of the Jaro River where it empties into Iloilo Strait, the site of the city of Iloilo was a natural choice for early development. By 1688, Iloilo had become the capital of Iloilo Province, which at that time included all of Panay and much of Negros. In 1855 the port of Iloilo was one of the earliest Philippine ports opened to foreign trade. The port and city received their greatest development during the late nineteenth and early twentieth centuries, largely as a result of commercial sugarcane developments on nearby Negros. As no suitable port or harbor facilities existed on Negros, Iloilo transshipped the cargoes from, or destined for, Negros; however, with the inevitable development of

shipping facilities on Negros, and increasing efficiency of lightering procedures, much of the Negros trade now bypasses the port of Iloilo. Nevertheless, the port of Iloilo continues to service a very rich rice-, sugar-, and
fish-producing hinterland on the island of Panay. The protected harbor of
Iloilo is provided by Iloilo Strait, which lies between Panay and Guimaras
Island. The deepwater port facilities are located along the strait, and
shallow-draft interisland vessels use the quay wharfage along the lower course
of the Jaro River. Iloilo is connected by rail with central and northern Panay,
and a good network of roads links Iloilo with all of the important towns on
the island. Iloilo is the center for a rather large home-textile industry,
particularly for piña and jusi cloth, and also is an important furniture-
manufacturing center. The city's population, which grew very rapidly until
the 1930's, has since grown much more slowly. In 1960 the population within
the chartered city limits of Iloilo was 150,000.

Bacolod, the capital city of Negros Occidental Province since 1890, is the
second-largest city in the western Visayas. In spite of the fact that it lacks
adequate port and harbor facilities, the city has experienced a continual
growth as the principal commercial and financial center for the large Negros
sugar industry. Bacolod is connected with most points in the province by an
excellent all-weather road system, much of which is concrete-paved. The
paving is financed by sugar revenues. Within the city are located the offices of
the numerous firms that cater to the sugarcane planters and sugar-mill
operators, such as farm-implement sales offices, fertilizer dealers, insurance
firms, and shipping offices, as well as the headquarters of the Planters'
Association, an association representing most of the large sugar-hacienda
owners, and the Sugar Exchange offices. Bacolod is a city of beautiful homes,
for many of the wealthy sugarcane planters maintain large residential
mansions in Bacolod, where they live with their families, commuting to their
haciendas during critical crop periods. In 1960 Bacolod had a population of
119,000 persons.

Roxas City is the principal commercial center for northern Panay, as
well as serving as the capital of Capiz Province. The city is situated along the
lower course of the Panay River, which is no longer navigable. Most of the
seaborne commerce is carried on at the outport of Port Capiz. Roxas City is
the terminus of the railroad from Iloilo. The city had a population of 14,000
persons in 1960.

The town of Fabrica, a large barrio within the municipality of Sagay in
northern Negros, is an interesting and rather exceptional Philippine barrio.
Fabrica is almost wholly an industrial community. Within the town are
located the administrative, milling, drying, and loading facilities of the largest

sawmill in the Philippines, and in addition, there is a large sugar central, with its associated distillery, several lumberyards and woodworking shops, and various service establishments. Fabrica is located along the Himuga-an River, approximately 7 miles above the river mouth. Lumber and sugar are lightered down the river, across the river bar, and loaded on overseas vessels standing offshore. In 1960, Fabrica had a population of approximately 9,000 persons.

The western Visayan region is highly urbanized, by Philippine standards, and the province of Negros Occidental is exceptionally so. Commercial agriculture appears to be largely responsible for the high degree of urbanization. Among the many lesser urban centers are: Binalbagan, Victorias, La Carlota, Talisay, Hinigaran, and Silay on Negros, and President Roxas on Panay. These are busy commercial towns that center around large centrifugal sugar mills. Most of these towns had poblaciones with 10,000–20,000 persons in 1960. Escalante, Toboso, and Cadiz on Negros, and Estancia and New Washington on Panay, are important fishing towns with populations of approximately 5,000. Kalibo, the capital of Aklan Province, and San Jose, the capital of Antique, combine important commercial services with their administrative functions.

THIRTEEN

~~~~~ *The Southern Country:*
Mindanao and Sulu

An Introduction to the Southern Philippines

The southern Philippines—those land areas lying south of about latitude 10°
and extending to within 4° 38′ north of the equator—is composed of two
major geographic units: the large island of Mindanao and surrounding
islands, and the numerous islands of the Sulu Archipelago. Actually the
southern Philippine realm consists of nearly 2,000 islands and islets of which
only 1,100 are named and only 116 have land areas exceeding one square
mile. This southern macroregion includes a land area of slightly more than
39,000 square miles, some 36,500 square miles of which falls on the large
main island of Mindanao. Thus, nearly 34 percent of the total Philippine
land surface is located in the south. On the other hand, the total population
of this macroregion, nearly 5.7 million persons in 1960, represents only 20
percent of the total Philippine population.

The population of the southern Philippines includes almost all of the
Moslem element of the Philippine population which, in the southern area,
constituted approximately 23 percent of the total population in 1960 (fig. 26a).
The Moslem Filipinos form the dominant socioreligious group in the
traditional Moslem provinces of Sulu and Lanao del Sur, and they constitute
important minority groups in the provinces of Cotabato and the two
Zamboangas. Pagan groups represent about 5 percent of the Mindanao
population.[1] Subanum, Manobo, Bukidnon, Bilaan, Tiruray, and other tribal

groups are thinly scattered in the more inaccessible forest lands on the island of Mindanao. Christian Filipinos are relative newcomers to the southern Philippines except along the north coast of Mindanao; however, so great have been their recent migrations, particularly during the twentieth century, that they now constitute 67.7 percent of the population.[2] Christians outnumber other religious groups througout the southern Philippines except in the two Moslem-dominated provinces.

Much of the distinctive character of Mindanao and the Sulus is due to their role as the meeting ground for the culturally diverse peoples of Moslem, Christian, and pagan faiths. Mindanao is nearly comparable in size to Luzon. Comparisons between these two largest islands of the Philippines show several marked geographic differences, as well as numerous points of similarity. Both of the islands contain extensive mountain systems; however, those on Mindanao generally are neither as high nor as continuous as those on Luzon, although they are much more complex geologically. Whereas Mindanao possesses the highest Philippine elevation on Mount Apo at 9,690 feet, Mount Pulog in northern Luzon is but a few feet lower at 9,606 feet. Both islands contain extensive lowlands and both support several major river systems. Vulcanism has played an important role in forming the landscapes of Luzon and Mindanao. Both islands have long and deeply embayed coastlines, with numerous large peninsulas and protected bays.

Mindanao and the Sulu Archipelago, however, have undergone a historical evolution very different from that of the rest of the Philippines. There has been a greater exposure on Mindanao to cultural currents emanating from Indonesia, and at the same time, relative isolation from the cultures that have been active in the central and northern Philippines. Except for the lengthy exposure of the northern coastal strip of Mindanao to Spanish cultural contacts, and the limited amount of influence surrounding the small Spanish fortress settlements at Dapitan and Zamboanga on Zamboanga Peninsula, and at Iligan, Cagayan de Oro, and Caraga, Spain was never able to control Mindanao effectively. As a result, Mindanao did not share proportionately in the cultural and economic development of the Philippines during the three hundred years of Spanish administration. The island remained geographically isolated and insulated from the rest of the Philippines, and even with the partial breakdown of isolation in the twentieth century, the interior land could be reached only by trails. Even now the transportation system of Mindanao is, by all standards, inadequte for the size and population of the island. Isolation gave to the Moslem and pagan populations an additional three hundred years in which to develop and solidify their cultures; particularly in the case of the Moslems, this was time in which to develop and strengthen from within those qualities with which they could resist later encroachments by migrant Christians. And most importantly, in the national sense, the lands of Mindanao remained relatively sparsely populated, in sharp contrast to the rapid "filling up" of many of the attractive lowland areas on Luzon and in the Visayan Islands. Only the north coast of Mindanao lay open to cultural and demographic influences emanating from the rest of the Philippines, and as a result, the culture and economy characteristic of this northern coastal strip are scarcely distinguishable from those of the central Visayan area.

Many of the deterrents to settlement and economic development which have operated on Mindanao in the past have, within recent years, been eliminated, or at least their influences have been lessened. The weakening or removal of these deterrents has acted as a tremendous stimulus to increased settlement, and contributed to an ever-increasing willingness on the part of the Mindanao residents to participate in national political and economic arenas. However, the removal of many of the obstacles to settlement and economic development have not been without attendant problems. The island of Mindanao has long been viewed and, unfortunately, continues to be viewed by most Filipinos as possessing vast expanses of empty arable land awaiting settlement. It is true that the island's overall average density of population reaches only two-thirds that of the national density. Furthermore, until World War II the population of Mindanao had expanded at a rate only slightly above that of the national increase. Since the 1948 census enumeration, however, the population of Mindanao has increased by well over a million new settlers, a population increment of one million beyond that to be expected by the excess of births over deaths. Whereas Mindanao contained only 8 percent of the national population at the dawn of the twentieth century, a figure that was probably somewhat underenumerated, by 1960 this proportion had increased to 19 percent. Most of this large and rapid population increase resulted from a massive voluntary migration, coming mainly from the overcrowded islands of the Visayan area, particularly from the islands of Cebu, Panay, Bohol, and Negros.

Although still carrying a pioneer-like atmosphere into most facets of its physical and cultural landscapes, the island of Mindanao can no longer be viewed as a limitless "Eldorado." Already the more favorably located and topographically suitable areas on the island support a considerable density of settlement. Although large areas on Mindanao are still available for future settlement, these must be viewed as having finite limits that will be reached and passed in the very near future, perhaps within a decade, if the present levels of migration continue. Furthermore, the recent patterns of settlement on Mindanao, with large blocks of land ending in single ownership, suggest the possibilities of developing land-tenure conditions reminiscent of those that continue to plague central Luzon.

Nevertheless, in broad economic assessment Mindanao continues to offer a rather respectable resource base. Dense tropical rain forests still cover large sections of the island, although their continuity is interrupted increasingly by broad expanses of cultivated fields, caingin clearings, and cogonales. Occurrences of elevated coral reef formation, various other calcareous materials, and considerable recent volcanic ash are extensive and widespread, and all of these parent materials, under proper circumstances, can contribute to a relatively fertile soil base. The climate in most parts of the island is humid, with abundant rains that show little seasonality. Most of the farmers are little concerned with the adequacy of its rainfall, although in a few isolated locales, such as at the head of Sarangani Bay, at the southern tip of Zamboanga Peninsula, and along sections of the north coast, there are precipitation regimes that seasonally approach dryland conditions. Winds of destructive intensity are rare. Mineral deposits are varied, of fair quality, and occur in amounts attractive for exploitation. Coal, copper, gold, chromite, manganese, and particularly iron ore, are present in relative abundance. The hydroelectric potential of the Mindanao rivers is estimated at nearly one million kilowatts, an amount equivalent to approximately 57 percent of the total Philippine hydroelectric potential.[3]

Although the island of Mindanao and the smaller islands of the Sulu Archipelago possess a number of elements of cultural homogeneity, three rather clearly distinguishable cultural regions have formed in the southern Philippines: (1) a narrow, densely settled Christian Filipino lowland area along the north coast; (2) a recent, predominately Christian Filipino pioneer settlement in the interior, east, and south of Mindanao; and (3) a Moslem-dominated western area, particularly in Lanao del Sur, Zamboanga del Sur, and the Sulus. However, certain physical geographic considerations, with attendant economic implications, dictate the finer geographic subdivision of the southern Philippines into six major regions on the island of Mindanao, and a seventh region that embraces the islands of the Sulu Archipelago. A narrow strip of densely settled lowlands located along the north coast constitutes the northern Mindanao region. The eastern Mindanao region is composed of a narrow, sparsely populated lowland coastal fringe, together with the Diuata Mountains and Pacific Cordillera, which lie immediately back of the eastern coastal strip. The Davao-Agusan Lowland region consists of a long, narrow structural trough sandwiched between the Pacific Cordillera and the ranges of central Mindanao. The southwestern Mindanao region includes the broad valley of the Rio Grande de Mindanao, several reentrant valleys, and the bordering Tiruray Highlands. All of the southwestern lowlands have been the targets for several recent large-scale government resettlement projects. The Bukidnon-Lanao Plateau region consists of an extensive 2,000-foot-high tableland that occupies the interior of the island in the north. The long, narrow, mountainous Zamboanga Peninsula region continues the island of Mindanao almost 150 miles southwestward to meet the Sulu Archipelago. The Sulu region, an archipelago of nearly 1,000 islands of medium to small size located in the extreme southwestern corner of the Philippine Archipelago, provides two discontinuous land bridges, leading from Mindanao to the larger Indonesian island of Borneo (Kalimantan).

The Visayan Fringe: Northern Mindanao

The northern coast of Mindanao is the region of densest settlement and the one with which the Spanish administration had its longest contacts and greatest influence. The proximity of the north coast of Mindanao to the central Visayan Islands and their people, combined with the strong similarities in landform and climate, have created a landscape along the north coast of Mindanao which is remarkably similar to that associated with the central Visayan area, and quite dissimilar from the remainder of Mindanao. Heavy population pressures, close Visayan ethnolinguistic ties, and similar crops and cropping patterns serve to heighten the Visayan-like character of northern Mindanao, and further set the north coast apart from the rest of the island. Whereas the remainder of Mindanao has a population that is generally characteristic of most pioneer areas—younger in age and strongly male-dominated—the population of northern Mindanao is slightly older and possesses a more equal number of females and males. Economically, the ties of the north coast are oriented away from trade centers on Mindanao and focus toward the premier Visayan commercial center of Cebu.

The narrow strip of coastal lowlands and bordering band of low foothills seldom exceeds 15 miles in width, except at the head of Panguil Bay in the municipalities of Kapatagan and Lala. The coastal lowlands extend from the Misamis Occidental–Zamboanga del Norte provincial boundary through coastal Misamis Occidental, Lanao del Norte, and Misamis Oriental eastward to the latter's boundary with Agusan province. The offshore island of Camiguin, which is administratively part of Misamis Oriental Province, also is included within the north coast region. The northern Mindanao region, thus constituted, includes a land area of approximately 2,800 square miles and in 1960 supported a population of nearly 873,000 persons.

THE PHYSICAL SETTING

Physiographically, northern Mindanao possesses a narrow coastal plain that averages only one to two miles in width and is absent along many sections of the coast. There are several narrow river floodplains that wind back toward the Bukidnon-Lanao Plateau escarpment. Behind the coastal plain and floodplains lie the foothills and lower slopes of the plateau escarpment. These units make up the physical landscape of the region. The coastal lowlands have been formed either as narrow coastal plains, in which limestone, sandstone, conglomerate, and other marine sediments are the dominant rock materials, or as small delta lands at the mouths of the numerous fast-flowing rivers. The larger and more important lowland areas lie along the Cugmen, Cagayan, Iponon, Rawan, and Liangan rivers. The hill lands, which accompany the coast a short distance inland, are composed mainly of Tertiary sediments. Further inland, and actually located outside of the region, the higher uplands of the Bukidnon-Lanao Plateau are composed largely of volcanics and undifferentiated metamorphic rocks, such as slate, schist, gneiss, and quartzite. The coastal lowlands attain their greatest width in southern Misamis Occidental and Lanao del Norte, where a low isthmus some 15 miles in width at the head of Panguil Bay provided the land connection between the main mass of the island of Mindanao and mountainous Zamboanga Peninsula (fig. 72). Important, but smaller areas of lowland are located at the heads of Macajalar and Gingoog bays. The nearly circular-shaped island of Camiguin in the Mindanao Sea is wholly volcanic in origin. Mount Hibokhibok (Catarman), located in the northwestern corner of the 96-square-mile island, is an active volcano whose explosive eruptions in 1951 rained death upon nearly 2,000 Camigueños and brought about a mass emigration from the island.

The physiographic environment of the northern Mindanao region offers a rather restrictive habitat to human occupance; lowland areas suitable for agriculture are at a premium, and the steep slopes and shallow soils of the adjacent uplands restrict agricultural expansion. Nor can one view the climatic conditions prevailing throughout most of this northern coast as other than restrictive to a productive agricultural occupance. If one can speak of a typical central-Visayan climate (see pages 445 and 446), one in which there is a long drought period in the spring months and relatively low annual precipitation, then northern Mindanao has this type of climate. Throughout the region, excepting a few more exposed locations, such as along the southeastern coast of Misamis Occidental and at the head of Panguil Bay, annual rainfalls range between 50 and 70 inches. This limited rainfall is distributed so that the period of maximum rains occurs during the summer and fall months and a rather severe drought season occupies the months of February, March, and April. The presence of porous limestone-derived soils in many parts of the region serves to heighten the effects of the climatic drought by creating a condition susceptible to severe edaphic drought. In essence, the climate and

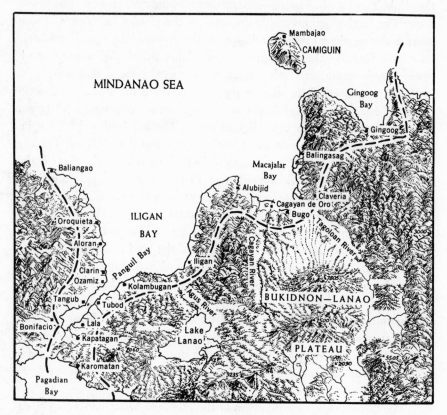

Fig. 72. Physiography of the northern Mindanao region.

conditions of soil moisture in northern Mindanao are practically the same as those experienced over the island of Cebu and in eastern Negros. Unfortunately most of the rivers of northern Mindanao are short with highly seasonal flows and are not suited for irrigation. Thus, the dry climatic conditions prevalent in the region cannot be alleviated by recourse to irrigation. The agriculture of most of northern Mindanao generally is restricted to the cultivation of a single crop within the span of one year, and in most cases, even this one crop must be carefully selected so as to be tolerant of the drier edaphic conditions. The lowlands at the head of Panguil Bay and along the

Misamis Occidental coast, on the other hand, benefit from exposures to both northeastern and southwestern seasonal air streams; that is, the latter can enter through the low saddle between Panguil and Pagadian bays. These areas receive rainfall that is more evenly distributed and in much greater quantity than elsewhere in the region. Clarin, in Misamis Occidental, receives an average annual precipitation of 208 inches.

Many of the soils of the coastal lowlands are derived from limestones, sandstones, and limey shales. The soils on the island of Camiguin, and of most of the lands lying adjacent to the plateau of northern Mindanao, are derived from thoroughly decayed volcanic materials. The soils are predominantly clays or clay loams. In general, their fertility is relatively high, although long and continued use and abuse of the land has robbed the soils of much of their inherent fertility. Accelerated soil erosion is evident everywhere and has been particularly encouraged by the removal of much of the original forest cover on the steeply sloping hills and escarpment land.

Virtually all of the original dense tropical rain-forest cover of northern Mindanao has been cleared from the lowlands and foothills in order to bring as much land as possible under cultivation. Where the cleared areas have not been cultivated permanently much of the land has regenerated in poor secondary forest growth or cogonales. Only two areas of mature commercial forest growth remain in the region. Commercial forests are found in western Lanao del Norte along the eastern shores of Panguil Bay, and at the head of Gingoog Bay in eastern Misamis Oriental. The richness of the forest resource in these two areas is attested by the presence of several large logging and sawmilling operations. Some of the finest forest timber in Mindanao is found at these two locations. Large reserves of dense commercial forests occupy much of the interior lands, and although located outside the region, these forest are accessible to the coast operations. Almon, apitong, bagtikan, kalunti, lanapua, tangile, and red and white lauans are the more common commercial timber species of northern Mindanao. Cogonales are not extensive in the region except in the foothill belt because land is at such a premium that extensive grasslands have not been permitted.

All in all, the physical environment of northern Mindanao has not been one that encourages a prosperous agricultural occupance, but since the physical conditions present in northern Mindanao are very similar to those found in much of the central Visayan area, the north coast has long been a favored migration target for peoples from the overcrowded islands of the Visayan group. Ease of accessibility has played an important role in facilitating these migrations, for the waters of the relatively narrow Mindanao Sea are all that separate the two areas.

THE CULTURAL SETTING

The most distinctive regional characteristic of northern Mindanao is supplied by its population. Along the north coast one is scarcely conscious that he is on the pioneer island of Mindanao, for the language, dialects, and religion, the numbers and densities of people, the age and sex composition of the population, and the whole gamut of demographic characteristics bespeak of a more mature and stable society than is typical of the island generally. People of central Visayan ethnolinguistic stock form an overwhelming majority of the northern Mindanao population. In 1960 Cebuano-speaking Filipinos, representing homelands in Cebu, Bohol, and eastern Negros, constituted 97 percent of the population of Misamis Occidental and 96 percent of the population of Misamis Oriental, and although long outnumbered by the Maranao-speaking Moslems in the old province of Lanao, they have rapidly increased their numbers in the north coast municipalities.[4] With the division of Lanao into two provinces in 1959, the northern municipalities were constituted as the province of Lanao del Norte in which Cebuano-speaking people make up 80 percent of the population and Christians outnumbered Moslems by a ratio of 4 to 1. Lanao del Sur retained an overwhelmingly Moslem population. Northern Mindanao is the most Hispanicized region of Mindanao. Roman Catholicism is strong almost everywhere, reflecting the rather close ties with which the Spanish maintained their control. These controls were especially strong and of long duration in Misamis Oriental Province where the settlement of Cagayan de Oro became an important mission station early in the seventeenth century.[5] Misamis (Ozamiz) and Iligan were early Spanish fortress settlements. The pan-Filipino catholicism movement, as represented in the Aglipayan, or Philippine Independent Church, also is quite strong in northern Mindanao and is particularly important in Misamis Occidental where the faith is followed by almost one-quarter of the population as compared to approximately 5 percent Aglipayans in the nation as a whole (fig. 26b). Small Moslem communities are found in Lanao del Norte, especially in the municipalities that lie away from the coast. Molsems are almost completely absent in the two Misamis provinces.

The density of settlement and the sex and age structure of the population contribute additional cultural elements that heighten the similarities between northern Mindanao and the central Visayas, and set the region apart from the rest of Mindanao. The arithmetic density of settlement along the north coast is nearly 50 percent higher than for the Philippines as a whole, and densities in northern Mindanao approximate those of the relatively crowded provinces of Albay and Ilocos Sur on Luzon, that is, approximately

300–310 persons per square mile of total area. Physiological densities also are high, although they stand only slightly higher than the national level. Nevertheless, one must keep in mind that the cultivated lands of northern Mindanao have rather severe environmental limitations, such as steep slopes, serious erosion, and unfavorable climatic conditions. The sex-ratio structure of the population of northern Mindanao is further evidence of the maturity of occupance. Generally in most newly settled areas males predominate overwhelmingly, and so they do in the frontier provinces of Mindanao; however, the ratio of males over females in the three provinces of northern Mindanao range between 101 and 107, as compared with male ratios of 117, 112, and 111 in Lanao del Sur, Cotabato, and Davao, respectively. Similarly, whereas a young population is normally thought to be characteristic of pioneer area, as it is throughout much of Mindanao, in the northern region the population is significantly older; a mean age of fifteen years in Bukidnon, Cotabato, and Davao can be compared with an age of sixteen years in the north coast region.

This north coastal strip also stands in sharp contrast to the rest of the island in terms of the population changes that have occurred through recent migrations. With the exception of the expanding industrial complex in the vicinity of the city of Iligan and the new agricultural areas in coastal Lanao del Norte, the regional population gain has failed to keep pace with the national increase. Whereas the Philippine population between 1948 and 1960 was increasing 41 percent, and that of the island of Mindanao increased by 87 percent, the population of Misamis Occidental grew by only 20 percent, and that of Misamis Oriental by a scant 5 percent. Only coastal Lanao del Norte reversed the trend of the region and expanded its population at a rate well above the national figure (105 percent). The large population increases in Lanao del Norte were encouraged by the development of the Maria Cristina Falls power complex and the several new settlement areas in the far west. A large number of north coastal people have emigrated to Zamboanga del Sur and nearby areas of interior Mindanao in Bukidnon. From Misamis Oriental the main streams of migration have been to Bukidnon and Cotaboto provinces, whereas the majority of the out-migrants from Misamis Occidental moved into neighboring sections of the Zamboanga Peninsula, particularly into the municipalities of Molave, Aurora, Tukuran, and Pagadian in eastern Zamboanga del Norte.[6] The out-migration of people from the north coast of Mindanao has not been uniform. The greatest percentage loss occurred on the offshore island of Camiguin where continued threats of volcanic eruption stimulated the exodus of large numbers of people. The population of Camiguin actually decreased by 25,000 persons, or 36 percent, between 1948 and 1960. The densely settled coast adjacent to the island of Camiguin, and the sparsely populated, rough interior lands in Claveria municipality, also experienced absolute decreases of population, although these were not as marked as on Camiguin. Conversely, most of the settlements located along Macajalar and Gingoog bays experienced an increase of population which exceeded the national average. The increase was particularly notable in the vicinity of the major regional urban center of Cagayan de Oro where an increase of nearly 70 percent occurred during the twelve intercensal years. None of the coastal municipalities of Lanao del Norte suffered any population decreases. Quite the contrary! The booming industrial complex near the city of Iligan and the rapid settlement of the agricultural lands in Kapatagan resulted in very rapid population increases. In Kapatagan municipality the large population increases between 1948 and 1960 necessitated the creation of the new municipality of Karomatan. Although no municipality in Misamis Occidental recorded an actual decline in population during the last intercensal period, the municipalities of Baliangao, Bonifacio, Clarin, and Tangub experienced virtual stagnation of their populations at 1948 levels, and in the province only the municipality of Aloran experienced a population growth in excess of the national average. The increase of population in Aloran was largely the result of the opening of new agricultural lands in the interior of the municipality.

In general, the population of the north coast of Mindanao is a coastal population, either living within one or two miles of the coast, or extending inland only where there are small floodplains (fig. 73). Most of the area located back of the coastal lowlands is sparsely settled, although what little population growth has occurred in the two Misamis provinces has taken place in this zone.

There is a relatively strong tendency for the population of northern Mindanao to congregate in urban centers. Within the provinces of Misamis Oriental and Lanao del Norte the actual percentage of the population living in poblaciones greater than 2,500 reached nearly 20 percent in 1960, a situation that is not unique on Mindanao except that there are no really large cities along the north coast to compare with the cities of Davao and Zamboanga. The two most important urban centers are Cagayan de Oro and Iligan. Cagayan de Oro, which has had a very long existence as a center of major industrial development, is the principal regional trade center for the entire north coast of Mindanao, as well as for northern sections of Bukidnon. Cagayan is the principal port for the north coast, the capital of Misamis Oriental Province, and a commercial and transportation center of considerable importance. With an urban population of nearly 25,000 in 1960, it ranked a poor third in size among the major cities in Mindanao. The city has occupied its present site along the right bank of the Cagayan River near the

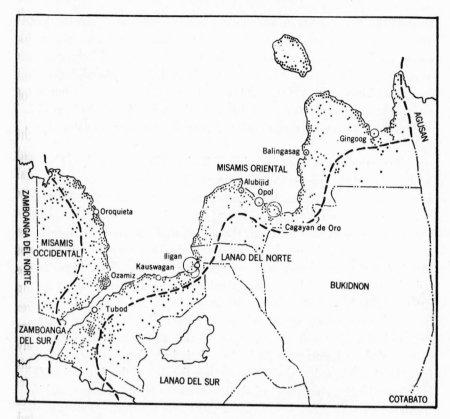

Fig. 73. The distribution of population in the northern Mindanao region, 1960.

head of Macajalar Bay since 1624. Across the river from the city proper is the satellite residential community of Carmen with a population of 4,000. Two miles downstream and at the mouth of the river is the outport of Julaojulao where there are deepwater port facilities for foreign and domestic shipping. The importance of Cagayan as a transportation center is strengthened by the fact that the city provides the only transportation window for the landlocked province of Bukidnon. Most of the commerce destined for Bukidnon passes through Cagayan. The city provides financial, administrative, and customs services for the five provinces of Agusan, Bukidnon, Misamis Oriental, Misamis Occidental, and Lanao del Norte. Through the port of Cagayan move large quantities of rice and corn which are produced within the Cagayan hinterland and are destined for the food-deficit areas of Manila and Cebu. Cagayan also serves as a port of export for substantial shipments of copra. Nearby, at Bugo are the wharf and cannery facilities of the Del Monte pineapple operations (Philippine Packing Corporation), and Cagayan functions as the main financial and trade center for this large export-oriented commercial enterprise. The Cagayan International Airport is the major airport on Mindanao from which feeder flights by DC-3 and lighter aircraft reach to all points on the island. Several times daily scheduled flights link Cagayan with Manila, Cebu, and Davao. In spite of its relatively important trade and transportation functions, however, the city and port of Cagayan fall within the commercial shadow of the central Visayan regional center of Cebu.

Iligan, the second city of northern Mindanao, is situated along the right bank of the Iligan River at the river mouth. Two deepwater piers are located adjacent to the city center. Iligan functions as the primary port for coastal Lanao del Norte and the interior lands of Lanao del Sur. Notwithstanding its important transportation function, the principal significance of Iligan stems from the important industrial developments that have occurred within the city during the past decade and are continuing to take place. Iligan is not only the major industrial center for Mindanao but also a rising center for the entire Philippines. The "boomtown" atmosphere of a modern expanding industrial community is very much in evidence at Iligan. Many of the stores are finished with rough siding, many of the streets are dirt, schools are overcrowded, and prices are high. Iligan's industrial growth stems largely from the presence, only a short distance from the city, of the Agus River. This large, even-flowing river rises in Lake Lanao on the interior plateau, and in its course of only 22 miles it makes a descent of 2,296 feet. Along the river course there are seven sites at which hydroelectric power can be generated with a minimum of capital outlay, with a total power potential estimated at 736,000 kilowatts.[7] Site No. 6 at Maria Cristina Falls, one mile above the river mouth, develops a hydraulic head of 507 feet. Here, the National Power Corporation (NPC) has installed two generators with a combined capacity of approximately 50,000 kilowatts. Three more generators are under construction at Site No. 6 with a combined capacity of 150,000 kilowatts of additional power. Several heavy power-consuming industries have located near Iligan and Maria Cristina because of the availability of relatively cheap electric power (around U.S. $0.0025 per kilowatt for industrial users). The National Steel Corporation's (NASSACO) electric furnace steel plant and rolling mill, a large fertilizer plant, a calcium carbide and ferroalloy plant, a flour mill, and a cement plant are now in operation. An integrated steel mill, an aluminum plant, and an additional fertilizer plant are planned for the near future. With the expanding output of low-cost electric energy, it is hoped that the Iligan area will become the "Pittsburgh" of Philippine basic industries. In 1960 the poblacion of Iligan had an urban population estimated at 25,000, although within the chartered city limits were more than 60,000 persons. The population of Iligan City had increased 130 percent in the twelve years preceding 1960.

No other city along the north coast has a population greater than 10,000 persons, and most of the towns have populations of considerably less than 5,000. Two towns stand out as somewhat larger with trade functions of a broader regional character. In the easternmost part of the region is the important logging and sawmilling center of Gingoog, with a population in 1960 of nearly 10,000. At the opposite end of the region along the shores of Panguil Bay in Misamis Occidental is the provincial capital of Ozamiz City, with a 1960 population of slightly less than 9,000 persons. Both of these centers have ports with fairly active seaborne trade, and both serve relatively large intraprovincial trade areas. Alubijid, Balingasag, Oroquieta, Kolambugan, and Kapatagan are among the larger and more important agricultural trade centers, and each had a 1960 population close to 5,000. Balingasag, Oroquieta, and Kolambugan also function as small ports. Oroquieta lies in the center of an important coconut plantation area, whereas Kolambugan is the site of a large sawmill. Alubijid and Balingasag serve as market towns for the surrounding agricultural lands. Kapatagan functions as the principal commercial center for the extensive newly settled areas of western Lanao del Norte. Mambajao, a small town in northeastern Camiguin, serves as that island's chief port and trade center.

All of the municipios along the northern Mindanao coast are served by the National Highway system, although road quality is well below minimum standards. Interregional highway connections are provided eastward along the coast to Butuan and Surigao and toward the west to Dipolog, Dapitan, and Pagadian on the Zamboanga Peninsula. The two interior through roads are the Sayre Highway, which turns inland near Cagayan and winds through Bukidnon Province and into the Cotabato Valley, and a second highway that leads from Iligan via Lake Lanao and Malabang, on the south coast, to Cotabato. There are numerous dirt tracks that lead short distances inland.

ECONOMIC ACTIVITIES

Agriculture is the dominant economic activity in northern Mindanao. Small-scale fishing and forest industries supplement the regional economy to which has been added the very important Maria Cristina industrial development. Each town of the region carries out those services normal to larger agricultural market towns, and is complete with bakeries, corn and rice mills, ice plants, electric power generators, and retail and wholesale outlets.

In its agricultural landscapes, northern Mindanao displays the same close similarity to the central Visayan area that it does in its physical and human environments. Corn occupies a position of considerably more significance than does rice. Northern Mindanao has a rather large deficiency of rice, and these deficiencies can be made up only by substantial and regular shipments from the southern Mindanao provinces of Cotabato and Davao. Most of the region's limited rice acreage is concentrated in western Lanao del Norte and coastal sections of Misamis Occidental. Wherever suitable lands for lowland rice can be found, such as on the floodplains and deltas of the small rivers, this grain is cultivated; however, suitable areas are limited, and so are the rice fields. In general, only one crop of rice is cultivated within a single year, for irrigation water is simply not available. Upland dry rice occupies about the same total area as wet-field rice. Corn, on the other hand, is much more tolerant of local climatic and topographic conditions, and nearly three-fourths of the total area devoted to food crops within the region is in corn. Two, and sometimes even three crops of corn are cultivated on the same fields within a single year. As a consequence, northern Mindanao has become a very large producer of corn and a prime supplier of that grain to Cebu and the central Visayan area.[8] Most of the region's corn surplus is grown in Lanao del Norte Province, particularly in the new agricultural settlement areas in the municipalities of Kapatagan, Lala, and Tubod, although important quantities also originate from the Iligan and Kolambugan areas. There are over one hundred small corn mills scattered throughout the region which process the local-grown corn. Of course corn supplies the bulk of the local diet, another similarity to the central Visayan area which, in part, reflects the strong Cebuano ethnolinguistic background of a majority of the population of northern Mindanao.

Coconuts also are of considerable importance in northern Mindanao, and both Misamis Oriental and Occidental are among the more important copra-producing provinces of the Philippines. There are especially extensive coconut plantings in the municipalities of Clarin, Ozamiz, and Oroquieta in Misamis Occidental and Gingoog in Misamis Oriental. A large coconut-oil mill and desiccated-coconut factory is located at Oroquieta. Most of the copra and desiccated coconut produced in northern Mindanao moves to Cebu awaiting overseas shipment.

Although as a region northern Mindanao does not bulk large in total Philippine timber production, it does possess two large logging and sawmilling operations. One is at Gingoog and the other is at Kolambugan in Lanao del Norte. Both operations represent corporate organizations, large capital investments, and daily sawmill capacities of 50,000 to 100,000 board feet. There are several smaller sawmills scattered through interior Misamis Occidental and in coastal sections of Misamis Oriental and Lanao del Norte. The region produces more than sufficient lumber to meet the regional consumption needs, and large quantities move to Cebu and Manila for consumption or export, or are shipped directly overseas from small company-owned piers near the sawmills.

Fishing is of local importance only. The relatively rich waters of the Mindanao Sea provide a good fishing ground, but fishing operations are not well-developed and fish supplies are insufficient for regional demands. The narrow extent of the coastal plain and lack of extensive estuarine areas have prevented the extensive development of fishponds. Much of the incoming freight received at the port of Cagayan is represented by shipments of fish and fish products, as fish is the most important inbound food commodity. The ports of Zamboanga and Cebu are the main suppliers of fish for northern Mindanao.

Another Far Coast: Eastern Mindanao

The eastern cordilleran lands, and the small, isolated plains along the Pacific shores of Mindanao constitute one of the least developed regions on the island of Mindanao. Uplands occupy more than 85 percent of the region, and lowlands are confined to a few small river estuaries and delta lands at the heads of Pujada, Cateel, Bislig, Lianga, and Lanuza bays, at the northern end of graben-like Lake Mainit, and on several of the islands lying off the northeastern coast. Where arable land is present, it is usually cultivated in subsistence crops or devoted to coconut plantings. Elsewhere, unless there are deposits of minerals or commercial forests present, the eastern coast of Mindanao is devoid of people. Roads are few and of very poor quality. Overland connections to the main highway system of Mindanao are restricted to three routes. Eastern Mindanao has failed to participate in the large population increases that have typified many areas of the island of Mindanao in the twentieth century.

The eastern Mindanao region includes all of the old province of Surigao, which is now divided into Surigao del Norte and Surigao del Sur, five municipalities in eastern Davao, and a narrow strip of eastern Agusan province (figs. 74, 75). The 4,600 square miles of eastern Mindanao supported a population of approximately 444,000 persons in 1960.

THE PHYSICAL SETTING

The Pacific Cordillera extends for 250 miles along the eastern coast of Mindanao. The western side of this highland system terminates abruptly at a major fault line, the Philippine Rift, which lies along the eastern side of the Davao-Agusan Trough. The eastern flanks of the cordillera slope less abruptly

Fig. 74. Physiography of northeastern Mindanao.

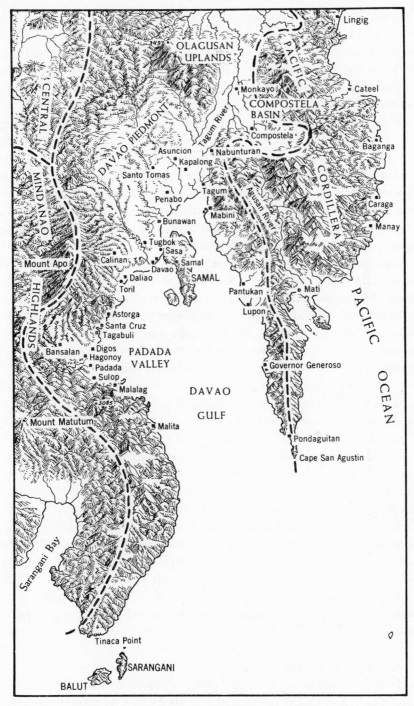

Fig. 75. Physiography of southeastern Mindanao.

into the Pacific Ocean; however, close offshore is the very steep descent into the Philippine Trough. The whole of the east coast of Mindanao appears as a drowned coastline that is island-fringed and deeply embayed, with small river deltas at the head of each bay. The Pacific Cordillera consists of two high, rugged mountain systems in the north and south, connected in the center by a series of low hills. The highest elevations in the Pacific Cordillera are reached in the south on Mount Tagdalit at 9,219 feet. Mount Hilonghilong, at 6,599 feet, is the highest peak in the northern highlands. There are two low passes through the central hill section; one is located behind Lianga Bay and the other is in back of Bislig Bay. The highlands are composed mainly of basement-complex materials, generally diorites, gabbros, basalts, and andesites, overlaid by a thin veneer of Tertiary sediments and volcanics. The structure of the Pacific Cordillera is essentially that of a fault-block mountain system, gently tilted toward the east. In the northern part of the highlands is a small graben that is occupied by Lake Mainit, the 52-square-mile, fourth largest lake in the Philippines. Lake Mainit is situated at an elevation of 82 feet and is drained southward by the Tubay River into Butuan Bay. A small horst closes off Lake Mainit from the Mindanao Sea to the west. The offshore islands of Dinagat, Siargao, Bucas Grande, and the several score smaller islands extend north and east of Surigao Peninsula, continuing the eastern cordilleran structures into Surigao Strait and Leyte Gulf.

None of the lowlands along the eastern coast exceeds 200 square miles in area. The largest plain lies behind Lianga Bay. Smaller lowlands, with areas of approximately 100 square miles each, are found at the heads of Pujada, Cateel, Bislig, and Lanuza bays, and north of the Lake Mainit area.

The whole of eastern Mindanao is swept by moist winds from the northeast during the months from early November through April or May. Rainfall amounts are very high everywhere except in the Pujada Bay area, averaging between 100 and 200 inches annually. Mati, somewhat sheltered from northeast and southeast air currents, receives only 55 inches annually. The rainfall maximums occur during the cooler months, although summers are by no means dry. Strong winds and typhoons are relatively rare. The slopes of the Pacific Cordillera are covered with a dense high-value dipterocarp forest. Almon, apitong, guijo, tangile, and white lauan, together with valuable stands of lanipau, mancono, red lauan, and sudiang, are found in abundance.

THE CULTURAL SETTING

The relative sparsity of settlement along the eastern coast of Mindanao cannot be laid to apathy on the part of early Spanish administration. Gold, the prime incentive to Spanish colonization in many other parts of the world, was present in limited quantities in the northern cordilleran lands of eastern Mindanao. Furthermore, the Jesuit mission settlement at Caraga in present-day Davao Province, which was founded in 1591, was the earliest Spanish-settled point on Mindanao. It appears that the natural limitations of eastern Mindanao—limited arable land, dense and virtually impenetrable tropical rain forests, and difficulties of mineral extraction—discouraged large-scale development or settlement then, as they do now. Instead, the regional population grew at a rate very nearly approximating the growth rate of the Philippines, and well below that of the rest of Mindanao. Even in the intercensal years 1948–1960 when the population of Mindanao was growing at a rate considerably in excess of that of the Philippine population as a whole, the eastern Mindanao region failed to keep pace with the national level. Several of the eastern Mindanao municipalities either lost population or were barely able to maintain their population totals even in the period from 1948 to 1960, as for example, Cantilan, Bacuag, Lanuza, and Tagana-an. On the other hand, in those few areas where a favorable resource base was present, such as at Bislig, Lingig, and Mati, the growth rates were double or triple the national figure. Generally the faster-growing areas reflected accessible mineral or forest resources. At present the pattern of population distribution in eastern Mindanao shows relatively dense settlement patterns on the offshore island of Siargao, on Surigao Peninsula in the vicinity of the city of Surigao and immediately to the south, and on the larger of the bayhead lowlands, particularly in the municipalities of Tandag, Tago, Hinatuan, Baganga, and Mati (fig. 23).

The ethnolinguistic composition of the population of Surigao Province is overwhelmingly Cebuano-speaking with small elements of Waray-speaking people from the eastern Visayan islands of Samar and Leyte. In the southern part of the region, in the province of Davao, the basic ethnolinguistic element in the population is also Cebuano, although there are important numbers of Davaweño, Panay-Hiligaynon, Waray-Waray, Mandaya, Tagalog, Ilocano, Bagobo, and Manobo peoples also. Most of the population is strongly Roman Catholic in religion, except on the northeastern islands where the Aglipayan church is relatively strong. The age structure of the population in eastern Mindanao indicates a population of normal characteristics, not one that is excessively young such as would be found in pioneer areas of settlement elsewhere on Mindanao. This would seem to indicate that eastern Mindanao has not been an important focus of in-migration, at least in recent years.

Agriculture is the dominant economic activity in the regional economy. Rice is the primary cultivated crop, with corn a poor second. Neither grain, however, is produced in quantities sufficient to meet regional demands, and approximately one-third of the rice and corn consumed in the region must be brought in from other areas on Mindanao. Rice is an important crop in the municipalities of Tago, Cantilan, Gigaquit, and Lianga, whereas corn cultivation is concentrated in Cantilan and Tago. Coconuts and coconut products, particularly copra, are of considerable importance throughout the region, and eastern Mindanao produces around 9 percent of the Philippine abaca crop. Both of these commercial crops are usually cultivated on small landholdings containing 3–5 acres only. The production of root crops such as camotes, cassava, potatoes and garlic, bananas, and beans is particularly important in eastern Mindanao, a reflection upon the failure to produce a sufficient amount of rice and corn. In general the regional agricultural production in foodstuffs rather clearly points up the restrictive agricultural environment. The regional economy is supplemented by several extractive industries, such as mining and forestry, thereby permitting the importation of foodstuffs from elsewhere.

Mining ranks second to agriculture in the economy of eastern Mindanao. The list of mineral deposits in the region is long and in many cases rather impressive, quantitatively. Looking to the future, the deposits of greatest interest are the lateritic iron ores present in northeastern Surigao and on several of the offshore islands, namely Homonhon and Manicani. These deposits consist of limonite ore and occur as a 1-inch- to 100-foot-thick overburden over an area of nearly 60 square miles. The reserves of limonite in Surigao Province are estimated at 1.15 billion tons of 47 percent iron-content ores in the surface mantle. None of this ore is being utilized at the present time because certain metallurgical properties of the ore, which Japanese metallurgists have successfully overcome in experimental smelting, make its present use economically marginal. There are soft and hard coking coals located in the hills back of Bislig with an estimated reserve of some one million tons. Gold has been mined in the northern highlands for a long time. Both lode and placer deposits have been attacked, and normally about one-sixth of the annual gold production of the Philippines comes from Surigao Province. There are some small deposits of relatively high-grade copper ore, ranging from 2½ to 5 percent copper content, found in the vicinity of Lanuza. Chromite ore occurs extensively over Dinagat Island, and relatively important deposits of nickeliferous iron ores are located at Nonoc on Dinagat. There are small recoveries of silver, lead, copper, and zinc. Little of eastern Mindanao has been systematically explored, but there is every indication that the list of mineral deposits will lengthen in the years ahead, and minerals should continue to play a vital role in the regional economy.

The forests of eastern Mindanao also are quite extensive and of good quality, and total production of lumber is approximately 5 percent of the Philippine lumber production. This production, however, is not a true indicator of the region's timber potential. The largest concentration of sawmill capacity is at Bislig Bay, with lesser concentrations in the forests behind Lanuza, Carrascal, Mati, Mainit, and Surigao.

In 1960 nearly 20 percent of the population of eastern Mindanao lived in poblaciones of more than 2,500 persons. Surigao, the capital of Surigao del Norte Province, is the largest city and major regional trade center for eastern Mindanao. The city occupies a site on a small peninsula located just south of the mouth of the Surigao River. Its port, Bilanbilan, is located at the southern tip of the peninsula where it projects into Port Surigao Bay, about one mile south of the city proper. Surigao is an important shipping point for copra and abaca. The city is linked by road with Butuan in Agusan Province and with a few of the east coast settlements located a short distance down the coast. In 1960 the population of Surigao was approximately 16,000. At the opposite end of the region is the port city of Mati, located at the head of Pujada Bay. Mati dominates much of the trade of the southeastern coast and is connected by road with the city of Davao. It serves a relatively productive agricultural hinterland and a small mineral industry. The population of Mati was approximately 7,800 in 1960. Cateel, Baganga, Manay, Tagana-an, Placer, Bacuag, Claver, Lanuza, Tandag, Marihatag, and Lianga are important small towns along the Pacific coast. All of them have populations between 2,500 and 5,000 persons and function as small interisland ports. Each serves a small agricultural development in its immediate hinterland. Tandag serves as the capital of the newly created province of Surigao del Sur.

The highway network of eastern Mindanao was very inadequate in the early 1960's. The major provincial highway parallels the east coast from Surigao southward only to Tago. Interregional connections exist between Surigao and Butuan along the shores of Lake Mainit, from Mati to Davao, and from Lianga across the eastern cordillera connecting with the Davao-Agusan highway. Elsewhere, roads extend only a few miles out from the major municipios. Thus, for most communities in eastern Mindanao transportation must be by coastal ship, and there are literally dozens of small ports along the east coast of Mindanao and in the islands to the northeast. Most of the ports are rather crude, offering at best a small pier jutting just barely into deeper water, and more often affording only a protected anchorage.

The Davao-Agusan Trough Country

The Davao-Agusan region coincides with one of the major physiographic units of the Philippines, the Davao-Agusan structural trough. This

120-mile-long longitudinal trough, with a maximum width of nearly 30 miles, extends from north to south through Mindanao. Actually the trough structure continues for many more miles beneath the waters of Butuan Bay and Davao Gulf (figs. 4*b*, 75). The Davao-Agusan region includes one of the largest lowlands in the Philippines and together with the surrounding uplands embraces an area of approximately 10,100 square miles. The Diuata Mountains and the various subranges of Mindanao's Pacific cordillera lands border the lowland to the east and form a relatively continuous barrier to easy access from the Pacific coastal lowlands. The high, rugged mountains of the several ranges of central Mindanao parallel the western side of the lowland, blocking easy ingress from Cotabato or the Bukidnon Plateau. Narrow belts of coastal lowlands accompany the margins of the trough where it plunges beneath the waters of Butuan Bay and Davao Gulf.

In contrast with many other areas of major lowlands in the Philippines, much of the Davao-Agusan Lowland does not constitute a major present focus of population. The swampy character of much of the lowland, and until recently, the almost complete absence of land-transportation facilities, have served to discourage large-scale migrations into the interior lands. Settlement has been fairly rapid during the twentieth century at the southern end of the lowland, but population densities remain well below the national averages, and much of the present-day occupance remains pioneer-like in character.

THE PHYSICAL SETTING

Geologically, the Davao-Agusan Trough appears to be a large structural downwarp, or possibly even a broad synclinal trough. The linear north–south orientation of the trough is the result of the north–south–trending arrangement of crystalline mountains on either side. Paralleling the valley along its eastern margins for a distance of over 200 miles, is the Pacific Cordillera of Mindanao. In all this distance the range is quite continuous, rising to summits generally exceeding 4,000 feet in altitude in the northern and southern sections. Two major breaks provide low pass routes through the cordillera land; one is located in back of Lianga Bay opposite the central Agusan Valley, and the other lies behind Bislig Bay to the south and opposite the southern Agusan Province area. West of the valley is a succession of mountain ranges that separate the Davao-Agusan Lowland from the lowlands of the valley of the Rio Grande de Mindanao and its tributaries, and the Bukidnon-Lanao Plateau. These mountain ranges, collectively referred to as the Central Mindanao Highlands, also trend nearly north–south, and they too are pierced by several low gaps or passes. Generally the higher sections of these central ranges lie in the north where most of the summits reach elevations of 4,000 to 5,000 feet; however, certain individual southern peaks are considerably higher. In the north the mountains are of complex structural origins, whereas in the south, beginning at a point near the head of Davao Gulf and continuing along the western Gulf's shores, the Central Mindanao Highlands are largely volcanic. Mount Apo, located 20 miles west of the city of Davao, attains an elevation of 9,690 feet, the highest point in the Philippines. Mount Apo is considered an active volcano. Mount Matutum, located 45 miles south of Apo, is a recently active volcano that reaches a height of 7,521 feet. In the recent geologic past most of the Davao-Agusan Lowland was occupied by a shallow arm of the sea. The present land surface is the result of very recent uplift. The floor of the lowland is covered with a thick mantle of recent marine and riverborne sediments reaching to depths of several hundred feet. The southern part of the Davao-Agusan Lowland, in the vicinity of the Philippine Rift (fig. 3), is a major focus of seismic activity, as is evidenced by the long series of earthquakes observed and carefully recorded by the Jesuit missionaries in that region. Their cause is probably geomorphic rather than volcanic. Small shocks have been more frequent in this region than in any other part of Mindanao.

Near the southern end of the lowland, a short distance south of the present provincial boundary between Agusan and Davao, lies the Olagusan Upland, which provides a low topographic divide across the trough from west to east. North of this 300-foot-high divide the drainage is dominated by the large, north-flowing Agusan River, whereas to the south the shorter Hijo, Saug, Tagum, and Libuganon rivers drain southward toward the head of Davao Gulf. The Agusan River is one of two great river systems on Mindanao, and ranks either second or third in length and size among the rivers of the Philippines. Its headwaters are located at the southern end of the Pacific Cordillera between the head of Davao Gulf and the Pacific Ocean near Mati. Near its source the river flows very close to the shores of Davao Gulf with only a low divide separating the river from what appears to have been its former outlet into the gulf. The Agusan flows northward for over 200 miles to its mouth in Butuan Bay. In its source region the Agusan flows in a deep, V-shaped valley in the mountainous country, finally breaking into the hill-encircled, nine-mile-long Compostela Basin in northern Davao. After again passing through upland country, the river debouches onto its main valley floor in the vicinity of the Davao-Agusan provincial boundary. Still nearly 80 miles above its mouth, the Agusan River flows the remainder of its course across its broad, nearly level valley. In this valley-proper section, several major tributary rivers join the main stream, including the Sumilao, Adgoan, Umayan, and Wawa rivers. The Agusan Valley proper probably contains a lowland area of about one-half the size of the Central Plain of Luzon, that is, about 2,100 square miles; but because of the presence of very large freshwater swamps in the middle section of the Agusan Valley, its potential arable area, though large, is considerably less than that of the Central Plain. These swamps are much larger than the Candaba Swamp of Luzon. Measuring nearly 40 miles in their combined north–south dimension during the rainy season, the swamps are reduced into a number of small lakes during low water. The Agusan River is navigable for vessels drawing 6 feet of water for a distance of 20 miles above its mouth, and smaller native craft or small boats with outboard motors can ascend the river for nearly 160 miles.

The drainage southward into the head of Davao Gulf is dominated by several short rivers. As the drainage divide of the Davao-Agusan Lowland lies much closer to Davao Gulf than to Butuan Bay the gradient of the lowland is such that southward-flowing rivers flow faster than those of the Agusan Valley, and as a result, the lands in the Davao area are much better drained. The largest of the southward-flowing rivers is the Libuganon whose source lies in the Central Mindanao Highlands. The Libuganon, together with the Saug and Tuganay, drain the northern and central sections of the Davao Piedmont, an extremely productive agricultural area that lies adjacent to the Central Mindanao Highlands in northwestern Davao. Along the shores of Davao Gulf there are several small lowlands. The largest of these lowlands, occupying the southern sections of the Davao Piedmont northwest and west of Davao City, is drained by the Davao and Talomo rivers. Another important alluvial plain, which contains an area of 220 square miles, is located south of Davao City in the municipalities of Padada, Digos, and Malalag. Smaller lowland areas are found scattered along the eastern shores of the Gulf of Mabini, Pantukan, and Lupon. Elsewhere most of the rivers that flow into the eastern and western margins of Davao Gulf descend abruptly from the uplands, leaving little room for the development of coastal lowlands.

The Davao Piedmont consists of a low rolling plain extending from Davao City northward to the Agusan border. With an average width of 20 miles, this piedmont land contains an extensive area of some of the finest agricultural land in the Philippines. Several first-class soil types are found on the piedmont, particularly the fertile San Miguel series.

Climatic conditions are relatively homogeneous throughout the Davao-Agusan Lowland, for although the quantities of precipitation received in the different sections of the region show considerable variation, the regime of rainfall is quite similar. No lowland station records a period of significant drought, as for example, a month with a mean monthly rainfall less than 2.4 inches. Throughout the lowland the period of maximum precipitation tends to coincide with the low-sun period. In the north the Agusan Valley receives well over 100 inches of rainfall annually. Surrounding Davao Gulf, the lowlands in the south, which are partially sheltered by the highlands, receive rainfalls that average between 60 and 80 inches annually. Where gaps exist in the central highlands, such as between Mounts Apo and Matutum and south of Matutum, southwestern air masses have better ingress and the annual precipitations increase to well over 100 inches in the gulf area. Nevertheless, even in the areas of relatively low precipitation amounts, there are few periods dry enough to affect crops. All of Mindanao lies south of the usual typhoon tracks, and the Davao-Agusan region is virtually free of the strong winds that accompany these storms.

Much of the region is still clothed in rich stands of tropical rain forest. Akle, ipil, narra, molave, yakal, tindalo, the lauans, apitong, tangile, and several other Philippine forest giants occur in dense stands throughout the region. Grasslands are not as extensive as in many other areas on Mindanao, for the presence of year-round rainfall precludes an environment that would favor their development. A few scattered mangrove forests can still be encountered in certain sheltered coastal areas along the gulf, particularly at Padada and near the town of Tagum at the head of the gulf. Extensive freshwater swamp and marsh vegetation accompanies much of the course of the Agusan River, particularly along the middle course where there are large swamps around Lake Linao.

The soils of the Davao-Agusan Lowland have developed under moderately high temperatures, evenly distributed rainfall, and in the main, a dense forest vegetation. Most of the soils are still in a virgin state, or have been put under cultivation only within the past few years. Generally they are less leached and eroded than the soils elsewhere in the Philippines. Their organic content is relatively high and most of the soils of the region can be considered as quite fertile. The soils in the southern part of the region show stronger affinities with volcanic parent-material derivations, whereas those in the north have been formed mainly from recent alluvium and sedimentary rock materials.

THE CULTURAL SETTING

Whereas a moderate degree of diversity exists within the Davao-Agusan region, there is also a considerable degree of homogeneity in its physiography, climate, soils, and natural vegetation. On the other hand, the northern and southern sections of the lowland have undergone very different historical occupances, and the resulting cultural patterns have developed along two distinct mainstreams. Furthermore, the present levels of economic development in the two areas make it quite clear that at least from the viewpoint of human occupance, it is necessary to subdivide the Davao-Agusan Lowland into two subsections; a northern Agusan Valley subregion and a southern Davao Gulf subregion.

Davao Gulf subregion. The Davao Gulf subregion includes the part of the Davao-Agusan Lowland which lies within the political area of Davao Province. It includes the lowland of the Compostela Basin, which is located along the upper reaches of the Agusan River, as well as the plains and piedmonts tributary to Davao Gulf. Although the Compostela area focuses on the Agusan River, it is included within the Davao Gulf subregion largely because the occupance of the basin has been linked closely with the settlement of the gulf area.

Little is known of the early occupance of the Davao Gulf area, and indeed, little is known of the region's history until shortly before the dawn of the twentieth century. The pre-Spanish occupance patterns appear to have been of several scattered tribal groups who lived mainly in the interior, and a sprinkling of small Moro coastal settlements. The Moros numbered between four and five thousand, and belonged to the Maguindanao Moslem group. These Moros occupied the coastal area from Sarangani Bay, in Cotabato Province, to the head of Davao Gulf, and along the eastern shores of the gulf south to Cape San Agustin. Although most of the Moro settlements were located along the coasts, a few were located along the lower courses of the larger rivers. At the time of the first permanent Spanish contacts in the nineteenth century, these Moros were occupying many of the sites that were later to become important towns of the present, including Tagum, Samal, Hijo, Matiao, and the largest Moro settlement at Mayo, which was to become part of Davao City.

In the nineteenth century the pagan peoples were loosely organized into several tribal groups whose scattered forest clearings in the upland areas were generally planted to maize, upland rice, taro, and abaca. Seven major pagan groups constituted the bulk of the population of the Davao area. The Manobo and Bagobo groups were the most numerous. The former occupied the central ranges to the west of the gulf and also appeared in the northern part of the province near the present Agusan border. The Bagobos occupied the area around the present-day city of Davao and also appeared farther south in what are now the municipalities of Digos, Padada, and Santa Cruz. In northeastern Davao were the Mandaya pagan groups. Ata occupied the lands northwest of the gulf and north of Davao City; Manggangan and Tagokaolo groups lived in northeastern Davao. Both were concentrated mainly in the area around Monkayo and Compostela, but the Tagokaolo were also found in the south around Malita and Malalag. Combined, these pagan groups constituted the most numerous element of the population, and even as late as the 1918 census they still made up 45 percent of the province's population. Their numbers, however, have failed to keep pace with the rapid in-migrations of the twentieth century. Nevertheless, they still numbered 82,000 in 1939, and even today they number around 17,000 and continue to dominate the occupance of much of the interior mountain country.

Although the Spanish made their first cursory contacts with the Davao Gulf region quite early in their administration, permanent Spanish settlement did not take place until the middle of the nineteenth century. Saavedra visited the small Sarangani Islands, which lie off the southwestern entrance to the gulf, in 1528, and Villalobos coasted along the Pacific shores of southeastern Mindanao in 1543. Caraga, a small coastal settlement on the Pacific coast of Davao, was the first permanent Spanish settlement on Mindanao. It was established early in the seventeenth century; however, the areas adjacent to Davao Gulf remained under the control of the Sultan of Mindanao until an expedition under the command of Don Jose Oyanguren succeeded in establishing effective Spanish control over the gulf in 1848. This Spanish businessman, formerly a resident of the Spanish settlement at Caraga, recognized the agricultural potential of the gulf, and in 1848, received authority from Governor Claveria to lead an expedition into the gulf area. In exchange for this military operation, Oyanguren was promised suzerainty over the area for a period of ten years, with a six-year period of trade monopoly. Neither promise was fulfilled, and until the end of Spanish rule in the Philippines, Spanish influence in Davao Gulf amounted to no more than the presence of a few priests and squads of soldiers.

The Spanish failed to generate any agricultural enthusiasm or other economic development. The main center of Spanish settlement at the inauguration of the American administration was at Vergara, the former Mayo and forerunner of the present-day capital city of Davao. At the end of the nineteenth century, smaller settlements, usually housing one or two Spanish priests, were located at Malag, Piapi, Digos, and Astorga in the Padada Valley, at Daliao, Bago, and Taoma in present-day Davao City, at San Jose on Samal Island, and at Pondaguitan on San Agustin Peninsula.

Mindanao was the last area in which American reorganization of Spanish political structure took place. Davao Province, as such, dates from 1914, but the internal subdivision and structuring of the region into municipalities was not completed until 1936. By that date Davao City had been chartered to include a large region of rural, agricultural territory, and the rest of the province had been divided into municipalities for which municipio administrative settlements had been chosen.

Following the transfer of Philippine administration to American authority, a few American and Filipino pioneer businessmen found their way to Davao in 1902 and began to clear the wilderness around the city. A few small plantations of abaca were developed by these men, but this earliest American occupance was not too successful because of the serious shortage of labor existing in the area. It was not until Mr. K. S. Ohta, a progressive Japanese businessman, began to transform the lands around Davao Gulf into large abaca and coconut plantations in 1904 that the present patterns of economic development of the Davao Gulf area began to emerge. In order to assure an adequate labor force for his plantations, Ohta at first imported 100 Japanese workmen from Philippine government construction projects in northern Luzon, and with this nucleus began the clearing of virgin farmlands around Davao City. Subsequent workers came directly from Japan. Japanese immigrations continued, and the numbers of Japanese colonists increased rapidly in Davao. By the 1939 census enumeration their numbers totaled nearly 18,000. These immigrants were carefully selected and came mainly from the Japanese island of Okinawa. The Japanese agricultural corporation secured agricultural land by outright purchase and through leasing arrangements with Filipino landowners. Eventually they controlled approximately 140,000 acres of prime agricultural land in Davao. This economic penetration by the Japanese resulted in their nearly complete domination over the growing, stripping, baling, and export of abaca in the Davao area. They instituted the very modern scientific agricultural techniques that typified the production of abaca in this southeastern region until the start of World War II. In continually increasing numbers the Japanese entered many other occupations in the region and soon gained a dominant position in general importing and exporting, retail merchandising, fishing, and logging and sawmilling. They also were important as builders, factory laborers, hairdressers, photographers, and housekeepers in the Davao area. They built Japanese schools and a hospital.[9]

At the conclusion of World War II, all Japanese nationals were repatriated to Japan, and the void they left in the agricultural economy was quickly filled by Filipino squatters. Immediately following the cessation of hostilities, a period of "butchering operations" on the old Japanese abaca plantations ensued. Unfortunately, the years of neglect of the plantations during the war had left their mark. Various plant diseases that previously had been kept in check now gained the upper hand, especially the abaca mosaic, and today the once rich abaca fields surrounding Davao City are plagued by lower yields and an inferior product.

The conclusion of World War II also found many Filipinos with a newly acquired pioneer psychology, one that the hardships of three years of Japanese military occupation had instilled. Apparently the Philippine population had acquired a greater mobility and a greater willingness to move to areas of greater economic opportunity. Since the war the population in the province of Davao has exceeded its expected natural increase by nearly 380,000 new settlers. This large increase took place between the two census years of 1948 and 1960, and except for the small NARRA project at Santo Tomas, was achieved largely through voluntary migrations, with a minimum of governmental assistance. The number of total in-migrants has meant that between 2,500 and 3,000 new settlers arrived in Davao Province each month. Most of the recent migration has been directed into the less densely settled areas of the Davao Gulf area. The Padada-Digos-Mainit river lowland in Santa Cruz municipality received about 140,000 of these new settlers, necessitating the creation of seven new municipalities. Davao City, which includes an area of 854 square miles within the chartered city limits, received 120,000 of the migrants. Smaller streams of migrants were directed into the lowlands at the head of the gulf, the small riverine plains along the eastern shores of the gulf, and along the upper Agusan River in the municipalities of Monkayo and Compostela. Approximately 700 new settler-families moved into the NARRA settlement at Tibal-og (Santo Tomas) between 1957 and 1960.

Whereas the population of Davao grew at a rate only slightly larger than the national average from 1903 to 1948, since 1948 the population of the province has expanded, both in terms of percent and in absolute numbers, at a rate that is exceeded by only two other provinces in the Philippines. The overall arithmetic density of population in Davao Province in 1960 was 120 persons per square mile, as compared to a figure of only 49 persons per square mile as recently as 1948. Physiological population densities, however, have remained close to the 600 persons per square mile of cultivated land reached in 1948, as new lands have been opened for settlement. Although Davao can support many more people than it now does, the province should no longer be viewed as the empty area of two decades ago.[10] The large-scale in-migrations have contributed a cosmopolitan character to the population of Davao; nevertheless, people from the crowded islands of the central Visayan group, primarily Bohol and Cebu, are in the majority.

Agriculture is the dominant economic activity in the southern Davao-Agusan Lowland, but the agricultural occupance characteristic of the Davao area is somewhat unusual. There is little agricultural diversification, and one farm usually concentrates on the cultivation of one crop only. In most cases the crops that are cultivated are cash crops. The economic considerations involved in the cultivation of the basic grains, rice and corn, in the Davao Gulf area are rather interesting. Davao is the leading corn-producing province in the Philippines by a wide margin, with nearly 600,000 acres devoted to its cultivation in 1960.[11] The production of corn in the province is equivalent to nearly five times the actual local needs. The large surpluses are shipped to Manila, Cebu, eastern Mindanao, and other food-deficit areas. Two crops of corn are usually cultivated each year, and sometimes a third crop is attempted. Corn also is frequently interplanted with upland rice, or it may be grown as a cover crop in young abaca and coconut plantations. Most of the cornfields in Davao are located on newly opened lands, and the yields are about 50 percent higher than those obtained in other parts of the archipelago. The largest corn acreage is concentrated in the Digos-Padada Valley, particularly in the new municipalities of Bansalan, Matanao, and Sulop, and on agricultural lands within the city of Davao (fig. 76). The corn is of the hard kernel variety, that is, white flint and yellow flint corns.

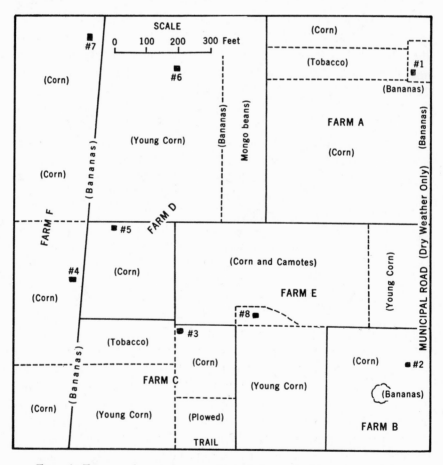

Fig. 76. Farms and crops in a newly settled area in Matanao, southern Davao, 1965.

Although the province of Davao produces corn in quantities well beyond those needed to satisfy actual provincial consumption, and ships large quantities to all food-deficit areas in other parts of the Philippines, the province continues to be a significant net-deficit region with regard to rice. Lowland wet-field rice is not a crop that usually makes an early appearance in newly settled regions. In keeping with other pioneer areas in eastern Mindanao, the province of Davao produces only 80 percent of its total rice requirements.[12] Little effort has been directed toward the improvement of rice yields in the region, and there has been little significant expansion of the area devoted to rice. The more important areas of rice cultivation in the Davao Gulf area lie in the municipalities of Hagonoy, Bansalan, Santo Tomas, and Panabo, and within the city of Davao. Upland and lowland rice can also be found in small, scattered patches throughout the province. It would appear that at least in the past, it has been more profitable to plant abaca and corn in the Davao area, depending upon the purchase of extra rice from the large surpluses of the neighboring province of Cotabato. The rice yields obtained within the gulf area approximate the national averages.

Regional food supplies are complemented by relatively large productions of various fruits, vegetables, and root crops. Sweet potatoes, gabi, cassava, peanuts, and yams are important root crops; and eggplant, tomatoes, beans, cabbage, and squash are the more common vegetables. Bananas, papayas, jackfruits, and durians are important fruits.

Davao has ranked as the leading province in the production of abaca since shortly after 1900; however, by 1960 its relative share of the total Philippine abaca acreage has fallen to 15 percent from a high of 22 percent in 1941, and Davao's share of abaca production stood at 18 percent, down from 35 percent in 1941. The abaca plant has been so characteristic of Davao that the plant and the name of the province became practically synonomous. The extensive cultivation of abaca in the Davao Gulf area has been largely in response to the presence of nearly ideal climatic conditions, with evenly distributed rains and the almost complete absence of strong winds; the well-drained, relatively fertile, volcanically derived soils; and particularly to the industry and vigor displayed by the early Japanese colonists in the years prior to World War II. Until 1941, most of the abaca in Davao was grown on large plantations; however, with the repatriation of Japanese agriculturalists, many of the plantations have been subdivided, and much of the present production originates from small farms. Furthermore, the main abaca-producing areas have been shifting into virgin lands farther north of the city of Davao in order to maintain high yields and to avoid the areas that have been infected with the abaca mosaic disease. Most of the abaca-stripping is accomplished in stations scattered throughout the abaca area, but baling of the loose abaca is performed at the towns of Sasa, Santa Ana, Madaum (Tagum), Pancho, and Kapalong. Two of the larger plantations use large decorticating machines. The abaca areas in Leyte, Samar, and the Bicol, which are relatively free from mosaic, have expanded at Davao's expense since World War II.

In spite of its large abaca production, Davao ships directly overseas only 3 percent of the Philippine abaca export product. Instead, most of the abaca produced in the Davao region moves via interisland vessels to Manila for transshipment. There are two reasons for this large in-transit shipment of abaca. First, differential freight rates for shipments to overseas markets exist between the various Philippine ports. The rate from Manila is substantially lower than from ports closer to the baling locations, such as Davao and Legaspi. This, in large part, is a reflection of the fact that the size of the shipment makes it less profitable for foreign vessels to call at ports other than Manila for loading abaca. In addition, there are the "customs of the trade" which strongly encourage the in-transit shipments through Manila. In situations where freight rates for abaca shipments are equal between Manila and other ports the "customs of the trade" is the dominant factor that explains the trade patterns.[13]

Coconuts rank above abaca among the commercial crops of the Davao Gulf subregion, both in terms of the acreage devoted to their cultivation and the value of production. Most of the lands devoted to coconuts are located along the shores of the gulf, particularly in the municipalities of Mati, Malita, Governor Generoso, Davao, and Baganga. The port of Davao serves as the main collection point for copra intended for eventual export from the several small producing areas in eastern Davao and southeastern Cotabato.

Davao Gulf agriculture is a mixture of food crops to be sold elsewhere in the Philippines and crops for eventual export. It is now, and should remain, one of the primary surplus-corn-producing areas of the Philippines.

Forestry, fishing, and mining contribute in small measure to the regional economy. Forest industries are of extraregional significance. The present merchantable timber reserves of Davao are estimated at 25 billion board feet, an amount that represents approximately 9 percent of the total merchantable timber reserve of the Philippines. There were twenty-four sawmills being operated in the Davao Gulf area in 1960 with a combined daily capacity of 154,000 board feet, or 5 percent of the total Philippine daily sawmill capacity. Most of the sawmills are located along the western side of the gulf, particularly within the city of Davao where the largest domestic market exists. At present the bulk of the logs come from the forests of the central mountains.

Lumber production is more than adequate for regional needs, and considerable quantities are exported from the small ports of Tambungon, La Paz, Tagabuli, Malalag, and Lupon. Davao is also an important supplier of lumber for markets in Manila and the central Visayas. Considerable timber is exported in log form to Japan and Europe.

The waters of Davao Gulf are relatively rich in fish resources, although at present they support only a moderate fishing industry with modest commercial overtones. Usually the region can supply its own fish requirements and on occasions small shipments are made to Cotabato and Zamboanga. The settlements of the two small islands of Sarangani and Balut, which lie off the southwestern entrance to the gulf, and many of the small communities near Cape San Agustin and Tinaca Point, are solely fishing villages. During the period of greatest Japanese agricultural development, the Japanese developed and controlled a very large part of the fishing industry in Davao Gulf. Nothing on a similar scale has replaced their operations.

Mining at the present time is restricted to a single operating company at Masara, Hope, and Hijo barrios in Mabini municipality. The main targets are the copper deposits, but there are small recoveries of lead, silver, and gold associated with the copper production.

Most of the modest industrial growth Davao has experienced has been in the agricultural-processing sector. Abaca-stripping mills and baling establishments, sawmills, and veneer and plywood plants, and the hundreds of rice and corn mills are widely scattered and are the dominant industries. Curiously, the corn mills have not fallen into the ownership of alien Chinese, as has been the case in most other Philippine rice and corn areas. The corn mills are concentrated mainly in Davao City, with roughly one-quarter of the region's mills, and the Padada Valley, with one-half; the remainder are located in the municipalities of Panabo, Samal, Hagonoy, and Compostela. In 1960 the Bureau of Census reported only 4,200 manufacturing employees in Davao, equivalent to only 2 percent of the Philippine manufacturing labor force.[14]

The Davao Gulf subregion is not well-supplied with overland communication facilities, and the lack of roads undoubtedly has delayed the economic development of southeastern Mindanao probably more than any other single factor. Two major highways provide the interregional overland connections, as well as serving most intraprovincial needs. A national highway runs south and west from Davao City to Cotabato Province and to a connection with the Sayre Highway. A new highway now connects Davao with the Agusan Valley and the north coast port of Butuan. This latter highway has acted as a tremendous stimulus to settlement along its entire length. Both of these major arteries are gravel-surfaced, all-weather roads except for small sections of concrete or asphalt roadway around the city of Davao. Small road grids service the Padada Valley and the lowlands northwest and north of Davao City. A poor road links Davao City with the eastern gulf towns of Pantukan and Mabini, and with the port city of Mati on the Pacific coast.

The city of Davao is the largest city on Mindanao, both in terms of its area and its total population. The chartered city limits include an area of 854 square miles, much of which is quite distinctly rural in character, and a 1960 population of 231,000. The urban population of Davao proper probably totals close to 100,000. The original city was built on a site at the mouth of the Davao River, but the present city occupies all of this original site and has spread over much of the broad piedmont plain. Port facilities were constructed at Santa Ana, which was then 2 miles from the town, although today the urban and port area have completely merged. The port of Davao, at Santa Ana, is very active in serving the smaller vessels engaged in Philippine interisland commerce. Deepwater port facilities have been constructed at Sasa, 5 miles north of Davao, and all foreign vessels and the larger interisland ships call there. The harbor for both port installations is provided by Pakiputan Strait, which is formed between the main island and the large offshore island of Samal. The port of Davao ranks fifth among Philippine ports in imports and third in the volume of its interisland commerce. Davao serves not only as the provincial capital for Davao province but also as the principal interregional center for all of southeastern and eastern Mindanao, a relatively productive though still lightly occupied hinterland. Several major regional offices for southern Mindanao, including the Sulus, are located in Davao, such as the new regional hospital and medical training center and offices of various national government bureaus. About fifty small ports lie within Davao's sphere of commercial dominance. Abaca, corn, and lumber are the principal items of commerce. Continued growth of the city is virtually assured as more and more settlers occupy the virgin lands surrounding Davao Gulf, for the city of Davao will remain the region's commercial focus.

The population of the Davao Gulf subregion is moderately urbanized with approximately 20 percent of the people living in Davao City proper or in municipality poblaciones with more than 2,500 persons. The following, with their 1960 poblaciones populations, are the major trade centers of the subregion: Digos (8,725), Bansalan (6,602), Padada (4,420), Malalag (5,242), and Santa Cruz (6,456) are the principal market towns for the important corn-producing area of the Padada, Digos, and Mainit river valleys. Santa Cruz, Digos, and Malalag are also small ports through which the surpluses of corn are shipped. Digos, the principal town of the valley, lies at the juncture of the Davao-Cotabato highway. Bunawan (2,821), Calinan (5,072), Toril (8,094), and Tugbok (4,595) are small market towns serving the extensive areas of abaca and coconut plantings in the rural areas southwest, west, and northwest of Davao, but within the chartered city limits. Panabo (5,539), Tagum (5,263), Asuncion (3,324), and Nabunturan (4,672) serve the important abaca-producing lands near the head of the gulf. Monkayo (3,679), located along the new Davao-Agusan highway, has become the major commercial center for the agricultural communities in the rich Compostela Basin. Lupon (4,356) and Mabini (5,947) are minor ports along the eastern side of the gulf, each controlling the trade of its small lowland. Malita (5,947) performs the same function along the southwestern coast. Mabini also services the Masara mining community. Santo Tomas (9,450) is a new town, settled largely since 1957 under the supervision of the NARRA program. The town was carefully laid out before the settlers arrived and retains the rectangular street patterns reminiscent of an American low-cost housing project. Church, school, town plaza, and public market sites have been carefully developed in conformity with a master plan (fig. 77).

The Davao Gulf subregion has grown tremendously in economic stature since the beginning of the twentieth century, although perhaps not as much as its enthusiasts would wish. If the city of Davao is not already the major regional center for the entire southern Philippines to the same extent that Manila and Cebu are for the northern and central Philippines, it soon will be.

The Agusan Valley subregion. The Agusan Valley subregion, the northern half of the Davao-Agusan trough, includes essentially the political area of the province of Agusan. Unlike the Davao Gulf subregion, all of the Agusan Valley focuses upon a single major river, the Agusan (fig. 74). Settlers have entered the Agusan Valley from the river mouth at Butuan Bay. In spite of early Spanish contacts and the establishment of mission stations upriver as early as the seventeenth century, most of the Agusan Valley has remained very sparsely settled until the present. Whereas the Davao Gulf subsection was gaining nearly 380,000 new settlers between 1948 and 1960, the province of Agusan added barely 100,000. Nearly two-thirds of the population of the province lives in the seven coastal municipalities located along Butuan Bay, and half of them reside within the chartered limits of the city of Butuan. Thus, the remaining population of nearly 100,000 is scattered over the 3,400 square miles of land in the central section of the Agusan Valley (fig. 23).

One of the main deterrents to settlement in the middle and upper courses of the Agusan River Valley can be tied rather closely to the lack of inland transportation facilities. Until 1960, no road of any kind penetrated

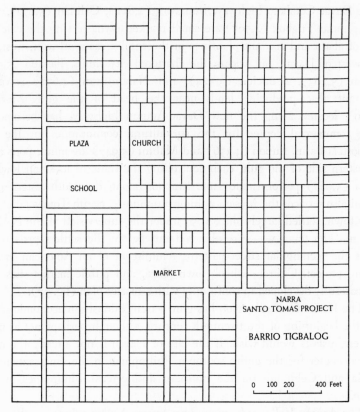

Fig. 77. Town plan of the poblacion of Santo Tomas (Barrio Tigbal-og), Davao. This National Resettlement and Rehabilitation Administration project settlement in Davao Province was settled between 1956 and 1960 mainly by Visayans.

into southern Agusan Province, and the rivers served as the only means of communication. Beyond the Agusan River some of the tributaries were navigable by small craft in the high-water season, which permitted trading between coastal folk and the thin scattering of pagan tribal peoples. Such points of trading contact as Esperanza and Talacogon, located on natural levees on the main Agusan River, represent old trading stations. Limited and seasonal river transport was not sufficient to encourage colonial settlement of the interior.

Another not so easily remedied deterrent to settlement in the upper Agusan Valley lies in the character of the drainage basin. Much of the basin in the southern section of the province is either seasonally flooded to a depth of several feet or is permanent swamp centering around a group of small lakes. The zone of annual flooding lies chiefly between Talacogon and

Bunawan, and involves an area of about 500 square miles. Surrounding this lowest sector exceptional flood conditions may affect another 300 square miles. Flood patterns in such exceptional years may reach as far north as Esperanza, and normally reach into the lower course of tributary streams. This zone of annual, and exceptional, flooding appears to be a result of quite recent subsidence in the basin floor, for only the lake margins and a few narrow strips behind the natural levees appear to have vegetative associations indicative of long-term swamp conditions. There are seven or eight localities with small and permanent bodies of water, although the smallest may dry up during exceptional dry seasons. Lakes Linao, Dagan, Mantood, and Adgoan are all-year water bodies. Here and there a hillock rises well above the level of highest flood within the floodable zone. The earliest Christian Filipino occupants pursuing dry-period agriculture within the floodable zone adopted such practices as living in houseboats, or of building their houses on log rafts that could float above the flood, that could be anchored, and that could be grounded where desired when the flood level receded. In this southern sector the nonfloodable lands west of the river are chiefly rolling uplands. Most of the best agricultural land in the southern sector lies east of the river well back from and above the floodable zone.

The province of Agusan, formerly called Butuan, was an early target for Spanish exploration and missionary activities. Pigafetta, the chronicler of Magellan's expedition, made mention of meetings with native chieftains from Butuan and the eastern Mindanao coastal settlement at Caraga. The settlement of Butuan, so-called from the name then applied to the Agusan River, was described as occupying a location near the mouth of the river and surrounded by broad plains with relatively dense populations. Even in early Spanish times it appears that Butuan was a major settlement. Apparently it was a port of call for vessels from Borneo and Luzon, for several ships were seen in Butuan Bay by members of Legaspi's expedition. They were reportedly trading for gold, wax, cinnamon, and slaves. In 1591, the encomienda of the "river of Butuan" was granted to the wife of one of the Spanish leaders, de Loarca, and at that time it included a population of approximately 4,800 persons.

The early Jesuits established a mission station of some stature at Butuan late in the sixteenth century. In the early seventeenth century the Recollects replaced the Jesuits at Butuan and going farther upstream, established mission stations at Linao, now Bunawan. This latter station, protected from Moro raids by its inaccessible interior location, was to remain active for several centuries; however, the central Agusan Valley was not to develop into an important Christian settlement area as a consequence. It is surprising that in view of the long period of Spanish occupance, at least in a missionary sense, the central Agusan area has not been more Hispanicized and more densely settled than it is. A large part of the indigenous population upriver was Christianized, but little new settlement ensued.

The modern political province of Agusan was first organized in 1914, but only those districts near to the coast were established as municipalities, and most of the whole central-to-southern sector was administered directly by the provincial government as municipal districts. Gradually provincial districts were formed with partial local governments, and this pattern remained operative as recently as the late 1950's. There have been numerous changes in the political structuring of the province, and it was a relatively easy matter for Butuan City, upon being chartered, to include a large area of the near-coastal interior lying athwart the Agusan River. The projection of the Davao-Agusan highway, the opening of the interior eastern section of the valley to settlement, and the eventual development of other elements of a road system throughout the province will carry with them the founding of a considerable number of new towns, the development of new local regionalism in political organization, and the maturing of the political structure of the province.

The population of the Agusan Valley underwent major changes in the early 1960's, increasing at a rate nearly double that which could be expected from the excesses of births over deaths. The large-scale migrations to Agusan are a relatively recent phenomenon. Tens of thousands of new settlers have entered the valley in the past decade, coming mainly from the Cebuano-speaking areas of Bohol, Cebu, and eastern Negros. More than 40 percent of the 1960 population of Agusan Province reported birthplaces other than Agusan. More than 80 percent of the present population of the province is of Cebuano origin, or at least claims Cebuano as its mother tongue. Although large numbers of migrants have settled in the coastal municipalities, there has been a significant migration toward the interior, particularly into the municipalities of San Francisco and Bunawan. Arithmetic population densities in the seven coastal municipalities averaged 182 persons per square mile in 1960, whereas in the eleven interior municipalities and municipal districts the densities were well below 30 persons per square mile.

Agriculture, forestry, and fishing are the principal economic activities, but only the forest industries can be considered well-developed. Agriculture does not play the dominant role in the Agusan Valley that it does in the Davao Gulf subregion. This is true despite the fact that climatic and soil conditions are well-suited to a greatly expanded agricultural occupance, except for the seasonally flooded condition of a share of the valley floor. Present agriculture is oriented toward general self-sufficiency. Rice is the leading food crop in terms of acreage and value, followed by corn and camotes. The coastal municipalities lead in the production of all agricultural crops. Each crop is produced in quantities sufficient to permit the sale of small surpluses. Coconuts are the principal commercial crop. Abaca, which used to be of considerable importance in the Agusan Valley, is no longer of major significance, as early exploitation was based upon the gathering of wild plants. The agricultural pattern will be a rapidly changing one in the coming decade.

The lumber industry, on the other hand, is of great importance to the economy of the valley, and nearly 10 percent of the national sawmill capacity is located within Agusan Province. Most of the sawmills are located on the coast, and all are of relatively large size, with daily capacities of 10,000 to 20,000 board feet. The mills represent fairly large capital investments, with 60 percent of the investment in Chinese hands. Butuan City, with nine sawmills, is one of the leading lumber centers in the Philippines. The small municipality of Nasipit, located 14 miles west of Butuan, is the headquarters of the Nasipit Lumber Company, one of the largest and most modern of Philippine plants, producing lumber, veneers, and wallboard, and having large timberland holdings along the lower Agusan River. The Agusan Valley also is an important source of export logs. Some of the lumber, and all of the logs, are exported directly overseas through the ports of Nasipit, Butuan, Magallanes, Cabadbaran, and Tubay. Most of the lumber goes to Manila and Cebu markets for consumption or reexport.

Commercial fishing is important in Butuan Bay and the rich waters of the Mindanao Sea, and sustenance fishing is extremely important along the lower Agusan River and in Lake Mainit; however, quantities are generally insufficient to meet local needs. The fish resource is present, but imperfectly developed.

Butuan, the capital city of Agusan Province, is the principal commercial center for the valley. Located approximately 6 miles upriver from Butuan Bay, Butuan's port functions are performed by its outport of Magallanes. By virtue of its position astride the lower Agusan, the city dominates all of the commerce to and from upriver ports; this is a position that the completion of the Davao-Agusan highway strongly reinforces, as the city is the highway's northern terminus. Butuan was originally situated along the west bank of the river, but it has spread out westward along the coastal plain, and in the early 1960's, was spreading both southward and eastward across the river. Its charter area takes in a large rectangular territory that centers along the Agusan River for about 20 miles, and much of the area still is in forest, with an increasing amount of agricultural land. Butuan does not strongly resemble the typical old towns and cities of the Islands; it has an Americanized atmosphere about it and displays some of the "urban sprawl" characteristic of the growing American industrial-trade city. Unfortunately, the city is flooded frequently by the river. In addition to its administrative and general commercial functions, Butuan is an important lumber town. In 1960 the city proper had a population of 25,000 persons, and within the chartered limits lived 82,000 persons.

Nasipit and Cabadbaran are small sawmill centers located along the coast, with 1960 populations between 6,000 and 7,000. Cabadbaran also processes and ships considerable quantities of copra from its surrounding hinterland. Buenavista and Carmen are small coastal towns that serve local agricultural areas. Bunawan Esperanza, Prosperidad, San Francisco, and Talacogon are market towns in the interior. Esperanza, Talacogon, and Bunawan are river-port towns on the Agusan. Prosperided and San Francisco are located in the fertile tributary valley of the Gibong River and lie a short distance west of Lianga Bay. Bunawan, San Francisco, and Prosperided also lie along the Davao-Agusan highway and have overland connections with Lianga in Surigao del Sur Province.

Hills, Valleys and Troughs: Southwestern Mindanao

Southwestern Mindanao includes two of the major physiographic regions of the island—the Cotabato Lowland and the Tiruray Uplands or Cotabato Cordillera (fig. 78). Obviously, the physiography of these two units is quite dissimilar; nevertheless, the two physiographic regions share a considerable range of economic and cultural similarity. The Moslems of the Cotabato Lowland and the pagan Filipinos in the Tiruray Uplands had considerable intercourse in the period before the coming of the Spanish, and during most of the 300-year Spanish administration. The uplands served as a peripheral settlement area for many lowlanders, and the political patterns on the lowlands often extended into the adjacent upland areas, especially from the small Moro settlements along the southwestern coast. The Moros often viewed the uplands as a place of refuge, and its inhabitants as a source of slaves. Surrounded as they were by lowland-dwelling Moros, the Tiruray looked upon the latter as their principal market and only contact with the outside world. The militant resistance by the Moros to encroachment by the Spanish resulted not only in the isolation of the lowlands from Hispanization, but the isolation of the upland areas as well. In their cultural-historical traditions the two physiographic regions of southwestern Mindanao merit single regional discussion.

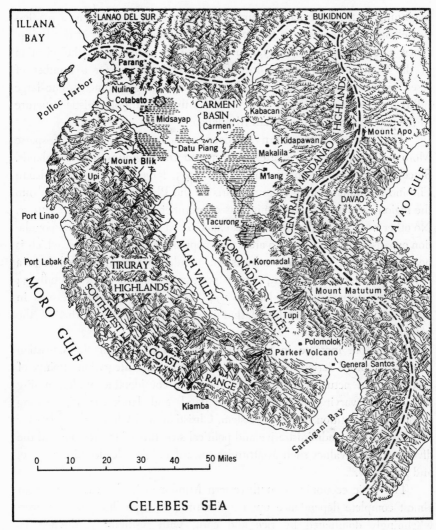

Fig. 78. Physiography of the southwestern Mindanao region.

As constituted, the southwestern Mindanao region embraces as area of approximately 8,800 square miles, an area split approximately equally between uplands and lowlands. In 1960 the region contained a population of slightly more than one million persons.

The principal regional characteristic of southwestern Mindanao is set by its distinctive pioneer occupance. In the years since 1948 more than 700,000 new settlers have arrived in the region,[15] and the region, which at the beginning of the twentieth century could have been described as a roadless wasteland, has now become the sixth most populous province in the Philippines. The large waves of migration were first set in motion by the selection of the Cotabato Lowland as one of the principal sites for a number of resettlement projects to be financed by the national government. The large influxes of migrants have, in turn, created a unique ethnolinguistic structure in the population of southwestern Mindanao.

The area of southwestern Mindanao was initially a region of sparse Moro settlement, with a scattering of pagan tribal groups in the uplands. Since about 1913, but particularly since 1945, large numbers of Christian Filipino migrants coming from all parts of the Philippine have moved into the region, so that now these migrants outnumber the original Moro settlers. No other area in the Philippines has experienced such a tremendous population expansion as the Cotabato area. The population of the province, which is nearly coincident with the southwestern Mindanao region, jumped from a crude population density of 14 persons per square mile in 1903, and only 34 persons per square mile as late as 1939, to a density of 130 persons in 1960—an average density figure that is still around one-half that of the national average.

The rapid increase in population, particularly within the Christian group, has posed serious problems of ethnoreligious integration. Points of potential and actual conflict which demand considerable understanding include the varying attitudes toward land and landownership; strong economic competition between Moslem, Christian, and Chinese; conflicts for domination of the administrative and political structure of the region; and the diverse cultural values such as attitudes toward religion, leadership, divorce, and polygamy.[16]

The basic economy of southwestern Mindanao is characterized by an almost complete dependence upon agriculture, an agriculture that is overwhelmingly dominated by rice and corn, with resultant production in amounts well above regional demands. Southwestern Mindanao has become one of the prime suppliers of foodstuffs to deficit areas in all parts of the Philippines.

THE PHYSICAL SETTING

The Cotabato Lowland is a large intermontane lowland that is half-graben in structure, with smaller synclinal embayments along its southern margins and two structural reentrants along the north. In its overall form the lowland measures approximately 50 miles in an east–west direction, and varies from 50 to 70 miles in length. The Cotabato Lowland is composed of five lowland subdivisions. The largest area of lowland is the Cotabato Valley itself. This extensive, low-lying, swampy plain, which is drained by the Rio Grande de Mindanao (Cotabato), the largest and longest river of Mindanao, includes a lowland area of well over 1,000 square miles. Recent uplift across the mouth of the river, which has formed the low Cotabato and Tinaco hills, has resulted in the impounding of river waters and the creation of two large swamp areas, the Libungan Marsh and the Liguasan Swamp. Together these two swamps cover a combined area of 450 square miles during normal water levels; however, the swamplands expand well beyond these limits when heavy seasonal rains and river floods inundate additional areas of the valley floor, and indeed, during heavy rains all of the lowland downstream from Lake Buluan looks like a vast lake from the air. The uplift across the river mouth also has resulted in the formation of two distributaries of the Rio Grande which, in turn, has resulted in considerable confusion as to the correct name of the river. The Cotabato and Tamentaka rivers are the two main distributaries of the master stream, the Rio Grande de Mindanao. The Rio Grande, rising far in the interior of Bukidnon Province, is variously known as the Cotabato, Mindanao, Rio Grande, and Pulangi. Throughout most of its course in its lower-valley section the river flows between natural levee banks that are only 3 to 6 feet above the waters. Several large tributaries join the Rio Grande along its lower course, including the Kabacan, Malabul, Mulita, Buluan, and Catisan rivers. Occasionally small hillocks, such as Cotabato Hill, Kudarangan Hills, and Kabalokan Hill, rise from the alluvium of the Cotabato Valley. In most instances the small hill lands are continuations of structures formed outside the region. The hills supply a local relief of several hundred feet to the Cotabato Valley.

Located upstream from the main Cotabato Valley in the northeastern corner of the province of Cotabato, and extending into the southern margins of Bukidnon Province, is the second of the Cotabato lowlands, the Carmen Basin. This broad synclinal basin gently plunges toward the south. The Rio Grande, in this section usually called the Pulangi River, flows across the basin floor, which is somewhat more elevated and less swampy than the lower Cotabato Valley. The Carmen Basin includes a lowland area of approximately 600 square miles.

The three synclinal embayments located along the southern margins of the Cotabato Lowland are the Allah, Alip, and Koronadal valleys, with extensions of the latter southward into the plain of the Buayan River at the head of Sarangani Bay. The long, narrow Allah Valley, sandwiched between the high eastern escarpment of the Daguma Range and the Roxas and Matulas ranges in the east, continues the Cotabato Lowland southwestward.

The Allah Valley measures approximately 30 miles in a northwest–southeast length, with an average width of 8 miles. Drainage is toward the northwest and the Cotabato River by means of the Allah, Banga, and Katilisan rivers. Most of the valley floor lies below the 1,000-foot contour. The Alip Valley, which continues the Cotabato Lowland southeastward, is located between the Alip Range on the west and the foothills of the Central Mindanao Highlands along the east. This youthful synclinal valley measures approximately 3 miles in width with a length of 15 miles. The Koronadal Valley in the south is the largest of the peripheral lowlands. With an average width of nearly 8 miles, the Koronadal extends for over 50 miles from the shores of Lake Buluan in the north to the head of Sarangani Bay. Structurally, the Koronadal Valley terminates at the low topographic divide located along the line between the Parker and Matutum volcanoes. North of the divide the drainage of the valley is dominated by the north-flowing Marbel River, whereas to the south, drainage is by way of the Buayan River into Sarangani Bay. The synclinal flexure responsible for the Koronadal Valley also projects into the Buayan Valley in the south, and both valleys are usually included under the name Koronadal Valley. The Koronadal lies between the high Roxas-Matulas-Parker Volcano mountain complex along the western margins, and the Quezon Range, a subsidiary range of the Central Mindanao Highlands, along the east. This latter range is dominated by the 7,500-foot-high Pliocene volcano, Mount Matutum. The floor of most of the Koronadal Valley is somewhat elevated, giving excellent drainage in most localities. The combined area of lowlands in southwestern Mindanao, including several smaller lowlands along the southwest coast, is approximately 3,500 square miles.

The Tiruray Highlands, or Cotabato Cordillera, occupy the extreme southwestern corner of Mindanao, and extend in an unbroken front along the Celebes Sea coast for more than 125 miles. The uplands have an average width of approximately 35 miles, and maximum elevations within them approach 4,000 feet. This upland area, horst-block in structure, is composed of four distinctive physiographic units. Fronting directly along the Celebes Sea is the 4,000-foot-high Southwest Coast Range. This first upland area presents rather abrupt slopes toward the south, and within a short distance offshore oceanic depths of 18,000 feet are encountered in the northern part of the Celebes Sea. The southern and western coasts of the coast range are generally terraced and sea-cliffed. The northern section of the Tiruray Highlands is composed of the Mount Blik Uplands, a cluster of Pliocene volcanoes with summits ranging between 3,000 and 4,000 feet in elevation. The eastern edge of the Tiruray upland area is formed by the Daguma Range, a narrow, linear mountain chain of fault-block origin. A high fault scarp lies along the eastern edge of the Daguma Range overlooking the Allah Valley. Between the Mount Blik Uplands and the Daguma Range is the Kulaman Plateau, an interior upland that lies at an elevation of approximately 3,000 feet. This highland basin measures approximately 50 miles by 25 miles and its surface is covered with a thick deposit of Tertiary sediments, consisting mainly of limestones, in which a youthful karst landscape has developed.

The topography of southwestern Mindanao is quite diverse; there are extensive areas of plains, including several well-drained areas as well as low-lying swampy lowlands, and there are rugged uplands. Considerable areas on the lowlands, and certain upland basins, are still only sparsely populated and offer excellent agricultural settlement possibilities. The poor drainage of much of the Cotabato Valley, and the inaccessibility of most other areas, remain serious problems that must first be overcome before the region develops to its full potential.

The position of the southwestern Mindanao region, at the southern edge of the Philippine Archipelago in latitude 7° North, insures a climate that is constantly warm and a location that is always close to the position of the Intertropical Convergence Zone. The exposed southwestern coast and most highland areas within the region receive abundant year-round rains averaging more than 100 inches annually. The lowlands, which generally lie behind uplands and are partially sheltered from moist air masses by their orographic effect, receive much less precipitation. Most of the lower and middle valley of the Rio Grande de Mindanao, including the Carmen Basin, receives an annual rainfall of 70–85 inches. The Allah, Koronadal, and Alip valleys receive only 50 to 60 inches of rainfall annually. The driest area in the region is the Buayan Plain at the head of Sarangani Bay, where the precipitation averages only 40 inches annually (General Santos, 38.45 inches). In this area climatic conditions typical of drylands are approached, and agriculture is possible only when supplementary irrigation waters are supplied. Fortunately, in most of southwestern Mindanao there is no real drought period, and only the Buayan Valley experiences a month when the average monthly rainfall is below 2.4 inches. December through March is the period of least rainfall throughout the region. In normal years the rainfall throughout southwestern Mindanao generally can be viewed as adequate and well-distributed for most agricultural purposes; however, farmers in the Allah, Alip, and Koronadal valleys periodically experience drought conditions sufficient to require replanting of the main grain crop, or cultivation of some of the "famine" root crops.

No complete soil survey has been undertaken in southwestern

Mindanao. Nevertheless, special surveys in the Koronadal and Allah valleys, and in the area surrounding Kidapawan, indicate an excellent soil base. Limestone and volcanic rocks are fairly widespread and usually give rise to an excellent agricultural soil. Much of the soil cover of the Cotabato Valley is swampy and poorly drained. Some of the finest agricultural land is found on the piedmont adjacent to the Central Mindanao Highlands.[17]

THE CULTURAL SETTING

Population and settlement have set the keynote of southwestern Mindanao. In 1960 the population of the region included approximately one million persons, and during the twelve intercensal years ending in 1960 the population of Cotabato Province had grown at a rate of 8.48 percent per year, the highest population growth rate of any province in the Philippines. At the end of this period the province of Cotabato ranked sixth in the size of its population, exceeded only by Rizal, Cebu, Negros Occidental, Leyte, and Pangasinan. The rapid growth of the southwestern Mindanao population in recent years has been the result of large-scale migrations. Several sections of the Cotabato Lowland, for example, Carmen, Koronadal, Allah, and Buluan, were chosen as sites for the resettlement projects subsidized by the national government, beginning in 1913. Although the numbers of settlers participating and the overall performance of these projects were somewhat disappointing, the programs served to initiate a tremendous voluntary migration to southwestern Mindanao. The influx of several hundred thousand migrants into southwestern Mindanao over the past decade, migrants who came mainly from Cebuano, Hiligaynon, Iloko, and Tagalog-speaking areas in the Visayan and Luzon areas, has brought into national focus and intensified many problems of ethnic stratification and integration. A considerable degree of skill and tolerance was called for in order to ensure a successful integration of the very sharp socioreligious differences between the resident Moslems and the immigrant Christians in the region—socioreligious differences that also had their manifestations in the economic and political sectors. Moslem Filipinos constituted approximately 35 percent of the population of Cotabato Province in 1960, a decrease in ratio of nearly 20 percent since the 1939 census. Christian Filipinos now make up approximately 55 percent of the population, as compared to only 35 percent in 1939. The tribal groups, consisting mainly of pagans living in the Tiruray Highlands and other inaccessible upland territory, constituted nearly 10 percent of the population in 1960, and the Chinese made up the balance. Thus, in a demographic sense the southwestern Mindanao region can be viewed as a sort of Philippine "melting pot," where Christian, Moslem, and pagan live together; one hopes they can live in peace.

The pre-Spanish occupance of southwestern Mindanao was by a predominantly Moslem Filipino population, with a sprinkling of Chinese traders and mountain tribesmen. The dominant Moslem group, the Maguindanao Moros, had their main living area near the mouth of the Cotabato River, but by the early fifteenth century, they had pushed up the river and crossed the drainage divide into the Davao Gulf area. This early Moro population was relatively sparse and quite static in total numbers. The Moros of Cotabato belonged to the Sultanate of Maguindanao, a relatively strong political unit centered on the lower Rio Grande de Mindanao Valley. The Maguindanao Moros are by tradition an inland-dwelling agricultural people who cultivate upland and lowland rice as their basic food crops. The Spanish authorities made numerous attempts to establish settlements near the mouth of the Rio Grande, but these were unsuccessful until late in the nineteenth century, and the Moros of the area maintained their militant resistance to Spanish authority. By the end of the Spanish era only a few Christians had managed to settle in southwestern Mindanao, and their total numbers probably were between one and two thousand. The Moros did not seem to mind the presence of the few Chinese traders who had migrated to the region. The Chinese merchants, usually without any deep religious convictions of their own, took up the Moslem faith if it was expedient, and frequently intermarried with the Moslem women. The resistance of the Moros to Hispanization (and Christianization) was succinctly summed up by an exasperated Jesuit priest.[18]

> We have no scruples in affirming and we do not believe that there is anyone who will be so rash as to deny that the principal obstacle in the way of reduction and civilization of Mindanao and Jolo is the Moslem population.

By 1900 the population of the southwestern Mindanao region stood at about 100,000 persons.[19] At this time most of the population was concentrated in the lower Rio Grande Valley. Lesser population concentrations were along the coast and in areas peripheral to the centers of greatest concentration. The upland areas were almost exclusively the home of primitive tribal groups.

The incoming American administration found southwestern Mindanao a virtual vacuum insofar as Spanish influence and control were concerned, and it was actually not until 1913 that a full measure of United States military and civil control was established in the area. In 1913 the first effective steps aimed toward the settlement of southwest Mindanao by Christian Filipinos were undertaken. The United States' Philippine administration felt that the settlement of the Cotabato area by outsider Filipino groups was advisable in order to facilitate the control of this Moro-dominated area and, at the same time, aid in the cultural integration of Christian and Moslem Filipinos. The increasingly acute problem of congested land settlement in central Luzon, along the Ilocos coast, and in central sections of the Visayan Islands, also could receive some benefit from the opening of new agricultural lands in Cotabato. Under the direction of the Insular Bureau of Lands, six settlement projects in Cotabato, with a total area of 35,000 acres, were thrown open to colonization between 1913 and 1917.[20] These early projects of government-subsidized pioneer colonization generally were considered failures, for when an assessment of the Bureau of Lands program was conducted in 1928 it was found that only 8,000 settlers and their dependents still remained in Cotabato. In 1935, under the commonwealth government, the National Land Settlement Administration (NLSA) was formed, and in 1938 the agency began an active settlement program. This agency, under the able direction of Major General Santos, planned the opening of 130,000 acres of land in the Koronadal Valley. The major Koronadal settlement project was divided into four settlement districts, which were, from north to south, Lagao, Polomolok, Tupi, and Marbel. Between February, 1939, and October, 1950, a total of 8,300 settler-families were settled in the Koronadal area under the auspices of NLSA. A similarly large area in the neighboring Allah Valley was thrown open to settlement at the same time, but without the NLSA's subsidy program. After 1950 the Land Settlement Development Corporation (LASE-DECO) replaced NLSA, and prior to its early demise in 1953, this corporation had managed to settle a total of 1,500 families, mostly in the Cotabato area. In 1954 President Magsaysay created the National Resettlement and Rehabilitation Administration (NARRA) with the threefold purpose of: (1) aiding the settlement of the relatively empty areas of the country, (2) settlement of large numbers of landless farmers upon farms of their own, and (3) resettlement of surrendered Huks (EDCOR). Major NARRA projects in Cotabato were located at Dulawan, Daguma, Koronadal, Allah, Carmen, and Columbio-Tulunan. By 1963 when NARRA was absorbed by the National Land Authority, it had settled a total of 11,000 settler-families in the Cotabato projects. Each of the settlement-project nuclei has become the site of an important market town or municipality poblacion, causing a wholesale reorganization of provincial political subdivision. With the balance of population rapidly shifting to southeastern Cotabato, the provincial capital was moved to Sultan Sa Barongis, which was nearer to the population center in 1960.

The importance of the various attempts to attract settlers to the relatively empty lands of southwestern Mindanao, and to the various settlement projects elsewhere in the Philippines, through government subsidies lies not in the actual numbers of people who participated directly in the programs, nor in whether these subsidized migrants have become permanent settlers in the migration areas, but in the tremendous stimulus these first projects gave to subsequent voluntary migrations. Literally hundreds of thousands of Filipinos have migrated to Mindanao at their own expense since the initial resettlement programs. The various government-sponsored projects demonstrated to the general public that the public domain in the Moro-occupied regions of Mindanao was safe to occupy, that the brief period of pioneer life was not to be feared, and the rewards of individual landownership merited a considerable sacrifice.

The population of the southwestern Mindanao region is concentrated at the mouth of the Rio Grande; in eastern piedmont areas near the Central Mindanao Highlands, particularly in the municipalities of Kidapawan, Makilala, and M'Lang; and in the lowland areas lying to the north and south of Lake Buluan, and continuing through the Koronadal Valley. Lesser concentrations are found along the middle course of the Rio Grande, between the municipalities of Datu Piang (Dulawan) and Kabacan, and along the northern and eastern shores of Sarangani Bay. The spectacular increase in the population of the Cotabato Lowland is almost wholly a phenomenon of the past two decades (figs. 79a, 79b). In earlier years the widespread prevalence of malaria, the general inaccessibility of the region, and the known or imagined hostility of the Moros combined to discourage settlement. As long as these deterrents were present, Cotabato's population increased at a rate considerably less than that of other parts of Mindanao. Between 1919 and the beginning of hostilities of World War II in 1941, the national government made several attempts toward making the lands of Mindanao more attractive to settlers by embarking upon the construction of major trunk roads that would link the major cities and settlement areas of Mindanao. Unfortunately, the main highway network of southwestern Mindanao was constructed very late in the prewar period, and at least in the minds of many Filipinos, the province of Cotabato maintained its reputation for Moro lawlessness through World War II. Only gradually has the image of a peaceful Cotabato been accepted in the northern and central parts of the Philippines.

The numbers of pagan tribal people within southwestern Mindanao have been steadily decreasing in the face of the large-scale Christian migrations and land settlement. The largest area of pagan peoples is in the Tiruray Highlands, where some 26,000 Tirrurai-speakers continue to occupy their

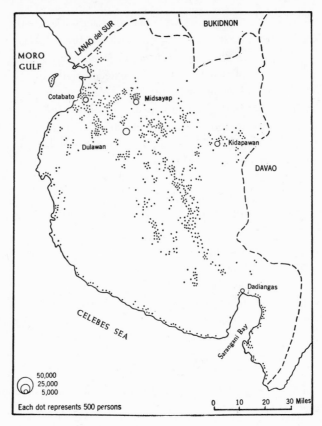

Fig. 79a. The distribution of population in Cotabato
Province, 1948.

steadily decreasing mountain homeland. Around the periphery of the Tiruray
uplands, Moros have been slowly infiltrating from the lowlands. Christian
Filipinos have moved into coastal areas of the Tiruray area, in the municipalities of Kiamba, Palimbang, Maitum, and Lebak in relatively large numbers,
chiefly following supplies of timber. Most of the Tiruray people continue to
practice shifting agriculture or relatively crude forms of sedentary cropping.
Hunting and gathering are still followed in some areas.

After World War II, a major trunk highway was constructed from Datu
Piang (Dulawan) through the Allah Valley, and improvements were made to
the Koronadal Valley highway. Both construction projects resulted in a
tremendous influx of new settlers. At first only a string of settlements were
made along the roads, but gradually people have moved back into the areas
located away from the main roads, and new dirt feeder roads have followed

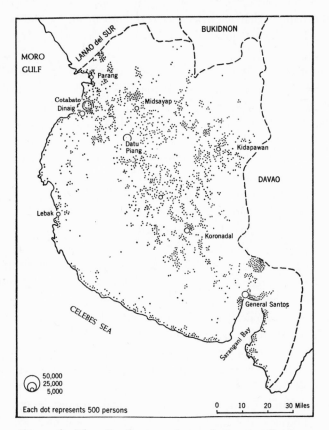

Fig. 79*b*. The distribution of population in Cotabato Province, 1960.

them. The lack of an adequate road network in the Cotabato Lowland, however, continues to restrict settlement, and in 1960 it was estimated that over 90 percent of the population of Cotabato Province lived within 10 miles of a road or shoreline.[21]

The large influx of people into the southwestern Mindanao region has been quite recent, much of it has been oriented toward an agricultural occupance, and there has been little development of any major urban centers in the region. Cotabato, with a 1960 population of 25,000, is the largest city in southwestern Mindanao. Cotabato served as the capital of Cotabato Province from 1914 to 1960, when the small town of Sultan Sa Barongis replaced it. Cotabato is located on the low, swampy interfluve land between the two main distributaries of the Rio Grande de Mindanao. The city lies along the southern banks of the Cotabato River some 3 miles above the river mouth.

One of the natural characteristics that continues to plague the city is poor drainage, a fact that is quite obvious at the airport after any heavy rain. Although the Cotabato River is navigable for larger vessels at Cotabato and for a short distance upstream, a shallow river-mouth bar prohibits their entrance. Small watercraft can ascend the Rio Grande and its major tributaries for considerable distances. Larger vessels, including all foreign shipping, use the facilities of the port of Parang, which is located on Polloc Harbor some 12 miles to the north.

Cotabato is an old city, and the derivation of its name, which means "fort," points to its earlier function. In spite of early beginnings, however, the city's population has remained relatively small for the principal commercial center of a region as large and as important as southwestern Mindanao. The more important functions of Cotabato include the providing of major retail, wholesale, shipping, and transportation services for the city and a part of the region. Cotabato's urban population is composed of several diverse ethnic groups. Most of the retail shops are owned by Chinese merchants, and the Cotabato Chinese Chamber of Commerce is a very strong organization, socially, politically, and economically. Christian Filipinos dominate the administrative and educational professions, especially the offices of the various provincial and national government agencies. Moros are especially active in port and various transportation activities.[22] Cotabato serves as a minor interisland port, airport, and highway terminus. If there is a primary regional center for the southwestern Mindanao region, the city of Cotabato must be considered as that center; however, the city's unattractive site and eccentric location have restricted development into a major commercial center approaching the stature of either Davao or Zamboanga.

Among the more important smaller urban centers of the region are the agricultural market towns of Datu Piang, Kidapawan, Koronadal, Midsayap, Sultan Sa Barongis, and General Santos. Each of these centers had a population in 1960 close to 10,000 persons in 1960. Datu Piang is the site of the principal ferry connection across the Rio Grande, and for a long time the town served as the seat of the Sultanate of Maguindanao. The trade area of Datu Piang includes most of the upper delta of the Rio Grande de Mindanao; much of the commerce from the new pioneer settlements in the lower Allah Valley also passes through Datu Piang. The town of Kidapawan is the primary commercial center for the important newly opened settlement areas on the lower western slopes of Mount Apo and the Carmen Basin. Koronadal is the principal commercial center for the Koronadal Valley projects of LASEDECO and NARRA. Midsayap, a market town north of the Rio Grande, serves the EDCOR projects of Gallego and Genio and various pioneer settlements located nearby in the foothills of the Midsayap Range. General Santos, the former town of Dadiangas, is the main shipping point and administrative headquarters for the Koronadal settlement projects. The small port town of Parang, situated at the head of Polloc Bay, is the major deepwater port of southwestern Mindanao and is classed as a national port. The small town of Sultan Sa Barongis, the former Lambayong, was established as the capital of Cotabato Province in 1960 in a move that was directed, in part, toward a readjustment of the eccentric location of capital to main areas of population. Taken a few months before designation of the new capital, the 1960 census listed the population of Sultan Sa Barongis poblacion at 3,800, a figure that has undoubtedly increased severalfold since the census enumeration. Each of these small urban centers provides retail and wholesale outlets, services, transportation facilities, and the other services normal to an important agricultural market center.

Most of the new towns of the Cotabato Lowland bear faint resemblances to the old towns built by the Spanish. Often not well planned, they may be centered around a single very wide street straddling the highway, with elongated margins and very few secondary streets. As the towns grow the laying-out of streets follows settlement in a somewhat haphazard manner. Early buildings are cheaply built of local materials, but later building gradually upgrades and improves appearances. Automotive service facilities frequently gain prominent positions in these settlements rather than the church, convent, municipio administrative structures, and homes of the leading families, as in the old Spanish towns.

No province in the Philippines has seen its minor civil divsions undergo such rapid and extreme change in the past decade. At least partly in response to large-scale migration, there has been a total of twenty-six new municipalities created in the province since 1948. Most of these new political units have been formed from the formerly large municipalities in the Allah and Koronadal valleys.

Twentieth-century road construction and settlement have gone hand in hand in southwestern Mindanao. Unfortunately, most of the region's roads are of extremely poor quality, usually dirt-surfaced, and many of the rivers must still be ferried. There still is little movement of passengers or cargoes interprovincially from Cotabato. The major trunk system serving southwestern Mindanao includes connections from Cotabato City through Kabacan to Davao Province, northward from Kabacan into Bukidnon Province and northern Mindanao (the Sayre Highway), and from Cotabato along the northern shores of Illana Bay and Lake Lanao into northern Mindanao. Major provincial roads run from Datu Piang through the Koronadal and

Allah valleys to the shores of Sarangani Bay. A short road leads south from Cotabato City into the Tiruray Highlands to the town of Upi. The present road network furnishes only the barest framework for minimum provincial and interprovincial transportation needs, and the quality and maintenance of the roads leaves a great deal to be desired. Overland bus and truck service in southwestern Mindanao are among the poorest in the Philippines.

Inland water transportation by launch, small craft, barge, and dugout is extremely important along much of the Rio Grande system. Much of the surplus rice and corn produced in inland municipalities moves overland to the river tributaries, and to Cotabato by water in small shipments.

Not only is agriculture the principal economic activity of the southwestern Mindanao region, it is almost the sole economic activity. The extremely rapid expansion of the agricultural area in recent years, owing to the large influx of population, has resulted in an equally large and rapid increase in agricultural production.[23] The leading crop in terms of total acreage is corn, but the area devoted to the cultivation of rice is nearly as large. The yields of both grains are slightly higher than those obtained at the national level, and both grains are produced in quantities considerably above regional requirements. Cotabato Province is an important supplier of these grains to the rest of the archipelago. Some 70,000 tons of shelled corn and nearly 100,000 tons of rough palay and milled rice are transported annually from the province by interisland vessels, particularly to deficit areas in the Visayas. The amount of land devoted to root crops also is quite large, reflecting the pressing need to secure early returns from the newly cleared pioneer farms. Coconuts and abaca are cultivated in small quantities at this still-early stage of agricultural occupance. Coffee, ramie, and pineapple are relatively new crops to the region, and although the area devoted to their cultivation is expanding, it is still relatively small. The Dole Corporation has recently developed a 20,000-acre lease-concession, which is planted in pineapple, on the slopes of Mount Matutum in the Koronadal Valley.

One aspect of crop productivity should be mentioned here, since there has been such a heavy influx of settlement within such a short period. In the tropics, it is characteristic of crop yields grown on lands cleared of forest to be very good for the first two or three years; then the yields decline steadily for about a decade, remaining relatively stable at a comparatively low level of yields for a considerable period after that. The early bountiful results from the Cotabato Lowlands may have been a factor in accelerating the rates of settlement. But once the lowlands are relatively filled up (and no more first-croppings can take place), and unless fertilization programs become standard cropping practice, neither the high yields nor the large surpluses of corn and rice may continue. Further increases in settlement-density patterns could then even negate the patterns of surpluses entirely.

The timber resources of southwestern Mindanao are quite large, but the lack of easy access to many of the forest lands has retarded their utilization. There are several small sawmills scattered through the region, with larger concentrations at Port Lebak, Nuling, and in the newly opened agricultural areas of Kidapawan, Makilala, and Carmen. Logs and lumber are shipped overseas through the ports of Parang, Lebak, Port Linao, and Davao.

All of the coastal settlements, as well as most river villages, participate in an extensive sustenance fishing industry. Whereas most of the commercial fish-catch, including mainly slipmouth, anchovy, nemipterid, and tuna, comes from the waters of Moro Gulf and Illana Bay, the rivers and lakes of the Cotabato Lowland supply important quantities of fish and fish products for local consumption. Although more so in the past, a relatively large crocodile catch comes from the Rio Grande de Mindanao. A total of approximately 9,000 acres have been developed into fishponds, and the potential fishpond area of the region totals an additional 175,000 acres, most of which is not suitable to other forms of use. Most of the population that lives adjacent to the coasts and rivers is self-sufficient in fish and fish products; however, inland communities are not so fortunate. The region occasionally ships small quantities of fish to Zamboanga and Davao.

Southwestern Mindanao is not a highly mineralized region. A few small deposits of iron ore and copper are located along the eastern flanks of the Tiruray Highlands and Central Mindanao Highlands; however, minerals play no significant role in the present economy of the region.

The limited development of manufacturing is restricted to local handicrafts and a few minor food-processing industries. Rice and corn mills are found in every poblacion, with somewhat larger concentrations in the municipalities of Midsayap, Koronadal, Kiamba, Tacurong, and Datu Piang. Home industries play a fairly significant role in southwestern Mindanao because of the general lack of marketing channels and facilities. The pineapple operations of the Dole Corporation will be the major industrial activity of southwestern Mindanao.

The Volcanic Highlands: Bukidnon and Lanao

The Bukidnon-Lanao Highlands region consists of a series of plateaus, highland basins, hills, and high volcanic ranges and peaks located in, and occupying nearly all of, north central Mindanao. This highland area, generally delimited by the 1,600-foot contour except in the south, extends eastward from near the shores of Panguil and Iligan bays to the high cordillera lands (Central Mindanao Highlands) which lie along the Bukidnon-Agusan provincial boundary. Included within this interior region is an upland area of approximately 5,000 square miles. Several broad expanses of relatively level arable land lie within the highlands, and owing to their elevations, they stand as islands of cooler temperatures. The lowland, coastal-living Filipinos have been slow to colonize the interior uplands of northern Mindanao, partly on account of the imagined or real hostility of certain of the indigenous people, and partly because of the region's general inaccessibility. An important exception to this general pattern of sparse settlement is found in the west, around the shores of Lake Lanao, where a dense Moslem settlement has been traditional since pre-Spanish times. The coastal lowlands bordering the Bukidnon area have had a long history of dense settlement by Visayan migrants, but it has only been during the past two decades, actually since the completion in 1941 of the Sayre Highway traversing Bukidnon, that the plateau lands in the east have experienced rapid settlement. No such migration has taken place in the Moro-dominated western uplands. The geographer-pedologist Robert Pendleton, writing in 1942, singled out the Bukidnon uplands as one of the prime areas of greatest potential for agricultural settlement in the Philippines, and during the past two decades migrants, coming mainly from the Visayan area, have arrived in ever-increasing numbers.[24]

Not all of the traditional Philippine crops appear to do well under the cooler temperatures of the uplands. Coconuts are completely absent. Since the streams are deeply entrenched into the plateau surface, it is very difficult to provide water for wet-field rice, and this widely cultivated Philippine crop is generally absent except in the vicinity of Lake Lanao. On the other hand, corn does extremely well, and many fruits and vegetables not usually associated with Philippine agriculture are now frequently grown in the cooler uplands.

The Bukidnon-Lanao Highland region embraces most of the areas of the provinces of Bukidnon and Lanao del Sur, together with adjacent sections of interior Lanao del Norte. The population of the 5,000-square-mile region in 1960 totaled approximately 650,000.

THE PHYSICAL SETTING

Basically the Bukidnon-Lanao region is constituted as a physiographic region, one of the major physiographic units of Mindanao, as recognized by Irving and Ranneft.[25] Coupled with the physiographic homogeneity, however, are close similarities in the climate, edaphic, and vegetational environments. Except for peripheral area, such as southern Bukidnon where the alluvial lowland of the Pulangi (Rio Grande de Mindanao) intrudes, and along other major river courses, the Bukidnon-Lanao Highland region is of volcanic origin. The region is generally delimited by the contact zone of volcanic rocks with underlying sedimentary and basement-complex materials. The eastern section of the region consists of the broad, deeply eroded, basalt plateaus of Bukidnon Province; the western segment, in the Lanao provinces, is basically formed by several chains of Miocene and Recent volcanoes with their lava flows standing as plateaus, but is dominated by the 134-square mile Lake Lanao (fig. 80). The plateaus have all been formed by extrusive vulcanism, mainly basalts and pyroclastics. Numerous isolated volcanic peaks and clusters of volcanic mountains project above the general level of the plateau surface. Mounts Katanglad and Kalatungan in central Bukidnon are especially prominent, reaching to 9,500 feet, whereas several peaks in the west (Mounts Ragang, Piagayunga, Butig, and Makaturing) in Lanao del Sur

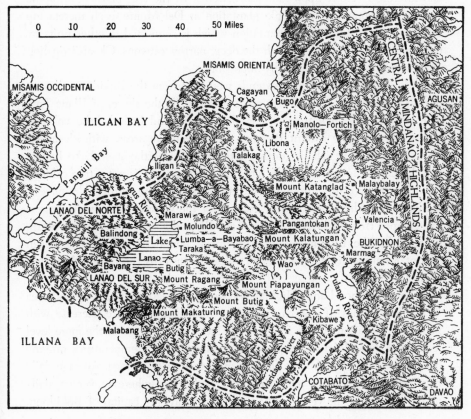

Fig. 80. Physiography of the Bukidnon-Lanao region.

Province rise to between 6,000 and 9,500 feet. Basalt and pyroclastic materials have spread out to great distances from the two high volcanoes of Katanglad and Kalatungan, and it is these long, gently sloping lava flows that are responsible for the plateau topography of most of Bukidnon Province. Between these two major volcanoes of Bukidnon, lying at an elevation of approximately 3,000 feet, is the broad Miaryan Plain. The main plateau of Bukidnon extends the north–south length of the province, sandwiched between the two volcanic masses of Katanglad and Kalatungan and the Central Mindanao Highlands. The northern and central sections of the plateau lie at elevations of 2,000 to 3,000 feet, descending to elevations under 1,000 feet in the south along the upper reaches of the Pulangi River. The numerous rivers of Bukidnon, among them the Cagayan, Tagoloan, Iponan, and Pulangi, have cut deep incisions into the upland surface. The canyons that have been formed usually have near-vertical walls of great height, making road construction very difficult and costly.

The meseta-like topography of Bukidnon Province has had important and interesting effect upon land-use patterns. In the area of the Philippine Packing Corporation's pineapple plantation at Del Monte, each meseta top contains a major unit of the plantation which is connected to other units by roads winding down and through the deep, narrow canyons. Cheap irrigation in this type of country is virtually impossible.

The Lanao volcanic area extends westward from the Bukidnon Plateau to near the head of Panguil Bay and southward to the shores of Illana Bay. The structure of the Lanao area is all volcanic, and includes the volcanic clusters surrounding Mount Ragang, the plateau-like areas, with elevations up to 4,000 feet, which lie north, northwest, and northeast of Lake Lanao, and the Lake Lanao basin itself. The Lake Lanao basin is not a true caldera, but originated possibly through a volcanic dam across the southern drainage of the basin or perhaps through the collapse of the volcano after much magma had escaped from its interior.[26] The Agus River drains the lake to the north. Close along the Bukidnon-Lanao provincial boundary and lying between Mount Kalatungan and the Ragang volcanic cluster is the broad Maridagao River Valley.

The Bukidnon-Lanao Highlands possesses the largest usable upland area in the Philippines. If one can assume a normal temperature decrease with increasing elevation of 1°F. for each 280 feet,[27] the majority of the more level sections of the upland will experience average monthly temperatures ranging between 71° and 74°, a very pleasant, near-temperate average. Average daily maximum temperatures reach into the high 80's, whereas average daily minimums are in the very low 60's at Malaybalay, the capital of Bukidnon, which is situated at an elevation of 2,300 feet. Rainfall is quite heavy throughout the region, with most agricultural areas receiving in excess of 100 inches annually. The higher mountain slopes that are well exposed to moisture-bearing air masses receive very heavy rains. Rainfall is fairly evenly distributed through the year, with the period of lightest rainfall occurring during the months of January, February, and March. Certain intermontane basins, such as at Manolo Fortich (Maluko) in northern Bukidnon, and areas located in the lees of high mountain ranges, receive annual rainfalls between 70 and 80 inches.

The heavy precipitation and near-tropical temperatures of the Bukidnon-Lanao Highlands undoubtedly supported an extensive and relatively dense tropical rain forest, and even today there are large prime commercial stands of molave, kamagon, tindalo, lumbayo, and red and white lauans. Approximately 40 percent of the region remains in commercial forests; [28] however, as a consequence of the Bukidnon peoples' widespread practice of shifting agriculture, there are extensive areas of grasslands on the plateaus and lower slopes of the mountains. Cogon is the dominant grass, but other grasses such as bagukbok, Johnson grass, redtop, silibon, and talahib occur over wide areas. The repeated firings of the grass-covered clearings for cattle pasturage have precluded their return to forest growth. The grasslands, however, are not without their benefits, for they retard soil erosion and at the same time furnish an excellent forage for a cattle industry, particularly in the province of Bukidnon. The mixed species composing the grassland plant cover are of much higher quality than the cogon-talahib covers of the lowlands.

The soils of the uplands can be classed as relatively fertile. In the moist highland climate the basic parent materials of volcanic ejecta weather quickly and deeply, giving rise to deep soils with a relatively high concentration of clay. The soils are brown to dark brown in color with characteristics of moderate to excessive drainage. At low elevations the soils are only mildly acidic, but their acidity increases sharply with altitude. The majority of the soils are deficient in phosphorous, potassium, and calcium. In general, they lend themselves to mechanization, especially where there are broad expanses of level land, such as on the Bukidnon Plateau.

THE CULTURAL SETTING

Physiography, climate, and soils have combined to create an extremely attractive agricultural potential in the Bukidnon-Lanao Highlands. Considerable contrasts in settlement patterns, agriculture, and other land-use patterns can be found in the Bukidnon-Lanao region which must be related to cultural differences of the settlers. Approximately one-third of the population of Bukidnon Province belongs to the Filipino enthnolinguistic group known as the *Bukidnons,* or "mountain people." Although many of these Bukidnons have accepted the ways of the migrant Cebuano-speaking population and now live among them as subsistence farmers, or serve as farmhands on the latter's plantations and cattle ranches, many others continue to follow their traditional way of life as caingineros in the more remote areas of the province. These original Bukidnon settlers are in the minority in their own homeland, however, having gradually been inundated by successive waves of lowland Filipino migrants coming mainly from the Cebuano-speaking areas in the Visayas, or from the province of Misamis Oriental on the north coast of Mindanao, where Cebuanes have long been in the majority. The *dumagats,* as the migrants are popularly called, have brought with them their characteristic central Visayan economy, centering around the cultivation of corn, camotes, and upland rice; and although subsistence farming is the rule, a good many migrants have developed extensive farms and ranches that contain hundreds and even thousands of acres, particularly in the plateau lands south and west of the capital city of Malaybalay. The large, successful pineapple plantation owned by the Philippine Packing Corporation (Del Monte) is located near the northwestern edge of the Bukidnon Plateau in the municipalities of Libona and Manolo Fortich. In contrast to the caingin and subsistence farms of the region, this 16,000-acre pineapple plantation is as modern as similar operations in Hawaii. Rubber, cinchona, oranges, coffee, and various vegetables also are raised commercially in the uplands. Then there are the occupance patterns associated with the Maranao Moslem population of the two Lanao provinces in the west, particularly those that have developed in the very densely settled area surrounding Lake Lanao in Lanao del Sur. Two large NARRA resettlement projects, at Maramag (Bukidnon) and Wao (Lanao del Sur), give additional variety to the patterns of land use.

The extensive areas of unused or underused agricultural land, climatic conditions conductive to an agricultural occupance with heavy rains and elevation-induced cooler temperatures, and generally peaceful political conditions in the east serve today as a strong magnet to attract thousands of new settlers from the more crowded areas of the Philippines; however, this area has not always functioned as a magnet. Historical evidence suggests a very early occupance of the region by various primitive tribal mountain peoples, including members of the Bukidnon, Manobo, Bagobo, and Negrito groups. The numbers were never very large, for even now their descendants number fewer than 75,000, and their impact upon the land was minimal except in the creation of broad expanses of grasslands through their caingin operations.

The first outsiders to enter the upland were coastal Filipinos of Malay extraction who settled in relatively large numbers in the west around the shores of Lake Lanao. These early Lake Lanao settlers eventually came under the sway of Islam in the fifteenth and sixteenth centuries. Known as the Maranao Moros, they remained militantly opposed to Spanish and early American attempts at pacification and colonization until their resistance was finally crushed by American military forces in 1913. The old Spanish fortresses at Iligan, Cagayan de Oro, and Malabang, and the maintenance of an American military base at Camp Keithley, Marawi City (Dansalan), attest to the bitterness of the struggle. The Maranao Moros, operating from a relatively secure stronghold in the vicinity of the lake, made periodic raids upon the Christian settlements in northern Mindanao and the Visayas until late in the nineteenth century. Today their descendants number nearly 400,000, nearly all of whom reside in the province of Lanao del Sur and neighboring municipalities of Lanao del Norte and Bukidnon. The Moros of the Bukidnon-Lanao region represent nearly 30 percent of all Philippine Moslems.[29]

The two provinces of Bukidnon and Lanao were organized in 1914 and were soon internally developed as to municipalities. In Bukidnon, local government has been chiefly in the hands of Christian Filipinos, and operations have been carried out as in any Christian province. In Lanao, on the other hand, affairs have been in the hands of the Moros, and although all the regular institutional forms and procedures are utilized, the Moro traditional sociopolitical structure has continued pretty much as in the past, administering local affairs in traditional ways via the newer machinery and institutions.

A certain degree of security gradually has been established in the Lake Lanao area, although this has not always been viewed with confidence by many Filipinos. Christian Filipinos from Cebu, Negros, Bohol, Panay, and Leyte have migrated into the peripheral Moro areas along the north coast of Mindanao around Iligan and Panguil bays, and in the south along the shores of Illana Bay. Within the newly created province of Lanao del Sur, Moslems outnumber Christians by a ratio of nearly 18 to 1, and within this province Christians form significant minority groups only in the capital city of Marawi (14 percent), the south coast port city of Malabang (21 percent), and in the municipality of Wao (71 percent), where the NARRA has been active. Moros are in the majority in the Lanao del Norte municipal districts of Nunungan, Pantao-Ragat, Munai, Baloi, Tangkal, and Matungao. Christians, on the other hand, have gained ascendancy along the north coast in Lanao del Norte, a factor that was one of the important considerations in the division of the former single province of Lanao in 1959. Christian Filipinos have succeeded in far outstripping in numbers the mountain peoples of Bukidnon. The NARRA-sponsored resettlement projects of Maramag, Pangantukan, and Wao reserved some 120,000 acres of near-virgin lands which have been thrown open to general settlement. Although NARRA directly settled relatively small numbers, the project has served to encourage large-scale voluntary migrations.

In general, population densities within Bukidnon are relatively light with an overall crude population density of slightly more than 60 persons per square mile for the province, and a maximum density of 120 persons per square mile in the southern municipality of Kibawe. The area that lies in the immediate vicinity of Lake Lanao, on the other hand, ranks among the more densely populated agricultural areas in the Philippines. More than 250,000 persons live within 3 miles of the lake shore, and agricultural population densities approach 1,600 persons per square mile. Other relatively dense concentrations of people are found in the newly settled areas near the head of Panguil Bay in Lanao del Norte, and along sections of the Sayre Highway in Bukidnon. Elsewhere, population is quite sparse, although much of the land is capable of supporting a relatively large agricultural occupance.

The only urban centers of more than local significance in the Bukidnon-Lanao Highlands are the two provincial capital cities of Marawi—formerly the town of Dansalan—and Malaybalay, and the newly chartered south coast city of Malabang. Marawi City, with a 1960 population of 8,000 in the city proper and 27,000 living within the chartered city limits, is the largest city of the region. Formerly serving as the capital of the province of Lanao, it has now become the capital of Lanao del Sur. Marawi is the cultural center of the Maranao Moros. Its dusty, crowded streets are lined with small shops displaying imported items or items of Philippine origin and the handicrafts produced by the Moros. Within the city are located numerous provincial administration buildings, several mosques, and a large public market, which is open every day. Marawi is an educational center with several elementary and secondary schools and the new State University of Mindanao. The university, opened in 1962, is designed to serve the needs of higher education in the southern Philippines, as well as serving as an instrument of social and cultural integration. Camp Keithley, the former headquarters of the American forces for the Mindanao military district, lies adjacent to the city.

Marawi City occupies low rolling hill land at the northern end of Lake Lanao. The Agus River, which drains the Lanao over the high plateau escarpment to the north, carries the lake past the city at an elevation of 2,297 feet above sea level. The hydroelectric potential of the upper Agus River augurs well for future industrialization in Marawi. The city is an important transportation center. A small wharf serves the busy small-launch traffic on the lake. Marawi and Iligan, the latter the capital of Lanao del Norte, share an airport located midway between the two cities. The National Highway connects Marawi with the north coast port city of Iligan 22 miles away, and with the south coast port of Malabang, 42 miles distant. The provincial capital status of Marawi has permitted a greater influx of Christian Filipinos, coming as representatives of the national government, then elsewhere in traditional Moslem Lanao del Sur.

Malaybalay, the capital city of Bukidnon Province, is situated on a broad plateau immediately east of Mount Katanglad. Its population of approximately 8,000 persons in 1960 makes it the largest urban center of the province. In addition to its administrative functions, Malaybalay serves as an important commercial center for the north and the larger farms in the south. Located astride the Sayre Highway between the provinces of Misamis Oriental, Cotabato, and Davao, it is an important highway transit town. Public and parochial secondary schools and the Normal College make it the center of higher education for the province.

Malabang, is the only port located within the Bukidnon-Lanao region; however, its commercial hinterland is restricted to the narrow coastal plain lying immediately to the northwest and southeast. Iligan, Cagayan de Oro, and Bugo, even though located outside the region, function as the principal ports for the Bukidnon-Lanao area. A chartered city since only 1962, Malabang has had a long settlement history. Dominating much of the coastline of Illana Bay and guarding the southern approaches to Lake Lanao, Malabang was the site of a Spanish fortress during the eighteenth century. The most recent development in Malabang's hinterland has been the relatively rapid growth of estate or plantation agriculture. Today the local area produces substantial quantities of copra, abaca, and cassava. The city is located along the Mataling River, a short distance from the mouth. The small port facilities maintain daily schedules with the ports of Pagadian, Parang, and Cotabato.

A second hierarchy of urban centers is formed by a relatively small group of agricultural market towns, including Kibawe, Libona, Manolo Fortich, Maramag, Talakag, and Valencia in Bukidnon, and Baloi, Balindong, Bayang, Molundo, Taraka, and Wao in Lanao. Each of these towns had an urban population between 2,000 and 3,000 in 1960 except Wao, which had a population of 6,000. The larger size of Wao is due to the extreme isolation of this important NARRA-inspired settlement.

Not only are there no large urban centers in the Bukidnon-Lanao Highlands, but outside of the main market towns practically none of the services usually associated with urban functions in Philippine towns are available. At best, the local barrio *tiendas,* or shops, will carry only a few items, such as needles and thread, tiny kerosene lanterns, a few tins of kerosene, cheap candy, and a few *gantas* of rice and corn.[30] The population of much of the region away from the commercially oriented areas is pretty much self-sufficient, requiring only a few items of manufacture or purchase in exchange for which they are prepared to barter surpluses of rice, corn, abaca, or local handicrafts.

Subsistence agriculture on the smaller landholdings still dominates the regional economy, but the larger holdings engage in commercial agriculture. Corn and rice are produced in quantities well beyond local regional needs, and large quantities of both grains move to coastal ports in Lanao del Norte and Misamis Oriental for shipment to food-deficit areas in the Visayas and Manila. There is an increasing trend toward an exchange or commercial economy. Both upland and lowland rice are cultivated on approximately equal areas; however, there are strong intraregional differences in rice agriculture. Nearly 85 percent of the lowland rice is grown in the western half of the region, mainly on the lake plain surrounding Lake Lanao. Approximately 40 percent of the lowland rice crop is grown under some form of water control in the municipalities of Butig, Pantao-Bayabao, Lumba-a-Bayabao, and Taraka. About one-quarter of the lowland fields carry a second crop of rice within the space of a single year. All the rice of Bukidnon is of the upland dry-field variety. Yields obtained in the Lake Lanao area are nearly one-quarter higher than those obtained nationally, whereas Bukidnon yields are lower than the national average by a similar proportion. Corn, the second-ranking grain, does extremely well throughout the region; however, it is more widespread in Bukidnon. Corn cultivation in Lanao is usually relegated to the poorer lands and steeper slopes, for the limited amounts of arable land are cultivated in wet-field rice wherever possible. In Bukidnon, on the other hand, the settlers from Cebu and Bohol, who form a majority of the population, have brought with them a long tradition of corn cultivation, and on fertile and recently occupied lands the yields of corn are nearly double those obtained nationally.

Elevations on the plateau are sufficiently high that a near-temperate regime is developed, and traditional crops, as well as many crops not usually associated with traditional Philippine tropical agriculture, are extensively cultivated. Coffee, cabbages, onions, and Irish potatoes are grown in relatively large quantities. There are also large acreages devoted to commercial production of jackfruit and mangoes, which do well in this region.

The most important fruit crop associated with the Bukidnon upland area, however, is the commercial plantings of pineapple at Del Monte.

Initiated on a very modest experimental scale in 1926, the Philippine Packing Corporation, a subsidiary of California Packing Corporation, now operates a 20,000-acre lease of which nearly 16,000 acres are devoted to the production of an excellent Smooth Cayenne pineapple that bears a fruit possessing the same excellent qualities of the Hawaiian-grown pineapple. The company also has branched into other food-processing activities, including the preparation of tomato sauce, tomato catsup, vinegar, and several pineapple-based canned fruit preparations such as a newly introduced tropical fruit salad and a pineapple-mango fruit dessert. A large modern cannery is located nearby on the coast of Misamis Oriental at Bugo, and the resultant fruit and juice pack represents an annual export valued at $8,000,000 to $12,000,000. Most of the fruit goes to the United States, with small shipments going to Canada and the countries of Western Euorpe. Nine out of ten cans of Del Monte Brand pineapple sold in the eastern United States are packed in Mindanao. A cattle-feeding industry has developed in association with the plantation, based upon the enriched pineapple wastes. Approximately 5,000 head of cattle are raised, and each month approximately 100–150 head are sent to markets in Cebu and Cagayan de Oro. A labor force of between 1,500 and 2,000 workers services the plantation. The company provides a hospital, schools, and a commissary, and supplies housing, electricity, and water. An additional 1,500 workers, mostly women, are employed at the cannery. The plantation occupies several small tablelands located at elevations ranging between 1,600 and 2,200 feet. The soils of the plantation fields are relatively fertile, having weathered from the deep deposits of volcanic materials ejected from Mount Katanglad, but they require rather heavy applications of lime and potash. Plant diseases and insect pests constitute a serious problem, and their control requires periodic sprayings with insecticides. Spraying of maturing plants with hormone mixtures ensures a relatively even ripening of fruit in whole field-block units, thus permitting the concentration of harvesting procedures. Numerous operations are fairly well mechanized to facilitate what is one of the most efficient agricultural undertakings in the Philippines. The overall operation of the Philippine Packing Corporation in Bukidnon has been so successful that the Dole Corporation has developed a new pineapple plantation and cannery in Cotabato Province on Mindanao, its first outside of the Hawaiian Islands.

The Bukidnon-Lanao region produces surpluses in almost all of its food crops. Abaca is the only important nonfood crop cultivated in Bukidnon Province, and approximately 6 percent of the total Philippine abaca harvest is produced in the province. Abaca is cultivated in Lanao, although the production is consumed locally in household industries. The areas planted in abaca in Bukidnon are located mainly along rivers and streams, and the plantings are, for the most part, small holdings averaging 1 to 3 acres in size. Nearly 27,000 acres were devoted to abaca in Bukidnon in 1960, with the main production centered in the municipalities of Malaybalay and Talakag. The nearly 10,000 acres of abaca in Lanao del Sur is located in Kapi municipality; it is hand-stripped and marketed in Malaybalay or shipped loose to Cebu.

For many years a cattle industry was of considerable importance. The extensive grass-covered plateau lands of Bukidnon are well suited to cattle grazing, particularly those that are covered with bagukbok, redtop, silibon, and cattail grasses. Prior to World War II, Bukidnon was the leading Philippine cattle province; however, wholesale slaughtering decimated the herds during the years of World War II. Even the breeding-stock was destroyed. Rehabilitation of the herds has been slow. Most of the cattle are imported breeds of Indian Nellore cattle. Today a few very large cattle ranches with several thousand head of cattle each are located in the Bukidnon municipalities of Maramag, Manolo Fortich, Libona and Malaybalay. Cattle are shipped live to markets in Cebu and Manila.

The economic development of the Bukidnon-Lanao region has suffered severely from the lack of transportation facilities. As it is basically an interior region, except for the coastal strip along Illana Bay which has been appended to the region mostly for convenience, though there are some strong cultural ties, a road system is the only answer to effective communications and active participation in the expanding national economy. Unfortunately, the rough topography of much of the Bukidnon-Lanao upland area imposes strong economic restrictions to road construction. Only the bare skeleton of a road network exists. Two major highways run longitudinally through the region, and both are poorly maintained gravel and dirt roads. In Bukidnon the Sayre Highway connects most of the important urban centers of that province with one another and with towns in the adjacent provinces of Cotabato and Misamis Oriental. There are a few feeder roads in the province, although at best these run only a few miles away from the main highway. Several bus companies provide relatively frequent service along the Sayre Highway. In Lanao del Norte the National Highway leaves the narrow north coast plain at Iligan, laboriously climbs the high escarpment over an extremely rough road to Lake Lanao, parallels the western side of the lake, and finally descends in a rough, winding road to Illana Bay at Malabang. There are even fewer lateral roads in the west, and there is not even a completed road around the densely settled eastern shores of Lake Lanao. The important NARRA settlement at Wao, located in the southeastern corner of Lanao del Sur, is virtually out of contact with the rest of the province during the rainy season.

The major port facilities for the region are provided in the neighboring provinces of Lanao del Norte and Misamis Oriental. Even today the lack of good roads remains the greatest single deterrent to increased settlement in the highlands, for not only does inaccessibility discourage initial settlement, but any cash-crop production from isolated areas on the plateau would have extreme difficulty reaching coastal markets.

Economic activities other than those directed toward an agricultural occupance do not occupy a position of any great strength in the Bukidnon-Lanao Highlands region. Logging and sawmilling are poorly developed, with less than 1 percent of the total sawmill capacity of the Philippines located within the region. This low figure should not be viewed as a reflection upon the wealth of the timber resources of the region, for it is substantial; rather it is a reflection of the inaccessibility of many of the commercial timber stands. Fishing is important in the waters of Lake Lanao, in some of the larger rivers, and along the southern shores facing Illana Bay; however, many interior communities never see fresh fish. Mineral resources are imperfectly known or of minor importance. Industries have not been attracted to the Bukidnon-Lanao area owing to its inaccessibility, lack of economic resources, and the relative sparsity of population for labor and markets. The gradual development of the hydroelectric potential of the Agus River will undoubtedly encourage some industrialization in the Marawi area in the relatively near future, but it is difficult to see why the more accessible coastal areas near Iligan should not absorb most of any industrialization program based on the Agus power. In short, although the Bukidnon-Lanao Highlands seem destined for a much greater development in the distant future, this development will, in the nearer future, be one of an increased agricultural nature.

The Peninsula of the Zamboangas

The westernmost region of Mindanao embraces most of the 150-mile-long, southwest–northeast–trending Zamboanga Peninsula, together with several adjacent large and small islands and islets, only eighteen of which have an area greater than 1 square mile. Never more than 50 miles in width, the peninsula of Zamboanga slims to a width of only 10 miles at the head of Panguil Bay in the isthmus where the peninsula joins the rest of Mindanao. Mountains and low rugged hill lands occupy most of the peninsula. There are few areas of lowlands, the largest of which are located at Dipolog, in northeastern Zamboanga, and on the Sibuguey and Baganian peninsulas in the south (fig. 81). The coastline of Zamboanga is quite irregular, particularly along the northern shores of Moro Gulf, and measures nearly 1,000

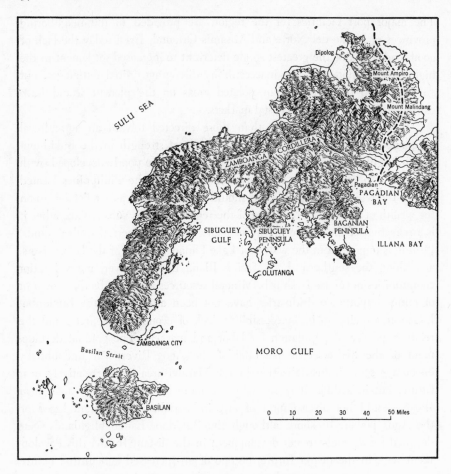

Fig. 81. Physiography of Zamboanga Peninsula.

miles in length. The Zamboanga region includes an area of approximately 6,500 square miles.

The Zamboanga region is located deep within the heart of the Moslem-dominated southwestern Philippines; however, the region lacks the overwhelming numbers of Moros which typify the populations of the adjacent areas to the west in the Sulu Archipelago, and to the east in the province of Lanao del Sur. In the two provinces of Zamboanga del Norte and Zamboanga del Sur, which occupy most of the peninsula, Christian Filipinos outnumbered Moslems by a ratio of nearly 4 to 1 in 1960. Moslems are more numerous only on the large island of Basilan which lies off the southwestern tip of the peninsula. If the island of Basilan is excluded from the region, the ratio of Christians to Moslems increases to 9 to 1. Although the ratio between

Christians and Moslems has been increasing sharply in favor of the former under the impact of large-scale postwar migration, Christians have been relatively numerous in the present province of Zamboanga del Norte since early in the Spanish era. The relatively numerous pagan population is now confined to the municipalities of Sindangan and Dumingag.

The Zamboanga Peninsula represents a historical cultural meeting ground between Moslem and Christian, and the outcome of these contacts has resulted in a blending of the two cultures which furnishes the outstanding regional characteristic. This character is most evident in the port city of Zamboanga, the regional commercial center that has functioned as the principal trade center for the southern and southwestern coasts of Mindanao as well as for the islands of the Sulu Archipelago.

THE PHYSICAL SETTING

The highlands that dominate the interior of Zamboanga Peninsula constitute the fourth of the major upland structural members of the island of Mindanao: the Pacific Cordillera, the Central Mindanao Highlands, Cotabato Cordillera, and the Zamboanga Cordillera. The Zamboanga Cordillera is separated from the main mass of Mindanao, except for the narrow horst that forms the isthmus between Pagadian and Panguil bays. Although physiographically part of Zamboanga Peninsula, the province of Misamis Occidental has already been discussed with the northern Mindanao region with which it shares strong cultural and economic ties. The Zamboanga Cordillera includes the northeast–southwest–trending main cordillera, which extends the length of the peninsula, and the lesser ridges of the Sibuguey and Baganian peninsulas in the southeast. All of the highlands merge in the volcanic complex of northeastern Zamboanga where the highest elevations in the region are found on the summits of Mounts Ampiro (7,212 feet) and Malindang (8,196 feet). These isolated volcanic mountain masses are located along the Zamboanga–Misamis Occidental provincial boundary. The main topographic divide of the peninsula has an elevation of approximately 2,000 feet, although there are numerous low gaps through the cordillera. Along the Sulu Sea coast the highlands descend precipitously, leaving little room for development of coastal lowlands. There are more gentle slopes toward the south and southeast, eventually leveling off to the broad shelf that is peripheral to Moro Gulf and the Celebes Sea. Along the south coast there are several deep coastal embayments, and at the heads of the bays are some of the larger lowlands, particularly along Sibuguey Gulf and Dumanquilas and Pagadian bays. The broad, gently sloping piedmont lands that lie south of Dipolog, and in the municipalities of Molave and Tambulig, are surfaced with volcanic materials ejected from Mounts Ampiro and Malindang and offer excellent agricultural sites. Elsewhere, lowland areas are confined to narrow coastal bands of sedimentary materials, formed largely of coralline reef materials, or to small river floodplains. The larger rivers of the peninsula include the Sibuguey, Salug, Sindangan, and Dapitan. Most of the offshore islands are low-lying and formed of coralline reef materials. The lack of large areas of lowlands along the north coast has certainly restricted settlement. Zamboanga del Sur, on the other hand, offers several excellent agricultural areas.

Basilan Island, located across a narrow strait from the south end of the mainland peninsula, is a large volcanic island surrounded by a cluster of islets, reefs, and rocks, and totals 495 square miles in area. About 25 miles north–south by 36 miles east–west, more than twenty volcanic peaks dot the Basilan skyline, topped by Basilan Peak (Lamitan Peak) at 3,316 feet in the south central sector. There is no regular arrangement of the volcanoes, so that a somewhat irregular physiography is present with a roughly radial pattern of drainage by short streams. Volcanic ash, tuffs, cinders, and flow basalts thickly cover the island, some sectors showing considerable etching by stream erosion, and other sectors showing but little erosional effect since the volcanic deposition. Scattered throughout the irregular topography are considerable areas of gentle footslopes, between-cone tablelands, and stream valleys that, with the irregular coastal lowlands, possess deeply weathered soils of good quality.

Precipitation conditions vary considerably over the region, although in most areas rainfall amounts are adequate for most forms of agriculture. In general, the early months of the year—January, February, March, and April—are drier; however, no real drought is experienced anywhere along the south-facing coast, and only in a few sheltered places along the northwest coast. A longer and more severe drought season, ranging from one to three months with less than 2 inches of rain monthly, is felt on the southern tip of the peninsula in the vicinity of Zamboanga City, and on nearby Basilan Island. Except at Zamboanga and on Basilan average annual precipitations exceed 80 inches everywhere, and along the south-facing Moro Gulf coast, precipitation is in excess of 100 inches. Most areas on Basilan receive annual precipitations between 60 and 70 inches. The driest locale in the region, and one of the driest in the Philippines, is Zamboanga City, with an average rainfall of only 43 inches. The greatest proportion of the rainfall is borne to the region on the summer "southwest monsoon" air masses, although the proximity of the Intertropical Front throughout the year ensures adequate moisture in most seasons. Strong winds are infrequent and typhoons practically unknown. Climatic conditions, in themselves, do not impose any restrictions on agriculture except in the vicinity of Zamboanga City.

The presence, however, of coralline parent materials in certain areas, such as at Zamboanga, on some of the smaller lowlands along the northwest coast, and on several of the offshore coral islands, while contributing parent materials from which relatively fertile soils are developed, also causes soils to be subject to edaphic drought. Many of the small river floodplains provide excellent sites for agriculture, especially where the alluvium is of volcanic origin, as on the Sibuguey and Baganian peninsulas. A relatively fertile soil base also has been provided by the weathering of volcanic ejecta in situ on the slopes of the volcanic masses of Ampiro and Malindang. On the other hand, where alluvium has originated from the basement-complex rocks of the cordillera the soil base is not very good. Most of the hill lands in the central and southern sections of the peninsula have been avoided by settlers, partially for this reason.

Commercial forests cover approximately 39 percent of the Zamboanga region. These are excellent stands of Philippine dipterocarps which contain considerable quantities of batitinan, betis, kalamansanai, kalunti, kato, and lumbayan, as well as the more common species, such as molave and the lauans. The volume of timber per acre is well above the average Philippine forest cover, particularly in the stands of Zamboanga del Sur and on Basilan Island. The region contains approximately 10 percent of the standing merchantable timber of the Philippines. Cogon grasslands, the aftermaths of the shifting agriculturists who have been quite numerous on the peninsula, scar many of the hill slopes and are particularly extensive in the municipalities of Dumingag, Liloy, Labason, and along the eastern shores of the peninsula facing Moro Gulf in Ipil municipality and Zamboanga City. Mangrove forests are quite extensive in the protected waters at the head of Sibuguey Gulf and along the shores of Sibuguey and Baganian peninsulas. In 1957 approximately 28 percent of the region had been cleared, and a large part of this was under active cultivation. This figure represents approximately 50 percent of the total alienable land.[31]

THE CULTURAL SETTING

The Spanish came into contact with sections of the Zamboanga Peninsula very early in their period of occupance, and maintained these contacts continuously throughout the nearly three hundred years of control, except for a brief period in the late seventeenth and early eighteenth centuries. Northeastern Zamboanga appears to have served as an in-migration area for Visayan peoples even in the pre-Spanish period, in the same fashion as did the rest of the north coast of Mindanao. Legaspi, touching at Dapitan in 1565, described it as an area of settlers from Bohol.[32] Dapitan, along with the town of Iligan, became a joint Jesuit cabacera, which in mid-seventeenth century was administering to 2,750 families, or nearly 11,000 persons.[33] From the very beginning of their Philippine occupance the Spanish authorities were in open conflict with the Moslem Filipinos who lived in western Mindanao and on the islands of the Sulu Sea. Early attempts to subjugate the Moros failed, and the Moros swiftly retaliated with a series of sanguinary raids upon the Christian settlements located along the northern coast of Zamboanga and in the Visayas. Basilan, Jolo, Tawi-Tawi, Siasi, Lanao, and Cotabato—all bastions of Moro strength—soon became bywords synonomous with Moro violence and piratical incursion.

These raids continued well into the nineteenth century.[34] Spanish military forces, in large part composed of Christian Filipino converts, directed early campaigns against the Sulu and Mindanao Moros in 1596, 1611, 1628, 1630, 1637, and 1638. In 1636, in an effort to control the Moro raids nearer their sources, Fort Pilar was established at the southern tip of the peninsula on the present site of Zamboanga City. Although abandoned in 1662, Fort Pilar was reestablished in 1719 and went on to become the most famous of the Spanish presidios in the Philippines. The presence of Spanish soldiery in the Zamboanga area fostered the development of two enclaves of Christian migrants from the Visayan area, one in the northeast in the vicinity of Dapitan and another in the southwest of Zamboanga. During the seventeenth century the Spanish priests were administering to 4,200 families in their residencia of Zamboanga.[35] By the close of the Spanish era, as many as 37,00 Christians were resident on the peninsula. The approximately 40,000 resident Moros and 20,000 pagans were still living pretty much out of contact with the Spanish at the end of the nineteenth century. The main Moro areas of concentration were on Basilan Island and along the shores of Moro Gulf, whereas pagans were chiefly scattered throughout the hill country of the interior.

The most immediate effect upon the population of the peninsula caused by the establishment of American control was an encouragement to further migration into the lands along the shores of the Sulu Sea, particularly in the vicinity of Zamboanga City and around Dipolog and Dapitan in the northeast. It was several years before American authorities effectively controlled the Moro Gulf area, and large-scale migrations by Christian Filipinos awaited the institution of greater political and military controls. Migration to southern Zamboanga spurted after 1918. By 1960 the population of southern Zamboanga had increased tenfold over that of 1903, as compared to a 255 percent increase of population in the nation as a whole during the same period. American commercial interests in the region were limited to exploitation of the rich timber resources of Basilan Island and the establishment of several small rubber plantations on Basilan and in the vicinity of Kabasalan at the head of Sibuguey Gulf.

By 1960 the two Zamboanga provinces had a combined population of slightly over one million persons. This population was distributed largely along the coasts, with greater numbers found in northeastern Zamboanga del Norte, particularly in the valleys of the Dapitan, Dipolog, and Lubungan rivers, in and adjacent to Zamboanga City, on Basilan Island, on the Baganian Peninsula, at the head of Pagadian Bay, and in the newly opened lands in the inland municipalities of Molave, Liargao, and Tambulig in eastern Zamboanga del Sur (fig. 82).

Crude population densities, while still well below the national average density, stood at approximately 172 persons per square mile in 1960, and approximately 650 persons occupied each square mile of cultivated land.[36] Post-World War II migrations have been especially large, particularly into the excellent, nearly empty agricultural areas at the head of Pagadian Bay. Nearly one-half (48 percent) of the 1960 population of Zamboanga del Sur reported birthplaces other than in the region.[37] Approximately 49 percent of this "alien" population had migrated to the province from elsewhere on Mindanao, 42 percent from the adjacent province of Misamis Occidental alone. Some 43 percent of the migrants reported birthplaces in the Visayan Islands; especially numerous were those with birthplaces on the islands of Cebu, Bohol, Negros, and Panay. The stream of migrants from the Visayas apparently has been of long standing, for the Cebuano dialect is dominant throughout the region. Luzon was reported as a birthplace of only 3 percent of the migrants.

Chavacano, a dialect that is a mixture of Malay and Spanish, and euphemistically referred to as "murdered Spanish," at one time was the dominant dialect in Zamboanga; however, in 1960 it was reported as the mother tongue of only 10 percent of the regional population. Tausog, Yakan, Samal, and Maguindanao are the major dialects spoken by the Moslem Filipinos who represent a block of 19 percent of the regional population. The greatest concentration of Moros in the region is found on the island of Basilan whereas smaller numbers occupy the lowlands at the heads of Sibuguey Gulf and Dumanquilas Bay and several of the small offshore coral islands (fig. 82). Moros are outnumbered by Christians in all municipalities of the region except those on Basilan Island and in the municipality of Sibuco. After World War II the movement of people to the Zamboanga

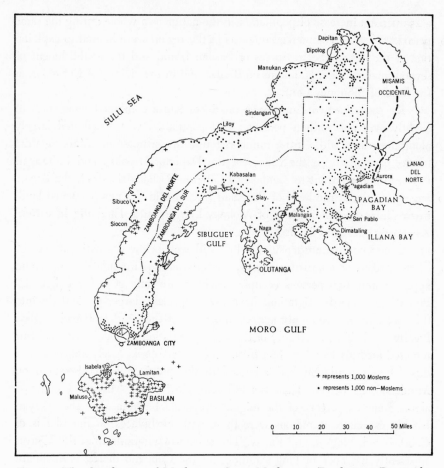

Fig. 82. The distribution of Moslems and non-Moslems in Zamboanga Peninsula, 1960.

Peninsula was so great that in 1952 it was considered desirable to split the single province of Zamboanga. The 12 political subdivisions (the city of Zamboanga and 11 municipalities) of the Zamboanga Province of 1948 had been subdivided into a total of 45 political units (the city of Zamboanga and 44 municipalities) by 1962. The creation of new municipalities has been greatest in Zamboanga del Sur where the six municipalities of 1948 had become 29 municipalities by 1962.

Although the population of the Zamboanga region is not strongly urbanized, five relatively important regional and subregional commercial centers have developed within the region. Zamboanga City is the primary regional center, serving not only the whole of the peninsula, but extending its commercial influence far toward the west into the Sulu Archipelago and eastward into adjacent sections of the provinces of Cotabato and Lanao del Sur. The site of Zamboanga at the southwestern tip of the island of Mindanao was chosen with strategic considerations in mind. All ships sailing from ports on Luzon and from the central and western Visayas, bound for ports in southern Mindanao, and using the approach route west of Mindanao, which is the most direct route, must sail through Basilan Strait and thus must pass within a mile or so of the city. Zamboanga's site is also strategically located with respect to foreign commerce, for it lies upon the main shipping routes between Indonesia and the Philippines. Because of its busy port functions Zamboanga has developed into a relatively important collection point for products produced within its trade hinterland and destined for overseas or interisland markets, such as copra, lumber, fish, and other minor products of the sea. Ten to twenty interisland vessels enter the port of Zamboanga daily, and as an interisland port Zamboanga probably ranks fourth among Philippine ports, surpassed only by Cebu, Manila, and possibly Iloilo.

Zamboanga's trade hinterland is truly interisland in character, or more properly "over-water." The city proper occupies a situation of strategic position rather than being located in the middle of a prosperous agricultural region. The coastal lowlands in the immediate vicinity of the city are extremely narrow and unproductive. Low, rough hills lie but a short distance inland. Unfortunately, the road network is also very poorly developed in the vicinity of the city. Except for the highway under construction between Zamboanga and the more important towns in Zamboanga del Sur, all roads serving the city are limited to the immediate vicinity. No overland connection exists between Zamboanga and the towns of northeastern Zamboanga del Norte. Instead, Zamboanga focuses its commercial life toward its port, which is alive with vessels calling from nearby Basilan Island, the Sulus, and the various small ports and settlements along Moro Gulf. The commercial stature of Zamboanga is attested to by the presence of numerous branch offices of Manila firms, shipping agencies, retail and wholesale outlets, and warehousing facilities. In 1960 the population of the city proper was approximately 30,000, and 131,000 people lived within the chartered city limits, which included an area of 645 square miles.

Pagadian, the second city of the peninsula, serves as the capital of the province of Zamboanga del Sur. Pagadian is located at the head of the Pagadian Bay in eastern Zamboanga del Sur and dominates the trade of the rapidly developing agricultural areas to the north and south of the city. Pagadian's busy waterfront has served as a reception center for tens of thousands of migrants who have settled in the pioneer areas in Pagadian's hinterland during the past decade. As the land has been occupied and agricultural productions increased, the port has originated large shipments of rice and corn to Manila and the Visayas. In 1960 the poblacion of Pagadian contained a population of approximately 18,000 persons.

Dapitan and Dipolog are the principal towns in the populous northeastern corner of Zamboanga del Norte. These two towns are located only 8 miles apart. Dipolog, the site of an important commercial airport and interisland shipping port, is the larger of the two cities. In 1960 Dipolog had a population of 15,000 in its poblacion. Dipolog serves as the provincial capital. Important roads lead south along the coast to the towns of Katipunan, Manukan, Sindangan, and Liloy, and southeast through the new municipalities of Polanco, Piñan, La Libertad, and Rizal, and into the province of Misamis Occidental. Dapitan is a small port town on Dapitan Bay. Its location north of the main areas of settlement in the province has precluded its development into a major commercial center. Dapitan was the locale of exile of the famous Filipino patriot Doctor Jose Rizal in 1892. In 1960 Dapitan proper had a population of approximately 8,000 persons.

Isabela is the largest and most important town on Basilan Island. Located midway along the north coast of the island opposite the city of Zamboanga, Isabela maintains frequent ferry connections with that regional center. The chief commercial significance of Isabela is associated with the numerous sawmills located in the town and nearby. In 1960 Isabela had a population of approximately 12,000 in its poblacion.

Thirteen other towns in the region are important as trade centers for small areas. Each of these centers had a population in its poblacion which ranged from 2,500 to 5,000 persons in 1960. Katipunan, Liloy, Manukan, and Sindangan are older settlements located along the coast of Zamboanga del Norte, and each serves a small agricultural hinterland. Piñan is a interior market town in the newly settled piedmont lands that lie south of Dipolog. Lamitan and Maluso are larger Moro towns on Basilan Island, and each possesses a limited agricultural hinterland. Ipil, Malangas, and Margosatubig are older settlements located along Moro Gulf. Each is an important fishing center, and Malangas has benefited from the recent development of the coal reserves located nearby. These latter three settlements have seen their populations expand rapidly in the past decade. Dumanlinao, Dumingag, and Tukuran are new towns located on Baganian Peninsula, and their populations also have increased very rapidly.

Agriculture dominates the economy of the Zamboanga region; however, fishing, logging, sawmilling, and mining make significant contributions to the regional economy. Rice is the leading crop, both in terms of the area devoted to its cultivation and the value of the product. Yields are well above national levels, in large part because of the virgin lands in the newly settled areas. Nevertheless, the Zamboanga region is unable to produce sufficient rice to meet regional demands. A very large rice deficiency exists in Zamboanga del Norte, much larger than can be met by the small rice surpluses of Zamboanga del Sur. The principal rice-growing area is located in eastern Zamboanga del Sur on the Sibuguey and Baganian peninsulas. Smaller rice areas are located on the river floodplains in northeastern Zamboanga del Norte. Upland rice is favored in the north, whereas lowland rice is cultivated more extensively in the south. Corn is the second most important crop and is usually produced in quantities well above regional consumption levels. Large quantities of corn move to deficit areas in the central Visayas. Zamboanga del Norte produces corn equivalent to 150 percent of its needs, and Zamboanga del Sur produces well over double its consumption levels. Corn is cultivated in roughly the same areas as rice.

Additional food crops include several root crops, vegetables, and fruits in quantities generally adequate to meet local needs. Camotes are particularly widespread, usually being grown as a "famine crop" or as a supplement to the rice and corn diet, particularly in the northeast.

Coconuts, abaca, and rubber are the principal commercial crops. Cultivation of the coconut palm is extremely widespread, and a band of palms usually fringes the shorelines throughout most of the region. Zamboanga City serves as the main collection point for copra produced in the Zamboanga region, as well as for much of that produced in the province of Cotabato and Lanao del Sur and on the islands of the Sulu Archipelago. Approximately 8 percent of the Philippine export copra is shipped overseas from within the Zamboanga region. A desiccated-coconut factory and coconut-oil mill are located at Zamboanga. A small quantity of abaca is produced in Zamboanga del Sur. Most of it is hand stripped, baled at Zamboanga, and shipped to Cebu or Manila for export. Five small rubber plantations, four on Basilan Island and the fifth at Kabasalan, produce most of the Philippine rubber. In 1924 two large American rubber companies attempted to secure landholdings of sufficient size to warrant commercial rubber production; however, the Philippine restriction of corporate landholdings to a maximum size of approximately 2,500 acres discouraged any large-scale investment in the industry. A number of small, mainly experimental plantations were established which today produce about 1,950 tons of rubber annually, 1,900 tons of which originate in Zamboanga del Sur.

Fishing, both commercially and for sustenance, is carried on extensively in the relatively rich waters of the Mindanao and Sulu seas, Moro and Sibuguey gulfs, and Illana Bay. In addition to a very large sustenance catch, approximately 2 percent of the Philippine commercial catch is landed at fishing ports within the region, and commercial vessels from as far away as Manila frequent the waters of Sibuguey and Moro gulfs. Slipmouths, anchovies, round scad, tuna, and sardines are the principal species caught. Kabasa-lan, Zamboanga, Malangas, Pagadian, Ipil, Siay, Naga, Dimataling, and San Pablo in Zamboanga del Sur, and Dipolog in Zamboanga del Norte, are the principal commercial fishing centers, although all coastal settlements partici-pate in inshore fishing. The Moros are particularly skillful fishermen. Small quantities of dried fish move out of the region to Davao, Cagayan de Oro, and Cebu. Shark fins, mother-of-pearl shells, sea snails, trochus shells, sponges, and trepang are exported from Zamboanga. Several fishponds have been established in Zamboanga del Sur in recent years, and a very great potential exists for their future expansion.

Mineral industries are relative newcomers to the economy of Zamboanga Peninsula, and although the scale of their present operations is relatively modest, their production is of considerable national significance. There are relatively large deposits of both coal and iron ore on the Sibuguey Peninsula north of the town of Malangas. The coal deposits are estimated to contain nearly 10 million tons of coal, some of which is of coking quality—a small quantity to be sure, but one that gains added significance in light of the general overall shortage of mineral fuels in the Philippines. The present production of Malangas coal is being shipped to the Iligan industrial area. The Upper-Sibuguey iron-ore deposits occur as hard, massive, heavy magnet-ite ores with iron contents ranging between 60 and 65 percent; the iron ore is low in phosphorus and sulphur. The mining company has built its own road system from docks at Pamintayan Point in Dumanquilas Bay to the deposits. Mining is by the open-pit method, and all iron ore is at present being shipped to Japan. Small deposits of relatively high-grade copper ore, ranging from 2 to 7 percent, have recently been opened in Molave municipality. Exploration for minerals on the Zamboanga Peninsula has been very incomplete, and undoubtedly there will be further commercial discoveries. Both coal and iron ore will gain considerable significance if the Philippines is able to establish an integrated steel mill at Iligan.

A logging and sawmilling industry is of long standing in the Zamboanga region, although most of the larger operations date since World War II. Eight percent of the Philippine sawmilling capacity is located within the region, and approximately 16 percent of the nation's total timber-cut originates there. Nearly one-half of the region's sawmill capacity is centered in six sawmills on

Basilan Island. Other smaller sawmills, aggregating a daily sawmilling capacity of 149,000 board feet, are located at Zamboanga City, along the coast of Zamboanga del Norte, and at Kabasalan, Ipil, Aurora, Malangas, Dumingag, and Pagadian in Zamboanga del Sur. The excellent stands of Philippine dipterocarps in Zamboanga are estimated to contain approximately 45 billion board feet of merchantable timber, some of which is of excellent quality. The Zamboanga forests contain an especially heavy volume of timber per acre.

Any interisland or intraprovincial communication except by water is extremely difficult. Zamboanga Peninsula has overland connections to central and eastern Mindanao from northeastern Zamboanga del Norte via northern Misamis Occidental, and from Pagadian into southern Misamis Occidental and Lanao del Norte. The major regional artery of land communication is the Zamboanga-Pagadian highway now under construction. A recently completed highway link crosses the peninsula from Liloy to Ipil. Regular commercial air service is maintained with Dipolog, Liloy, Ipil, Siocon, Pagadian, and Zamboanga. There are perhaps a dozen important and hundreds of lesser ports scattered throughout the region, and some kind of shipping service is maintained between all of them. Zamboanga, Pagadian, Pulanan (Dipolog), and Malangas are among the more important Philippine interisland ports.

The Far South: The Sulu Archipelago

A host of medium-sized islands and tiny islets set as jewels in a tropical sea sums up the simple basic setting of the Sulu Archipelago, the southernmost sector of the Philippine island world. All of the unit-measures of Sulu are diminutive when compared to the main sectors of the Philippines and Indonesia; and the little archipelago, both physically and culturally, is a sort of mosaic miniature of the whole Malaysian realm. Interwoven into the somewhat exotic historical connotations of this Sulu "little sea world" are such intriguing elements as the sea-gypsy Samal Laut peoples, the older Sulu population that turned into fanatic Moslem raiders and traders; the historical role as meeting ground of sea-traders from many realms; the Spanish struggle for political control of the sea lanes; the international diplomatic contests for political control of the region; the quiet but long-present Chinese wholesale traders and merchants; the lure of such exotic tropical products as pearls, corals, shells, sharks' fins, and birds' nests; the near-constant danger accompanying the lone alien stranger intruding from the outside world; the magic of such place names as Tawi-Tawi, Sanga-Sanga, Jolo, Pangutaran, and Cagayan Sulu; and the romantic stories of men such as the Moslem missionary-adventurer Abu Bakr, who came to the Sulus in the mid-fifteenth century to bring the Moslem faith to the population, but stayed to marry the princess daughter of an island ruler, inherit the title of Sultan, formulate political codes of statehood, and turn the local island principality into a regional Moslem island state that made its influence felt from North Borneo to Luzon over nearly two centuries. The Sulu Islands are a part of the Philippines; yet their peoples have lived a life somewhat outside the patterns prevailing in other parts of the Philippines, and even today they live somewhat apart from the main currents of Philippine life.

The total accounted area of the Sulu Archipelago, as a physical region, normally is considered to be just under 1,600 square miles, with the islands scattered over many thousands of square miles of sea area. In modern times the Basilan island group has been politically and economically attached to the political structure of the Zamboanga provinces, and the distant Cagayan Sulu island group has been included in the political structure of Sulu Province. Sulu Province as a political area is normally listed at 1,038 square miles. In 1960 the population of the province was 326,898.

THE PHYSICAL SETTING

The Sulu Archipelago forms a southeastern rampart of the Sulu Sea and a northwestern rampart of the Celebes Sea; it continues a double structural zone from the Zamboanga Peninsula southwestward toward Borneo (fig. 83). Two submarine ridges stand close to present sea level in long curving arcs. The westernmost, or northernmost, is a platform-like ridge upon which are perched numerous coral reef islands chiefly making up the Pangutaran group of islands. The eastern, or southern, ridge has a few points above present sea level which show up as islands composed of sedimentary-metamorphic rocks, but chiefly this ridge is capped by young volcanoes. Many of the islands in this latter chain are covered by flow basalts, tuffs, ashes, and cinders, and many of them are high islands capped by dormant or recently active volcanoes and cinder cones.[38]

The northernmost of the double island chain is Basilan Island, just off the southern tip of Zamboanga Peninsula. (Basilan Island is here included in the physical setting for the sense of completeness only.) The southernmost islands lie within the Tumindao Reef complex and the southern Sibutu Island reef complex, just off the coast of northeastern Borneo, although reefs and very small islets continue beyond the Philippine political limit to join the Semporna Peninsula of Borneo. For convenience the dozen volcanic islets in the Cagayan Sulu group are classified as part of the Sulu Archipelago, although they are located quite far out to the west in the Sulu Sea. The seventy-eight islands over 1 square mile each in area total 1,566 miles, and the

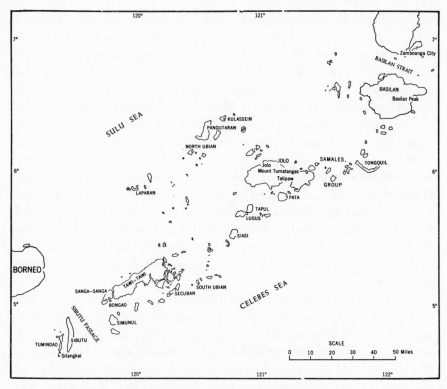

Fig. 83. The Sulu Archipelago.

remainder of the islets, reefs, and rocks are of little consequence as land sections of the archipelago, although they figure significantly in the life of the population in other ways.

The definition of an island, in the Sulu Archipelago, is open to arbitrary classification.[39] Although the tidal range is nowhere over 4 feet, this is sufficient to separate numerous reefs, rocks, and islets at high-tide periods which are joined at low-tide periods. The short-term patterns of physical change among coral reef islands and shoals also contribute to the confusion in classification. Tapul Island, south of Jolo Island, is a nearly circular volcanic mass surmounted by several cones, the tallest of which is about 1,600 feet in elevation. The island slopes away from a central height to a firm shoreline possessing a very narrow fringing coral reef, and there is no question that it is one island with an area of 10.54 square miles. Kulassein Island, on the other hand, one of the northernmost of the Pangutaran group, is normally considered a single island having an area of 6.70 square miles, even though there are five separate bits of land at normal tide levels. Inside a circular fringing reef there are a few bits of open, shallow water, but much of the lagoon is almost filled with mangrove growth, and is exposed at low tide. Tongquil Island, between Jolo and Basilan islands, normally is considered a single island with an area of 18.89 miles; however, in the 1940's it consisted of more than twenty bits of land within a fringing roof. More than half the area then was mangrove swamp, awash at high tide but exposed at low tide. The sand barrier just inside the fringing reef often changed shape and elevation, and channels into the lagoon opened and closed. Barrier beach sections grew strand vegetational covers during periods of accretion, only to lose both the cover and the sand at other periods. Both in the western structural platform and along the volcanic platform, major island units and reef-and-island units change shape, size, and degree of separation as a result of storm action, the filling of lagoons by sediment and organic matter, the growth or aging of coral formations, volcanic action, and eustatic shifts in relative level of elevation. In the historical sense the precise patterning of the Sulu Archipelago has been subject to detailed change in form and numbers, and the elements of change continue to operate.

Among the seventy-eight larger islands three stand out in size and conformation. These are Basilan, 495 square miles, previously described under the Zamboanga region; Jolo, 345 square miles; and Tawi-Tawi, 228 square miles. The first two are high islands marked by the rounded contours of volcanoes and cinder cones, some of which stand sufficiently close to shorelines to give conformation to those shorelines. Both Basilan and Jolo possess rolling to smooth lowlands and areas of intermediate elevation surfaced with tuffs, ashes, and cinders, with the graceful sloping forms of volcanoes and cinder cones standing above them. Both islands appear to have sedimentary cores, although volcanic materials almost totally cover them. Elevations on Basilan range above 3,000 feet, and the top elevation on Jolo is Mount Tumatangas, toward the western end of the island, at 2,664 feet. Both islands possess numerous short streams providing good supplies of fresh water, and both have considerable arable land that has been put into agricultural use. Tawi-Tawi, on the other hand, is an island composed of old sedimentary-metamorphic rocks, and it possesses a rather hilly landscape, although there are a number of rough ridges of moderate relief with elevations reaching toward 1,900 feet. It has not proved as attractive to land settlement as Basilan and Jolo, and most of its area is still heavily wooded. Its fringing reefs, islets, bays, channels, and lagoons, on the other hand, have long proved attractive to boating populations, and most of the settlement patterns are those of the littoral or the off-island fringes.

Among the varied shapes and sizes of islands, and among the different landscapes of the Sulu Archipelago, a wide variety of local environments is to be found. Both Basilan and Jolo are large enough and of such conformation that in the interior the "land environment" becomes noticeable in the long stretches of cultivated fields, open parklands, and areas of forest; and the road-and land-transportation systems become significant. On most of the small islands one cannot lose sight of the sea, and the "littoral environment" becomes the significant pattern. In the fringing reef-linear islet-interior lagoon situation the "sea environment" becomes the dominant aspect, as it also does in the small islet clusters. Relatively flat islands occur as volcanic, sedimentary, and coralline islands; and rocky, rough, and high islands are both sedimentary and volcanic in composition of country rock. Some of the sedimentary islands are rocky-surfaced and uncultivable; Bongao and Simunul are such, and the occupance is by fisherman only. Coralline islands sometimes possess no soil sufficiently matured for agricultural use, and they may lack supplies of fresh water. Laparan and South Ubian are such islands, but a great many of the smaller islets of coral origin also belong in this group. Some of the larger coralline islands afford water resources relatively fresh except after extended dry periods. There are many islets frequented by fishermen who carry in their water supplies. There are a number of islands possessing both coralline fringes and rocky sedimentary cores, such as Pangutaran, Sanga-Sanga, Secuban, and Sibutu. Low, rocky hills top the sedimentary sectors, supplies of fresh water are available, and on the larger of such islands there frequently are expanses of land possessing developed soils adequate to agricultural occupance. Siasi, Pata, Lapac, Tapul, and Cagayan Sulu are topped by volcanoes or cinder cones whose surfaces chiefly are in slopes dropping away from centrally placed crests toward lowland shorelines. Such islands frequently are surfaced by soil covers sufficiently developed that they may be cultivated right up to their volcanic craters. In almost all of the volcanic islands, supplies of groundwater are perched high on the islands, issue from highly situated springs, and provide adequate supplies for all purposes. Cagayan Sulu has two high crater lakes of fresh water.

The general climatic description for the Sulu Archipelago is humid tropical in all respects, locally ranging from Af to Am in the Köppen classification, and from humid to subhumid in the Thornthwaite classification (figs. 11, 12). Annual precipitation totals range from about 50 inches in a few local rain-shadow situations to about 90 inches on exposed upland localities. The months of February through April are apt to experience dry spells of sufficient duration that freshwater supplies on coralline islands may run low or give out, and soil dryness becomes a problem on sandy or cinder surfaces. Temperature conditions are ameliorated by the marine location, and the seasonal ranges are slight, although sensible temperature differences occur both seasonally and from lowlands into some of the crests of the high islands.

Almost all of the islands of the archipelago were heavily forested at one time, but fuelwood cutting, timber cutting, agricultural clearing and burning, and pasture burning have deforested many of the islands occupied by agricultural settlers. A number of the islands containing a sedimentary rock base still carry heavy vegetational covers; Tawi-Tawi is perhaps the most notable. Basilan Island until recently was still heavily forested back from the littoral, but commercial timbering is reducing the forest cover steadily. Jolo has long had much of its upland surface in cogon grass. A great many of the low-lying islands carry heavy strand vegetational covers, and many lagoons are partially filled with mangrove swamp covers. A number of tree species either are fire-resistant or are specially prized, and numerous upland areas now are mixed tree-and-grass parklands.

Almost none of the Sulu islands possesses significant mineral resources, as far as current surveys would indicate. Small volumes of a number of ores, such as iron, copper, and manganese, have been reported from such sedimentary islands as Tawi-Tawi, but mineral survey has not been extensive to date.

Various groupings of the islands of the two Sulu chains have been common. Each large island is surrounded by a cluster of small islands, islets, rocks, reefs, and shoals. It is common to refer to the Jolo and Tawi-Tawi groups for the political province, as the Basilan group belongs to Zamboanga. Groupings up to thirteen in number can be selected for specific purposes or for maps of different scales. Easily distinguishable on most maps are such cluster-groups as Basilan, Samales, Jolo, Pangutaran, Tapul, Tawi-Tawi, and Sibutu, from north to south, with the Cagayan Sulu group offset far to the west (fig. 83).

Under the influence of the monsoon trade-wind system, the major ocean-current structure, and the general pattern of tidal movements, there is variation in the seasonal pattern of air and water movements that affect the Sulu Sea–Sulu Archipelago–Celebes Sea area as a whole. Within and close around the archipelago, however, there are locally varied and rather complex patterns of local currents and air movements. The latter are of only minor interest for the regional generalization, and even for interisland shipping and air traffic; but for the population of the archipelago the seasonal and local patterns of air and water movement are of major significance. In and around many of the island clusters the patterns of offshore reefs, channels, rocks, and islets, create local conditions that affect local sailing craft and conditions for appropriation of corals, shells, pearls, and fishery produce for that share of the population dependent upon these activities as a part of their regular economy. Particularly is this important in the patterns of local movement for the sea-gypsy Samal Laut population. This "local wind-and-water geography" is of an order impossible to generalize upon in a study such as this, but its variety and intricacy is an element in the local measure of attractiveness of selected islands and islets for residence and for economic exploitation. Some islands lacking fresh water and land suitable for agriculture are among the most attractive to the boat-dwelling populations, to the fishermen, and to divers for pearl, coral, and shell.

THE CULTURAL SETTING

The traditional distinctiveness of the Sulu "little sea world" comes forward out of the past with little specific and factual reference until the relatively modern period; the pattern of reference is that of the fabled island world as a meeting ground for seafaring peoples from afar, about which seafarers tell tall tales. The very mobility of these island peoples, and their occupance of the littorals only, produced patterns of constant change yielding few kinds of marks on islands and islets resembling those marks made on "land environments" in other parts of the world. In the last few centuries occupance has become more normally that of the land environment on the larger islands. What may be described in this century as the prevailing pattern of occupance, therefore, contains many very old elements but also numerous elements of relatively recent origin.

A large share of the present population may be identified ethnically as Tausog (Tausug, Tausuug, Suug, Sulu) with reference to peoples who have preferred to live on shore, or along shore, in pile-built villages and hamlets, carrying on a living style that normally includes elements of agricultural land-use complemented by some form of fishery activity in, and trading activity on, the nearby sea. These are the peoples who first turned to the Moslem faith in the fifteenth century, who built principalities, political states, and small sea-empires, and who turned traders and raiders, preying upon the islands to the north and south from the sixteenth to the early nineteenth centuries. These also are the peoples who have resisted the imposition of the civil rules of modern political statehood in the last century, and who sometimes still are described by other Filipinos and news reporters as rebels, bandits, and pirates. Various amounts of intermarriage between the Tausog and other ethnic elements, including Chinese and recent Indonesian immigrants, have somewhat diluted the unity of the old ethnic strain. About two-thirds of the total population of Sulu Province (238,000 in 1960) claimed Tausog as their mother tongue.

Another element in the population of the archipelago may be described ethnically as Samal Laut (Samal, Laut, Orang Laut, Sea Samal, Shore Samal, and other combinations, sometimes involving Badjao, Bajao, Bajau), with reference to several groups of peoples who normally have preferred living on boats, or in boat-and-shore or fringe-of-the-shore environments involving primary dependence on the sea and only a complementary participation in activities relating to a land environment. Historically there appears to be more than one ethnic element summarized under the heading of Samal Laut, although the differences may be chiefly in the degree of acceptance of shore-living and the land environment rather than properly ethnic distinctions. It is clear, however, that there has been progressive change in their patterns of preference, and that linguistic and cultural differentiation has been a continuing process in this island world. Some groups now remain within one regional orbit, to be thereby distinguished from other groups who remain in a separate regional orbit. It is still possible to distinguish the Samal Laut proper (Orang Laut, "people of the sea"), who constitute the sea-gypsy groups; the Shore Samal, who have become less mobile; and the groups distinguished as Badjao, who speak languages separable from Samal. There are, of course, further distinctions to be made by differing criteria, such as North Ubian Badjao (Pangutaran Island group) and the Sanga-Sanga Badjao (from the Tawi-Tawi Island group).

The 1960 Philippine census distinguished only between Samal and Badjao speakers, and cultural, regional, and linguistic variations are thereby disguised, although these are recognized in local living situations (fig. 84). The 1960 census enumerated 68,793 people claiming Samal as a mother tongue, and 12,232 claiming Badjao as their mother tongue.[40] In broad terms, Samal and Badjao speakers both are Samal peoples as far as ethnic stock is concerned, and this is the only division made by the Census Bureau, although other linguistic divisions could be distinguished on dialectic bases or on the factor of grouped residence-bases on different island clusters.

By far the great majority of the Samal people also adopted the Moslem faith by the late eighteenth century and many of them, either independently or as agents of the Moslem political states, did considerable raiding and trading during the sixteenth to nineteenth centuries. Many of the Samal groups, particularly from the smaller islands, maintained strong patterns of mobility, ranging seasonally from the Borneo and Celebes coasts northward to the Visayan Sea waters. The Sulu and Celebes seas, and the coasts surrounding these two seas, formed their territorial range, and the islets, reefs, and shoals throughout the range formed their fishing grounds, anchorages, and camp sites. During at least the eighteenth and nineteenth centuries, groups of Samal from particular islands (Pangutaran and Tawi-Tawi island groups,

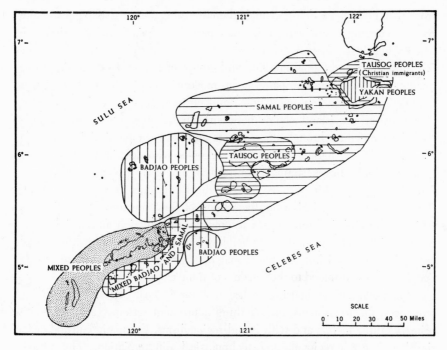

Fig. 84. Peoples of the Sulu Archipelago.

notably) established temporary bases of operations at various coastal fringes within the territorial range, only to shift these bases to other coastal locations in time for specific reasons. During the late nineteenth century there began the modern political process of identification of peoples with particular territories. North Ubian Badjao groups then operating out of North Borneo bases have become classified as Borneans, whereas relatives who continued operating out of North Ubian island bases have come to be regarded as Filipinos. That some Mindanao Moslem groups (chiefly Maguindanao ethnic stocks) and Sulu Moslem groups (Tausog ethnic stocks as opposed to Samal stocks) participated in this same kind of temporary mobility has complicated very greatly the patterns of ethnonationalistic affiliation of seafaring, fishing, trading-raiding peoples throughout the zone from Celebes and Borneo to Mindanao. The forced cessation of the raiding-piracy aspect of their living pattern has required these groups to depend more heavily on their fishery economy or to take up life ashore. The number of Samal who remain purely sea gypsy (Orang Laut) has declined in the past century, and most families and groups now claim a house or a village ashore on some one island, even though they may spend a large share of their time aboard a boat and away from that home base. Most Samal, therefore, are now classifiable as Shore Samal, referring to an increase in their participation in land activities, residence ashore, agricultural economy, and normal commercial economy.

Both Sulu and Samal families, and groups of families, still decline to be totally tied down by the patterns of modern political nationalism, tariff boundaries, immigration regulations, and customs requirements. The near-continuity of the island chains between Mindanao and Borneo facilitates small-boat mobility through these waters and between political landfalls on either side of the national boundaries. Peoples who describe themselves as fishermen raid villages, smuggle contraband, and carry passengers back and forth. Numerous Chinese have entered the Philippines from Borneo along this route, and there still is a northward flow of Borneans into the Philippines which defies statistical reporting. Customs and immigration authorities of the countries involved are not entirely helpless in trying to stop smuggling, illegal entry, and "piracy," but the traditional patterns of life do continue among peoples long accustomed to the freedom of these tropical waters.[41]

Such matters as housing styles, tool types, boat styles, yearly living sequences, dietary systems, and clothing adornment systems vary both with primary ethnic factors and with island regionalisms. Economic cultural criteria show ethnic, regional, and technological differentiation. The proper Orang Laut still rarely sleep ashore, do not own or cultivate land, fish for particular kinds of subsistence fish, produce particular items derived from the sea for frequent petty sale ashore, move in small groups of related or friendly families, and shift within their own annual travel circuits. Badjao-speaking peoples of the Tawi-Tawi group may fish regularly for particular subsistence fish, fish both for shark and for shell for salable products, and carry out a travel circuit from a home base on a particular island where homes are surrounded by spasmodically cultivated kitchen gardens. Shore Samal of Jolo Island may reside ashore most of the year, carrying on some cropping activities on small bits of owned or rented land, complemented by regular subsistence fishing in nearby waters only; they may also prepare for sale excess fish catches at particularly good periods, and then engage in pearl fishing at certain periods of the year. Tausog residents on Jolo or Basilan may be primarily farmers growing rice, manioc, and coconut; they may maintain kitchen gardens, may hire out as casual labor sometime during the year, or may even participate occasionally in the fishing operations of a crew boat. Within the hundreds of islands arranged in clusters there are many different kinds of local situations, both ashore and on the sea, and living patterns are almost as varied as these can be in the present century within this large island cluster.

Within the above-patterned cultural milieu the growth of population and the development of land environment characteristics is apt to lag. Settlements rarely developed permanence and public architecture, and although trading centers have operated as meeting places for many centuries, there are no old cities and highly developed urban complexes. Pile-built hamlets, villages, towns, and trading ports had little durability and disappeared with the cessation of maintenance. Until rather recently no island contained a very large permanently resident population. Even the development of political statedom by the Moslem datus and sultans, in the late fifteenth to early nineteenth centuries, produced very few marks of permanence on the landscapes, for they chiefly were constructs of religious-secular power dependent upon personal loyalties and administrative militancy.

The Spanish, in 1876, burned the chief Tausog-Samal pile-built shore-margin settlement of Jolo, on the northwest coast of Jolo Island, in a last effort at political control. On the long gentle slope above the shore the Spanish built a three-street, landed-site town of brick and stone, surrounded by a wall and appropriate further fortification, and they also built a stone pier out from the shore into the harbor. This gave the Sulu Archipelago, in the physical sense, perhaps its first permanent urban settlement. The municipality of Jolo is but a small one, and the 1960 population of 33,259 may be considered an urban one, of which some 3,300 lived within the old Spanish walled town that now is the poblacion.

Only three other poblaciones in Sulu Province exceeded 2,500 in 1960, those of Siasi at 4,973, Sitangkai at 3,328, and Talipaw at 3,099. The settlement of Sitangkai is on a tiny islet of the same name, near the southern end of the Tumindao Reef complex. Until very recently, at least, the islet contained no supply of potable water, and the whole of its nonmarine food supply had to be imported. Although Sitangkai is the seat of a municipality, it still is less of a city than a large fishing camp and processing site, for its local waters are a primary center of the sponge, shell, clam, and bêche-de-mer fishery. Siasi, on the other hand, in the Tapul island group, located on the west coast of the volcanic island of Siasi, on a spit of land at a break in the reef on Siasi Channel, has developed characteristics of a land town. It has fair port facilities for small interisland ships and local craft, the skeleton of a street plan, shore buildings including warehousing and public buildings, a mixed population, some processing activities, a piped water system derived from springs high on the island's volcanic peak, and local roads leading out of town to coastal hinterlands. Talipaw (formerly Bilaan) is an inland, land-built town in an agricultural area, and it is the only land trading center of the province which may be described this way. Located just west of the constriction in the island of Jolo, Talipaw is located in the longitudinal lowland running east–west through the island, and is a local road-transport center and market town.

Although there are now other permanent land-sited villages located on several islands in the Sulu chain, few of them are as yet more than residential villages. Some of these will in time develop into small regional ports, when well situated on the interisland traffic lanes. On Jolo Island one or two of the other landed villages beyond Talipaw may develop into local regional centers or market towns.

Technically, roads could be built on quite a number of islands in the Sulu chain, but within the province, Jolo is the only one that has more than purely local, short-reach roads. Both Tawi-Tawi and Sibutu are large enough that in the course of time road systems might prove useful. Elsewhere there is nowhere for roads to go, and there will be no more than short roads and trails leading away from the immediate ports or landings. Jolo Island, in 1960, had some 150 miles of roads, providing a fairly close network giving access to all lowland sectors of the island. Port facilities, in modern terms, are available only at Jolo. Elsewhere only minimal facilities are available for more than small craft. The watercraft of most peoples in the islands do not require the technical facilities of modern ports and, from the local point of view, this lack of development presents no particular hardships.

THE ECONOMIC ACTIVITIES

A little over one-third of the total land area of Sulu Province, in the late 1950's, was classifiable either as forest covered or swamp surfaced. About 15 percent of the total area was in forest of commercial utility. Out of the total forested land a fair share may eventually be usable as farmland, either for pasturage or for crop production. About a third of the total area was in farms, and the area may be expanded further when needed. The marine resource range continues of regular utility, since little of it has been heavily over-worked commercially. A portion of the swamp-marsh-lagoon area represents potential aquatic land resource, although almost no attempt has been made so far at pond development and the cultivation of fishery products on a controlled basis. Without significant mineral resources the patterns of present and future economic development of the province lie within the agricultural and marine resource ranges. A portion of the landed area never can be strongly developed in agricultural patterns, since it represents either hard rock surface or low-lying coralline islands, islets, and beach ridges without developed soils and groundwater sufficient to support crop production.

Over the long past the land areas have served as landfalls, anchorages, sources of water, wood, and plant products to be appropriated by sea-going peoples dependent chiefly on the marine resource. Within recent centuries the slow development of land resources on the larger and more easily usable islands has taken place. Over half the surface of Jolo Island has been cultivated at one time or other, and much of the island today is in cogon grass or parkland cover, currently not being used in crop production but available for such operations. Much of Tawi-Tawi and Sibutu currently are in forest cover of some degree of utility, although much of the cover has been cut through or picked over for much of its higher-value product. Many of the smaller volcanic islands have been cropped over at some time in the past century or two by shifting cultivators, and few of them possess forest covers of real utility. Several of the higher islands either are now being cropped right to their crests or stand in cogon grass covers.

The total range of marine resources tapped in some degree within the Sulu chain runs to hundreds of species of faunal aquatic life, and to dozens of species of seaweeds and associated plants. Although many of these items, such as pearls, have a romantic lure, fascination, and an individual high value for a prize product, the marine resources do not represent high income resources unless they are tapped in well-organized industrial terms, in large volume, followed by organized merchandising. Little has been done on these lines in the Sulu region in terms of modern economic development, so that the fishery economy has represented a subsistence-pattern resource capped by a relatively cheap commercial market resource. Button shell, mother-of-pearl, coral, shark fins, bêche-de-mer, birds' nests, and turtle eggs are all competitive market items dependent upon particular cultural customs or preferences. The relative closure of the mainland China market in recent years has distinctly lowered the outlet for the shark-fin, bêche-de-mer, and birds' nest products; the creation of plastics and other synthetics has put pressure on the button shell and mother-of-pearl product, and the pearl, coral, and shell-collector market is a luxury market of limited capacity and highly competitive with the products from other parts of the world. Present development of this marine resource range remains near subsistence levels as a low-income producer under present technologies and economic organization, so that the Sulu population engaging in this range of economic activity now is held to a low-income economic operation.

The 1960 census enumerated just over 52,000 dwelling units classified as family residences in Sulu Province, but of these nearly 15,000 were ranked as makeshift affairs, with the inference that they were temporary or casually used. About 127,000 persons were indicated as married, widowed, or divorced, and the number of family units cannot be far from 65,000. The total number of farms stood at just over 21,000 in 1960. These figures suggest that agriculture does not yet dominate the economic activity of the Sulu population, and that a considerable share of that population does not maintain permanent, sedentary homes on land. The number of boat-living families is not revealed by the census tabulations, but a goodly share of those dwelling units reported as makeshift probably include the land bases of residence for many of the families whose lives are still primarily oriented toward the sea and mobility of movement.

The 21,000 farms are chiefly small, ranging from a half acre to about 6 acres in size, and well over three-fourths of them are farmed by owners. In terms of normal classification, farms ranked as coconut, rice, abaca, and root-crop farms are the chief types throughout the Sulu region, although there are numerous mixed-crop farms. In relative acreage strength the crops stand in the following order: coconut, rice, cassava, corn, and abaca. In the frequency of cultivation of food crops on farms, however, manioc stands well ahead of all other crops, being found in small patches on seven out of ten farms. This is the only region in the Philippines in which manioc has this relative importance. Of the other crops bananas show up on about three out of ten farms, coconuts are present on about eight out of ten, and mangoes, corn, and abaca are found on about two out of ten farms. Rice occurs on about half of the farms. In matters of crop disposal manioc is very strongly a home-use subsistence crop, but small shares of it move to local markets for internal regional use. Rice, bananas, mangoes, and corn are chiefly subsistence crops, with small shares reaching local markets within the archipelago to provide for the local deficit consumption patterns. Abaca and coconut are almost entirely commercial crops sold off the farms, eventually moving to Jolo for export from the region either to Zamboanga or directly to the main export markets. Such crop plants as yams and sweet potatoes, eggplant, squash, tobacco, and pineapple show up on under 10 percent of all farms. The usual tropical fruits are to be found, on perhaps one farm in five, but the total plantings are quite small, and they are either grown for local consumption, as with the durian, papaya, avocado, and lanzone, or represent specialty crops for market disposal, such as the mangosteen. Coffee plantings are fairly widely scattered, but cacao plantings had not become numerous in the Sulu region by the late 1950's, unlike the pattern in some other parts of the Philippines. Certain traditional crops, such as kapok, and betel nut, show up on one farm in six, oriented toward local markets and consumption.

In regional terms Jolo, of course, is the chief agricultural island, and more than 50 percent of the total farms, farm area, and production is centered here. Other islands significant as agricultural areas include Siasi, Tapul,

Cagayan Sulu, Lapac, and Pangutaran. Sibutu and Tawi-Tawi are but scantily developed so far, though cattle raising has been present on both islands for many decades, and most of the reserve agricultural land lies on these two islands. A good many of the smaller islands have small bits of cultivation, particularly patches of manioc and coconut plantings, but the total share of these small islands does not bulk large.

Although fishery activities are present throughout the whole of the Sulu island chain, many of the more significant operations are concentrated around particular islands, or island clusters, wherein local aquatic ecology produced hydrologic environments of particular qualities. The four primary localities are around the islands of Jolo, Siasi, Tawi-Tawi, and Sitangkai; secondary in importance are the Samales island cluster, Pangutaran, Bongao, Laparan, and Sibutu. Sponge gathering is common at all of them, although the market for sponges is not well developed and the fishery is a minor item. Some sixty species of sea cucumbers (chiefly *Holothuria* spp.) are gathered and processed as bêche-de-mer (trepang) from waters around Jolo, Siasi, Bongao, and Sitangkai. Sun-dried or smoked, and sold to Chinese wholesalers, this product traditionally has gone to the Chinese mainland, but currently there are restrictions on the marketing pattern. Waters around Tawi-Tawi and Sitang-kai have provided the largest share of the top and turban shells (*Trochus* and *Turbo* spp.) destined for the button trade, with a share of the meaty tissue forming a local food supply. Small shares of the button shells come from a variety of local island waters. The waters around Jolo Island have been the chief source of pearls and black coral. Mother-of-pearl material from a variety of shells comes out of the waters around many islands, but the highest quality shell comes from Jolo and Tawi-Tawi, and the mother-of-pearl fishery actually ranks near the top of the income sources for the Sulu region. Various giant clams yield a meat that when dried goes under the name *manankay,* and is produced from the waters around a number of islands; but Sitangkai is the center of this fishery activity. Turtle catching and gathering of turtle eggs are chiefly practiced in the southern zone.

More normal fishing operations range widely through the whole Sulu island chain and well into the waters of both the Celebes and Sulu seas. Fishing for the herrings, sardines, mackerels, tunas, and skipjacks has its seasonal patterns in different localities, reaching its maximum intensity in the period from December to May. A traditional and old fishery pattern, this usual fishing activity today yields a small volume for export outside the Sulu region, but remains not well developed in commercial terms by local popula-tions. There are a host of fish species ecologically localized around various of the reefs and shoals throughout the region which provide fresh fish products for local consumption by the land populations of the region, and subsistence fisheries are carried on in the traditional manner.

Mineral industries, in the normal sense, play no role in the economic life of the Sulu region so far. Forest industries are not currently significant. At one time or other in the last century timber cutters have worked through such islands as Tawi-Tawi and Sibutu, and have cut out considerable timber for export to northern Philippine markets. Local transport problems between the forest and the shore have restricted such activity chiefly to the cutting of poles, material for railroad ties, or the extraction of particularly valuable woods.

Secondary economic activity within the Sulu region remains chiefly related to processing procedures. Rice milling, copra processing, and abaca processing are of more than a household industry category, but these are the chief activities. Fish processing, such as drying, smoking, curing, and the preliminary processing of shell products, is chiefly restricted to operations enabling the products to be marketed as durable, transportable commodities rather than as finished products. On Jolo Island, and particularly in the city of Jolo, there are the beginnings of other forms of industrial activity, but even here the level of operations is but very slightly advanced.

Traditional handicrafts are of greater significance here than anywhere else in the Philippines except possibly among the Maranao Moslems of the Lake Lanao region. The building of watercraft and their accessories forms a group of traditional skills of superior technology. The fabrication of tools and weapons in iron and bronze was highly developed. The working of brass, bronze, copper, silver, and gold, both for utensils and for art goods that combined coral and shell was perhaps the best in the Philippines. Textile making here showed greater variety in handling materials and colors than elsewhere. Many of these products were for domestic use, but a variety of the metal, coral, pearl, and shell handicrafts long have been among the export-barter goods exchanged by the natives of the archipelago with the traders frequenting Sulu waters. Such fabrication patterns were individualistic or family-organized, and somewhat opportunistic as to barter patterns, and although production of some items continues for the modern curio trade, such handicrafts do not represent a significant potential economic development.

With the advent of modern patterns of trade, customs controls, and other regulatory arrangements, much of the traditional meeting ground and barter trading that enlivened life in the Sulu Islands has ceased. There still is the modern smuggling trade, of course, but no index of its importance in the economic life of the Sulu population is readily available. Obviously, it continues, and various of the island populations engage in it to greater or lesser degree.

Regular trade movements, chiefly of the Philippine interisland shipping fleet, tie the Sulu Archipelago into the economic structure of the Philippines. The northward flow of copra, abaca, shell products, coral, pearls, and fishery products, which cannot be provided more easily by the smuggling-trade connections with Borneo markets, provide a regional export that pays for the southward flow of manufactured goods and consumer products. The Sulu level of living, and the regular entry of many of the consumers goods, lags behind the general Philippine level. Except for the two towns of Jolo and Siasi, the 1960 census records for Sulu show very close to the lowest frequency of such items as radios in the home, piped water, electric light, and improved domestic facilities. The volumes of goods moving, and the frequency of shipping connections with Zamboanga and other ports, indicate that little beyond the minimal connections are maintained, and that the region does not yet effectively participate in the improving economic life of the northern islands, or even that of many sectors of Mindanao. The Sulu region remains a subsistence region oriented toward a traditional pattern of life which is closely connected with the sea.

In part, of course, the slow pace of entry into the modern Philippine economic structure is due to the attitudes of the Sulu population. Traditionally rebellious against Spanish civil authority, the Moslem population continued to fight against American imposition of civil government, and still continues the same struggle against contemporary Philippine administration.[42] What is termed lawlessness and civil unrest by northern Christian Filipinos, national government civil servants, and military agencies alike is chiefly directed against the imposition of what the Sulu residents think of as outside rule. The continuance of such conditions right into the 1960's handicaps the regional development of a more active economy integrated into the national economy of the modernizing Philippines. At the same time, the zealous Sulu defense of their distinctive way of life constitutes a protest against the trend toward uniformity which characterizes the development of any modern national state.

Statistical Appendix

Table 1   PRINCIPAL ISLANDS OF THE PHILIPPINES (Areas and populations [a])

Rank by size	Island name	Province	Area (in sq. mi.)	Population (000 omitted) 1903	Population (000 omitted) 1960
1	Luzon	—	40,420.0	3,798.5	12,875.1
2	Mindanao	—	36,536.7	499.6	5,358.9
3	Samar	Samar	5,050.2	222.7	735.7
4	Negros	—	4,905.5	460.7	1,862.5
5	Palawan	Palawan	4,550.2	10.9	104.5
6	Panay	—	4,446.0	743.6	1,746.6
7	Mindoro	—	3,758.5	28.3	291.1
8	Leyte	—	2,785.5	357.6	1,072.6
9	Cebu	Cebu	1,707.3	592.2	1,185.6
10	Bohol	Bohol	1,492.2	243.1	529.2
11	Masbate	Masbate	1,262.2	29.4	280.3
12	Catanduanes	Catanduanes	552.4	39.2	156.3
13	Basilan	Zam. del Sur	495.0	27.0	127.1
14	Marinduque	Marinduque	346.8	50.6	112.0
15	Jolo	Sulu	344.8	44.7	165.6
16	Busuanga	Palawan	343.6	4.3	13.2
17	Dinagat	Surigao	309.3	5.2	19.5
18	Tablas	Romblon	265.0	24.6	74.1
19	Polillo	Quezon	233.7	2.2	18.4
20	Tawi-Tawi	Sulu	228.5	1.2	7.7
21	Guimaras	Iloilo	223.4	21.3	56.1
22	Biliran	Leyte	192.2	19.1	68.7
23	Sibuyan	Romblon	173.2	10.7	25.1
24	Siargao	Surigao	168.6	9.5	37.0
25	Burias	Masbate	163.6	1.6	15.8
26	Culion	Palawan	150.4	1.0	4.8
27	Siquijor	Negros. Or.	129.7	46.0	59.1
28	Ticao	Masbate	129.0	10.1	47.4
29	Dumaran	Palawan	125.8	2.0	5.0
30	Balabac	Palawan	125.1	0.4	2.8
31	Camiguin	Misamis Or.	96.0	30.7	37.1
32	Samal	Davao	95.9	1.1	33.1
33	Panaon	Leyte	78.0	8.6	29.0
34	Olutanga	Zam. del Sur	77.6	[b]	16.6
35	Lubang	Occ. Mindoro	73.9	6.3	14.1
36	Alabat	Quezon	73.8	4.5	21.3
37	Calayan	Cagayan	72.8	0.7	3.4
38	Camiguin	Cagayan	63.4	0.1	1.1

Table 1—Continued

Rank by size	Island name	Province	Area (in sq. mi.)	Population (000 omitted) 1903	Population (000 omitted) 1960
39	Bucas Grande	Surigao	50.5	0.8	4.8
40	Bugsuk	Palawan	46.9	b	0.4
41	Bantayan	Cebu	44.8	18.3	45.8
42	Homonhon	Samar	40.2	1.2	2.3
43	Linapacan	Palawan	39.9	b	1.2
44	Daram	Samar	39.3	3.5	25.4
45	Sibutu	Sulu	39.1	0.2	5.4
46	Poro	Cebu	38.7	8.5	20.1
47	Pangutaran	Sulu	36.8	0.6	8.1
48	Fuga	Cagayan	35.7	b	0.8
49	Panglao	Bohol	35.1	14.4	25.4
50	Batan	Albay	34.8	5.3	10.0
51	Pacijan	Cebu	33.8	8.1	20.9
52	Patnanongan	Quezon	33.5	b	2.7
53	Itbayat	Batanes	32.7	1.2	2.4
54	Romblon	Romblon	31.7	9.3	16.7
55	Ilin	Occ. Mindoro	29.6	0.6	4.9
56	Siasi	Sulu	29.6	11.8	19.3
57	Cabarruyan	Pangasinan	29.5	b	14.6
58	Babuyan	Cagayan	27.7	b	b
59	Coron	Palawan	27.6	b	0.4
60	Cagraray	Albay	27.5	1.1	10.8
61	Batan	Batanes	26.9	5.3	6.2
62	Cagayan Sulu	Sulu	26.1	2.4	10.8
63	Rapu-Rapu	Albay	24.8	1.6	6.8
64	Dalupiri	Cagayan	23.8	0.2	b
65	Mactan	Cebu	23.6	17.5	50.0
66	Cuyo	Palawan	22.5	7.5	17.1
67	Balut	Davao	22.0	b	2.9
68	Semirara	Antique	21.7	0.2	1.5
69	Vitali	Zam. del Sur	20.3	b	3.3
70	Jomalig	Quezon	19.9	b	1.3
71	Lapinpin	Bohol	19.8	1.3	9.6
72	Maytiguid	Palawan	18.9	0.1	0.5
73	Tongquil	Sulu	18.9	0.6	1.3
74	Nonoc	Surigao	18.8	b	1.2
75	Pata	Sulu	18.0	1.0	5.3
76	Sanga Sanga	Sulu	17.8	0.2	4.2

Table 1—Continued

Rank by size	Island name	Province	Area (in sq. mi.)	Population (000 omitted) 1903	Population (000 omitted) 1960
77	Sacol	Zam. del Sur	17.1	b	4.4
78	Sibay	Antique	16.4	0.7	1.2
79	Tandubato	Sulu	16.4	0.5	b
80	Siminul	Sulu	15.8	1.3	6.0
81	Pandanan	Palawan	15.8	0.1	0.4
82	Lapac	Sulu	15.6	1.1	7.8
83	Lugus	Sulu	14.8	4.9	8.1
84	Baliungan	Sulu	14.8	b	0.2
85	Sarangani	Davao	14.0	b	1.8
86	Buad	Samar	13.9	2.3	11.5
87	Laparan	Sulu	13.7	b	b
88	Capul	Samar	13.6	2.3	7.3
89	Ponson	Cebu	13.3	4.6	8.8
90	Quinasalag	Camarines Sur	12.8	b	1.4
91	Ramos	Palawan	12.7	b	0.4
92	Sabtang	Batanes	12.5	1.7	1.7
93	Batag	Samar	12.3	0.1	4.6
94	Laoang	Samar	12.2	b	16.2
95	Batas	Palawan	12.2	b	0.1
96	Maricaban	Batangas	12.0	3.7	7.6
97	Carabao	Romblon	11.2	1.4	2.7
98	Dalupiri	Samar	11.1	2.0	5.9
99	Tagapulan	Samar	11.1	2.3	4.6
100	Talikud	Davao	11.1	b	3.0
101	Banton	Romblon	10.9	3.0	6.1
102	Maripipi	Leyte	10.8	1.9	7.1
103	Talim (L. de Bay)	Rizal	10.7	b	14.1
104	Ambil	Occ. Mindoro	10.7	0.1	0.3
105	Tapul	Sulu	10.5	0.4	6.9
106	Cabucan	Sulu	10.3	0.0	0.4
107	Palaui	Cagayan	9.9	0.0	b
108	Pilas	Zam. del Sur	9.8	0.5	7.9
109	Caluya	Antique	9.5	1.1	2.9
110	Almagro	Samar	8.8	b	6.2
111	Tuluran	Palawan	8.8	0.5	b
112	Calagnaan	Iloilo	8.6	1.1	2.2
113	San Miguel	Albay	8.4	4.1	5.0
114	Pagbilao Grande	Quezon	8.4	b	1.6

Table 1—Continued

Rank by size	Island name	Province	Area (in sq. mi.)	Population (000 omitted) 1903	Population (000 omitted) 1960
115	Mantangule	Palawan	8.4	b	b
116	Bongo	Cotabato	8.2	b	2.4
117	Santo Niño	Samar	8.1	1.8	5.6
118	Simara	Romblon	8.0	1.9	6.5
119	Santiago	Pangasinan	7.9	1.5	6.2
120	Maestro de Campo	Romblon	7.8	1.0	3.0
121	Poneas	Surigao	7.6	b	b
122	Panducan	Sulu	7.5	0.2	0.9
123	Capual	Sulu	7.4	0.2	0.5
124	East Bucas	Surigao	7.3	b	3.4
125	Calicoan	Samar	7.3	b	2.5
126	Lahuy	Camarines Sur	7.2	b	1.9
127	Malamaui	Zam. del Sur	7.0	0.8	5.0
128	Tumindao	Sulu	7.0	0.3	1.8
129	Mahanay	Bohol	6.8	0.3	1.0
130	Golo	Occ. Mindoro	6.8	0.4	1.2
131	Calabete	Quezon	6.8	0.2	1.1
132	Kulassein	Sulu	6.7	b	b
133	Bilatan	Sulu	6.7	0.2	0.6
134	Cap	Sulu	6.5	b	b
135	Verde	Batangas	6.5	1.5	5.3
136	North Ubian	Sulu	6.5	4.7(?)	1.1
137	Manuk Manka	Sulu	6.4	0.1	2.7
138	Volcano (Taal Lake)	Batangas	6.3	b	1.7
139	Masapelid	Surigao	6.3	b	1.0
140	Pan de Azucar	Iloilo	6.2	0.7	2.2
141	Bancalan	Palawan	6.1	b	0.2
142	Iloc	Palawan	6.1	b	0.3
143	Palasan	Quezon	5.9	b	0.5
144	Cabingaan	Sulu	5.8	2.1	0.6
145	Biri	Samar	5.8	0.5	2.1
146	Agutaya	Palawan	5.8	1.5	2.5
147	Bulalacao	Palawan	5.8	b	b
148	Simisa	Sulu	5.6	b	b
149	Secuban	Sulu	5.6	b	3.8
150	Boayan	Palawan	5.4	b	b
151	Middle Bucas	Surigao	5.3	b	b
152	Tagubanhan	Iloilo	5.3	2.0	1.8

Table 1—Continued

Rank by size	Island name	Province	Area (in sq. mi.)	Population (000 omitted) 1903	Population (000 omitted) 1960
153	Bucutua	Sulu	5.2	b	1.4
154	Olango	Cebu	5.1	1.1	5.3

ª Island areas are rounded to the nearest tenth of a square mile. Populations are rounded to the nearest hundred.

ᵇ This information is not available, as census reports do not indicate a formal barrio organization on these islands, and therefore there is no separate census tract. This normally indicates a lack of sedentary residence.

SOURCES: Island areas were calculated by the Philippine Bureau of Coast and Geodetic Survey; populations were calculated from the *Census of the Philippines*, 1903, 1960.

Table 2 PROVINCES BY AREA AND POPULATION, 1960

Province	Area (in sq. mi.)	Population
Abra	1,535	115,193
Agusan	4,461	271,010
Aklan	702	226,232
Albay	985	514,980
Antique	973	238,405
Bataan	530	145,323
Batanes	81	10,309
Batangas	1,222	681,414
Bohol	1,589	592,194
Bukidnon	3,202	194,368
Bulacan	1,031	555,819
Cagayan	3,476	445,289
Camarines Norte	815	188,091
Camarines Sur	2,034	819,565
Capiz	1,016	315,079
Catanduanes	584	156,329
Cavite	497	378,138
Cebu	1,965	1,332,847
Cotabato	9,188	1,029,129
Davao	7,595	893,023
Ilocos Norte	1,313	287,335
Ilocos Sur	996	338,058
Iloilo	2,055	966,266
Isabela	4,117	442,062
La Union	576	293,330
Laguna	679	472,064
Lanao del Norte	1,194	270,603
Lanao del Sur	1,495	378,327
Leyte	2,420	1,172,972
Manila	14	1,138,611
Marinduque	370	114,586
Masbate	1,563	335,971
Misamis Occidental	749	248,371
Misamis Oriental	1,467	388,615
Mountain	5,528	435,839
Negros Occidental	3,060	1,332,323
Negros Oriental	2,218	597,761
Nueva Ecija	2,040	608,362
Nueva Vizcaya	2,688	138,090

Table 2—Continued

Province	Area (in sq. mi.)	Population
Occidental Mindoro	2,270	84,316
Oriental Mindoro	1,685	228,998
Palawan	5,751	162,669
Pampanga	846	617,259
Pangasinan	2,073	1,124,144
Quezon	4,613	653,426
Rizal	718	1,456,362
Romblon	524	131,658
Samar	5,185	867,994
Sorsogon	827	347,771
Sulu	1,038	326,898
Surigao	2,815	359,997
Tarlac	1,179	426,647
Zambales	1,434	213,442
Zamboanga del Norte	2,285	281,429
Zamboanga del Sur	4,232	742,404
Total	115,600	27,087,685

Table 3 SELECTED SMALL ISLANDS BY AREA AND POPULATION

Island	Municipality	Province	Area (in sq. mi.)	Population in 1960
Aguada	Capul	Sulu	1.26	949
Alad	Romblon	Romblon	1.12	715
Baluc Baluc	Basilan City	Zambo. del Sur	2.63	1,702
Banaran	Tandu Bas	Sulu	2.38	5,162
Basbas	Tandu Bas	Sulu	2.59	385
Borocay	Malay	Aklan	3.96	2,378
Cabilao	Loon	Bohol	2.88	2,767
Camandag	Santo Niño	Samar	3.60	2,671
Catalaban	Sulat	Samar	1.00	1,265
Dudangan	Tandu Bas	Sulu	3.76	742
Gigantangan	Calubian	Leyte	1.86	1,425
Hibuson	Lorete	Surigao	4.03	880
Igbon	Concepcion	Iloilo	2.69	1,190
Jaguilao	Jetafe	Bohol	1.55	763
Jao	Talibon	Bohol	1.98	2,524
Latuan	Tandu Bas	Sulu	2.02	1,440
Limasawa	Padre Burgos	Leyte	3.44	1,874
Manicani	Guiuan	Samar	4.31	1,341
Pangangan	Calape	Bohol	2.00	2,728
Panobulan	Nueva Valencia	Iloilo	1.28	488
Saluping	Basilan City	Zambo. del Sur	1.70	1,368
Sibale	Surigao	Surigao	1.34	1,207
Sicogon	Carles	Iloilo	4.20	1,874
Tamuk	Basilan City	Zambo. del Sur	1.32	1,341
Tubabao	Guiuan	Samar	2.21	1,772

NOTE: No island smaller than 1.0 sq. mi. is included, since area data on the very small islands was not available.

SOURCES: Island areas were taken from lists provided by the Philippine Coast and Geodetic Survey for the year 1962; populations are from *Census of the Philippines, 1960*.

Table 4 MEAN MONTHLY TEMPERATURES FOR SELECTED PHILIPPINE STATIONS (In degrees Fahrenheit)

Station	Years of Record	Jan.	Feb.	March	April	May	June	July	Aug.	Sept.	Oct.	Nov.	Dec.	Annual
Basco	46	72.4	72.5	75.4	79.2	81.5	83.4	82.7	82.2	81.5	79.9	76.7	73.4	78.5
Aparri	47	74.7	73.2	73.4	76.7	79.7	81.4	82.4	81.9	81.4	80.8	79.4	77.2	78.5
Laoag	41	77.0	78.2	81.0	83.4	84.0	83.4	81.9	81.0	81.7	81.4	80.0	78.9	81.0
Vigan	47	77.7	78.0	80.4	82.5	83.5	82.5	81.0	80.2	80.6	81.0	80.4	79.0	80.6
San Fernando	38	77.0	77.2	80.2	83.5	84.4	83.2	81.7	81.5	81.2	81.0	79.4	78.5	80.8
Baguio	47	61.7	61.9	63.9	65.5	66.0	66.0	64.5	64.2	64.4	64.4	63.9	63.4	64.2
Echague	32	74.7	75.5	70.0	82.5	84.4	84.5	83.0	82.7	82.0	79.9	77.4	75.7	80.0
Dagupan	47	77.9	78.5	80.8	83.2	83.4	82.5	80.6	80.6	80.6	81.0	79.9	78.7	80.6
Tarlac	32	78.3	79.4	82.2	84.7	84.7	83.7	81.5	81.5	81.4	81.4	79.9	79.0	81.5
Manila	75	76.2	77.0	79.4	82.0	82.7	81.9	80.2	80.4	79.9	79.4	78.2	76.9	79.5
Silang	24	75.5	76.0	77.5	79.5	78.7	77.4	76.0	76.5	76.7	76.9	76.5	75.4	76.9
Batangas	32	78.5	79.2	82.0	84.2	84.2	83.5	81.7	81.9	81.0	80.6	79.9	79.0	81.4
Atimonan	38	77.4	77.5	79.5	81.9	82.7	82.2	81.4	81.5	80.6	80.4	79.9	78.5	80.2
Baler	45	76.0	76.2	77.7	79.9	81.9	82.5	82.2	82.7	81.5	80.0	79.0	77.4	79.7
Naga	37	77.2	77.0	78.7	80.6	82.7	82.7	82.2	82.5	81.9	80.6	79.4	78.1	80.2
Legaspi	47	78.2	78.2	79.7	81.5	82.5	82.2	81.2	81.2	80.6	80.8	79.9	79.2	80.4
Romblon	46	79.9	79.7	82.0	84.2	85.0	84.2	83.0	83.2	82.7	82.4	81.7	80.4	82.4
Masbate	45	79.2	79.9	81.5	83.5	84.7	84.3	83.2	83.2	82.7	82.5	81.5	80.4	82.2

Roxas	47	78.1	78.0	79.9	81.7	82.4	81.5	80.6	80.6	80.0	80.0	79.9	79.4	80.2
Iloilo	47	78.1	78.5	80.2	82.0	82.2	81.2	80.2	80.2	79.9	79.9	79.5	78.9	80.1
Bacolod	25	78.6	78.9	80.2	82.2	82.9	81.5	79.9	79.9	80.0	80.2	79.5	79.4	80.2
Dumaguete	38	79.0	79.0	80.2	81.5	81.7	81.4	81.4	81.9	81.5	80.8	80.6	80.2	80.7
Cebu	47	78.8	78.9	80.2	81.9	82.6	82.0	81.4	81.5	81.2	80.8	80.2	79.7	80.7
Ormoc	38	77.4	77.3	78.5	79.5	80.2	80.0	81.7	80.2	79.9	79.0	78.5	78.3	79.2
Tacloban	46	77.9	77.8	79.4	80.8	81.9	81.4	81.2	81.7	81.4	80.4	79.5	78.9	80.2
Borongan	47	78.1	78.0	79.2	80.2	81.1	81.4	81.4	81.7	81.7	80.4	79.7	79.4	80.2
Tagbilaran	38	78.3	78.1	79.4	80.6	81.7	81.2	81.4	81.4	81.2	80.4	79.7	79.0	80.2
Jolo	52	79.2	78.9	79.2	80.2	80.6	80.0	80.6	80.2	80.2	79.9	79.5	79.5	79.8
Zamboanga	49	79.5	79.4	79.7	80.2	80.4	79.9	79.7	79.7	79.7	79.7	79.9	79.9	79.9
Cagayan de Oro	40	78.1	78.5	79.7	81.5	82.4	81.4	81.2	81.2	81.0	80.2	79.9	78.9	80.2
Cotabato	38	81.0	81.6	82.7	83.4	82.9	81.9	80.8	80.8	81.2	81.7	81.7	81.4	81.7
Surigao	47	78.1	77.8	78.7	79.7	81.0	81.2	81.4	81.7	81.4	80.6	79.4	78.7	79.9
Davao	47	79.2	79.5	80.4	81.7	81.5	80.4	80.0	80.4	80.6	80.6	80.4	79.5	80.4

SOURCE: Philippine Weather Bureau.

Table 5 MEAN MONTHLY PRECIPITATION FOR SELECTED PHILIPPINE STATIONS (In inches)

Station	Years of Record	Jan.	Feb.	March	April	May	June	July	Aug.	Sept.	Oct.	Nov.	Dec.	Annual
Basco	46	9.1	5.3	5.2	3.8	8.5	8.6	12.6	15.9	13.9	14.7	13.7	12.8	124.0
Aparri	47	5.7	3.2	2.2	1.9	4.5	6.8	7.9	9.4	11.3	14.6	12.9	8.6	89.0
Aguneran	9	0.4	0.5	0.4	1.5	1.3	2.6	2.8	4.0	4.4	5.4	7.8	4.2	35.2
Laoag	41	0.2	0.2	0.2	0.4	7.3	12.1	22.2	25.2	15.8	7.1	1.9	0.6	93.0
Vigan	47	0.1	0.3	0.3	0.8	7.7	14.6	27.2	28.5	16.2	5.7	1.7	0.6	103.5
San Fernando	38	0.3	0.3	0.4	0.9	7.1	13.0	23.8	26.4	15.9	5.6	1.9	0.8	96.3
Baguio	47	0.8	0.7	2.0	4.9	14.3	16.4	38.5	42.1	25.9	14.7	6.5	2.4	169.2
Echague	32	2.4	1.5	2.4	3.3	6.8	4.4	7.8	8.2	9.3	9.0	10.3	6.7	72.1
Dagupan	47	0.4	0.5	1.0	3.4	8.0	12.4	21.8	21.5	15.1	6.9	3.3	1.1	95.3
Tarlac	32	0.3	0.5	0.9	2.4	7.5	10.2	16.1	15.8	11.5	6.5	3.3	1.3	76.1
Olongapo	22	0.2	0.2	0.1	1.1	12.9	20.6	38.8	35.6	27.0	9.9	4.7	1.7	152.8
Manila	75	1.0	0.5	0.7	1.3	5.1	10.0	17.0	16.6	14.0	7.6	5.7	2.6	82.0
Silang	24	1.6	0.9	1.2	1.5	7.8	10.8	17.9	16.6	13.0	7.4	7.5	4.3	90.3
Batangas	32	1.0	0.7	0.4	1.3	4.4	6.2	11.9	10.4	10.7	7.4	7.4	4.5	66.3
Atimonan	38	8.1	4.4	3.1	3.3	5.8	7.4	8.0	6.4	11.2	15.0	17.6	15.1	105.4
Baler	45	8.0	6.7	8.2	11.2	11.1	9.1	10.3	7.2	11.7	14.9	15.9	15.3	129.6
Naga	37	4.5	3.2	2.7	3.4	6.1	8.0	10.8	7.4	11.5	11.5	12.2	11.4	92.6
Legaspi	47	14.8	10.6	8.4	5.9	6.8	7.7	9.4	8.1	9.8	12.5	18.9	20.2	133.1
Baras	13	18.0	16.0	15.1	5.8	8.1	8.9	14.1	8.6	14.6	31.6	43.2	32.0	215.8
Romblon	46	4.6	3.2	2.4	2.7	5.6	8.5	11.1	8.6	9.1	12.3	11.9	9.3	89.2
Masbate	45	7.2	4.6	3.2	1.3	4.2	6.1	7.2	6.8	6.9	7.2	8.8	10.3	73.7

Station														
Puerto Princesa	9	1.4	0.6	2.4	1.4	5.0	6.3	7.1	7.1	8.9	7.6	8.7	4.9	61.3
Roxas	47	5.5	3.4	2.1	2.1	7.1	10.6	10.4	8.9	10.0	14.5	11.7	8.9	95.2
Iloilo	47	2.4	1.6	1.4	2.0	6.2	10.5	15.8	14.6	11.5	10.6	8.3	4.9	89.7
Bacolod	25	3.9	2.3	1.6	1.5	7.0	8.9	14.8	12.0	11.3	10.3	9.3	6.8	89.7
Dumaguete	38	4.0	2.9	2.2	1.8	4.5	6.1	5.5	4.3	5.6	7.6	7.1	5.5	56.9
Cebu	47	4.2	2.8	2.1	1.8	4.8	7.1	7.7	5.8	7.5	8.1	6.5	5.6	64.0
Ormoc	38	6.9	4.5	3.9	3.2	4.3	7.7	10.9	8.9	10.9	10.1	19.2	8.3	89.8
Tacloban	46	13.0	8.2	7.2	5.1	6.3	6.9	6.4	5.2	6.1	8.3	11.5	14.3	98.4
Borongan	47	25.2	17.3	14.2	10.2	10.5	9.1	7.5	5.9	7.1	13.2	21.6	25.8	167.6
Tagbilaran	38	5.1	3.6	3.6	4.9	4.6	5.6	7.8	5.2	6.6	8.8	8.2	6.2	70.3
Jolo	52	4.3	4.3	4.3	5.7	8.3	8.5	6.7	6.8	7.5	8.7	8.5	6.8	80.2
Zamboanga	49	2.1	2.2	1.5	2.0	3.6	4.3	4.8	4.4	4.8	5.6	4.7	3.5	43.4
Clarin	9	15.8	7.6	13.4	7.4	13.5	17.4	17.4	17.3	16.6	21.9	30.6	29.2	208.2
Cagayan de Oro	40	3.7	2.2	1.8	1.3	5.1	8.8	9.2	7.7	8.6	7.8	5.2	4.8	66.2
Marawi	16	6.5	5.4	5.5	7.3	11.9	14.3	10.4	9.0	13.0	10.8	9.0	8.2	111.3
Cotabato	38	3.3	3.5	3.5	5.9	8.6	9.4	10.7	9.4	8.8	11.0	7.4	4.2	85.7
Dadiangas	4	2.0	2.5	3.2	2.2	4.3	4.7	3.6	4.5	3.4	3.8	3.2	2.7	39.9
Surigao	47	22.0	15.1	14.2	9.9	6.7	4.9	6.8	5.2	6.7	11.0	16.8	24.9	144.2
Davao	47	4.7	4.2	4.9	5.6	9.2	8.6	6.9	6.4	7.0	7.7	5.6	5.8	76.4

Source: Philippine Weather Bureau.

Table 6   SPECIES OF FISH COMMONLY CAUGHT IN PHILIPPINE WATERS

English nomenclature	*Philippine nomenclature*	*Latin nomenclature*
Anchovy	Dilis, tuakang, dumpilas	*Stolephorus commsonii, S. indicus, Scutengraulis hamiltonii*
Barracuda	Asogon, torcillo	*Sphyraena jello, S. obtusata*
Big-eyed scad	Matang baka	*Caranx crumenophthalmus*
Bonito	Katchorita	*Euthynnus yaito*
Caesio	Dalagang bukid	*Caesio cunning, C. chryosozomus, C. caerulaureus, C. lunaris, Pinjalo typus*
Cavalla	Talakitok, garapeche	*Caranx armatus, C. malabaricus, C. stellatus, C. sexfasciatus, C. speciosus*
Common climbing perch	Martiniko	*Anabas testudineus*
Crevalle	Salay-salay	*Caranx djodaba, C. kalla, C. leptolepis*
Croaker	Kabang, alakaak	*Sciaena dussumieri, S. indica, Pseudosciaena anea*
Flying fish	Bolador	*Cypselurus oligolepis*
Freshwater catfish	Hito	*Clarias batrachus*
Garfish	Kambabado, batalay	*Ablennes hians, Tylosurus giganteus, T. strongylurus*
Gizzard shad	Suogan, kabasi	*Nematolosa nasus, Anodontostoma chacunda*
Goatfish	Saramulyete	*Upensoides sulphureus*
Goby	Bianga pute	*Glossogobius giurus*
Grouper	Lapo-lapong senorita, Lapo-lapo, lapo-lapong liglig, garopa, kolapo	*Variola louti, Epinephelus undulosus, E. megachir, E. corallicola, E. merra, E. fuscoguttatus, Plectropomus maculatus, P. oligacanthus, Anyperodon leucogrammicus, Cromileptes altiveles*
Grunt	Labian	*Plectorhinchus pictus*
Hairtail	Balila	*Trichiurus haumela*
Halfbeak	Buguing	*Hemiramphus georgii, H. far*
Hardtail	Oriles	*Megalaspis cordyla*
Herring	Tunsoy, lapad, tuabak	*Sardinella fimbriata, S. perforata, Ilisha hoevenii*
Leaf fish	Dahong gabi	*Platax orbicularis*
Leather jacket	Dorado	*Scomberoides lysan*
Lizard fish	Kalaso	*Saurida tumbil, Trachinocephalus myops*

Table 6—Continued

English nomenclature	Philippine nomenclature	Latin nomenclature
Mackerel	Hasa-hasa, alumahan, tangigi	*Rastrelliger brachijosomus, R. chrysozomus, Cybium commerson*
Milkfish	Bangos	*Chanos chanos*
Mojarra	Malakapas	*Gerres filamentosus*
Moonfish	Chabita	*Mene maculata*
Moray	Pabukang benhe	*Gymnothorax pictus*
Mullet	Banak, talilong	*Mugil caeruleomaculatus, M. vaigiensis, M. melinopterus, M. dussumieri*
Nemipterid	Bisugo	*Nemipterus japonicus, N. tawnipterus*
Pomfret	Duhay	*Stromateus niger*
Porgy	Malaking mata, bitilla, mahuwana	*Monotaxis grandoculis, Lethrinus opercularis, Argyrops spinifer*
Runner	Salmon	*Elagatis bipinnulatus*
Sardine	Tamban	*Sardinella longiceps*
Sea catfish	Kanduli, bongoan	*Arius manillensis, A. thalassinus, A. leistetocephalus*
Shark	Pating, pating inflesa, binkungan	*Scoliodon palasorrah, Carcharias melanopterus, Sphyrna zygaena*
Siganid	Samoral	*Teuthis javus*
Silver bar	Parang-parang	*Chirocentrus dorab*
Slipmouth	Sapsap, hualing, dalangat, e-im, dalupani	*Leiognathus* spp.
Snapper	Maya-maya, iso, dolesan	*Lutjanus* spp.
Sole	Dapang sinilas, tambiki	*Cynoglossus puncticeps, Solea humilis*
Spadefish	Kitang	*Scatophagus argus*
Surgeon fish	Labahita	*Acanthurus bleekeri*
Tarpon	Buan-buan	*Megalops cyprinoides*
Tenpounder	Bidbid	*Elops hawaiiensis*
Threadfin	Mamale, mamalang bato	*Eleutheronema tetradactylum, Polynemus microstoma*
Tuna	Albacora	*Neothunnus macropterus*
Whiting	Asohes	*Sillago sihama, S. maculata*

Table 7   SPECIES OF TIMBER TREES COMMONLY LOGGED

Common name [a]	Scientific name
Group 1	
Akle	*Albizzia acle*
Aranga	*Homalium* spp.
Bansalagin	*Mimusops parviflora*
Banuyo	*Wallaceodendron celebicum*
Batikuling	*Litsea leytensis*
Batitinan	*Lagerstroemia periformis*
Betis	*Madhuca betis*
Dañgula	*Vitex aherniana*
Dao	*Dracontomelum dao*
Duñgon	*Tarrietia sylvatica*
Ebony	*Diospyros ferrea*
Ipil	*Intsia* spp.
Kaburo	*Phoebe sterculiodes*
Kalamansanai	*Neonauclea calycina* and spp.
Kalantas	*Toona* spp.
Kamagong	*Diospyros discolor*
Kulilisiau	*Machilus philippinensis*
Malabuñga	*Nothaphiobe malabuñga*
Mancono	*Xanthostemon verdugonianus*
Margapali	*Dehaasia triandra*
Molave	*Vitex parviflora*
Narra	*Pterocarpus* spp.
Sañgilo	*Pistacia chinesis*
Supa	*Sindora supa*
Tambulian	*Eusideroxylon zwageri*
Teak	*Tectona grandis*
Tindalo	*Pahudia rhomboidea*
Urung	*Fagraea cochinchinensis*
Yakal	*Shorea gisok, S. astylosa, S. seminis, S. malibato, Hopea plagata*
Group 2	
Akleng-parang	*Albizzia procera*
Alupag	*Euphoria* spp.
Alupag-amo	*Litchi philippinensis*
Amayan	*Angelesia splendens*
Anubing	*Artocarpus cumingiana*
Balu	*Cordia subcordata*
Banaba	*Lagerstroemia speciosa*

Table 7—Continued

Common name [a]	Scientific name
Bitanghol	*Calophyllum blancoi*
Bitaog	*Calophyllum inophyllum*
Bolong-eta	*Diospyros philosanthera*
Caña-fistula	*Cassia fistula*
Duñgon-late	*Heritiera litoralis*
Gisok-gisok	*Hopea philippinensis*
Guijo	*Shorea guiso*
Katmon	*Dillenia* spp.
Kayu-galu	*Sindera galedupa*
Lanete	*Wrightia laniti*
Makaasim	*Zyzygium* spp.
Malabayabas	*Tristania decorticata* or *littoralis*
Malakadios	*Beilschmiedia cairocan*
Malugai	*Pometia pinnata*
Manggachapui	*Hopea acuminata* or *foxworthyi*
Manggis	*Koompasia excelsa*
Mapilig	*Xanthostemon bracteatus*
Maranggo	*Azadirachta integrifoliola*
Narek	*Balanocarpus cagayanensis*
Narig	*Vatica* spp.
Pagatpat	*Sonneratia alba*
Sudiang	*Ctenolophon philippinensis*
Tabau	*Lumnitzera littorea*
Tamayuan	*Strombosia philippinensis*
Tañglin	*Adenanthera intermedia*
Tukang-kalau	*Aglaia clarkii*
Group 3	
Agoho	*Casuarina equisetifolia*
Almaciga	*Agathis alba*
Amugis	*Koordersiodendron pinnatum*
Anislag	*Securinega flexuosa*
Antipolo	*Artocarpus blancoi*
Apitong	*Dipterocarpus grandiflorus*
Bagras	*Eucalyptus deglupta*
Bahai	*Ormosia calavensis*
Batino	*Alstonia macrophylla*
Batukanag	*Aglaia bicolor*
Bayanti	*Aglaia llanosiana*
Binggas	*Terminalia comintana*

Table 7—Continued

Common name [a]	Scientific name
Bulala	*Nephelium mutabile*
Gisihan	*Aglaia laevigata*
Harras	*Garcinia ituman*
Kaliñgag	*Cinnamomum mercadoi*
Kalumpit	*Terminalia edulis*
Kamatog	*Erythrophloeum densiflorum*
Kamuning	*Murraya paniculata*
Kato	*Amoora aherniana*
Kayatau	*Dysoxylum turczaninowii*
Kuling-manuk	*Aglaia luzoniensis*
Lamio	*Dracontomelum edule*
Lamog	*Planchonia spectabilis*
Lanipau	*Terminalia crassiramea*
Lanutan	*Bombycidendron* spp.
Liusin	*Parinarium corymbosum*
Lumbayau	*Tarrietia javanica*
Malabatino	*Paralstronia clusiacea*
Malaguijo	*Shorea plagata*
Malakamanga	*Reinwardtiodendron celebicum*
Malakauayan	*Podocarpus* spp.
Malapinggan	*Trichadenia philippinensis*
Malasaging	*Aglaia diffusa*
Malasantol	*Sandoricum vidalii*
Malatumbaga	*Aglaia harmsiana*
Malibayo	*Berria cordifolia*
Mangkas	*Sideroxylon ferrugineum*
Mayapis	*Shorea squamata*
Miao	*Dysoxylum euphlebium*
Nangka	*Artocarpus heterophylla*
Nato	*Palaquium luzoniense*
Oak	*Quercus* spp.
Pahutan	*Mangifera altissima*
Palosapis	*Anisoptera thurifera* or *mindanensis*
Piagau	*Xylocarpus molucensis*
Pine, Benguet	*Pinus insularis*
Pine, Mindoro	*Pinus merkusii*
Red lauan	*Shorea negrosensis*
Salakin	*Aphanamixis cumingiana*
Santol	*Sandoricum koetjape*
Talisai	*Terminalia catappa*

Table 7—Continued

Common name [a]	Scientific name
Talisai-gubat	*Terminalia oocarpa*
Tañgile	*Shorea polysperma*
Tibigi	*Xylocarpus granatum*
Toog	*Petersianthus quadrialata*
Tugbok	*Stemonurus secundifolius*

[a] Species are listed in the three groups normally classified by the Philippine Bureau of Forestry for commercial lumber purposes. Group 1 includes the chief hardwoods employed in furniture and fine lumbers; Group 2 comprises chiefly general construction woods and soft "Philippine mahogany" woods; Group 3 comprises chiefly woods of lesser utility, rough construction woods, and scarce woods; however the list is subject to periodic rearrangement according to criteria set by the Bureau of Forestry.

SOURCE: *Important Commercial Timbers of the Philippines* (Tamesis and Aguilar), Popular Bulletin no. 32 (Manila, 1953).

Table 8 LAND SUBJECT TO SOIL EROSION, 1949 (By province)

Province	Total area (in sq. mi.)	Percent subject to erosion
Batangas	1,191	83.1
Cebu	1,880	76.3
Ilocos Sur	1,037	73.8
La Union	530	70.3
Batanes	76	67.9
Masbate	1,571	66.1
Bohol	1,575	66.0
Abra	1,469	65.1
Iloilo	2,048	63.5
Cavite	498	60.6
Rizal	805	58.4
Capiz	1,703	55.2
Marinduque	355	51.7
Negros Occidental	2,989	49.7
Tarlac	1,175	48.4
Ilocos Norte	1,308	46.7
Pangasinan	2,029	46.2
Mindoro	3,891	45.7
Antique	1,034	45.6
Bukidnon	3,104	42.7
Pampanga	827	42.6
Mountain	5,458	42.5
Sulu	1,086	41.5
Leyte	3,084	41.0
Albay	996	40.5
Catanduanes	552	39.9
Negros Oriental	2,053	35.5
Camarines Sur	2,060	34.3
Zambales	1,408	33.7
Isabela	4,069	32.9
Nueva Ecija	2,120	31.1
Romblon	512	30.9
Bulacan	1,021	26.6
Sorsogon	793	24.7
Misamis Oriental	1,512	24.6
Nueva Vizcaya	2,627	22.4
Laguna	465	21.8
Cagayan	3,470	21.4
Misamis Oriental	802	21.3

Table 8—Continued

Province	Total area (in sq. mi.)	Percent subject to erosion
Quezon	4,616	19.8
Bataan	517	19.4
Cotabato	8,868	15.6
Lanao	2,575	14.7
Camarines Norte	829	14.3
Zamboanga	6,517	12.0
Davao	7,529	10.5
Samar	5,309	10.5
Palawan	5,693	7.8
Surigao	3,079	5.7
Agusan	4,120	4.5
Philippines	114,830	29.9

Source: J. P. Mamisao, "Soil Conservation Problems in the Philippines," *Journal of the Soil Science Society of the Philippines* 1 (1949), 1–18.

Table 9   POPULATION BY LANGUAGE SPEAKERS, 1960

SPECIFIED MOTHER TONGUES

Mother tongue	Total (in thousands)	Percent	Mother tongue	Total (in thousands)	Percent
Cebuano	6,529.8	24.1	Calagan-Caragan	13.4	a
Tagalog	5,694.0	21.0	Yogad	13.4	a
Iloco	3,158.5	11.7	Badjao	12.6	a
Panay-Hiligaynon	2,817.3	10.4	Ivatan	11.8	a
Bikol	2,108.8	7.8	Isinai	11.5	a
Samar-Leyte	1,488.6	5.5	Pinalawan	11.2	a
Pampango	875.5	3.2	Tagakaolo	11.0	a
Pangasinan	666.0	2.5	Spanish	9.6	a
Maguindanao	358.8	1.3	Ata	9.3	a
Tausog	307.5	1.1	Tagabili	8.7	a
Aklanon	304.8	1.1	Banuanon	8.0	a
Ilanum	268.1	1.0	Mangyan	6.7	a
Hamtikon	262.0	1.0	Tinggian-Itneg	6.3	a
Ibanog	178.7	0.7	Agutayano	6.2	a
Maranao	150.6	0.6	Kalamian	6.1	a
Masbate	136.0	0.5	Tagbanua	5.5	a
Chavacano	126.5	0.5	Palanon	3.8	a
Samal	126.1	0.5	Indonesian	3.7	a
Chinese	122.9	0.5	Ilongot	3.6	a
Bilaan	94.7	0.3	Negrito	2.7	a
Subanon	81.8	0.3	Kalibugan	2.4	a
Bontoc	78.1	0.3	Molbog	2.2	a
Ifugao	74.9	0.3	Sangil	1.8	a
Zambal	72.8	0.3	Dumagat	1.6	a
Kangkanai	71.3	0.3	Banton	1.1	a
Cagayano	71.6	0.3	Hindi	0.9	a
Bukidnon	70.5	0.3	Cagayan de Oro	0.6	a
Davaweno	68.7	0.3	Batac	0.5	a
Itawis	64.7	0.2	German	0.488	a
Inibaloi	63.0	0.2	Kulaman	0.471	a
Yakan	58.1	0.2	Manguangan	0.457	a
Manobo	46.8	0.2	Japanese	0.429	a
Kalinga	46.6	0.2	Belgian	0.365	a
Malaueg	36.5	0.1	Dutch	0.238	a
Apayao-Isneg	33.0	0.1	French	0.212	a
Bagobo-Guiangga	31.7	0.1	Mamanwa	0.151	a
Tirruarai	26.3	0.1	Kapul	0.093	a

Table 9—Continued

Mother tongue	Total (in thousands)	Percent	Mother tongue	Total (in thousands)	Percent
Mandaya	24.3	0.1	Tap	0.081	a
Bolinao	23.2	0.1	Pullon-Mapun	0.029	a
English	21.5	0.1	Kene	0.024	a
Palawano	18.9	0.1	Others	1.475	a
Romblon	17.7	0.1			
			Total [b]	27,087.7	100.0
Gaddang	13.8	0.1			
Caviteno	13.5	a			

Table 9—Continued

MAJOR MOTHER TONGUES BY PROVINCES, 1960° (In thousands)

Province	Total	Tagalog	Cebuano	Iloco	Panay-Hiligaynon	Bikol	Samar-Leyte	Pampango	Pangasinan
Abra	115.2			89.6					
Agusan	271.0	2.7	218.7	4.6	9.5		6.9		
Aklan	226.2	1.4			1.6				
Albay	514.9	2.6				509.5			
Antique	238.4			1.9	9.3				
Bataan	145.3	123.0						16.7	
Batanes	10.3								
Batangas	681.4	675.6				1.0			
Bohol	592.2		591.1						
Bukidnon	194.3	2.0	102.0	4.9	9.9		1.9		
Bulacan	555.8	537.1	1.8	3.0	1.7	3.1	2.3	3.5	1.3
Cagayan	445.3	4.5		289.3					
Camarines Nor	188.0	87.9	1.3			95.7			
Camarines Sur	819.5	32.0				781.9			
Capiz	315.0				313.9				
Catanduanes	156.3					155.5			
Cavite	378.1	358.0	1.1	1.3	1.6	1.2	1.9		
Cebu	1,332.8	3.6	1,313.6		1.9		3.2		
Cotabato	1,029.1	22.1	151.7	98.0	222.8	3.0	6.0	3.2	2.9
Davao	893.0	19.6	599.5	19.4	37.8	1.0	20.5		1.7

	1	2	3	4	5	6	7	8	9
Ilocos Norte	287.3			283.7					
Ilocos Sur	338.0			329.7					
Iloilo	966.2	2.1	1.1		958.5				
Isabela	442.0	20.4		294.9				1.1	2.8
La Union	293.3	1.8		274.9					6.7
Laguna	472.0	453.3	1.2	4.3	1.0		1.4	1.1	1.1
Lanao del Nor	270.6	1.9	217.8		3.6	5.7	1.1		
Lanao del Sur	378.3	1.5	8.5	2.7	5.8				
Leyte	1,172.9	1.4	673.8				494.6		
Manila	1,138.6	734.7	29.7	75.7	29.2	46.2	49.9	50.2	28.4
Marinduque	114.5	113.4							
Masbate	335.9		107.3		29.6	62.4	1.3		
Misamis Occ.	248.3		242.6		1.0				
Misamis Or.	388.6	5.0	371.3						
Mountain	435.8	9.6		83.4				1.1	12.6
Negros Occ.	1,332.3	4.5	328.6		992.8				
Negros Or.	598.7		564.7		30.2				
Nueva Ecija	608.3	386.7	1.2	205.0		1.0		6.4	4.0
Nueva Vizcaya	138.0	4.1		107.3					
Occ. Mindoro	84.3	54.3		12.6	6.3		1.3		
Or. Mindoro	229.0	178.6		9.8	7.4		1.2		
Palawan	162.6	15.4	2.6	3.8	7.9				

Table 9—Continued

Province	Total	Tagalog	Cebuano	Iloco	Panay-Hiligaynon	Bikol	Samar-Leyte	Pampango	Pangasinan
Pampanga	617.2	20.0	1.2	4.9	1.3	1.4	1.1	579.1	1.7
Pangasinan	1,214.1	8.0		527.8				1.7	555.4
Quezon	653.4	582.0	2.2	21.2	1.0	38.0	1.5		1.0
Rizal	1,456.3	1,134.4	26.6	76.5	34.5	44.8	36.9	31.0	26.0
Romblon	131.6				57.7				
Samar	868.0	1.5	26.6				836.8		
Sorsogon	347.7	1.1				344.4			
Sulu	326.9	1.4	1.9						
Surigao	360.0	1.2	349.5		1.9		4.9		
Tarlac	426.6	18.7		223.9				169.5	9.9
Zambales	213.4	49.4		83.3		1.3	1.3	3.3	2.6
Zambo. del Nor	281.4		219.2	1.2	3.0				
Zambo. del Sur	742.4	7.0	361.3	10.3	25.6		3.4		
Total [b]	27,087.6	5,694.0	6,529.8	3,158.5	2,817.3	2,108.8	1,488.6	875.5	666.0

Table 9—Continued

PERSONS ABLE TO SPEAK TAGALOG, ENGLISH, AND SPANISH, 1960, BY AGE CLASS (In thousands)

Age class	Population	Tagalog	English	Spanish
Under 10 Years	8,941.8	2,325.2	498.5	10.6
10 to 29 Years	10,661.6	6,197.2	6,921.3	260.9
30 to 49 Years	5,116.5	2,577.3	2,671.6	172.8
50 Years and Over	2,367.5	917.2	697.3	115.8
Total [b]	27,087.6	12,019.2	10,689.1	558.6

[a] Less than 0.1 percent.

[b] Individual totals do not add owing to rounding in both columns.

[c] Blanks represent unit totals of less than 1,000 for the language of the province.

SOURCE: *Census of the Philippines*, 1960. Eighty-four specified languages are listed by the dentifications employed by the Bureau of Census and Statistics, of which ten are not properly native to the Philippines.

Table 10   POPULATION BY RELIGIOUS AFFILIATION, 1960 [a] (By province)

Province	Total (in thousands)	Roman Catholic	Agli-payan	Iglesia ni Kristo	Protes-tant	Moslem
Abra	115.2	95.8	6.5	1.0	7.2	
Agusan	271.0	243.5	12.1	2.6	8.0	0.1
Aklan	226.2	214.2	7.0	0.4	2.1	
Albay	514.9	508.7		1.4	2.4	
Antique	238.4	160.6	61.8	0.5	13.6	
Bataan	145.3	130.3	7.1	4.0	3.1	
Batanes	10.3	10.1			0.2	
Batangas	681.4	664.0	4.0	5.3	4.8	
Bohol	592.2	570.3	12.6	0.8	6.3	
Bukidnon	194.3	159.8	5.2	0.6	12.9	2.7
Bulacan	555.8	527.3	7.0	9.4	9.2	
Cagayan	445.2	377.5	42.5	4.0	13.7	
Camarines Nor.	188.1	185.9		2.4	0.8	
Camarines Sur	819.5	787.2	19.2	2.9	6.5	
Capiz	315.0	304.9	3.1	1.2	4.3	
Catanduanes	156.3	155.7		0.2	0.1	
Cavite	378.1	324.9	30.7	8.0	11.6	
Cebu	1,332.8	1,294.7	19.6	3.4	8.2	
Cotabato	1,029.1	467.8	15.1	8.9	78.1	356.4
Davao	893.0	778.0	5.2	5.9	46.6	22.8
Ilocos Norte	287.3	115.7	157.9	3.6	7.9	
Ilocos Sur	338.0	293.3	16.4	2.9	17.6	
Iloilo	966.2	862.2	71.5	2.2	24.8	0.3
Isabela	442.0	314.8	72.7	9.7	31.0	
La Union	293.3	268.6	5.6	2.3	11.7	
Laguna	472.0	409.6	44.9	7.2	6.3	
Lanao del Norte	270.6	198.2	5.7	1.6	5.3	56.5
Lanao del Sur	378.3	19.9	0.6	0.4	0.9	355.7
Leyte	1,172.9	1,127.3	26.4	2.7	10.0	
Manila	1,138.6	1,056.6	9.8	16.6	24.2	22.0
Marinduque	114.5	108.4	4.9	0.7	0.1	
Masbate	335.9	313.6	13.9	1.9	3.1	
Misamis Occ.	248.3	168.0	61.2	1.8	11.6	0.1
Misamis Or.	388.6	338.3	37.4	1.0	5.6	0.6
Mountain	435.8	231.5	8.9	2.2	69.0	
Negros Occ.	1,332.3	1,188.4	74.3	8.6	48.7	
Negros Or.	597.7	489.3	67.4	3.7	32.2	
Nueva Ecija	608.3	491.5	66.7	19.2	21.6	0.1
Nueva Vizcaya	138.1	84.0	12.4	4.9	84.0	0.4

Table 10—Continued

Province	Total (in thousands)	Roman Catholic	Agli- payan	Iglesia ni Kristo	Protes- tant	Moslem
Occ. Mindoro	84.3	70.3	6.5	2.6	2.7	
Or. Mindoro	229.0	203.4	4.5	4.7	8.1	0.1
Palawan	162.6	116.5	0.7	0.9	10.3	12.7
Pampanga	617.2	574.5	9.5	15.6	14.1	
Pangasinan	1,124.1	942.6	105.2	20.4	33.9	0.2
Quezon	653.4	625.7	3.3	11.3	4.7	0.2
Rizal	1,456.3	1,348.5	36.9	24.0	32.8	0.6
Romblon	131.6	100.0	25.5	0.8	3.3	
Samar	868.0	832.7	21.6	1.6	10.3	
Sorsogon	347.7	343.2	0.4	1.6	1.3	
Sulu	326.9	10.0			0.9	310.9
Surigao	360.0	304.2	42.3	1.6	7.6	0.1
Tarlac	426.6	318.5	70.8	15.1	14.0	0.2
Zambales	213.4	139.4	56.0	7.2	8.3	0.1
Zambo. del Norte	281.4	226.2	3.0	0.4	8.7	16.2
Zambo. del Sur	742.4	490.1	8.9	4.2	33.1	178.2
Total [b]	27,087.6	22,686.1	1,414.4	270.1	785.4	1,317.4

[a] The 1960 census recorded 39,631 Buddhists and 574,549 "others." Of the Buddhists a total of 22,035 were resident in Manila and 3,647 were resident in Rizal. Every province except Batanes had resident Buddhists, chiefly numbering a few hundred per province.

[b] Totals do not add owing to rounding. Blanks indicate numbers under 100.

SOURCE: *Census of the Philippines, 1960.*

Table 11   SCHOOL ATTENDANCE

POPULATION BY EDUCATIONAL ACHIEVEMENT, 1960
(By provinces)

	Ten years old and over			Six years old and over		
					Attended	
Province	Total (in 000's)	Literate (in 000's)	In per- cent	Total (in 000's)	School (in 000's)	In per- cent
Abra	79.1	54.8	69.3	93.1	20.0	21.5
Agusan	173.3	136.2	78.6	208.2	39.8	19.1
Aklan	153.5	104.6	68.2	183.0	40.0	21.9
Albay	341.1	252.9	74.1	407.6	91.2	22.4
Antique	164.2	105.8	64.4	192.8	36.0	18.7
Bataan	93.4	77.4	82.9	113.0	26.1	23.2
Batanes	7.5	6.1	81.4	8.6	2.1	24.7
Batangas	460.7	332.9	72.3	543.3	117.0	21.5
Bohol	410.7	283.7	69.1	479.0	81.0	16.9
Bukidnon	122.0	77.9	62.9	148.1	26.3	17.8
Bulacan	382.1	327.2	85.6	448.8	104.3	23.2
Cagayan	293.3	206.5	70.4	350.3	65.2	18.6
Camarines Norte	120.2	108.1	89.9	145.4	34.8	24.0
Camarines Sur	541.6	417.9	77.1	649.9	148.2	22.8
Capiz	205.5	126.8	61.7	248.8	47.7	19.2
Catanduanes	106.0	84.7	79.9	125.3	27.9	22.3
Cavite	259.2	216.8	83.7	304.4	74.6	24.5
Cebu	908.0	576.9	63.5	1,072.0	202.7	18.9
Cotabato	681.1	362.9	53.3	818.1	127.4	15.6
Davao	571.2	379.6	66.5	691.1	133.8	19.4
Ilocos Norte	207.0	147.5	71.3	238.6	48.5	20.3
Ilocos Sur	240.0	172.1	71.7	278.1	56.2	20.2
Iloilo	663.9	513.8	77.4	781.3	158.4	20.3
Isabela	284.6	207.7	73.0	342.0	69.1	20.2
La Union	199.7	151.5	75.9	235.5	51.4	21.8
Laguna	310.0	259.3	83.6	370.4	89.0	24.0
Lanao del Norte	174.7	114.2	65.4	210.8	34.9	16.6
Lanao del Sur	258.2	188.8	73.1	309.6	31.2	10.1
Leyte	780.1	516.4	66.2	932.2	179.2	19.2
Manila	827.1	756.4	91.5	940.0	304.7	32.4
Marinduque	75.1	59.3	78.9	90.4	20.0	22.2
Masbate	212.5	127.0	59.8	259.5	47.9	18.5
Misamis Occ.	166.6	127.3	76.4	198.1	42.5	21.5
Misamis Or.	250.8	193.2	77.0	303.1	65.8	21.7
Mountain	294.7	154.6	52.5	346.7	73.1	21.1

Table 11—Continued

Province	Ten years old and over			Six years old and over		
	Total (in ooo's)	Literate (in ooo's)	In per-cent	Total (in ooo's)	Attended School (in ooo's)	In per-cent
Negros Occ.	875.9	594.0	67.8	1,056.0	201.2	19.1
Negros Or.	397.3	217.2	54.7	476.4	74.0	15.5
Nueva Ecija	403.2	322.7	80.0	479.5	102.6	21.4
Nueva Vizcaya	89.1	62.7	70.3	107.7	23.6	22.0
Occ. Mindoro	56.2	43.2	76.9	65.5	13.8	20.8
Or. Mindoro	145.5	105.2	72.3	175.7	37.9	21.6
Palawan	110.3	65.8	59.7	130.0	22.0	17.0
Pampanga	408.8	321.5	78.7	487.2	117.5	24.1
Pangasinan	762.9	594.1	77.9	901.0	216.2	24.0
Quezon	425.4	361.7	85.0	509.4	105.9	20.8
Rizal	1,008.9	903.9	89.6	1,169.2	333.7	28.5
Romblon	84.4	57.5	68.1	102.4	23.0	22.5
Samar	578.7	370.6	64.0	691.9	138.6	20.0
Sorsogon	228.2	182.0	79.8	274.0	69.3	25.3
Sulu	223.9	63.2	28.2	267.6	33.4	12.5
Surigao	241.8	180.5	74.7	286.9	56.7	19.8
Tarlac	282.8	214.3	75.8	336.7	75.6	22.5
Zambales	141.7	122.6	86.5	168.0	43.7	26.0
Zambo. del Norte	181.6	106.3	58.5	220.2	42.1	19.2
Zambo. del Sur	478.7	235.9	53.0	580.6	91.1	15.7
Total	18,145.8	13,073.7	72.0	21,557.5	4,541.7	21.1

SCHOOL ATTENDANCE BY AGE GROUPS, 1960
(Six years and over)

Age group	Total population (in ooo's)	Attended school (in ooo's)
6–18	9,169.9	4,033.1
19–29	4,903.5	408.8
30 and over	7,484.1	99.9
Total	21,557.5	4,541.8

Table 11—Continued

SCHOOL ATTENDANCE BY CLASS OF SCHOOL, 1960
(Six years and over)

School	Total attended (in 000's)
Elementary	11,979.1
Secondary	2,368.6
College	928.2
No school	6,282.4
Total	21,558.3

NOTE: Not all totals are equivalent owing to rounding.
SOURCE: *Census of the Philippines, 1960.*

Table 12   COMPARATIVE POPULATION BY PROVINCES (In thousands)

Province	1876°	1903	1918	1939	1948	1960
Abra	28.1	51.8	72.7	87.7	86.6	116.2
Agusan	—	30.6	44.7	99.0	126.4	271.0
Aklan	a	a	a	a	a	226.2
Albay	259.0	240.3	323.2	333.9	394.6	515.0
Antique	108.2	134.1	154.9	199.4	233.5	238.4
Bataan	50.9	46.7	58.3	85.5	92.9	145.3
Batan	—	8.3	8.2	9.5	10.7	10.3
Batangas	331.8	257.7	340.1	442.0	510.2	681.4
Bohol	233.8	269.2	358.3	491.6	553.4	592.2
Bukidnon	—	21.1	48.5	57.5	63.4	194.4
Bulacan	247.2	223.7	249.2	332.8	411.3	555.8
Cagayan	90.2	156.2	190.1	292.2	311.0	445.3
Camarines Norte	186.2	239.4	270.8	{ 98.3	103.7	188.1
Camarines Sur				385.6	553.7	819.5
Capiz	213.1	230.7	292.6	405.0	441.8	315.0
Catanduanes	b	39.4	63.5	98.5	112.1	156.3
Cavite	131.6	134.7	157.3	238.5	262.5	378.1
Cebu	417.5	653.2	855.0	1,068.0	1,123.1	1,332.8
Cotabato	—	125.8	171.9	298.9	439.6	1,029.1
Davao	—	65.4	108.2	292.6	364.8	893.0
Ilocos Norte	170.0	178.9	219.1	237.5	251.1	287.3
Ilocos Sur	200.8	187.4	217.4	271.5	276.2	338.0
Iloilo	435.9	410.3	502.9	744.0	816.3	966.2
Isabela	35.3	76.4	112.9	219.8	264.5	442.0
La Union	100.7	137.8	160.5	207.7	237.3	293.3
Laguna	141.1	148.6	195.5	279.5	321.2	472.0
Lanao del Norte	—	22.0	91.4	243.4	343.9	{ 270.6
Lanao del Sur						378.3
Leyte	239.1	388.9	597.9	915.8	1,006.9	1,172.9
Manila	93.6	219.9	285.3	623.4	983.9	1,138.6
Marinduque	38.1	51.6	56.8	81.7	85.8	114.5
Masbate	17.1	43.6	67.5	182.4	211.1	335.9
Misamis Occidental	81.0	175.6	198.9	{ 210.0	207.5	248.3
Misamis Oriental				213.8	369.6	388.6
Mountain	—	135.8	242.3	296.8	278.1	435.8
Negros Occidental	201.0	{ 308.2	396.6	824.8	1,038.7	1,332.3
Negros Oriental		201.4	272.5	394.6	443.4	597.7
Nueva Ecija	117.2	134.1	227.0	416.7	467.7	608.3
Nueva Vizcaya	27.2	20.0	35.8	78.5	82.7	138.0

Table 12—Continued

Province	1876[c]	1903	1918	1939	1948	1960
Occidental Mindoro ⎞ Oriental Mindoro ⎠	19.7	39.5	71.9	131.5	167.7	⎧ 84.3 ⎩ 229.0
Palawan	16.4	35.6	69.0	93.6	106.2	162.6
Pampanga	207.9	223.7	257.6	375.2	416.5	617.2
Pangasinan	269.2	397.9	565.9	742.4	920.5	1,124.1
Quezon	121.3	153.0	212.0	358.5	416.7	653.4
Rizal	191.8	150.9	230.2	444.8	673.0	1,456.3
Romblon	31.0	52.8	64.6	99.3	108.7	131.6
Samar	180.2	266.2	379.5	546.3	757.2	868.0
Sorsogon	b	120.0	178.4	247.6	291.1	347.7
Sulu	—	90.5	172.7	247.1	240.8	326.9
Surigao	59.0	115.1	122.1	225.8	264.9	360.0
Tarlac	92.2	135.1	171.8	264.3	327.0	426.6
Zambales	90.7	59.9	83.7	106.9	138.5	213.4
Zamboanga del Nor ⎞ Zamboanga del Sur ⎠	—	98.0	147.3	355.9	521.9	⎧ 281.4 ⎩ 742.4
Total	5,501.3	7,635.4	10,314.3	16,000.3	19,234.1	27,087.7

ᵃ Included in Capiz through 1948 census.

ᵇ Included in Albay in 1876.

ᶜ This is church data from the 1903 census; it does not include Mountain Province, most of Mindanao, or Sulu.

Table 13 POPULATION DENSITIES BY PROVINCE, 1960

Province	Persons/sq. mi. cultivated area	Cultivated area *
Abra	75.0	998.5
Agusan	60.7	769.8
Aklan	322.3	1,056.2
Albay	522.5	1,193.5
Antique	244.8	942.3
Bataan	274.1	1,543.0
Batanes	127.6	719.9
Batangas	557.5	1,369.1
Bohol	372.5	1,183.9
Bukidnon	60.7	310.7
Bulacan	538.8	2,057.7
Cagayan	128.1	800.4
Camarines Norte	237.1	621.2
Camarines Sur	403.0	811.0
Capiz	309.9	1,007.2
Catanduanes	277.8	801.6
Cavite	760.7	1,750.5
Cebu	678.4	2,358.7
Cotabato	112.0	417.3
Davao	117.6	612.4
Ilocos Norte	218.9	1,786.6
Ilocos Sur	339.4	2,335.0
Iloilo	470.1	1,120.7
Isabela	107.4	588.7
La Union	508.8	2,189.5
Laguna	694.8	1,465.4
Lanao del Norte	226.7	842.2
Lanao del Sur	253.0	841.3
Leyte	382.9	1,051.9
Marinduque	319.4	685.4
Masbate	215.0	568.2
Misamis Occidental	331.7	930.0
Misamis Oriental	264.9	786.0
Mountain	78.8	974.6
Negros Occidental	435.4	1,026.1
Negros Oriental	269.5	989.8
Nueva Ecija	298.2	733.4
Nueva Vizcaya	51.4	844.5

Table 13—Continued

Province	Persons/sq. mi. total area	Cultivated area *
Occidental Mindoro	37.1	364.8
Orinetal Mindoro	135.9	673.8
Palawan	28.3	388.9
Pampanga	733.1	1,908.4
Pangasinan	542.4	1,787.4
Quezon	141.7	739.6
Rizal	2,028.4	19,394.9
Romblon	251.5	758.6
Samar	167.4	674.6
Sorsogon	420.6	865.1
Sulu	315.0	1,048.3
Surigao	130.6	642.8
Tarlac	361.9	984.0
Zambales	148.8	1,956.6
Zamboanga del Norte	120.0	608.5
Zamboanga del Sur	193.8	672.9
Philippines (excl. Manila)	224.3	949.9
Philippines	234.1	991.6

* Provincial areas have been computed from *1960 Census of the Philippines, Agriculture*, table 1, entitled "Total Number and Area of Farms Classified According to Use, by Municipalities, May, 1960." The physiological densities are computed from the same table (for cultivated lands) by combining the areas listed in temporary crops, lying idle, permanent crops, and in permanent pasture.

Table 14   CHARTERED CITIES, AREAS, AND POPULATIONS

Number	Name	Province	Charter date (mo/yr)	Charter area (in sq. mi.)	Charter area (1960 census pop.)	Urban area (1960 pop. est.)
1	Bacolod	Negros Occ.	6/38	60.6	119,315	93,000
2	Baguio	Mountain	8/09	18.8	50,436	50,000
3	Basilan	Zam. del Sur	6/48	512.0	155,712	20,000
4	Butuan	Agusan	6/50	209.9	82,485	31,000
5	Cabanatuan	Nueva Ecija	6/50	74.4	69,580	35,000
6	Cagayan de Oro	Misamis Or.	6/50	159.3	68,274	35,000
7	Calbayog	Samar	7/48	348.7	77,832	40,000
8	Caloocan	Rizal	⎰1/62	21.5	145,523	120,000
9	Canlaon	Negros Or.	⎱6/61	62.0	22,884	14,000
10	Cavite	Cavite	5/40	4.5	54,891	55,000
11	Cebu	Cebu	10/36	108.4	251,146	225,000
12	Cotabato	Cotabato	6/59	67.9	37,499	30,000
13	Dagupan	Pangasinan	6/47	14.3	63,191	20,000
14	Danao	Cebu	6/61	41.4	32,826	10,000
15	Davao	Davao	10/36	853.7	225,712	85,000
16	Dumaguete	Negros Or.	7/48	21.5	35,282	35,000
17	Gingoog	Misamis Or.	6/60	156.2	56,677	10,000
18	Iligan	Lanao del Nor	6/50	282.0	58,433	31,000
19	Iloilo	Iloilo	10/36	21.6	151,266	150,000
20	Lapu Lapu	Cebu	6/61	22.4	48,546	40,000
21	Legaspi	Albay	6/59	59.3	60,593	60,000
22	Lipa	Batangas	6/47	90.5	69,036	20,000
23	Lucena	Quezon	6/61	26.4	49,264	28,000
24	Manila	Manila	7/01	14.3	1,138,611	1,138,000
25	Marawi	Lanao del Sur	7/40	8.7	26,910	22,000
26	Naga	Camarines Sur	6/48	29.9	55,506	35,000
27	Ormoc	Leyte	10/47	179.1	62,764	17,000
28	Ozamis	Misamis Occ.	6/48	59.5	44,091	19,000
29	Pasay	Rizal	6/47	5.4	132,673	133,000
30	Quezon City	Rizal	10/39	64.1	397,990	380,000
31	Roxas	Capiz	4/51	38.9	49,326	19,000
32	San Carlos	Negros Occ.	6/60	162.6	124,750	36,000
33	San Pablo	Laguna	5/40	82.7	70,680	30,000
34	Silay	Negros Occ.	6/57	82.9	60,324	28,000
35	Tacloban	Leyte	6/52	38.9	53,551	36,000
36	Tagaytay	Cavite	6/38	28.5	7,203	6,000

Table 14—Continued

Num-ber	Name	Province	Charter date (mo/yr)	Charter area (in sq. mi.)	Charter area (1960 census pop.)	Urban area (1960 pop. est.)
37	Toledo	Cebu	6/60	67.6	63,881	18,000
38	Trece Martires	Cavite	5/54	1.5	4,422	4,000
39	Zamboanga	Zam. del Sur	10/36	546.1	131,489	28,000

SOURCES: Area of chartered cities calculated from data from Bureau of Census and Statistics, 1963. The 1960 populations for chartered city areas are from *Census, 1960*. Urban area estimates for 1960 were calculated by the authors, and rounded to the nearest thousand.

Table 15 INDICATED NET MIGRATION, BY PROVINCE, 1939–1960
(Migrants and their descendants)

Province	Net in-Migration
Rizal	703,329
Cotabato	523,037
Davao	397,666
Zamboanga del Sur	374,805
Camarines Sur	166,603
Lanao del Sur	134,525
Agusan	103,369
Lanao del Norte	102,544
Bukidnon	96,920
Manila	83,070
Oriental Mindoro	72,349
Isabela	69,843
Quezon	46,414
Zamboanga del Norte	46,365
Zambales	32,389
Masbate	27,036
Misamis Oriental	26,642
Camarines Norte	21,633
Occidental Mindoro	18,225
Nueva Vizcaya	5,185
Palawan	4,085
Bataan	511

Province	Net out-Migration
Cebu	475,356
Leyte	377,521
Iloilo	293,326
Bohol	240,074
Pangasinan	132,829
Ilocos Sur	121,632
Ilocos Norte	114,888
Misamis Occidental	107,245
Antique	99,193
Nueva Ecija	97,195
Sulu	91,459
Aklan	72,785
Capiz	72,031
Sorsogon	71,493
Negros Oriental	70,413
Batangas	66,927

Table 15—Continued

Province	Net out-Migration
Mountain	66,754
Negros Occidental	64,120
La Union	58,297
Samar	56,875
Albay	50,330
Cagayan	49,509
Romblon	36,565
Abra	33,414
Cavite	25,768
Marinduque	23,843
Surigao	22,432
Tarlac	20,933
Pampanga	18,073
Catanduanes	10,503
Bulacan	7,607
Batanes	5,794
Laguna	1,124

Table 16　COMPARATIVE CROP AREAS, 1948 AND 1963 (In thousands of acres)

Crop	1948	1963
Rice	4,501	8,008
Corn	2,493	4,816
Root crops	674	653
Vegetables	288	306
Fruits	505	975 [a]
Tobacco	80	240
Total domestic [b]	8,620	15,003
Coconut	2,596	3,439
Abaca	568	449
Sugarcane	202 [c]	639
Total export [b]	3,500	4,694

[a] Includes some items not included in 1948 total.

[b] Totals do not add because they include unlisted minor items.

[c] Figure was abnormally low owing to war damage to sugar centrals and delayed replanting programs.

SOURCES: 1948 data from *Philippine Census, 1948.* 1963 data from Agricultural Economics Division, Department of Agriculture and Natural Resources.

Table 17 CROP AND ANIMAL FREQUENCIES ON FARMS, 1948 AND 1960 (In thousands)

Crop or animal	Primary farm (1948) [a]	Farms growing 1948	Farms growing 1960
Rice	784	1,147 [b]	1,468
Corn	254	603 [c]	966
Coconut	233	656	1,015
Abaca	23	144	140
Sugarcane	13 [d]	97	53
Tobacco	2	109	175
Root crops	48		
Sweet potatoes (camote)		467	368
Manioc (cassava)		294	288
Yams (all kinds)		101	
Peanut		56	91
Vegetables	1.5		
Eggplant		179	185
Taro (gabi)		137	112
Squash		86	84
Tomato		81	88
Mung bean		66	117
Bamboo		65	235
Ampalaya (cucurbit)		59	41
Patola (gourd)		53	19
Fruits and nuts	24		
Banana		1,056	879
Jackfruit		467	103
Papaya		288	171
Mango		273	207
Star apple			74
Malungay		270	25
Santol		175	29
Pomelo		164	22
Soursop		160	18
Betel nut		154	7
Avocado		136	85
Orange		134	117
Siniguela		95	17
Tamarind		87	5
Kamachile		80	2
Sugar apple		80	13
Calamondin		79	—

Table 17—Continued

Crop or animal	Primary farm (1948) [a]	Farms growing	
		1948	1960
Breadfruit		69	12
Lanzon		65	20
Tambi		59	3
Pineapple		53	122
Lemon		52	3
Pili nut		52	7
Chico		—	10
Kapok		137	16
Coffee		120	155
Cacao		114	42
Livestock	0.1	—	—
Pigs		1,100	1,446
Carabao		935	1,395
Cattle		177	348
Goats		121	296
Horses		89	50
Poultry	0.1	—	—
Chickens		1,352	1,757
Ducks		60	115
Others [e]	256	—	—
Total farms	1,638		2,166

NOTE: Occurrences of crops and animals on less than 50,000 farms were omitted. This involved about twenty fruits and about fifty vegetables reported in 1948 census.

[a] Number refers to farms on which the specified crop is the first crop grown on more than 50 percent of the land cultivated.

[b] Includes 756 farms growing first-crop lowland rice and 391 farms growing upland rice. Second- and third-crop lowland rice farms were not counted to avoid duplication, but a small amount of duplication may be involved between the two classes totaled.

[c] Includes only farms reported growing first-crop corn. Second- and third-crop corn farms are not included to avoid duplication.

[d] Totals of both primary farms and farms growing are probably still too low, representing war damage.

[e] Under "Others" were classified all farms not having at least 50 percent of the cultivated land in a single crop. These are chiefly very small farms.

SOURCES: Philippine agricultural censuses, 1948 and 1960.

Table 18   VEGETABLE CROPS COMMONLY GROWN, 1948 AND 1960 [a]

	1948 [b]			1960		
Crop	Leading province or region	Number of farms	Total Acres	Leading province or region	Number of farms	Total Acres
Eggplant	Pangasinan-Ilocos	179,715	35,920	Pangasinan–Nueva Ecija	184,883	75,433
Taro	Leyte-Samar	137,590	47,069	Leyte-Samar	112,532	54,932
Squash	Pangasinan	86,641	9,830	Batangas	83,295	8,724
Tomato	Pangasinan	81,331	19,695	Nueva Ecija–Tarlac	87,984	19,705
Mung beans	Pangasinan	66,463	53,139	Visayas	117,421	115,788
Ampalaya	Pangasinan	58,924	7,577	Central Plain–Ilocos	42,463	5,288
Patola	Pangasinan	53,305	6,200	Batangas	41,457	3,108
Onion	Negros-Bohol	50,969	8,173	Davao	40,795	8,600
Green corn [c]	—	—	—	Visayas	55,564	14,820
Ginger	Nueva Vizcaya	43,803	4,715	Mountain	13,632	2,336
Singapore bean	Pangasinan-Ilocos	29,546	6,550	d	d	d
Chile peppers	Pangasinan	21,273	2,193	d	d	d
Pechay	Mountain	16,410	1,302	Mountain	2,672	674
Garlic	Batangas	12,356	1,620	Ilocos	23,967	6,888
Cucumber	Lanao	10,163	1,350	d	d	d
Watermelon	Pampanga	8,851	5,510	Batangas	6,422	4,989
Soybean	Pangasinan	8,345	3,020	Visayas	4,948	4,120
Cabbage	Mountain	6,360	2,808	Mountain	6,834	7,237
Radish	Pampanga	5,582	2,286	Cavite	2,429	d
Vine pepper	Leyte	3,697	615	—	d	d
All other beans	—	51,040	10,628	—	54,738	14,538
All others	—	—	55,273	—	145,559	54,224
TOTAL			285,473			401,404

a The 1960 data is suspect in many cases. It is obvious that the census did not gather data for 1960 on certain crops. Further, the published data in the provincial summaries exhibits numerous omissions and discrepancies. The 1960 data are included in the table, but are not to be regarded as definitive, for many of the crop areas seem too low.

b A farm that had over half its acreage in vegetable crops was classified as a vegetable farm in 1948. Of the 1,519 farms so classified, 817 were located in the four provinces of Mountain, Nueva Ecija, Pampanga, and Pangasinan; however, only Romblon and Zamboanga provinces had no such farms. A total of 8,698 acres were included in vegetable farms in 1948, and the average size of a vegetable farm in that year was 7.6 acres. Data of this degree of analysis had not yet been published for the 1960 census when this volume went to press.

c Data not recorded by 1948 census.

d Data either lacking or very faulty for 1960.

SOURCE: *Census of the Philippines*, 1948 and 1960.

Table 19   FRUITS AND NUTS COMMONLY GROWN, 1948 AND 1960

		1948		1960 [a]	
		Number of	*Total hills/trees*	*Number of*	*Total hills/trees*
Crop	*Leading province/region*	*farms*	*(in thousands)*	*farms*	*(in thousands)*
Banana	Leyte-Samar	1,056,717	51,486.6	947,496	76,314.0
Jackfruit	Visayas	467,527	2,814.6	103,048	936.8
Papaya	Visayas	288,409	2,220.0	172,141	3,184.7
Mango	Lanao-Cotabato	273,396	1,045.8	207,221	1,208.7
Malungay	Cebu-Negros	270,722	2,059.9	33,979	906.4
Santol	SE Luzon–Samar	175,892	494.9	29,390	127.5
Pomelo	Pangasinan-Ilocos	163,991	518.5	22,172	132.7
Soursop	Pangasinan	160,474	599.5	17,211	86.1
Betel nut	Visayas-Lanao	154,051	2,113.3	7,201	391.4
Avocado	Southwest Luzon	136,490	767.5	85,077	630.6
Orange	Batangas	134,733	541.6	85,707	790.5
Siniguela	Visayas	95,187	372.3	17,708	118.0
Tamarind	Pangasinan	87,822	184.2	5,129	20.9
Sugar apple	Batangas	80,043	521.0	11,123	335.2
Kamachile	Pangasinan-Ilocos	79,870	330.5	1.665	24.6
Calamondin	Batangas-Quezon	79,575	506.0	13,165	638.8
Breadfruit	Visayas	69,087	254.1	11,959	56.8
Lanzon	Laguna-Batangas	65,635	776.0	20,298	646.7
Tambi	Visayas	59,508	234.1	3,307	9.1
Pineapple	Samar-Leyte, Bukidnon	53,406	25.1 [b]	122,786	
Lemon	Bicol-Samar	52,718	274.4	3,008	44.2
Pili nut	Bicol-Samar	52,650	276.2	7,121	65.5
Tangerine	Batangas	49,593	395.6	30,341	1,575.3
Caimito	Pangasinan-Ilocos	48,617	221.9	73,820	532.1
Cashew nut	Pangasinan-Zambales	43,634	244.8	8,021	266.9
Makopa	Visayas-Lanao	32,853	76.7	2,917	227.6
Dalayap	Pangasinan	29,605	221.2	c	c
Chico	Quezon	24,455	166.0	10,162	71.5
Durian	South Mindanao–Sulu	18,251	136.0	6,031	39.4
Marang	Lanao, Sulu	17,193	139.5	4,616	35.8
Guava	Central Plain, Visayas	15,039	209.7	14,620	211.4
Lime	Bicol-Samar	6,910	20.6	140	0.9
Duhat	Pangasinan-Ilocos	4,134	19.8	5,610	21.4
Lumbang nut	Quezon, NE Mindanao	3,840	45.8	887	16.5
Mangosteen	Sulu	2,414	16.2	727	10.0
All Others	—	8,257 [d]	44,879.0	17,889 [e]	c

[a] The 1960 census obviously involves incomplete reporting for many items and this data should not be regarded as highly reliable.

[b] The figure for pineapple is given in acres.

[c] Data not available.

[d] Involves probable duplication of farms growing, but the total of trees is as reported, for the fruits Mabolo, Kamias, Cainistel, Carambola, Custard apple, Katuray, and Iba.

[e] Involves probable duplication of farms growing Cainistel, Mabolo, Carambola, Kamios, and others unspecified.

SOURCE: *Census of the Philippines*, 1948 and 1960.

Table 20 BEVERAGE CROPS GROWN, 1948 AND 1960

| | 1948 | | | | 1960 [a] | | | |
	Number of farms	*Total acres*	*Plants (in thousands)*	*Production (in millions)*	*Number of farms*	*Total acres*	*Plants (in thousands)*	*Production (in millions)*
Crop								
Cacao	114,200	b	943	3.2 [c]	40,264	16,451	1,803.5	6.7 [c]
Coffee	120,600	b	5,045	8.6 [c]	153,489	75,000	48,444.2	56.9 [c]
Coconut	b	b	502	96.3 [d]	b	b	1,803.7	349.2 [d]
Buri [e]	b	b	b	b	b	b	b	b
Nipa [e]	b	b	b	b	b	b	b	b

[a] Data for 1960 may not be highly reliable owing to uneven reporting of provincial returns.

[b] Data not available.

[c] Totals are in pounds.

[d] Totals are in liters of tuba.

[e] The census has not tabulated data on either buri or nipa palms grown and tapped for tuba production, although both are significant in amount.

SOURCE: *Census of the Philippines,* 1948 and 1960.

Table 21   MINOR CROPS GROWN, 1948 AND 1960

Crop	1948				1960 [a]			
	Number of farms	*Acres*	*Trees (in thousands)*	*Production (in thousands of lbs.)*	*Number of farms*	*Acres*	*Trees (in thousands)*	*Production (in thousands of lbs.)*
Cotton	9,187	3,509	—	1,163.8	449	3,585	—	1,445.8
Kapok	137,000	—	779.2	3,544.8	16,164	2,941	313.9	2,714.3
Maguey	20,195	19,834	—	12,500.2	3,596	2,225	—	1,129.3
Ramie	590	1,630	—	869.0	308 [a]	1,257 [a]	—	746.6 [a]
Buri	7,001	—	172.4	1,016.4 [b]	8,396	3,446	1,494.4	6,912.0 [b]
Nipa	[c]	[c]	[c]	[c]	3,333	5,652	2,208.8	30,771.3 [b]
Rubber	2,882	—	52.9	1,586.2	70 [a]	10,979 [a]	—	2,532.8 [a]
Bamboo	65,121	—	638.3	[c]	[c]	—	[c]	[c]

[a] Data for 1960 may not be highly reliable. The provincial summaries for the 1960 census do not give data for Cotabato Province, where both ramie and rubber are fairly new crops.

[b] In pounds of leaves utilized in various handicraft manufactures. Additionally, nipa palm leaves form a significant raw material used in housing construction for walls and roofs.

[c] Data not available.

SOURCE: *Census of the Philippines,* 1948 and 1960.

Table 22 SUMMARY OF CROP AREAS, YIELDS, AND VALUES, 1960 [a]

Crop	Acres (in thousands)	Area index (1955 = 100)	Yields (in millions of lbs.)	Production index (1955 = 100)	Value in pesos (in millions)
Primarily domestic food crops					
Rice	8,166.9	124.5	8,226.9	116.8	711.9
Corn	4,558.3	132.9	2,563.4	151.3	149.7
Root crops	720.1	b	3,119.8	b	87.1
Vegetables, beans, peanuts	447.2	b	485.3	b	41.3
Citrus fruits	56.5	b	95.4	b	10.5
Other fruits and nuts (excl. pineapple)	733.6	b	1,191.3	b	69.0
Sugarcane c	93.4	70.1	117.0	97.0	12.7
Coffee	75.2	158.6	56.9	369.5	38.1
Cacao	16.3	101.7	6.7	202.0	9.0
All others	19.8	b	b	b	5.4
Subtotal	14,837.3				1,134.7
Primarily commercial crops					
Coconut	2,616.7	97.5	2,458.2	97.5	389.6
Sugarcane d	504.7	95.6	3,038.6	111.0	337.2
Abaca	433.7	80.7	207.8	90.4	58.8
Tobacco	236.7	182.2	140.8	212.4	73.4
Pineapple e	55.9	87.4	294.6	129.7	19.5
Rubber	12.7	b	6.8	b	3.4
Kapok	8.4	114.2	7.1	115.8	1.1
Ramie	4.2	58.3	4.9	130.8	1.1
Maguey	7.1	96.0	4.6	b	0.05
Cotton	5.5	86.5	2.7	518.9	0.02
Subtotal	3,885.6				884.17
Total	18,722.9				2,018.87

ᵃ Totals listed will not necessarily agree with totals of other tables or textual statements, as these figures are interpolations of annual totals calculated from data supplied by the Department of Agriculture and Natural Resources. Their overall reliability is possibly somewhat greater than that of the incomplete data contained in the Provincial Summaries constituting the first volume of the *Census of Agriculture, 1960.*

ᵇ Data not available.

ᵉ Refers to sugarcane grown primarily on small farms, refined in traditional refineries into *muscovado* and *panocha*, and used in home dietary, seldom entering foreign trade.

ᵈ Refers to sugarcane refined by modern centrifugal processes in sugar centrals to produce refined white sugar, which goes primarily into the export trade.

ᵉ Includes acreage and yield data for domestic small-farm pineapple and piña fiber, and for the commercial pineapple grown in Bukidnon Province, Mindanao, most of which enters foreign trade.

SOURCE: *Raw Materials Resources Survey Bulletin, Tables for Agriculture: 1958 to 1963.* National Economic Council, Office of Statistical Coordination and Standards (mimeographed: Manila, January, 1965).

Table 23   IRRIGATED LAND, 1960 (By province)

Province	Total farms	Total farms irrigated	Acres irrigated
Nueva Ecija	58,566	25,524	179,916
Pangasinan	87,253	29,798	111,771
Cotabato	114,615	15,050	38,913
Pampanga	26,203	12,918	83,789
Tarlac	35,606	10,860	81,738
Isabela	56,755	8,775	64,189
Mountain	53,470	36,450	63,193
Camarines Sur	66,731	11,105	55,899
Iloilo	74,876	9,470	51,612
Bulacan	31,854	10,586	50,920
Ilocos Norte	36,088	24,945	47,930
Negros Occidental	59,234	3,438	44,582
Laguna	24,426	9,008	43,744
Albay	39,341	11,833	42,348
Lanao del Sur	30,510	6,416	41,137
Nueva Vizcaya	16,246	9,967	37,359
Leyte	82,245	11,885	35,716
Cavite	23,905	5,795	32,565
Quezon	58,158	9,363	30,556
Antique	26,195	7,186	28,466
Ilocos Sur	27,319	11,138	25,315
Abra	15,842	6,843	21,942
Sorsogon	28,609	7,421	21,041
Cagayan	50,535	5,450	19,736
Bohol	58,979	14,677	19,301
Bataan	6,874	3,127	18,893
Zamboanga del Sur	63,079	3,065	17,470
La Union	24,344	7,302	15,320
Oriental Mindoro	23,053	2,751	14,707
Zambales	12,468	2,682	11,149
Misamis Occidental	22,633	5,461	9,246
Davao	92,243	1,925	8,705
Camarines Norte	14,084	1,716	8,300
Southern Leyte	23,499	4,045	7,398
Occidental Mindoro	8,273	1,350	7,280
Negros Oriental	61,864	2,224	7,233
Aklan	22,415	2,564	6,793
Surigao del Norte	20,028	1,658	6,262
Catanduanes	16,062	2,543	5,950

Table 23—Continued

Province	Total farms	Total farms Irrigated	Acres irrigated
Batangas	55,095	1,245	5,419
Samar	95,626	1,384	5,117
Masbate	31,868	1,369	5,053
Palawan	19,213	1,215	4,791
Rizal	10,522	1,634	4,653
Capiz	28,905	1,190	4,552
Agusan	23,677	918	4,497
Bukidnon	23,341	466	4,327
Misamis Oriental	34,346	1,323	3,875
Marinduque	13,367	1,208	3,190
Surigao del Sur	19,662	874	3,138
Cebu	114,615	1,750	2,992
Romblon	14,982	626	2,226
Lanao del Norte	27,053	266	2,078
Zamboanga del Norte	29,511	496	1,735
Sulu	21,356	127	220
Batanes	1,761	none	none
Philippines	2,164,365	374,405	1,533,490

SOURCE: *1960 Census of the Philippines, Agriculture*, I, Report by Provinces.

Table 24   LIVESTOCK AND POULTRY POPULATIONS, 1939, 1948, AND 1960 (In thousands of head)

Item	1939 ª	1948	1960
Carabao	2,918	1,964	3,467
Cattle	1,349	511	1,206
Pigs	4,348	2,850	5,898
Goats	402	326	1,219
Sheep	37	9	15
Horses	340	146	297
Chickens	25,360	19,840	42,775
Ducks	691	577	2,484
Geese	29	5	97
Turkeys	43	7	166
Pigeons	180	10	333

ª The data for 1939 are here given to supply a more normal comparative base than is provided by the 1948 data, at which time populations had not recovered from effects of World War II.

SOURCE: Data for 1939, 1948, and 1960 are from the various agricultural censuses.

Table 25 FISHERY YIELDS, 1947–1963 (In metric tons)

Year	Commercial [a]	Municipal and [b] sustenance	Fishponds [c]	Total
1947	63,028.0	167,633.3	20,788.6	251,449.9
1948	41,995.5	130,052.3	23,030.7	195,078.5
1949	54,826.6	158,668.7	24,507.8	238,003.1
1950	47,932.9	146,793.1	25,463.7	220,189.7
1951	69,027.4	197,393.1	29,669.2	296,089.6
1952	73,315.0	208,706.5	31,038.2	313,059.8
1953	72,888.4	199,266.1	33,471.7	305,626.1
1954	103,220.3	205,370.6	35,034.0	343,625.0
1955	107,210.2	213,983.3	36,733.5	362,927.1
1956	106,659.3	243,509.1	38,479.8	393,648.2
1957	93,948.1	253,808.0	39,413.8	387,169.9
1958	111,876.6	257,165.5	57,624.4	426,666.4
1959	117,818.2	260,573.0	58,090.0	436,481.2
1960	120,021.6	264,481.0	60,119.6	444,622.1
1961	125,626.4	268,448.2	60,824.6	454,899.2
1962	150,036.5	272,475.0	61,436.1	483,947.6
1963	208,747.9	276,562.1	62,044.5	547,354.2

[a] Includes all fishing vessels (over 3 tons gross) licensed by the Philippine Fisheries Commission.

[b] Includes fishing done in fishing vessels (3 tons gross capacity and below) and that done without the use of such vessels for subsistence reasons.

[c] Includes all developed brackish-water ponds where juvenile or immature bañgos (*Chanos chanos*) or other kinds of fish and crustaceans are introduced, fed, protected, and eventually caught.

SOURCE: *Fisheries Statistics of the Philippines, 1958–63.*

Table 26 SELECTED PHILIPPINE MINERALS, PRODUCTION 1946–1964

Year	Gold (oz.)	Silver (oz.)	Copper (metric tons)	Mercury (flasks)[a]	Zinc (metric tons)	Refractory Chromite (metric tons)	Metallurgical Chromite (metric tons)	Iron ore (metric tons)	Manganese (metric tons)	Cement (barrels)[b]	Coal (metric tons)	Total value (in thousands of pesos)[c]
1946	297	913	0	0	0	58,000	0	0	0	304,897	48,427	3,997
1947	65,487	44,186	3,223	0	0	189,499	5,604	0	3,322	785,137	73,732	24,193
1948	209,225	150,760	2,043	0	0	232,778	24,075	18,289	25,565	703,939	87,748	37,293
1949	287,844	218,419	7,007	0	0	165,340	81,404	370,172	26,288	1,204,692	123,336	59,290
1950	333,991	216,034	10,387	0	0	208,665	41,846	599,095	29,867	1,749,637	158,822	81,370
1951	393,602	274,602	12,712	0	155	301,835	32,736	903,282	22,343	1,850,927	150,691	116,680
1952	469,408	693,751	13,241	0	1,596	491,150	52,364	1,170,350	20,627	1,855,772	139,440	144,314
1953	480,625	572,046	12,715	0	747	468,549	88,541	1,217,864	21,508	1,741,185	154,905	145,833
1954	416,052	527,160	14,349	0	0	388,590	62,595	1,424,898	9,393	1,585,860	119,627	147,093
1955	419,112	502,069	17,461	635	0	535,262	59,745	1,432,712	11,912	2,396,673	130,243	167,781
1956	406,112	541,168	26,963	3,015	950	581,685	127,370	1,440,232	4,414	2,616,795	151,708	196,710
1957	379,982	479,216	40,382	3,363	302	612,158	113,358	1,346,363	30,231	2,996,350	191,151	227,497
1958	422,833	497,987	47,030	3,321	0	381,821	34,489	1,098,732	22,308	3,772,727	107,780	217,760
1959	402,615	504,085	49,521	3,500	5	534,535	118,952	1,230,193	34,804	4,277,425	139,853	264,851
1960	410,618	1,133,343	44,010	3,041	4,978	606,013	128,426	1,138,770	17,318	4,661,469	147,857	274,245
1961	423,983	812,793	51,875	3,167	3,313	495,819	144,483	1,170,548	18,640	5,975,029	152,328	326,638
1962	423,394	675,570	54,728	2,767	4,460	433,085	98,202	1,386,959	11,686	5,633,390	162,978	401,841
1963	376,006	838,304	63,986	2,651	3,893	373,342	85,779	1,384,704	6,435	5,577,927	156,535	433,296
1964	425,770	907,504	60,457	2,496	2,136	381,820	86,260	1,366,922	7,439	7,042,586	114,936	478,653

[a] One flask is equivalent to 76 pounds.   [b] One barrel is equivalent to four bags of 94 pounds each.
[c] With the adoption of new exchange rates in 1961/62 the value of the Philippine peso declined from 2 pesos equals U.S. $1 to approximately 3.8 pesos equals U.S. $1.

SOURCE: Bureau of Mines, *Mineral News Service*, no. 52 (1965).

Table 27　ROADS AND TRAIL SYSTEMS BY CLASSES, 1965 (In miles)

Area	First class	Second class	Third class	Total roads	Trails	Total roads and trails
National roads and trails						
Luzon	3,868	703	146	4,717	641	5,358
Visayas	2,217	318	73	2,608	144	2,752
Mindanao	2,145	402	48	2,595	170	2,765
Subtotal	8,230	1,423	267	9,920	955	10,875
Provincial/city roads and trails ª						
Luzon	3,330	2,522	1,109	6,961	1,380	8,341
Visayas	2,025	2,219	953	5,197	824	6,021
Mindanao	952	1,527	1,415	3,894	587	4,481
Subtotal	6,307	6,268	3,477	16,052	2,791	18,843
Total	14,537	7,691	3,744	25,972	3,746	29,718
Regional recapitulation ᵇ						
Luzon	7,198	3,225	1,255	11,678	2,021	13,699
Visayas	4,242	2,537	1,026	7,805	968	8,773
Mindanao	3,097	1,929	1,463	6,489	757	7,246

ª Includes both urban streets and rural highways maintained within limits of chartered cities.

ᵇ Not included in "Regional recapitulation" are 1,061 miles of paved municipal road and 8,899 miles of unpaved municipal road; these are not ranked by classes. Municipal roads are those located chiefly within poblaciones, roads leading to barrios, and roads connecting with provincial and national highways.

SOURCE: Retabulated from data available as of June 30, 1965, provided by the Chief Highway Engineer, Department of Public Works, Manila.

Table 28 HIGHWAY AND ROAD DENSITIES IN THE PHILIPPINES, 1955 (By province)

Province	All roads km/100 km²	Surfaced roads km/100 km²
Laguna	47.27	28.55
Cavite	42.89	19.21
Rizal	39.29	33.24
Batanes	33.84	14.89
Cebu	29.13	20.90
Bohol	26.68	10.86
Marinduque	26.31	7.00
La Union	25.87	12.07
Pampanga	24.95	12.56
Pangasinan	24.63	15.57
Batangas	23.54	11.52
Iloilo	22.92	12.49
Ilocos Norte	20.92	7.50
Bataan	20.54	11.09
Romblon	20.49	7.65
Albay	20.31	11.15
Bulacan	20.17	9.85
Catanduanes	18.70	14.05
Sorsogon	18.59	13.64
Tarlac	18.24	10.65
Negros Occidental	17.86	8.11
Ilocos Sur	17.76	9.06
Basilan City	17.03	3.78
Misamis Occidental	16.30	10.58
Nueva Ecija	15.94	10.85
Capiz and Aklan	14.43	10.53
Misamis Oriental	14.37	5.56
Leyte	14.09	7.87
Antique	13.71	10.44
Negros Oriental	12.42	8.78
Camarines Norte	11.45	8.49
Camarines Sur	11.11	5.55
Sulu	10.65	8.22
Philippine national average	(10.51)	(5.64)
Abra	9.64	4.14
Zambales	8.79	4.96
Lanao	8.54	1.37
Mountain	8.11	4.29

Table 28—Continued

Province	All roads km/100 km²	Surfaced roads km/100 km²
Cagayan	7.43	5.96
Masbate	7.08	5.49
Samar	6.93	3.08
Quezon	6.25	2.86
Mindoro	5.35	2.23
Surigao	5.32	2.46
Davao	5.14	1.18
Nueva Vizcaya	4.66	2.91
Isabela	4.57	3.10
Bukidnon	4.48	1.94
Cotabato	3.58	1.26
Zamboanga	3.35	0.97
Agusan	3.31	2.29
Palawan	2.62	1.52

SOURCE: Data from the Stanford Research Institute study.

Table 29   SELECTED TRANSPORT DATA, 1961

Type of establishment	Number of establishments	Number of Employees	Gross receipts (in pesos)
Rail	2	9,982	30,317,000
Bus (TPU) ᵃ	1,047	26,282	141,966,000
Jeepney (TPU) ᵇ	2,447	8,092	23,292,000
Jeepney (AC) ᶜ	1,813	4,599	11,769,000
Calesa ᵈ	7,331	9,784	7,722,000
Taxicab	93	8,554	46,327,000
Tricycle and pedicab ᵉ	1,059	1,709	1,408,000
Freight truck	944	8,150	40,278,000
Ocean transport	11	1,915	56,056,000
Coastal steamship	883	11,847	107,494,000
Coastal launch, banca, etc.	919	3,091	4,465,000
Air transport	2	2,634	39,639,000
Total (selected establishments)	16,551	96,639	510,234,000
Total (all transportation establishments) ᶠ	17,199	129,377	595,215,000

ᵃ Public utility passenger buses follow fixed schedules and routes.

ᵇ Public utility passenger jeepneys (converted wartime jeeps) follow fixed schedules and routes.

ᶜ AC jeepneys are for hire, but are not required to follow fixed schedules or routes.

ᵈ A horse-drawn passenger cart.

ᵉ Both are bicycle-drawn passenger vehicles.

ᶠ Total transport figures include, in addition to the enumerated items, delivery services, arrastre services, stevedoring, and airfield operational personnel.

SOURCE: *Economic Census of the Philippines, 1961: Transportation and Communication*, Vol. VII, Part A.

Table 30 SELECTED CATEGORY BREAKDOWN ON INDUSTRIAL ESTABLISHMENTS HAVING MORE THAN TWENTY EMPLOYEES EACH, 1960

Category	Number of establishments	Number of employees
Foods and kindred products (20) [a]	315	42,777
Beverages (21)	62	8,837
Tobacco products (22)	53	12,906
Textiles (23)	81	24,441
Apparel and related products (24)	385	16,362
Wood products (25)	180	17,351
Furniture and fixtures (26)	60	3,030
Paper and allied products (27)	57	4,498
Printing and publishing (28)	93	9,123
Leather and products (29)	21	1,172
Rubber products (30)	30	4,950
Chemical and allied products (31)	112	11,035
Petroleum, coal, and miscell. (32, 39) [b]	75	4,361
Nonmetallic mineral products (33)	74	7,264
Base-metal products (34)	25	3,367
Nonelectrical fabricated metals (35)	115	11,581
Nonelectrical machinery (36)	42	3,396
Electrical machinery products (37)	49	6,883
Transport equipment (38)	55	5,650
Total	1,884	199,094

[a] The number in parentheses is the standard industrial classification category number.

[b] Arbitrarily grouped to conceal specific identity.

SOURCE: *Annual Survey of Manufactures, 1960*, Bureau of Census and Statistics, Manila, 1962.

Table 31   GEOGRAPHICAL DISTRIBUTION OF INDUSTRIAL ESTABLISHMENTS AND EMPLOYEES, 1960

Region	Number of establishments with more than twenty employees	Percent	Number of employees	Percent
Philippines	1,884	100.0	199,094	100.0
Metropolitan Manila	1,016	53.9	101,645	51.1
Manila City	458	24.3	44,904	22.6
Suburban area	558	29.6	56,741	28.5
Outside Metropolitan Manila	868	46.1	97,449	48.9
Ilocos-Mountain	17	0.9	1,741	0.9
Cagayan Valley	16	0.9	1,761	0.9
Central Luzon	143	7.6	12,237	6.1
Southern Luzon	354	18.9	40,281	20.2
Bicol	26	1.4	1,304	0.7
Western Visayas	82	4.3	18,171	9.1
Eastern Visayas	119	6.3	7,762	3.9
Southwestern Mindanao	57	3.0	4,254	2.1
Northeastern Mindanao	54	2.9	9,907	5.0

SOURCE: *Annual Survey of Manufactures, 1960*, Bureau of Census and Statistics. Manila, 1962.

Table 32   SELECTED MANUFACTURING DATA, 1960

Item	Total	Manila percentage
Total establishments with over 5 employees	7,221	39.2
Average employment in total establments	248,781	48.7
Establishments with over 20 employees	1,884	53.9
Average employment in establishments with over 20 employees	199,094	51.1
Manufacturing receipts, in millions of pesos	3,668.5	50.7
Costs of materials, in millions of pesos	2,003.8	52.3
Value added by mfg., in millions of pesos	1,664.7	48.2
Book value of fixed assets, in millions of pesos	1,318.8	41.6
Capital expenditures, in millions of pesos	258.1	44.3
Electrical energy used, in millions of kwh	2,069.2	66.9

SOURCE: *Annual Survey of Manufactures, 1960*, Bureau of Census and Statistics, Manila, 1962.

Table 33 INDEXES OF THE PHYSICAL VOLUME OF PHILIPPINE PRODUCTION (1955 = 100)

Year	Combined	Agriculture	Manufac- turing	Mining
1949	56.3	59.8	46.9	47.5
1950	62.4	64.4	56.6	61.1
1951	72.0	73.8	66.4	76.2
1952	77.4	79.4	69.9	93.7
1953	84.0	85.2	79.0	98.3
1954	92.7	94.0	88.8	92.0
1955	100.0	100.0	100.0	100.0
1956	108.6	106.1	115.7	110.8
1957	116.2	110.2	125.0	123.7
1958		110.9	134.6	122.5
1959		117.5	145.8	132.4
1960		120.8	150.5	126.7
1961		120.6	160.5	134.3
1962		129.8	169.7	136.6
1963		137.6	180.2	134.1

SOURCE: *Central Bank News Digest.*

Table 34 NATIONAL INCOME BY INDUSTRIAL ORIGIN, 1949–1962 (In millions of current pesos)

Industrial category	1949	1950	1951	1952	1953	1954	1955	1956	1957
Agriculture	2,308	2,505	2,787	2,806	3,009	3,118	3,161	3,175	3,230
Mining	40	55	79	98	107	105	121	122	142
Manufacturing	440	502	630	639	834	850	1,001	1,195	1,292
Construction	276	239	237	221	236	205	230	296	328
Trade	709	752	838	809	780	781	861	999	1,057
Transport, and communication	193	205	228	242	242	235	250	286	322
Public admin. and defense	377	386	431	487	544	574	648	679	685
Other services	1,121	1,278	1,257	1,252	1,263	1,277	1,352	1,662	1,762
National Income	5,464	5,922	6,487	6,554	7,015	7,145	7,624	8,414	8,818

Industrial category	1958	1959	1960	1961	1962	1963	1964	1965
Agriculture	3,364	3,405	3,523	3,858	4,246	5,132	5,437	5,778
Mining	138	170	177	209	261	280	310	375
Manufacturing	1,474	1,703	1,815	2,090	2,399	2,686	3,036	3,072
Construction	281	330	343	428	390	544	553	638
Trade	1,096	1,162	1,231	1,410	1,530	1,682	1,950	2,066
Transport and communication	327	347	385	416	446	465	476	478
Public admin. and defense	705	763	879	984	1,115 }			
Other services	1,847	1,734	2,251	2,351	2,475 }	4,003	4,424	4,823
National Income	9,232	10,015	10,604	11,746	12,862	14,792	16,096	17,230

SOURCE: Central Bank, *Economic Indicators*, and A. B. Abello, *Patterns of Philippine Public Expenditure and Revenue* (Quezon City: University of the Philippines, Institute of Economic Development and Research, 1964).

Table 35   SELECTED FOREIGN TRADE STATISTICS

VALUE AND BALANCE IN FOREIGN TRADE
(In millions of dollars)

Year	Total trade	Imports	Exports	Balance
1899	34.1	19.2	14.8	− 4.4
1905	63.5	30.0	33.4	+ 3.4
1910	90.3	49.7	40.6	− 9.1
1915	103.1	49.3	53.8	+ 4.5
1920	300.5	149.4	151.1	+ 1.7
1925	268.6	119.7	148.8	+ 29.1
1930	251.2	123.1	133.1	+ 10.0
1935	187.4	85.0	102.4	+ 17.4
1940	290.6	134.7	155.9	+ 21.2
1946 [a]	360.0	295.8	64.2	−231.6
1950	679.9	341.9	331.0	− 10.9
1955	948.2	547.6	400.6	−147.0
1960	1,164.0	604.0	560.0	− 44.0
1965	1,631.0	835.3	795.7	− 39.6

COMMODITY PATTERNS IN IMPORTS AND EXPORTS
(In millions of dollars)

Item	1929	1941	1949	1959	1964
Imports					
Cottons, rayons, other textiles, and manufactures	32.5	30.3	105.0	38.6	50.9
Grains and preparations	13.5	8.5	44.4	66.0	126.0
Dairy products	3.8	5.6	23.4	2.6 [b]	4.4 [b]
Iron and steel mfrs.	21.9	29.3	63.8	73.5	99.6
Transport equipment	9.0	[c]	31.0	149.3	262.5
Petroleum products	11.1	14.9	27.6	59.7	69.5
Paper products	7.5	6.5	24.0	19.6	27.8
Tobacco products	3.2	8.3	17.7	2.0	1.5
Miscellaneous	44.7	32.2	230.1	112.3	159.8
Total	147.2	135.6	567.1	523.6	802.0
Exports					
Coconut products	52.1	31.7	129.4	183.7	241.2
Sugar products	53.2	28.6	45.2	120.6	159.0
Abaca	28.4	17.5	28.9	38.8	35.7
Pineapple	—	2.5	6.8	9.2	10.9
Embroideries	7.8	3.6	6.0	8.5	28.5
Timber and lumber	3.6	4.4	3.2	97.8	176.3
Copper ores	[e]	[e]	[e]	16.1	33.8

Table 35—Continued

Item	1929	1941	1949	1959	1964
Iron ores	d	d	d	9.0	12.6
Chrome ore	d	d	2.7	16.7	11.1
Tobacco products	8.7	3.6	2.0	8.4	16.8
Gold bullion	7.4	47.0	23.6	e	14.3
Miscellaneous	10.7	22.2	31.6	67.9	309.9
Total	164.5	161.1	255.8	528.2	888.2

CHIEF DIRECTIONS OF TRADE
(Volume in millions of dollars)

Country	1910	1920	1930	1940	1946	1950	1955	1960	1965
United States	32.8	200.9	188.1	234.3	295.9	1,001.6	605.0	549.4	673.1
Great Britain	13.4	17.3	9.4	5.5	3.7	21.3	18.0	34.4	41.4
Indonesia	9.1	2.7	3.1	4.6	2.5	9.3	27.5	40.6	19.4
France	8.8	2.9	2.8	1.8	3.1	5.6	f	5.8	17.5
Spain	3.5	6.5	5.8	1.7	1.5	4.2	f	4.3	5.8
China	3.3	13.0	7.7	4.9	9.8	0.4	—	—	17.6
Japan	2.9	33.5	17.3	29.8	—	72.46	105.5	291.1	408.6
Hong Kong	1.7	7.5	.2	2.8	3.9	22.6	11.5	8.0	9.2
Canada	.3	1.0	.4	2.2	8.3	26.4	20.0	18.4	28.1
Thailand	.3	4.3	.2	1.9	3.4	2.6	f	0.2	15.0
Mexico	f	f	f	.2	6.8	f	f	1.5	5.0

a Data for 1945, terminal year of World War II, neither available nor representative.
b Probably understated by inclusion of some items under "Miscellaneous."
c Included under "Iron and steel mfrs."
d None then exported.
e Separate figure not available.
f Separate total either not available or below U.S. $100,000.
SOURCE: United Nations *Yearbook on International Trade*, various other yearbooks, annual summaries, statistical bulletins, and personal communications from the Bureau of Census and Statistics, Manila, and Central Bank of the Philippines.

Table 36   DIRECTION OF FOREIGN TRADE, SELECTED YEARS, 1948–1963 (Percent of trade with selected countries)

Year	Total trade (in millions of dollars)											
1948	887.41	75.1	2.0	0.4	2.3	0.6	1.0	1.5	0.7	0.4	0.2	15.8
1951	890.06	67.3	7.1	3.0	1.4	0.8	2.2	2.1	2.4	1.2	0.6	11.9
1952	782.40	69.1	6.6	1.4	2.7	0.9	1.5	2.6	1.4	0.5	0.5	12.8
1953	847.95	71.4	8.2	2.6	2.4	1.2	1.4	1.7	1.2	0.8	0.5	8.6
1954	887.80	64.5	9.0	4.8	1.5	2.2	1.6	2.1	1.4	1.2	0.7	11.0
1955	948.25	62.7	11.0	4.1	2.0	2.2	1.9	2.0	1.0	1.1	1.1	10.9
1956	959.63	56.8	13.7	5.2	2.3	3.2	2.3	1.8	1.8	1.4	1.1	10.4
1957	1,046.17	54.0	14.5	5.6	2.7	3.5	2.9	1.8	2.1	1.2	1.0	10.7
1958	1,055.41	49.0	16.4	5.4	3.7	3.5	2.4	1.2	1.3	1.3	0.5	15.3
1959	1,053.07	49.8	21.0	5.2	4.1	3.6	2.9	1.5	1.2	0.9	0.2	9.6
1960	1,164.26	46.3	25.0	5.0	2.5	4.0	3.0	1.3	1.2	0.7	0.4	10.6
1961	1,152.85	51.8	21.4	4.0	2.1	4.2	2.8	1.1	1.0	0.7	0.1	10.8
1962	1,146.55	47.7	20.9	4.8	1.9	5.6	2.8	1.6	0.8	1.2	0.2	12.5
1963	1,363.19	45.1	22.9	6.3	1.4	6.6	3.0	1.4	0.5	0.7	0.1	12.0

SOURCE: United Nations, *Yearbooks of International Trade Statistics.*

Table 37   CLASSIFIED RANKING OF SEAPORTS

A. Customs ports of entry (regularly manned by customs staff)

Aparri, Cagayan	Jose Panganiban, Camarines Norte
Batangas, Batangas	Legaspi and Tobaco, Albay
Cagayan de Oro, Misamis Oriental	Manila
Cebu, Cebu	Maasin, Leyte del Sur
Davao, Davao	Masao, Agusan
Dumaguete, Negros Oriental	San Fernando, La Union
Iligan, Lanao del Norte	San Jose, Samar
Iloilo, Iloilo	Tacloban, Leyte del Norte
Jolo, Sulu	Zamboanga, Zamboanga del Sur

B. Subports (enterable by arrangement with nearest customs port of entry) [1]

Bislig, Surigao del Sur	Ozamis, Misamis Occidental
Catbalogan, Samar	Pulupandan, Negros Occidental
Claveria, Cagayan	Siain, Quezon
Dadiangas, Cotabato	Surigao, Surigao del Norte
Limay, Bataan	Tagbilaran, Bohol

C. National ports (open to all domestic shipping) [2]

Balabac, Palawan	Makar, Cotabato
Balanacan, Marinduque	Malangas, Zamboanga del Sur
Basco, Batanes	Mariveles, Bataan
Batobato, Sulu	Masbate, Masbate
Bongao, Sulu	Nasipit, Agusan
Borongan, Samar	Nasugbu, Batangas
Bulan, Sorsogon	Pagadian, Zamboanga del Sur
Butuan, Agusan	Palawan, Zamboanga del Norte
Cagayan de Sulu, Sulu	Pandan, Ilocos Sur
Calapan, Oriental Mindoro	Parang, Cotabato
Calbayog, Samar	Puerto Princesa, Palawan
Capiz, Capiz	Romblon, Romblon
Contra Costa, Batanes	San Carlos, Negros Occidental
Culion, Palawan	San Jose de Buenavista, Antique
Gaan Bay, Ilocos Norte	San Vicente, Cagayan
Hinigaran, Negros Occidental	Siasi, Sulu
Hondagua, Quezon	Sitangkai, Sulu
Jimenez, Misamis Occidental	Solvec, Ilocos Sur
Kawit Island, Cebu	Sual, Pangasinan
Magallanes, Sorsogon	Taganak, Sulu
Salomague, Ilocos Sur	Virac, Catanduanes

Table 37—Continued

D. Provincial and municipal ports

This grouping includes several hundred local ports, few of which possess docking facilities, warehousing, or cargo-handling equipment capable of servicing even medium-sized ships or significant cargoes. Some form of pier, quay, or wharfage is normally available for small ships and launches; most such ports have roads into hinterlands.

[1] The list of subports is periodically subject to change according to conditions of trade in hinterland regions.

[2] National ports normally are built and maintained by the Department of Public Works. The list of national ports is periodically subject to change. National ports normally possess fair docking facilities for medium-sized to small ships; they also possess some warehousing, and have good transport connections to hinterlands.

SOURCE: Data on ports of entry and subports as of October, 1966, from the Deputy Commissioner of Customs, Manila.

Notes

Notes to Chapter 1

1. Some of the most recent evidence supporting structural relationships between the Philippines and areas to the north is discussed in C. S. Ho, "Geologic Relationships and Their Comparison between Taiwan and the Philippines," *Philippine Geologist,* XV (1961), 59–95.

2. Grant W. Corby, *et. al., Geology and Oil Possibilities of the Philippines,* Republic of the Philippines, Department of Agriculture and Natural Resources, Bureau of Mines, Technical Bulletin no. 21 (Manila, 1951).

3. Bailey Willis, "The Philippine Archipelago: An Illustration of Continental Growth," *Proceedings of the Sixth Pacific Science Congress, 1939,* I (Berkeley, 1940) 185–200.

4. R. W. Van Bemmelen, *The Geology of Indonesia,* Vol. IA (The Hague: Government Printing Office, 1949).

5. Edward F. Durkee and Selmer L. Pederson, "Geology of Northern Luzon, Philippines," *Bulletin of the American Association of Petroleum Geologists,* 45 (1961), 137–167.

6. Clarence R. Allen, "Circum-Pacific Faulting in the Philippines-Taiwan Region," *Journal of Geophysical Research,* 67 (1962), 4795–4812.

7. Earl M. Irving, "Geological History and Petroleum Possibilities of the Philippines," *Bulletin of the American Association of Petroleum Geologists,* 36 (1952), 452.

8. The spelling of all island names, and their areas, are taken from *Geographical Data of the Philippines,* Republic of the Philippines, Bureau of Coast and

Geodetic Survey (1962). The names and heights of all mountains are from *Philippine Islands,* 1:250,000, Army Map Service, Corps of Engineers, Series S501 (1954–1957). Table 1 in the appendix of the present study lists the 154 islands of the Philippines possessing areas greater than 5 square miles.

9. Juan S. Teves, "On the 'Haycock' Hills of Bohol: An Interesting Geomorphic Feature," *Philippine Geographical Journal,* II (1954), 57–60.

10. Earl M. Irving, "Physiographic Observations on Mindanao by Aerial Reconnaissance, and Their Geological Interpretation," *Philippine Journal of Science,* 81 (1952), 141–169; T. S. M. Ranneft, *et al.,* "Reconnaissance Geology and Oil Possibilities of Mindanao," *Bulletin of the American Association of Petroleum Geologists,* 44 (1960), 529–568.

11. Irving, *op. cit.,* p. 159.

Notes to Chapter 2

1. R. G. Hainsworth and R. T. Moyer, *Agricultural Geography of the Philippine Islands—A Graphic Summary,* United States Department of Agriculture (Washington, 1945), p. 8.

2. All temperatures are given in degrees Fahrenheit.

3. Florencio Tamesis and Luis Aguilar, *Important Commercial Timbers of the Philippines,* Republic of the Philippines, Department of Agriculture and Natural Resources, Popular Bulletin no. 32 (Manila, 1953), p. 52.

4. M. A. Estoque, *An Analysis of Rainfall in Manila,* Philippine Weather Bureau (Manila, 1952), I, 7 (mimeographed).

5. Jose Coronas, "The Climate and Weather of the Philippines, 1903 to 1918," in *Census of the Philippine Islands, 1918,* I, 379–380.

6. Thomas E. Thorp, *High Velocity Winds in the Philippines,* Indiana University Foundation (Bloomington, 1962).

7. H. J. de Boer, "On the Relation between Rainfall and Altitude in Java, Indonesia," *Chronica Naturae,* 106 (1950), 424–427.

8. C. K. Stidd and L. B. Leopold, "The Geographical Distribution of Average Monthly Rainfall, Hawaii," *Meteorological Monographs,* I (1951), 24–33.

9. D. H. Grist, *Rice,* (London: Longmans, Green, 1953).

10. E. C. J. Mohr and F. A. VanBaren, *Tropical Soils,* (New York: Interscience, 1954), p. 71.

11. W. Köppen, "Klassifikation der Klimate nach Temperatur, Niederschlag und Jahrelauf," *Petermanns Geographische Mitteilungen,* 62 (1916), 197–203.

12. E. DeMartonne, *Traité de Géographie Physique* (Paris: Librairie Armand Colin, 1909), 205–225.

13. G. H. Hargreaves, "Areas in the Philippines Where Rice Can Be Grown without Irrigation," *Philippine Geographical Journal,* IV (1956), 69–71.

14. W. Köppen and K. Geiger, *Handbuch der Klimatologie,* IC (Berlin: Gebrüder Borntraeger, 1936).

15. C. W. Thornthwaite, "An Approach toward a Rational Classification of Climate," *Geographical Review*, XXXVIII (1948), 55–94.

Notes to Chapter 3

1. *Labor in the Philippines*, U.S. Department of Labor, Bureau of Labor Statistics (Manila, 1956) p. 15; Frank H. Golay, *The Philippines: Public Policy and National Development* (Ithaca: Cornell University Press, 1961), pp. 32–33 and n. 1; A. Barrera, "Inventory of Philippine Soils," pp. 107–123, and J. P. Mamisao, "Soil Conservation in the Philippines," pp. 124–145, both in *Proceedings of the Interdisciplinary Symposia of the 1961 National Science and Technology Week*, National Science Development Board (Manila, 1961).

2. Pendleton published two early soil studies on the Negros Island sugarcane fields; the first on the La Carlota district in 1925, the other on the Silay-Saravia area in 1930.

3. The six provinces surveyed by 1939 were Bulacan, Rizal, Cavite, Batangas, Pampanga, and Tarlac.

4. Chiefly in the *Journal of the Soil Science Society of the Philippines* (1949 to the present).

5. "Formation of Soils," in H. G. Byers, *et. al.*, *Soils and Men: Yearbook of Agriculture, 1938*, United States Department of Agriculture (Washington, 1938), p. 948.

6. Rosario A. Aspiras and Martin V. Tiangco, "Potential Demand for Phosphate Fertilizer in the Philippines," *Journal of the Soil Science Society of the Philippines*, II (1950), 75.

7. Hugh Popenoe, "The Influence of the Shifting Agricultural Cycle on the Soil Properties in Central America," *Proceedings of the Ninth Pacific Science Congress, 1957*, VII (Bangkok, 1959), 72–77.

8. Dioscoro S. Rabor, "The Status of Conservation in the Philippines," *Proceedings of the Tenth Pacific Science Congress, 1961* (Honolulu, 1961), mimeographed paper.

9. Botanical nomenclature is used here only once, when the plant is first mentioned. A complete list of common species is presented in appendix table 7.

10. Harold C. Conklin, *Hanunóo Agriculture: A Report on an Integral System of Shifting Cultivation in the Philippines*, FAO Forestry Development Paper no. 12 (Rome, 1957), p. 128.

11. See the general discussions of the subject in E. Banks, *Bornean Animals* (Kuching, Sarawak: Kuching Press, 1949); T. D. Carter, J. E. Hill, and G. H. H. Tate, *Mammals of the Pacific World* (New York: Macmillan, 1945); P. H. Darlington, Jr., *Zoogeography: The Geographical Distribution of Animals* (New York: John Wiley & Sons, 1957); J. Delacour and E. Mayr, *Birds of the Philippines* (New York: Macmillan, 1946); G. H. H. Tate, *Mammals of Eastern Asia* (New York: Macmillan, 1947).

12. For a discussion of the continuing importance of hunting to a specific shifting-cultivator population, see H. C. Conklin, *op. cit.*; for the relative significance of hunting to all shifting-cultivator populations, see J. E. Spencer, *Shifting Cultivation in Southeastern Asia,* University of California Publications in Geography, vol. 19 (1966).

Notes to Chapter 4

1. It is often customary to speak of a four-level structure: the chief, the noble, the freeman, and the dependent-slave. Actually no one simple generalization covers the whole Philippines. We have combined the chief and the nobility. The bottom class is often termed slave erroneously. There were varying levels of dependency, from what might be termed sharecropper (not a slave at all), to term-debtor (an economic function, such as a bonded debtor, arising from economic causes), to judicial dependent (poachers who ran afoul of the "laws" of the datu), to captive dependent (those caught in interregional raids, or purchased captives of slaving sallies). Dependency often was hereditary, but there were bewildering complications in the regional variance of such patterns, further complicated by social obligational rules of reciprocity which functioned both upward and downward. Elevation in social status was possible, but sinking into dependency, particularly economic-service dependency, was far more common. The preservation of many of these relationships into modern time accounts for much of the economic and social dependency found among the "depressed tenancy" of the modern Philippines. See J. L. Phelan, *The Hispanization of the Philippines* (Madison: University of Wisconsin Press, 1959), and see M. R. Hollnsteiner, *Reciprocity in the Lowland Philippines,* Institute of Philippine Culture, Paper no. 1 (Quezon City: Ateneo de Manila University Press, 1961), and its revised version, *The Dynamics of Power in a Philippine Municipality* (Quezon City: University of the Philippines, 1963).

2. Phelan, *op. cit.*

3. D. V. Hart, *The Philippine Plaza Complex: A Focal Point in Culture Change,* Yale Southeast Asia Studies (New Haven: Yale University Press, 1955).

4. See Phelan, *op cit.*, p. 124, for a table listing early, late, and contemporary names for the various units, and see fig. 18 of the present study.

5. During the late nineteenth century the Spanish population in the Philippines increased markedly, but even in 1903 the census tabulated less than 4,000 Spanish as resident in the Islands.

6. Phelan, *op. cit.*, pp. 95–98, 115–120, discusses the encomienda, comments on the substitution of the Spanish system for the older one, and concludes that too little is yet known of transitional process to clarify the origins of the great estates. The three paragraphs preceding the citation of this note in the text are but a summary generalization of the probabilities of a complex development.

7. The 1903 census judged literacy as the ability to read or write any

language, but estimated that not more than 10 percent of the population could speak Spanish. The 1960 census recorded 558,000 persons (2.1 percent of the total population) as able to speak Spanish.

8. It should be noted that neither was imposed upon the Filipinos, but that these were two of the things for which the Filipinos had rebelled against Spanish political control. It is true that English was imposed as the language of instruction throughout the school system.

9. See the effective discussion of these two features, government and education, in R. A. Smith, *Philippine Freedom, 1946–1958* (New York: Columbia University Press, 1958).

10. It is true that late in the Spanish period a British-built rail line did link both northwest and southeast Luzon with Manila, that public roads were not entirely American, and that a few ports were minimally equipped; but in broad terms the American period began a new era.

11. The aim of the following paragraphs is not to depreciate the American actions in supervising Filipino modernization, but to point out the significant fact that American action did not totally remove many of the problem situations that made for trouble during the Spanish period and have continued to be problem situations right down to the present. Many of these issues are geographically significant to the whole of the Philippines, whereas others are regionally significant in certain parts of the Philippines.

12. The significance of title lies in the fact that a land title offers collateral for the borrowing from legitimate lending agencies of capital funds with which the land can be productively developed. Lacking title, most occupants of land are forced to seek credit from private sources charging very high interest rates. Title could be secured after provision of description by private survey, but few small farmers needing credit have been able to afford the costs of private survey. In the United States, in contrast, the cadastral land survey was completed for most of the country west of the Appalachians long before settlement took place so that land titles could be secured at the time of settlement or claim establishment.

13. In economic and political literature this concept normally is termed "caciquism," an adaptation of a term applicable to the role of the Latin-American Indian cacique, or chief, in the Spanish era.

14. A notable beginning in northern Luzon established a skeleton road network into Mountain Province, but this was more a political administrative measure aimed at future regional development.

15. Negros and Panay islands have various narrow-gauge light rail lines or nets, but these are private lines used only in sugarcane or timber transport, and they do not provide general public transport. The Cebu rail line became inoperative during World War II, and has not been restored.

16. For example, buses normally carry such cargo, in small lots, as demanded by passengers, make pickup and discharge stops at passenger demand, and generally provide far more service on the semirural run than is customarily the case in the United States. The World War II jeep was rebuilt into the "jeepney," a

ten-passenger taxi that is a remarkable adaptation of American transport equipment to Philippine conditions.

17. The traveler in hinterland areas still runs into the question of bread-eating versus rice-eating, but increasingly the facilities for both dietary patterns are widely available.

Notes to Chapter 5

1. Data from official censuses are used without efforts to evaluate or recon-stitute them. There is evidence of underlisting in recent censuses, but no adequate data is available for truly critical analyses of census tabulations.

2. Francisco V. Nazaret and Felisa R. Barretto, *Concepts and Definitions of Urban Rural Areas in the Philippines,* Bureau of Census and Statistics (Manila: mimeographed, n.d.), discusses several criteria, each of which produces a different percentage answer.

3. Only very small numbers of immigrants have come into the Philippines since the seventeenth century, and in the present century the official net immigra-tion has amounted to less than 2,000 per year.

4. Physiological density in this section (and in appendix table 13) is defined as the ratio of total population to land now in cultivation, that is, land listed as in temporary or permanent crops, in fallow, or in pasture, rather than to arable or cultivable land.

5. Until the late nineteenth century the militant Moro population of Mindanao fought off immigrant Christians, raided the islands to the north, and generally retarded southward migration out of the Visayas. Until after 1900 Christian occupation was only a thin fringe along the very north coast of Mindanao.

6. Though the word "ethnic" is not a synonym for "racial" in the strict biological sense, it will be used here as an approach to this meaning. Strict biological distinctions cannot be made clearly in dealing with the Filipinos, for cultural criteria have always been used, with the result that use of the term "ethnic" is fairly accurate.

7. One thesis has it that the immigrant Moslem groups both conquered and absorbed many of the proto-Malay groups, yielding the modern Moslem population of the Sulu Islands and parts of Mindanao. See H. W. Krieger, *Peoples of the Philippines* (Washington, D.C.: Smithsonian Institute, 1942), p. 34; F. C. Cole, *The Peoples of Malaysia* (New York: D. Van Nostrand & Co., 1945), p. 195.

8. "Igorot," perhaps the best-known name for "pagan people," has been loosely used and does not truly indicate unity in language, culture, or regionalism. In the early American period the term "Igorot" was applied to almost all the non-Christian peoples of Luzon.

9. In Mindanao the term "Bukidnon" was in early use for all non-Christian and non-Moslem peoples, and like "Igorot," is not a proper unit-term, even though it is a precise term for one culture group.

10. The Mangyan are not one people in historicocultural terms. There are eight or more linguistic groups who seldom intermarry, who preserve their own precise cultures, and who are classified as one chiefly because they are pagan and preserve their pre-Christian forms of culture and economy.

11. Canada in 1960 had a population of 17,200,000, and officially the country is bilingual. About three-fourths of Quebec's 4,300,000 inhabitants claim French as their mother tongue. The Philippines may well be the fourth-ranking country employing English as the language of instruction in the schools.

12. The table is from *Census of the Philippines, 1960: Population and Housing, Summary,* Bureau of Census and Statistics (Manila, 1963), p. 14.

13. On the arrival of the Spanish a few barangays were larger than these figures indicate. Owing to the mobility of the pre-Spanish population, shifts in size and location were rather common through time. For notes on the pre-Spanish and early Spanish patterns, see J. L. Phelan, *The Hispanization of the Philippines* (Madison: University of Wisconsin Press, 1959), pp. 15–17, 121–129.

14. Nuclear or single families are bound together into groups by several kinds of social and economic ties that involve obligation and reciprocity. Both within and beyond nuclear-family units related by blood and marriage such times provide a degree of solidarity to village and hamlet communities which is similar but not equivalent to the socioeconomic relationships maintained within the extended family system; see M. R. Hollnsteiner, *The Dynamics of Power in a Philippine Municipality,* (Quezon City: University of the Philippines, 1963).

15. Manila was set apart from the provincial structure by royal charter in 1574, and reaffirmed in 1901 by the United States as a federal district. All other city charters are post-1900. See J. E. Spencer, "The Cities of the Philippines," *Journal of Geography,* LVII (1958), 288–293.

16. The village cockpit conceivably may lay claim to such temporal status, and the house of the datu often was larger than others. Such buildings as the "men's house" found among some of the proto-Malay culture groups were no different than other housing and cannot be construed as formal public architecture.

17. A. Ravenholt, *The Philippines* (Princeton: Van Nostrand, 1962), pp. 148–149, suggests that schoolhouse architecture was introduced from the American Midwest, and that government buildings are derived from the "Potomac Greek" of the federal and state capitols of the United States.

18. There are regional differences. Around the Manila urban area many villages are larger than normal, since urban workers prefer to commute. On the Negros Island sugarcane farms villages are found that are above average in size and villages in Surigao Province seem to be larger than normal.

19. Phelan, *op. cit.,* p. 122, noted 6,000 barangays for 1768; the 1903 census suggested "about 13,400 barrios." The 1960 figure excludes about 1,200 barrios that form the poblaciones of the municipalities, and the averages for barrio and village populations, likewise, exclude the poblacion barrios.

20. The term *pueblo* properly referred to the town, and the term *cabecera* was properly applied to the administrative center of a parish, which comprised the

formal, permanent church, a regularly assigned resident priest, and the church residence and school; however, the two terms often were indiscriminately applied to the town.

21. The municipality is the primary regional political unit of the Philippines. Comprising a group of barrios, the municipality corresponds somewhat to the county in the United States. The town serves as the "county seat"; it contains the poblacion and provides most of the secondary services. Municipalities are grouped into provinces, which correspond to American states.

22. From Phelan, *op. cit.*, pp. 167–176, who gives the lists of cabecera churches up to 1655 by the several religious orders establishing them.

23. Some of the Cagayan Valley settlements did not remain town settlements, and a few others elsewhere did not mature into large modern towns, but the generalization is sound.

24. The friendly sense of hospitality among Filipinos is such that in the past very few towns possessed hotels and related services, making it somewhat awkward for a traveler who did not have friends or relatives in the community. With greatly increased mobility and travel volume, purely friendly hospitality no longer serves the current need, and hotels are being established in many of the larger towns on frequented transport routes. Nevertheless, the Philippine town still retains certain features that distinguish it from towns elsewhere in the world.

25. Log and bamboo palisades protected settlements on both sides of the Pasig River mouth when the Spanish arrived. Similar fortifications on the south bank of the Pasig were extended by the Spanish, but these were burned several times by attackers. Stone fortifications began with individual blockhouses, built in the 1580's, which later were linked by the walls of the Intramuros to enclose an area of about ½ square mile. Repeated repairs were made until into the nineteenth century.

26. See Phelan, *op. cit.*, pp. 97–98, 145–146, and n.2, p. 178. See also Conrado Benitez, *History of the Philippines*, (Boston: Ginn and Company, 1940), pp. 22–234, on the variation in Spanish, Japanese, and Chinese resident populations.

27. In the course of time the Intramuros proved too small for the growing Roman Catholic institutions; and convents, schools, and locality-centered parish churches grew more important and significant. The religious focus of much of Filipino life made these parish centers significant elements of decentralization. Retail markets established near several of the plazas drew additional retailing activities and created decentralized patterns to native retail trades; the concentrations of foreign clothing and consumer goods within the Escolta sector and of hardware and machinery within the Rosario sector formed a different pattern. High-class residential siting outside of Intramuros spread in several directions, leading to the development of numerous zonations of residential patterns. The early development of the handicraft industries in Binondo, the tobacco manufacturies in Paco, and the embroideries in Malate sector suggests a decentralized yet zonal pattern for the productive activities.

28. A widely quoted figure for 1896 gave a total of 340,000 for Manila. See J. Foreman, *The Philippine Islands* (2nd ed.; New York: Scribner, 1906), p. 355. A Board of Health census for 1901 yielded a total of 244,000; the census of 1903 gave the total for the city of Manila, itself, as 219,000.

29. In the development of the port facilities dredging deepened an anchorage inside a breakwater, and extended the land area seaward from the walls of the Intramuros, creating a new sector known as the Port Area, in which numerous government offices were located and where facilities for handling international cargo have concentrated.

30. As of the 1960 census period this was true. New city charters continue to be granted municipalities, and in 1962 a fourth city, Caloocan, was chartered.

31. The destruction of the Intramuros area during World War II almost completely depopulated that small sector and less than 1,000 persons resided there in 1948. By 1960 the population had grown markedly over that of 1948. Other similar short-term changes in internal trends have taken place, but these are not considered here. Though Quezon City was named the national political capital in 1950, national government offices still were widely scattered in Manila in 1960; the President's executive mansion, Malacañang Palace, and the headquarters of the Philippine Congress remained in the city of Manila in 1965.

32. This trend is evident within the political limits of Manila itself, as well as in the surrounding areas. The inner Binondo sector contained 16,000 people in 1903 and the same number in 1960; Ermita held 18,000 in 1903 and 12,000 in 1960; San Nicolas held 33,000 in 1903, reached a peak of 41,000 in 1948, and declined to 33,000 in 1960. Sampaloc, an outer suburb of the political unit of Manila, conversely, held 18,000 in 1903, 233,000 in 1948, and 287,000 in 1960; Malate held 9,000 in 1903, 66,000 in 1948, and 69,000 in 1960. Quezon, as an outer municipality only, held 3,000 people in 1903, but its population rose to 108,000 in 1948 afer Quezon was chartered Quezon City, and grew to 398,000 in 1960 as the move toward the national capital gathered speed. Makati, as a rural municipality in 1903, held only 2,000 people; its population reached 41,000 in 1948, and 114,000 in 1960 after Makati became a residential and industrial suburb.

33. The Philippine Congress, in a move to restrict the patronage power of the President, has passed legislation making elective the offices of Mayor and City Council member in some cities; changes in this tug-of-war will continue in the future. Congress has declined to legislate the chartering of some cities in the contest for political power, and chartering is to some extent a function of the strength of a political party at a particular time.

34. This issue is not to be confused with the situation obtaining in the United States in which metropolitan regions receive quasi-official status for census purposes or in which there is changing policy with regard to the administration of public services. In the Philippines some chartered cities do receive some services from national government bureaus rather than from provincial bureaus, but the sources of the motivations involved are quite unlike those of the American

situation. Urbanization has certain modern conventional criteria that go unstated, even though these must vary among different cultures. The 1960 census statistics for some of the Philippine chartered cities indicate, among other things, extremely low ratios for piped water to individual houses, for electric lighting, flush toilets, cooking fuels other than traditional ones, multiple housing, and for owned versus rented housing. Such data cannot be broken down for the central and rural sectors of the cities, but the overall ratios are very low for all cities outside the Manila metropolitan zone, and indicate that normal American criteria do not yield totally effective results.

35. Area was reported to be 546.2 square miles in 1963; whether this was the area at the time of the 1960 census is uncertain. Dates for changes in area are also uncertain in the instances cited in later paragraphs of this chapter.

36. See F. L. Wernstedt, "Cebu: Focus of Philippine Interisland Trade," *Economic Geography,* vol. 32 (1956), and E. L. Ullman, "Trade Centers and Tributary Areas of the Philippines," *Geographical Review,* vol. 50 (1960), for supporting data.

37. During World War II the Philippines suffered as much material damage as almost any region elsewhere, but though dietary patterns were somewhat restricted, it is very doubtful if they declined to the level of national biological malnutrition.

38. Regional concentration of certain of the American crop plants has occurred since their introduction as dietary staples or complements. Thus, in the central Visayan Islands, where there is less rainfall and more porous soil, corn has become a key crop and a dietary staple. Coarsely ground and cooked as though it were rice, corn is a staple food; corn-eating is a mark of the Cebuano and the Boholano, and its use has spread to those areas in Mindanao which Cebu and Bohol migrants have gone.

39. The preference for highly milled rice over lightly milled or unmilled rice, for white sugar over brown, for white flour over brown, and for everprocessed food merely parallels changing world patterns. The problems of malnutrition that result from such changes are little greater in the Philippines than elsewhere in the world, though the rectification programs resulting from nutritional education are perhaps somewhat more slowly instituted in the Philippines than in some parts of the Occident.

40. Perhaps the one disease in which this is somewhat untrue is malaria. In the earlier periods, and on the expanding frontiers of settlement, malaria has been as serious in parts of the Philippines as elsewhere in the tropics.

41. See Phelan, *op. cit.,* pp. 99–108, for discussion of the contrasts between the Philippines and Mexico in these matters.

Notes to Chapter 6

1. The first volume of the 1960 census dealing with agriculture has appeared, issued in 1965; however, the bases for data collection were not regular

and were not comparable to those of the 1948 census, and the provincial summaries presented in the first volume are either incomplete or faulty, or both. It may be that the data will be restated in later volumes still to be published, but as our study goes to press we regret that it is impossible to present a full range of 1960 data comparable with that in the 1948 volume. We have presented all the 1960 data available from any source, and we retain the 1948 tables as more fully indicative of the general patterns.

2. The total lowland irrigated rice acreage increased from 1,370,000 in 1939 to 1,533,000 in 1960, but during the same period the unirrigated lowland acreage total increased from 1,925,000 to 3,230,000, and the upland rice acreage total increased from 1,000,000 to 1,720,000. Data from *The Philippines: Long-Term Projection of Supply and Demand for Selected Agricultural Products,* U.S.D.A., Regional Analysis Division, Economic Research Service. ERS-Foreign-34 (1963), p. 110, and *Census of the Philippines, 1960.*

3. See J. L. Phelan, *The Hispanization of the Philippines* (Madison: University of Wisconsin Press, 1959). Phelan discussed the rise and decline of the role of the encomienda as a grant of annual tribute collectible from a given population, or the population of a given area, in the form of produce, labor service, or money. He itemized the decline of private grants and the rise of crown grants during the seventeenth century, but did not deal fully with the subject of church grants. He also suggested that tenancy was a phenomenon related to the nineteenth century and the Filipino adoption of Spanish concepts of landownership and tenure, although it was beyond his purpose to deal fully with the whole subject of land systems and the rise of tenancy.

4. There are several different ways in which tenants pay their costs, such as crop-share, cash and share, and cash-lease, with variations in provision of work animals, seed, fertilizer, and planting-harvest labor.

5. Some kind of government resettlement agency has been in operation almost continuously since early in the American period. These programs have shown that frontier areas are able to be occupied peaceably, but the actual numbers of settlers relocated by such programs have been quite small.

6. D. G. Salita, "Agricultural Problems: Ownership, Tenancy, and Credit," in R. Huke, *Shadows on the Land* (Manila: Bookmark, 1963), pp. 196–199; and *Census of the Philippines, 1960: Agriculture, Summary.* Tenancy rates vary depending upon classes of landownership considered under tenure. In 1960 only 44 percent of Philippine farms were being cultivated by full-owners. An additional 14 percent were cultivated by part-owners.

7. The provision of effective, controlled water supply may, of itself, raise rice yields from the present average of about 1,000 pounds per acre to a figure of about 1,600 pounds, other conditions remaining appropriately stable. Recent evidence from integrated programs suggests that yields of about 2,000 pounds per acre are certainly attainable on a significant share of the total lowland rice land of the Philippines, and that under the best of conditions Filipino farmers can better that yield. A considerable financial investment will be required to spread such

yield patterns widely throughout the archipelago, and numerous changes in the structure of rice agriculture will be required to enable widespread adoption of such integrated programs.

8. Phelan, *op. cit.*, p. 111 and accompanying footnote, suggests that Filipinos did not accept corn readily, and that it was little grown in the early period, noting the high price of corn as compared to rice. This is standard crop history everywhere in the Orient, in terms of the competition between rice and corn in areas producing good rice yields. Nevertheless, the plant spread and gradually won its acceptance in those areas in which rice growing was not productive for environmental or other reasons. This process often took considerable time in many areas.

9. The term "corn rice" refers to a coarse-ground corn in which the particles are about the size of rice grains. It is cooked to a waterless consistency and eaten as one would eat boiled rice.

10. The taros serve as the base for particular food dishes. Purple yams, *ubi* (*Dioscorea alata* Linn.), are made into sweet puddings, particularly at Christmas, and on certain other religious holidays. Ice cream made with purple yams will be eaten by the well-to-do who no longer eat yams as a food staple. Manioc flour sometimes is used in filling out wheat flour, to be eaten by all classes in the various breadstuffs. Particular regional dishes, delicacies, and snacks are prepared from each of the root crops and consumed regularly by children and adults of all classes.

11. Fern tips and the growing tips or buds of wild taro, bananas, palms, and many other wild plants furnished a good share of the edible "vegetables" to the customary shifting cultivators who gathered these from the regenerating forest ranges around their homesites.

12. Even Batanes Province, in the far north, is included in this statement. For practical purposes, however, the Batanes Province region is one in which there is no commercial production of any of the fruits, and the plantings are no more than token plantings.

13. When fiber is the end product desired the young fruit is cut out of the growing plant, forcing the leaf growth, in order to produce longer leaves than are normal to the plant when grown for fruit.

14. *Cattle ranches, animal pastures, pasturelands, cattle ranges,* and related terms in the Philippines refer almost entirely to lands deforested and overgrown by rank tropical grasses, and properly constitute the parang lands and the tropical grasslands. These are pasturelands by default only. Annual burning to rid the land of the old, inedible growth does not constitute effective control, although it does make possible good browse for a few weeks after the burn as the new growth begins. See comments in the section "Livestock and Poultry" in this same chapter.

15. The Philippine water buffalo is termed carabao. Long present in the Islands, the breed is slightly lighter in weight than the best stock of the Asian mainland, and also differs from this stock in color. Recent importation of mainland breeding stock for upgrading local carabao attaches the name "buffalo" to the mainland stock, but only breed variation is involved, not speciation.

16. Variation in the production cycle depends upon local regional climate and upon whether the crop is from an initial planting or is a ratoon crop grown on last year's rootstock. Initial plantings in Luzon may sometimes be harvested in even less than twelve months. Labor needs are concentrated in a six-month portion of this cycle.

17. The long-term contracts specify such items as the shares of sugar to be received by the growers and millers, procedures for estimating sugar content of delivered cane, stalkage that can be cut and delivered, and cane varieties to be grown; annual working agreements further specify cane-cutting patterns and schedules, delivery schedules for daily mill-run quotas, and replanting patterns. The cooperative system involves integration of many complex elements between growers and millers not required in the same way in other countries.

18. The treaty agreement of 1956 specified an annual quota of preferential-duty sugar at 850,000 tons, plus provision for quota adjustment; sugar preferentially admitted has been close to 1,000,000 tons per year. The agreement also specified an increasing duty-pattern, beginning in 1956, by which Philippine exports to the United States after 1974 will pay such duties as are applicable to all other suppliers of the American market. This will place Philippine sugar production under increasing cost-patterns, and may require changes in the whole structure of the industry.

19. Since 1960 and the closure of Cuban sugar supplies the United States and many other countries have been forced to seek substitute sugar supplies. In crop year 1963–64 a total of 639,000 acres of land in the Philippines was devoted to commercial sugarcane. Furthermore, there are plans for the establishment of three new sugar centrals in the Visayas.

20. There continues to be a small production of muscovado in such forms as the cake *panocha,* but this actually supplies a specialty-item market rather than a basic demand for sugar. Various other domestic uses, such as *basi,* a cane juice beverage, are in this same category.

21. Actually the Spanish monopoly operated only within a few sectors of Luzon. In the mid-nineteenth century tobacco growing by farmers outside the monopoly system expanded in the Visayan Islands, and government depots bought up some leaf tobacco for inclusion within the Luzon monopoly operations. By about 1850 inefficiencies in monopoly operation had become a factor in tenancy development in parts of central to northern Luzon, as government payments often were diverted from distribution to the farmers forced to grow the crops. Abuses became so great that the monopoly system was abolished in 1882. See J. Foreman, *The Philippine Islands* (New York: Scribner, 1906), pp. 292–299, for a general discussion of nineteenth-century tobacco growing; or F. H. Sawyer, *The Inhabitants of the Philippines* (London: Low, Marston and Co., 1900), for various comments on the local operation system.

22. A. Cutshall, "Tobacco Growing in the Philippines." *Transactions of the Illinois Academy of Science,* 52 (1959), 33–44.

23. These terms are employed in the proper sense that the level of living is

that actually achieved, and the standard of living is that to which the population aspires.

24. The Philippine peso in 1960 was equivalent to U.S. $0.50, but translation into United States currency yields no proper comparisons of annual income values. These data are rough estimates only, subject to many kinds of differentials, and are provided only to give a sense of comparison of ranking income utility among the major crops. Devaluation of Philippine currency in 1961 has made the peso equivalent to approximately U.S. $0.26.

Notes to Chapter 7

1. A. W. Herre, *Check List of Philippine Fishes,* Research Report no. 20, U.S. Fish and Wildlife Service (Washington: Government Printing Office, 1950).

2. Personal communication, Republic of the Philippines, Department of Agriculture and Natural Resources, Bureau of Fisheries, February 11, 1960.

3. *Ibid.*

4. D. M. Bunag, "Common Philippine Market Fish," *Philippine Fisheries Yearbook, 1953,* I (1954), 209–216; and table 24, entitled "Productivity of commercial Fishing Vessels, by Fishing Grounds, by Kind, and by Quantity, 1962," in *Fisheries Statistics of the Philippines, 1962* (Quezon City: Philippine Fisheries Commission), pp. 35–43.

5. Manual E. Medina, "Status of the Fishing Industry in Cebu, Bohol and Negros Oriental," *Philippine Fisheries Yearbook, 1953,* I (1954), 101, 225.

6. Porfirio R. Manacop and Cipriano Menguito, "Philippine Commercial Fishing Craft and Gear," *Philippine Fisheries Yearbook, 1953,* I (1954), 197–205.

7. Santos B. Rasalan, "Types of Philippine Fish Corrals," *Philippine Fisheries Yearbook, 1953,* (1954), 112–114, 323, 325.

8. Arthur C. Avery, *Fish Processing Handbook for the Philippines,* U.S. Fish and Wildlife Service, Research Report no. 26 (Washington: Government Printing Office, 1950).

9. L. Ma. Rivera and Associates, *Directory of Industrial Establishments in the Philippines,* Department of Commerce and Industry, Bureau of Commerce (Manila, 1958), p. 96.

10. Wallace E. McIntyre, "Philippine Fish Culture," *Scientific Monthly,* 78 (1954), 86–93; *Fisheries Statistics of the Philippines, 1962,* pp. 78–79.

11. D. V. Villadolid and P. A. Acesta, "Culture Tilapia for Food and Profit," *Philippine Fisheries Yearbook, 1953,* I (1954), 30, 260–265.

12. *Fisheries Statistics of the Philippines,* 1962, pp. 83–87.

13. *An Economic Analysis of Philippine Domestic Transportation,* Stanford Research Institute (Menlo Park, 1957), Vol. II, tables 5, 6.

14. Winslow L. Gooch, *Forest Industries of the Philippines,* Bureau of Forestry and Philcusa (Manila, 1953), p. 14, unnumbered table.

15. *Ibid.,* p. 20.

16. The authors purposely have not entered Latin binomials for every native wood at this point, but these are given in appendix table 7. Readers interested in woods and wood characteristics are referred to Florencio Tamesis and Luis Aguilar, *Important Commercial Timbers of the Philippines,* Republic of the Philippines, Department of Agriculture and Natural Resources Popular Bulletin no. 32 (Manila, 1953).

17. The statistics of the 1960 census indicate that wood is the chief fuel used in cooking in an overwhelming proportion of the homes of every Philippine city, including Manila.

18. Mineral production statistics are from *Base Metals Monthly Report, 1961, Annual,* Base Metals Association of the Philippines (Manila, n.d.) p. 114.

19. Benjamin M. Gozon, "Mineral Resources Development in the Philippines," in *Proceedings of the Interdisciplinary Symposia of the 1961 National Science and Technology Week,* Area II, National Science Development Board (Manila, 1963), p. 9.

20. See Felix M. Keesing, *The Ethnohistory of Northern Luzon* (Stanford: Stanford University Press, 1962), *passim,* for notations on mining and trading of gold from the north Luzon hill country as typical of pre-Spanish and early Spanish conditions.

21. Estimates are from *Copper Deposits of the Philippines,* Republic of the Philippines, Department of Agriculture and Natural Resources, Bureau of Mines, Special Projects Series, Publication no. 16 (Manila, 1956); and from company reserve estimates in *Philippine Mining Yearbook,* 1959, 1960.

22. *Chromite in the Philippines,* Republic of the Philippines, Department of Agriculture and Natural Resources, Bureau of Mines, Information Circular no. 15 (Manila, 1953); *Philippine Mining Yearbook,* 1959, p. 60.

23. *Mineral Trade Notes,* U.S. Department of Interior, Bureau of Mines, 50 (1960), 20.

Notes to Chapter 8

1. Much of the material in this transportation section is based upon the analysis of Philippine transportation made by the Stanford Research Institute at the request of the Philippine government: *An Economic Analysis of Philippine Domestic Transportation* Stanford Research Institute (Menlo Park, 1957), 7 vols. The reader is also referred to F. L. Wernstedt, *The Role and Importance of Philippine Interisland Shipping and Trade,* Cornell University, Southeast Asia Program, Data Paper no. 26 (Ithaca, 1957), 132 pp.; and Edward L. Ullman, "Trade Centers and Tributary Areas of the Philippines," *Geographical Review,* L (1960), 203–218.

2. Best estimates suggest that there are probably more than 6,000 vessels in the Philippines operating on some kind of commercial basis (*An Economic Analysis of Philippine Domestic Transportation,* III, 23). Not included in this

total are thousands of *bancas,* which are moved by oar and/or sail and are not engaged in commercial operations in the traditional sense of the word. These small boats are used for a variety of personal purposes in much the same way that Americans rely upon personal automobiles. They are used for family travel from island to island or to market, for commuting, for transporting personal cargoes, and for subsistence fishing. Commercial fishing operations are conducted from about 1,000 or more vessels. The larger fishing vessels, operating from bases at Manila and Cebu primarily, have gross tonnages of 30–100 tons and are included within the commercial fleet as enumerated above.

3. Several thousand miles of privately operated trackage exists in the primary sugarcane-growing localities, but these do not serve general transport requirements.

4. A short rail line extending southward from Fabrica, Negros Occidental, is privately operated by a lumber company, and though not legal public carriers, its logging trains are used by a large local population in spite of the company's objections.

5. In 1960 first-class roads totaled 12,100 miles that were all-weather, graded, and hard-surfaced or graveled. Second-class roads totaled 7,600 miles; these were graded, drained, but not hard-surfaced. The remainder were third-class roads, which were unimproved as to drainage, grading, and surfacing. National roads are those main traffic routes that connect provincial capitals, important commercial centers, national airports, and seaports. Provincial roads connect one municipality with another.

6. *Journal of Philippine Statistics,* Bureau of Census and Statistics, 13 (1960), 100–101.

7. The economic history of the Spanish colonial period in the Philippines is not given adequate presentation, particularly with regard to nonagricultural aspects. See Conrado Benitez, *History of the Philippines,* (New York: Ginn and Co., 1926), and later editions, for general comments on all of these phases mentioned.

8. Handicraft textile spinning and weaving operations in cottons and fine grades of abaca tended to decline, whereas the availability of imported textile yardage promoted the growth of tailoring, dressmaking, and the slow growth of apparel manufacturing. The handicraft manufacture of fine-grade abaca products shifted to the processing of larger volumes of medium-grade fibers for the export trade in raw fiber; there occurred the rise of the handicraft embroidery industry producing export goods (often from imported textile yardage) in the fine linens.

9. Even now, Philippine statistical compilations, and the procedures involved, are relatively new and not yet comprehensive, as Filipinos are unaccustomed to statistical reporting of all economic activities. Currently the distinction between handicraft and industrial operations may actually be determined by whether data can be secured on the particular activity. The tendency is to set a minimal employee number on the definition of factory, whereas earlier reporting included everything on which any amount of data could be secured. So far the data

for Manila tends to predominate, and that for other areas is fragmentary, incomplete, and sometimes unclearly defined.

10. In 1934 and early 1935 legislative enactments by the United States Congress and the Philippine legislature arranged a ten-year period of home rule during which the Philippines prepared for its total independence in 1945. Henceforth, governmental policy toward, and control over, industrialization was in the hands of the Filipinos in practical terms. See R. A. Smith, *Philippine Freedom, 1946–1958* (New York: Columbia University Press, 1958), for the texts of the enactments, and a discussion of the political aspects.

11. Some government organizations preceded the commonwealth. For a tabular listing of the concerns and the changes that occurred over the years, see A. V. H. Hartendorp, *History of the Industry and Trade of the Philippines,* (Manila: American Chamber of Commerce of the Philippines, 1958), pp. 49–63.

12. For a discussion of these relationships and the changing legislation, see R. A. Smith, *op. cit.;* S. Jenkins, *American Economic Policy toward the Philippines* (Stanford: Stanford University Press, 1954); A. V. Castille, *Philippine Economics* (Manila: privately printed, 1949).

13. Jenkins, *op. cit.*

14. See several chapters in F. H. Golay, *The Philippines: Public Policy and National Economic Development* (Ithaca: Cornell University Press, 1961) covering the social environment of economic policy and an analysis of the postwar recovery pattern.

15. G. P. Sicat, "The Structure of Philippine Manufacturing: Prospects for the 1960's," in *The Philippine Economy in the 1960's,* Institute of Economic Development and Research, University of the Philippines (Quezon City, 1964), pp. 188–200.

16. *Ibid.,* pp. 191–192.

17. The results are published in the *Annual Survey of Manufactures,* Bureau of Census and Statistics, Manila. Additional economic data is available in the annual *Central Bank Statistical Bulletin.*

18. This is the definition of the Bureau of Census and Statistics, employed in the *Annual Survey of Manufactures, 1960,* and reflected in the relevant appendix tables of this study.

19. The Central Bank of the Philippines in the early 1960's defined Greater Manila as including the eight units of the Manila Metropolitan Area and the two additional municipalities of Navotas and Malabon, on the north bay side. Other references to Greater Manila include one or more of the additional towns listed.

20. Benitez, *op. cit.,* pp. 98–102, summarizes the subject of pre-Spanish trade; and Hartendorp, *op. cit.,* pp. 1–4, provides a short summary. Paul Wheatley, "Geographical Notes on Some Commodities Involved in Sung Maritime Trade," *Journal of the Malayan Branch, Royal Asiatic Society,* 32 (1961), 1–139, discusses many of the commodities traded and includes the Philippines as a source and as a market.

21. The precise rank of commodity groups in the export and import lists has

shifted from time to time, and is further commented on in a later paragraph of this chapter.

22. By the Treaty of Paris, December 10, 1898, which ended Spanish sovereignty, Spain retained equal tariff treatment on Spanish exports to the Philippines for a ten-year period, influencing the directional movement of both island exports and imports in the first decade of the twentieth century.

23. Golay, *op. cit.*, pp. 163–182.

24. The formal opening of customs offices seldom was quickly followed by the active entry of ships and movement of commodities, and various dates are attached to port openings. Several other ports were formally opened but attracted no commercial activity. Only Manila, Cebu, and Iloilo retained permanent customs offices and functioned continuously as ports for foreign commerce until the end of Spanish sovereignty.

25. See table 37 for the lists of open ports as of 1966. Special permits allow special cargo movements into certain other ports, and make possible shipments of particular exports from many national and municipal ports, as isolated instances.

26. Copra, as an unprocessed, dried, coconut-meat export product, has faced little competitive or limiting tariff patterns; but such processed coconut products as coconut oil, when exported, compete with domestic production of fats in several countries, including the United States, and import tariff levies on coconut oil act to retard the Philippine export of such products. The export of coconut oil was helped considerably by the reduction of trans-Pacific freight charges on vegetable oils in 1962.

27. Sapanwood, as a source of dyes, was in the late nineteenth century a more important export than that of logs, timber, or lumber.

28. Quotas for the duty-free export maximum into the United States have been present for cordage products, for pearl or shell buttons, for sugar, coconut oil, cigars, other tobacco products, and rice. These quotas have had an effect both upon production and upon the export volumes; adjustments in legal quotas, and altered practical application of quota limits, have occurred. Only rice has not been thus affected; as the Philippines normally are short of rice, there has been no export pattern in the product. For notes on quotas see R. A. Smith, *op. cit.*, and Jenkins, *op. cit.*

29. World War II, of course, seriously affected the balance of trade as a result of the tremendous destruction, causing a serious inbalance in Philippine economy. Very tight exchange and trade controls during the early 1950's slowly restored a controlled pattern of balance which will also continue to affect total Philippine trade in the near future.

30. As pointed out in the previous section on manufacturing, the textile import led to a decline in native textile production but to a rise in dressmaking, tailoring, and clothing manufacture; footwear manufacturing has risen as a result of the import of leathers and rubbers.

31. Reference is to such shifts as the decline in betel chewing with the rising

preference for white teeth. Changing preferences led to the consumption of coffee, chocolate, beer, and the soft drinks over the traditional "tuba"; the shift in tobacco preferences led to a huge increase in import of cigarettes and cigar and cigarette tobaccos.

32. See Golay, *op. cit.,* for a thorough discussion of the various aspects of Philippine economic policy.

33. C. B. Elliott, *The Philippines* (Indianapolis: Bobbs-Merrill, 1917), p. 332.

34. For an extended treatment of the development of interisland shipping and flow patterns in the 1950's see Wernstedt, *op. cit.*

35. There have been local regions in which Filipino opposition to Chinese merchants prevented their participation in trade during certain periods between the mid-nineteenth century and the present, but these are exceptions to the general situation.

36. See Ullman, *op. cit.,* pp. 203–218, for a discussion of the arrangement of the hierarchical patterns of trade centers and the delimitation of trade regions.

Notes to Chapter 9

1. Data pertaining to island groupings, numbers, and areas are from *Geographical Data of the Philippines,* Bureau of Coast and Geodetic Survey (Manila, 1962).

2. Latest population data is from *Census of the Philippines, 1960: Population and Housing,* Bureau of the Census and Statistics (Manila, 1963), Vol. I: *Report by Provinces.*

3. Data pertaining to the political areas of provinces, cities, municipalities and municipal districts is from *Estimated Total Area of the Philippines, 1963,* Bureau of the Census and Statistics (Manila, 1963).

4. Norton Ginsburg, *Atlas of Economic Development* (Chicago: University of Chicago Press, 1961), table 30, p. 72.

5. C. S. Ho, "Geologic Relationships and Their Comparison between Taiwan and the Philippines," *Philippine Geologist,* XV (1961), 59–95.

6. *Philippine Coast Pilot,* Republic of the Philippines, Department of National Defense, Bureau of Coast and Geodetic Survey (Manila, 1954), Part I, *Sailing Directions for the Coasts of Luzon, Mindoro and Visayan Islands,* p. 23.

7. D. B. Paguirigan, M. E. Gutierrez, *et al., Wrapper Tobacco,* Philippine Department of Agriculture and Natural Resources, Bureau of Agriculture, Bulletin 41 (1927), p. 120.

8. F. M. Sacay, T. T. Quirino, and G. B. Fernandez, "An Economic and Social Study of Tobacco Farming in Isabela," *Philippine Agriculturist,* XXXIII (1949), 88–96; Felix M. Keesing, *The Ethnohistory of Northern Luzon* (Stanford: Stanford University Press, 1962); and *Census of the Philippines, 1960.*

9. *An Economic Analysis of Philippine Domestic Transportation,* Stanford

Research Institute, II (1952), 260–262, Table V-II, "Estimates of Total Accessible Forest."

10. Conrado Benitez, *History of the Philippines* (Boston: Ginn and Company, 1940), p. 178.

11. *Ibid.*, pp. 208, 222, 241, 268.

12. Sec. 9, "Tobacco Inspection Regulations for Leaf and Manufactured Products of Tobacco," Bureau of Internal Revenue, (March 1, 1918). The italics are the authors'.

13. Juan P. Mamisao, "Soil Conservation Problems in the Philippines," *Journal of the Soil Science Society of the Philippines*, I (1949), 15.

14. Bruno Lasker, *Filipino Immigration to Continental United States and Hawaii* (Chicago: University of Chicago Press, 1931).

15. *Census of the Philippine Islands, 1903,* U.S. Bureau of the Census, I (Washington, 1905), 421–422; Emma H. Blair and James A. Robertson, *The Philippine Islands, 1493–1898* (Cleveland: Arthur H. Clark, 1903), VIII, 105–108.

16. *Philippine Agricultural Situation,* Philippine Department of Agriculture and Natural Resources, Agricultural Economics Division (1959), I, 30.

17. Natividad V. Garcia, *A Study of the Socio-Economic Adjustments of Ilocano Villages to Virginia Tobacco Production,* Community Development Research Council, Abstract Series no. 15 (Quezon City, 1962).

18. *Industrial Philippines,* Republic of the Philippines, Philcusa, Industrial Development Branch (Manila, 1953), pp. 1–40.

19. Temperature regimes do not have enough contrast between cool season and hot season for some of the fruits, and warm-season temperatures remain too low for many other fruits.

20. Often it is suggested that the Spanish either made no effort to control the highlands or failed completely. Although they never succeeded in bringing the region under control, they did keep working at the problem. Gold-searching expeditions and punitive expeditions following raids on the lowlands marked the early era; the middle period saw the establishment of mission stations on the fringes and the maintenance of a fairly stable military boundary around the highlands; in the late nineteenth century a few Spanish military posts and missions were established in the highlands themselves. See J. L. Phelan, *The Hispanization of the Philippines,* (Madison: University of Wisconsin, 1959), pp. 137–144, for a summary; see Keesing, *op. cit.,* for many of the details of expeditions, mission stations, and military posts.

21. There is no point in questioning the accuracy of the census at this point, for there obviously is a cultural bias in claiming or admitting such culture traits as form of religion and literacy, and the bias can be that of the inhabitant as easily as that of the census taker. Mountain Province, as of 1960, is not the same area as that included in the 1903 political units. An interesting study probing the weaknesses of census attempts to determine literacy is that by John E. DeYoung and Chester L. Hunt, "Communications Channels and Functional Literacy in the

Philippine Berrio," *Journal of Asian Studies,* XXII (1962), 67–77. In this study the statement is made that functional literacy is probably 20 percent below the census figure.

22. See F. C. Cole, *The Peoples of Malaysia* (New York: Van Nostrand, 1945), pp. 149–172, for a discussion of the Tinguians; see also Keesing, *op. cit.,* for a study concerned with all the issues here suggested.

23. This section has drawn on the suggestive, but incomplete, conclusions of F. M. Keesing, *op. cit.* The volume was not complete at Keesing's death, and it contains a few inconclusive suggestions. The summary here presented is also only suggestive.

24. Census data are presented as tabulated; linguistic subdivisions of the census, and placement therein during census taking, may not accord fully with current linguistic studies of the languages of northern Luzon. See table 9.

25. See Keesing, *op. cit.,* for scattered comments on early trade.

26. Except for a section of the eastern part of Abra, areas formerly included in surrounding provinces but roughly belonging in the highlands region were incorporated into Mountain Province, to the end that the province fairly closely approximates the highland region.

27. Such village poblaciones do not properly constitute urban places, even though several are above the 2,500 lower limit employed in studies of urbanism.

28. Bontoc, Ifugao, Kankanai, Inibaloi, Kalinga, and Apayao, in that order.

Notes to Chapter 10

1. *Census of the Philippine Islands, 1903,* Census Bureau (Washington, 1905), I, 421–23.

2. D. Z. Rosell, "Two Years of PHILCUSA-FOA Pump Irrigation Program in the Philippines," *Philippine Geographical Journal,* III (1955), 9–30.

3. *Fisheries Statistics of the Philippines, 1962,* Department of Agriculture and Natural Resources, Bureau of Fisheries, Fisheries Economics and Statistics Section (Quezon City, 1963), pp. 39–40.

4. Admittedly this is a crude and somewhat artificial measure of urbanization; however, it follows the United Nations definition of an urban settlement: *Population Growth and Manpower in the Philippines,* United Nations, Department of Economic and Social Affairs, Population Studies no. 32 (New York, 1960), p. 48.

5. Quoted in Albert Kolb, *Die Philippinen* (Leipzig: Koehler, 1942), pp. 379–380.

6. Emma H. Blair and James A. Robertson, *The Philippine Islands, 1493–1898* (Cleveland: Arthur H. Clark, 1903), III, 141–172.

7. The most recent eruption, in 1965, covered villages and fields on the slopes of the small volcano in the lake, causing some loss of life locally, but there was no damage beyond the outer margins of Taal Lake. The eruption in 1911 was a rather destructive one, spraying ash over a wide area. Previous eruptions were

frequent, but the only other serious one was that of 1754. The peculiar land-and-water construct of the Taal areas has resulted in a local conundrum: What is the lake within an island within a lake within an island within a lake? Answer: Green Lake in Volcano Island in Taal Lake in Luzon Island in the Pacific Ocean.

8. During early to middle Spanish times Cavite was a shipbuilding center, using timber cut from the hill country of southern Cavite and northwest Batangas.

9. Protests of taxation, labor drafts, product exactions, and in Batangas, of invasions of private crop fields by church cattle were normal and chronic problems encountered everywhere; but these were mild in comparison with the troubles raised by the Moros and the North Luzon Highlanders. A number of national patriots active against Spain in the late nineteenth century are native to the region. Jose Rizal was born in Laguna; Emilio Aguinaldo was a native of Cavite; and Apolinario Mabini was a native of Batangas.

10. Joaquin Martinez de Zuñiga, *Estadismo de las Islas Filipinas* (Madrid, 1893), I, 318–319.

11. *Proceedings of the Interdisciplinary Symposia of the 1961 National Science and Technology Week,* Republic of the Philippines, National Science Development Board (Manila, 1963), I, 135 ff., table 1.

12. See Frank Lynch, *Social Class in Bikol Town,* University of Chicago, Philippine Studies Program, Research Series, no. 1 (1959), particularly map 3.

13. Jose G. Gutierrez, "Corn Production and Consumption Requirements," *Philippine Agricultural Situation,* II (1960), 23–25. See tables 5, 6.

Notes to Chapter 11

1. *The Current Status of the Malaria Eradication Program in the Philippines: A Special Report to the Secretary of Health,* Republic of the Philippines, Malaria Eradication Project (Manila: May, 1961). See accompanying map.

2. For a detailed cultural anthropologic study of the Hanunóo, the most numerous of the pagan groups on Mindoro, see the excellent monograph by Harold E. Conklin, *Hanunóo Agriculture in the Philippines,* FAO Forestry Development Paper no. 12 (Rome, 1957), 195 pp.

3. *Soil Survey of Palawan Province, Philippines,* Republic of the Philippines, Department of Agriculture and Natural Resources, Bureau of Soils, Report no. 27 (Manila: Bureau of Printing, 1960).

Notes to Chapter 12

1. There are those who would exclude from the Visayan group the islands of Masbate, Burias, and Ticao; however, they are so included here following such authoritative sources as Worcester, Kolb, the Bureau of Census, and the Human Relations Area Files study by the University of Chicago's Philippines Studies

Program. Marinduque, although not part of the Visayas, is included because there is no other convenient place to include it.

2. *Census of the Philippines, 1960: Population and Housing, Summary,* Republic of the Philippines, Bureau of Census and Statistics (Manila, 1963).

3. R. W. Van Bemmelen, *The Geology of Indonesia* (The Hague: Government Printing Office, 1949), IA, 36.

4. H. Otley Beyer, *Philippine Saga* (Manila, 1947).

5. P. San Buenaventura, "Reforestation of Imperata Waste Lands in the Philippines," *Proceedings of the Ninth Pacific Science Congress, 1957,* II (Bangkok, 1958), 54.

6. *Philippine Coast Pilot,* Republic of the Philippines, Department of National Defense, Bureau of Coast and Geodetic Survey (4th ed.; Manila: Bureau of Printing, 1954), Part I: *Sailing Directions for the Coasts of Luzon, Mindoro, and Visayan Islands,* pp. 13–22.

7. Mike McIntyre, "Typhoons as a Retarding Influence on the East Coast of Samar," *Philippine Geographical Journal,* I (1953), 122–126.

8. Thomas E. Thorp, *High Velocity Winds in the Philippines* (Bloomington: Indiana University Press, 1962), pp. 46, 55, 61.

9. *An Economic Analysis of Philippine Domestic Transportation,* Stanford Research Institute (Menlo Park, 1957), II: *The Demand for Transportation: Commodity Flows and Passenger Movements,* 258–262.

10. A. R. Kinkel, L. M. Santos–Yniga, S. Samaniego, and O. Crispin, *Copper Deposits of the Philippines,* Bureau of Mines, Special Projects Series no. 16 (Manila, 1956), pp. 253–275.

11. Joaquin Martinez de Zuñiga, *Estadismo de las Islas Filipinas,* quoted in *Census of the Philippine Islands, 1903* (Washington, 1905) I, 440.

2. Joseph E. Spencer, *Land and People in the Philippines* (Berkeley and Los Angeles: University of California Press, 1952), pp. 41, 45, 57.

13. *Fisheries Statistics of the Philippines, 1962,* Philippine Department of Agriculture and Natural Resources, Bureau of Fisheries (Quezon City, 1963).

14. *Ibid.,* pp. 78–79.

15. Juan S. Teves, "On the 'Haycock' Hills of Bohol: An Interesting Geomorphologic Feature," *Philippine Geographical Journal,* II (1954), 57–60.

16. Estimates of arable land are based upon total cultivated lands plus areas that are not in crops but are suitable for agricultural purposes, that is, neither too steep nor too eroded. See: *Soil Survey of Bohol Province, Philippines,* Report no. 15, 1952; *Soil Survey of Cebu Province, Philippines,* Report no. 17, 1954; *Soil Survey of Negros Oriental Province, Philippines,* Report no. 26; Republic of the Philippines, Department of Agriculture and Natural Resources, Bureau of Soils (Manila: Bureau of Printing, 1960).

17. Karl J. Pelzer, *Pioneer Settlement in the Asiatic Tropics,* American Geographical Society, Special Publication no. 29 (New York, 1948), p. 253; *Census of the Philippines, 1960* (Manila, 1963), Vol. II: *Migration.*

18. Frederick L. Wernstedt, *The Role and Importance of Philippine Interisland Shipping and Trade,* Cornell University Southeast Asia Program, Data Paper no. 26 (Ithaca, 1957), p. 45.

19. Bruno Lasker, *Filipino Immigration to Continental United States and Hawaii* (Chicago, 1931).

20. *Crop, Livestock and Natural Resources Statistics, 1958 and 1959,* Republic of the Philippines, Department of Agriculture and Natural Resources, Agricultural Economics Division (Manila, 1963).

21. *Soil Survey of Cebu Province, Philippines,* Republic of the Philippines, Department of Agriculture and Natural Resources, Soil Report no. 17 (Manila, 1954), p. 115.

22. *An Economic Analysis of Philippine Domestic Transportation,* II, 108–109.

23. *Crop, Livestock and Natural Resources Statistics, 1958 and 1959,* p. 3.

24. Coal industry statistics are from *Mineral Resources of the Philippines,* Republic of the Philippines, Department of Agriculture and Natural Resources, Bureau of Mines, Information Circular no. 19 (Manila, 1955), pp. 98–102.

25. Data secured from Domestic Division, Sugar Quota Administration, Manila 1959.

26. Emma H. Blair and James A. Robertson, *The Philippine Islands, 1493–1898* (Cleveland: Arthur H. Clark, 1903), III, 169–170.

27. Manuel Buzeta and Felipe Bravo, *Diccionario Geografico, Estadistico, Historico de las Islas Filipinas* (Madrid, 1851).

28. Martinez de Zuñiga, *op. cit.*

29. *Census of the Philippine Islands, 1903,* Census Bureau (Washington, D.C., 1905).

30. Francisco V. Nazaret and Felisa R. Barretto, *Concepts and Definitions of Urban-Rural Areas in the Philippines,* (mimeographed, n.d.).

31. *Fisheries Statistics of the Philippines, 1962.*

Notes to Chapter 13

1. *The Philippines,* Human Relations Area Files (New Haven, 1955), I, 293; *Census of the Philippines, 1960: Population and Housing,* Bureau of Census and Statistics (Manila, 1963).

2. In the southern Philippines area the religious breakdown is: 59.9 percent Roman Catholic, 23.0 percent Moslem, 3.9 percent Protestant, 3.5 percent Aglipayan, and 0.5 percent Iglesia ni Cristo. See *Census of the Philippines, 1960: Population and Housing.*

3. *Multiple Purpose River Basin Development,* United Nations, Flood Control Series 8 Part 2A, *Water Resources Development in Ceylon, China, Taiwan, Japan and the Philippines* (Bangkok, 1955), p. 190.

4. This statement is not to imply that the majority of the present northern

Mindanao population has been migrant to the region. The Cebuano-speaking people have been migrating into this area for centuries. The percentages cited represent migrants and their descendants.

5. Francis J. Madigan, "The Early History of Cagayan de Oro," *Philippine Studies,* II (1963), 76–130.

6. *Census of the Philippines, 1960,* Vol. II: *Migration Statistics,* appendix.

7. *Multiple Purpose River Basin Development,* Part 2A, pp. 100, 109–110.

8. In 1959, Misamis Oriental produced a surplus of 16,000 metric tons of corn, and Lanao (the single undivided province) had a surplus of 25,000 metric tons. See Jose S. Gutierrez, "Corn Production and Consumption Requirements," *Philippine Agricultural Situation,* II (1960), 10–25.

9. Albert Kolb, "Die japanische Ackerbaukolonie in Davao, Philippinen," *Koloniale Rundschau,* 29 (1939), 209–218.

10. The National Economic Council considered that two-thirds of the 1,367,000 acres of arable land in Davao had been disposed of by 1957.

11. Gutierrez, *op. cit.*

12. Jose S. Gutierrez, "Rice Production and Consumption Requirements," *Philippine Agricultural Situation,* I (1960), 13–33.

13. *An Economic Analysis of Philippine Domestic Transportation,* Stanford Research Institute (Menlo Park, 1957), II, 206.

14. *Annual Survey of Manufactures, 1960,* Bureau of the Census and Statistics (Manila, 1963).

15. This figure is not completely accurate since many of the people listed beyond the normal population increase represent children born to new settlers *after* they migrated to the region.

16. Chester L. Hunt, *Cotabato: Melting Pot of the Philippines,* UNESCO National Commission of the Philippines (1954); and Hunt, *Ethnic Stratification and Integration in Cotabato,* paper presented at the University of Chicago Mindanao Conference, 1955.

17. Robert L. Pendleton, "Land Utilization and Agriculture of Mindanao, Philippine Islands," *Geographical Review,* 32 (1942), 210; and "Glimpses of Cotabato Province," *Philippine Agriculturist,* 23 (1935), 738–741.

18. *Census of the Philippines, 1903* (Washington, 1905), I, 573, quoting a commentary written in 1901.

19. The 1903 census of the Cotabato Commandancia included a region whose area was 11,786 square miles with a population of 128,000 persons. This area was about 30 percent larger than the area of the present province of Cotabato.

20. Pikit, Silik, Peidu Pulangi, Pagalungan, Glan, and Talitay. See Karl J. Pelzer, *Pioneer Settlement in the Asiatic Tropics,* American Geographical Society, Special Publication no. 29 (New York, 1948), p. 129.

21. Canute VanderMeer and Bernardo C. Agaloos, "Twentieth Century Settlement of Mindanao," *Papers of the Michigan Academy of Science, Arts and Letters,* 47 (1962), 548. It should be remembered that the road density of Cotabato Province in 1955 was only 3.58 kilometers of roads per 100 square

kilometers of area (see appendix table 28); only three Philippine provinces had sparser networks.

22. Hunt, *Ethnic Stratification and Integration in Cotabato*.

23. Between 1948 and 1960 the area devoted to rice in Cotabato Province increased from 244,000 acres to 595,000 acres, and that of corn from 95,000 acres to 346,000 acres. Proportional increases also occurred in the areas devoted to root crops, vgetables, and fruits.

24. Pendleton, *op. cit.*, pp. 180–210.

25. Earl M. Irving, "Physiographic Observations on Mindanao by Aerial Reconnaissance and Their Geological Interpretation," *Philippine Journal of Science*, 81 (1952), 141–169; T. S. M. Ranneft, R. M. Hopkins, A. J. Froelich, and J. W. Gwinn, "Reconnaissance Geology and Oil Possibilities of Mindanao," *Bulletin of the American Association of Petroleum Geologists*, 44 (1960), 529–568.

26. Irving, *op. cit.*, pp. 159, 167; Warren D. Smith, *Geology and Mineral Resources of the Philippines*, Department of Agriculture (1924), p. 210.

27. Sverre Petterssen, *Introduction to Meteorology* (New York: McGraw-Hill, 1958), p. 11.

28. *Raw Materials Resources Bulletin*, National Economic Council (1959), with additional corrections.

29. Mamitua Saber, "Some Observations on Maranao Social and Cultural Transitions," paper presented at the Second Annual Sociological Convention, Xavier University, Cagayan de Oro, 1963, 12 pp. (mimeographed).

30. One *ganta* is a unit of dry measure equivalent to three liters, or 25 *gantas* equal one *cavan*. Just as the American bushel varies in weight, so does the *cavan*.

31. *Proceedings of the Interdisciplinary Symposia of the 1961 National Science and Technology Week*, National Science Development Board (Manila, 1963), II: *Natural Resources*, 136, 146.

32. *Census of the Philippine Islands, 1918*, Census Office (Manila, 1920), I; *Geography, History, and Climatology*, 276.

33. John L. Phelan, *The Hispanization of the Philippines* (Madison: University of Wisconsin Press, 1959), p. 197 n. 6.

34. *Ibid.*, p. 137. Phelan speculates that if the principal Spanish base had remained in the Visayas, Mindanao might well have been conquered in the sixteenth century.

35. *Ibid.*, p. 197 n. 6.

36. *Proceedings of the Interdisciplinary Symposia*, II, 136, 146.

37. *Census of the Philippines, 1960*, Vol. II: *Migration Statistics*.

38. R. W. Van Bemmelen, *Geology of Indonesia* (The Hague: Government Printing Office, 1949), Vol. I, *passim*.

39. P. J. Wester, *Mindanao and the Sulu Archipelago*, Bureau of Agriculture, Bulletin no. 38 (2nd ed., revised; Manila: Bureau of Printing, 1928), pp. 99–106; N. M. Saleeby, *The History of Sulu*, Philippine Bureau of Science,

Division of Ethnology, Vol. IV, Part II (Manila: Bureau of Printing, 1909); reprinted for the Filipiniana Book Guild (Manila; Carmelo and Bauermann, 1963). Depending on how the number of islands is accounted, there are "about 400" in the Sulu group, but the normal accounting for 7,100 (7,108) islands of the Philippines includes 958 Sulu islands in the whole minor archipelago from Basilan to Buli Nusa, south of Tumindao.

40. Combining the linguistic returns for Zamboanga del Sur (to include the Basilan island group) and Sulu provinces, the mother-tongue figures become: Tausog, 296,130; Samal, 115,056; Badjao, 12,506. Both Tausog and Samal speakers are numerous in the Basilan island cluster, whereas Badjao peoples are chiefly southern-western in location within the Sulu Archipelago. For Sulu Province alone only 35,200 (10.8 percent) admitted ability to speak Tagalog in 1960; 52,000 (15.9 percent) claimed ability to speak English; only 1,407 (0.4 percent) admitted ability to speak Spanish. (*Census of the Philippines, 1960.*)

41. It is almost impossible to distinguish between various groups of Bornean and Sulu peoples on casual inspection. Powerful outboard motors enable persons intent on smuggling to outrun Customs craft, and island-hopping fishermen intent on their own pursuits can play hide-and-seek endlessly with the few official personnel who can be assigned preventive tasks.

42. The Spanish never successfully organized either a military or a civil government in the Sulu area. An American military government area was organized in 1903, and Sulu was established as a civil province in 1914. The Sultan of Sulu abdicated his secular power only in 1915, retaining his religious leadership. The Moslem Sultanate was abolished only in 1940, but self-styled "chieftains" (termed rebels, outlaws, and bandits outside Sulu) have repeatedly rallied portions of the populace to militant protests, and such protest continues in the 1960's.

Bibliography

Bibliographies

Huke, R. E. *Bibliography of Philippine Geography, 1940–1963: A Selected List.*
Geography Publications at Dartmouth, no. 1, 1964. Department of Geography.
Hanover: Dartmouth College, 1964. 84 pp. This is the most recent comprehen-
sive bibliography, and it includes a section on bibliographies.

Significant Philippine Journals and Recurrent Reports

Annual Survey of Manufactures. Vol. I. Manila: Bureau of Census and Statistics,
for the National Economic Council, 1958.

Central Bank of the Philippines. Annual Report. Manila: Central Bank of the
Philippines. Published annually since 1949.

Economic Indicators. Vol. I. Manila: Department of Economic Research, Central
Bank of the Philippines, 1949. Semiannual.

Journal of East Asiatic Studies. Manila: University of Manila. Quarterly since
1952.

Journal of Philippine Statistics. Manilia: Bureau of Census and Statistics.
Published quarterly. Postwar publication began in 1947.

Philippine Geographical Journal. Manila: Philippine Geographical Society.
Published quarterly since 1953, but somewhat irregular in appearance.

Philippine Journal of Agriculture. Manila: Bureau of Plant Industry, Department
of Agriculture and Natural Resources. Published quarterly under this title since
1930.

Philippine Journal of Forestry. Manila: Bureau of Forestry, Department of Agriculture and Natural Resources. Published quarterly since 1938.

Philippine Journal of Science. Manila: Institute of Science and Technology.
Published quarterly since 1906.

Philippine Journal of Soil Conservation. Manila: Bureau of Soil Conservation,
Department of Agriculture and Natural Resources. Published quarterly since
1953.

Philippine Social Sciences and Humanities Review. Quezon City: University of
the Philippines. Published quarterly under the present title since 1949.

Philippine Sociological Review. Quezon City: Philippine Sociological Society,
University of the Philippines. Published quarterly since 1953.

The American Chamber of Commerce Journal. Manila: American Chamber of Commerce of the Philippines. Published monthly since 1921.

The Philippine Geologist. Manila: Geological Society of the Philippines. Published quarterly since 1946.

The Philippines; A Handbook of Information. Manila: Philippine Information Agency, Office of the President of the Philippines. Supposedly Annual since 1960.

The Silliman Journal. Dumaguete, Negros Oriental: Silliman University. Published quarterly since 1954.

Census Reports

U.S. Bureau of the Census. *Census of the Philippine Islands, 1903*. Washington: Government Printing Office, 1905. 4 vols.

Census Office of the Philippine Islands. *Census of the Philippines, 1918*. Manila: Bureau of Printing, 1920–1921. 4 vols.

Commission of the Census, Philippine Commonwealth. *Census of the Philippines, 1939*. Manila: Bureau of Printing, 1940–1943. 5 vols.

Bureau of Census and Statistics. *1948 Census on the Philippines: Population Classified by Province, by City, Municipality, and Municipal District, and By Barrio*. Manila: Bureau of Printing, 1951. This is a preliminary summary volume on population.

Bureau of Census and Statistics. *Summary Report of the 1948 Census of Agriculture*. Manila: Bureau of Printing, 1952. This is a preliminary summary volume for agriculture.

Bureau of Census and Statistics. *Census of the Philippines, 1948*. Manila: Bureau of Printing, 1952–1956. 4 vols. in 7 parts.

Bureau of Census and Statistics. *Special Bulletin no. 1: Population of the Philippines by Province and Municipality, February 15, 1960*. Manila: Bureau of Census and Statistics, 1960. This is a preliminary summary report of population only.

Bureau of Census and Statistics. *Census of the Philippines, 1960*. Manila: Bureau of Census and Statistics. Vol. 1: Report by Province, Population and Housing, issued in 1962–1963. Vol. 2: Summary Report, Population and Housing, issued in 1963. Vol. 2: Appendix, Migration Statistics, issued in 1963. Economic Census of the Philippines, 8 vols.; Vol. 1: Report by Province, Agriculture, issued in 1965.

Books, Reports, and Significant Articles

Agpalo, R. E. *The Political Process and the Nationalization of Retail Trade in the Philippines*. Quezon City: University of the Philippines, 1962.

Barrera, A. *Handbook of Soil Surveys for the Philippines.* Manila: Department of Agriculture and Natural Resources, Bureau of Soils, 1961.

————. "Classification and Utilization of Some Philippine Soils," *Journal of Tropical Geography,* 18 (1964) 17–29.

Barton, R. F. *The Kalingas, Their Institutions and Custom Law.* Chicago: University of Chicago Press, 1949.

Bemmelen, R. W. Van. *The Geology of Indonesia.* The Hague: Government Printing Office, 1949. 2 vols.

Benitez, Conrado. *History of the Philippines: Economic, Social, Political.* Boston: Ginn and Co., 1940.

Blair, E. H., and J. A. Robertson. *The Philippines, 1493–1898.* Cleveland: Arthur H. Clark Co., 1903–1909. 55 vols.

Bureau of Mines. *Philippines Department of Agriculture and Natural Resources. Mineral Resources of the Philippines.* Information Circular no. 19. Manila: Bureau of Mines, 1955.

Carroll, J. J. *The Filipino Manufacturing Entrepreneur: Agent and Product of Change.* Ithaca: Cornell University Press, 1965.

Castro, A. A., *et al. An Economic Survey of the Limay, Bataan, Area.* Quezon City: Institute of Economic Development and Research, University of the Philippines, 1960.

Collier, R. W. *Barrio Gacao, A Study of Village Ecology and the Schistosomiasis Problem.* Quezon City: Community Development Research Council, University of the Philippines, 1960.

Conklin, Harold C. *Hanunóo Agriculture in the Philippines.* Rome: FAO, United Nations, 1957.

Corby, G. C., *et al. Geology and Oil Possibilities of the Philippines.* Technical Survey no. 21. Manila: Bureau of Mines, 1951.

Cutshall, A. *The Philippines: Nation of Islands.* Princeton: D. Van Nostrand Co., 1964. Original Searchlight paperback.

Dalisay, A. M. *Development of Economic Policy in Philippine Agriculture.* Manila: Phoenix Publishing House, 1959.

Dawson, O. L. "Philippine Agriculture, a Problem of Adjustment," *Foreign Agriculture,* 4 (1940), 383–456.

Depperman, C. E. *Some Characteristics of Philippine Typhoons.* Manila: Weather Bureau, 1939.

Diaz, R. C., *et al. Case Studies of Farm Families, Laguna Province, Philippines.* Los Baños, Philippines: University of the Philippines, 1962.

Diettrich, S. deR., *The Philippine Islands.* New York: Doubleday, 1961.

Durkee, E. F., and S. L. Pederson. "Geology of Northern Luzon," *Bulletin of the American Association of Petroleum Geologists,* 45 (1961), 137–68.

ECAFE. *Multiple Purpose River Basin Development.* Part 2A: *Water Resource Development in Ceylon, China (Taiwan), Japan, and the Philippines.* Bangkok: ECAFE, for United Nations, 1955.

Foreman, J. *The Philippine Islands: A Political, Geographical, Ethnological, Social, and Commercial History of the Philippines.* 2d ed. New York: Scribner, 1906.

Friend, T. *Between Two Empires: The Ordeal of the Philippines, 1929–1946.* New Haven: Yale University Press, 1965.

Garcia, N. V. *A Study of the Socio-Economic Adjustments of Two Ilocano Villages to Virginia Tobacco Production.* Quezon City: Community Development Research Council, University of the Philippines, 1962.

Golay, F. H. *The Philippines: Public Policy and National Economic Development.* Ithaca: Cornell University Press, 1961.

Gooch, W. L. *Forest Industries of the Philippines.* Manila: Bureau of Forestry, and Philippine Council for United States Aid, 1953.

Goodstein, M.E. *The Pace and Pattern of Philippine Economic Growth: 1938, 1948, and 1956.* Cornell University. Southeast Asia Program. Data Paper no. 48. Ithaca: Cornell University Press, 1962.

Haas, W. R. *The American Empire.* Chicago: University of Chicago Press, 1940.

Hainsworth, R. G., and R. T. Moyer. *Agricultural Geography of the Philippine Islands: A Graphic Summary.* Washington, D.C.: U.S. Department of Agriculture, 1945. This summarizes the generally unavailable 1939 census for agriculture.

Hart, D. V. *The Philippine Plaza Complex: A Focal Point in Culture Change.* Yale Southeast Asia Studies. New Haven: Yale University Press, 1955.

Hartendorp, A. V. H. *History of Industry and Trade in the Philippines.* Manila: American Chamber of Commerce of the Philippines, 1958.

———. *History of Industry and Trade of the Philippines: The Magsaysay Administration.* Manila: Philippine Education Company, 1961.

———. "The Proposed Land Reform Act," *The American Chamber of Commerce Journal,* 39 (1963), 164–184.

Hayden, J. R. *The Philippines: A Study in National Development.* New York: Macmillan Company, 1942.

Hollnsteiner, M. R. *The Dynamics of Power in a Philippine Municipality.* Quezon City: Community Development Research Council, University of the Philippines, 1963.

Houston, C. O., Jr. "Rice in the Philippines Economy, 1934–1950," *Journal of East Asiatic Studies,* 3 (1953), 13–85.

———. "The Philippine Coconut Industry, 1934–1950," *Philippine Geographical Journal,* 1 (1953), 61–90.

Huke, R. E., et al. *Shadows on the Land: An Economic Geography of the Philippines.* Manila: Bookmark, 1963.

Hunt, C. L. "Moslem and Christian in the Philippines," *Pacific Affairs,* 28 (1955), 331–349.

Hunt, C. L., et al. *Sociology in the Philippine Setting.* 2d ed. Quezon City: Phoenix Publishing House, 1963.

Irving, E. M. "Review of Philippine Basement Geology and its Problems," *Philippine Journal of Science,* 79 (1950), 267–308.

———. "Submarine Morphology of the Philippine Archipelago and its Geological Significance," *Philippine Journal of Science,* 80 (1951), 55–87.

———. "Physiographic Observations on Mindanao by Aerial Reconnaissance, and the Geological Interpretation," *Philippine Journal of Science,* 81 (1952), 141–169.

Jenkins, S. *American Economic Policy toward the Philippines.* Stanford: Stanford University Press, 1954.

Keesing, Felix M. *The Ethnohistory of Northern Luzon.* Stanford: Stanford University Press, 1962.

King, P. B., and E. M. McKee. "Terrain Diagrams of the Philippines," *Bulletin of the Geological Society of America,* 60 (1949), 1829–1836.

Kinkel, A. R., Jr., *et al. Copper Deposits of the Philippines.* Special Projects Publication no. 16. Manila: Bureau of Mines, Department of Agriculture and Natural Resources, 1956.

Kolb, A. *Die Philippinen.* Leipzig: Koehler, 1942.

Krieger, H. W. *Peoples of the Philippines.* Publication 3694. Washington, D.C.: Smithsonian Institute, 1942.

Kroeber, A. L. *Peoples of the Philippines.* New York: American Museum of Natural History, 1919; rev. ed. 1928, reprinted 1943.

Lande, C. H. *Leaders, Factions, and Parties; The Structure of Philippine Politics.* Yale Southeast Asia Studies. New Haven: Yale University Press, 1965.

Lynch, F. *Social Class in a Bicol Town.* University of Chicago. Philippine Studies Program. Chicago: University of Chicago Press, 1959.

Malcolm, G. A. *The First Malayan Republic.* Boston: Christopher Publishing House, 1951.

Manalo, E. B. "The Distribution of Rainfall in the Philippines," *Philippine Geographical Journal,* 4 (1956), 104–67.

O'Neill, J. F., *et al. A Report on Nonmetallic Minerals.* Manila: Bureau of Mines, Department of Agriculture and Natural Resources, 1957.

Ortigas, F., Jr. *Planting Rice is Never Fun.* Manila: Alemars, 1953.

Pacis, V. A. *Philippine Government and Politics.* rev. ed. Quezon City: Bustament Press, 1963.

Pelzer, Karl J. *Pioneer Settlement in the Asiatic Tropics.* Special Publication no. 29. New York: American Geographical Society, 1948.

Pendleton, R. L. "Land Utilization and Agriculture of Mindanao, Philippine Islands," *Geographical Review,* 32 (1942), 180–210.

Phelan, J. L. *The Hispanization of the Philippines: Spanish Aims and Filipino Responses, 1565–1700.* Madison: University of Wisconsin Press, 1959.

Philippine Studies Program. University of Chicago. *Area Handbook of the Philippines.* New Haven: Human Relations Area Files, 1956. 4 vols.

Philippines. National Economic Council. Water Resources Planning and Development Committee. *Water Resources of Central Luzon*. Manila: National Economic Council, 1961.

Pittman, R. S., *et al*. *Notes on the Dialect Geography of the Philippines*. University of North Dakota. Summer Institute of Linguistics. Grand Forks, North Dakota: University of North Dakota, 1953.

Polson, R. A., and A. P. Pal. *The Status of Rural Life in the Dumaguete City Trade Area, Philippines, 1952*. Cornell University. Southeast Asia Program. Data Paper no. 21. Ithaca: Cornell University Press, 1956.

Rabor, D. S. "Zoogeography of Negros Island and the Visayan Province, or Central Philippines," *Philippine Geographic Journal*, 7 (1963), 179–191.

Ramos, C. P. "Manila's Metropolitan Problem," *Philippine Journal of Public Administration*, 5 (1961), 89–117.

Ranneft, T. S. M., *et al*. "Reconnaissance Geology and Oil Possibilities of Mindanao," *Bulletin of the American Association of Petroleum Geologists*, 44 (1960), 529–568.

Ravenholt, A. *The Philippines, A Young Republic on the Move*. Princeton: D. Van Nostrand Co., 1962.

Rivera, G., and R. T. McMillan. *The Rural Philippines*. Manila: Philippine Council for United States Aid, 1952.

———. *An Economic and Social Survey of Rural Households in Central Luzon*. Manila: Philippine Council for United States Aid, 1954.

Robinson, B. B., and F. L. Johnson. *Abaca, A Cordage Fiber*. Agricultural Monograph no. 21. Washington, D.C.: U.S. Department of Agriculture, 1953.

Schurz, W. L. *The Manila Galleon*. New York: Dutton, 1939.

Sicat, G. P., *et al*. *The Philippine Economy in the 1960's*. Quezon City: Institute of Economic Development and Research, University of the Philippines, 1964.

Smith, R. A. *Philippine Freedom, 1946–1958*. New York: Columbia University Press, 1958.

Spencer, J. E. *Land and People in the Philippines: Geographic Problems in Rural Economy*. Berkeley and Los Angeles: University of California Press, 1952.

———. "The Abaca Plant and its Fiber, Manila Hemp," *Economic Botany*, 7 (1953), 195–213.

Stanford Research Institute. *An Economic Analysis of Philippine Domestic Transportation*. Menlo Park, Calif.: Stanford Research Institute, 1957. 7 vols.

Starner, F. L. *Magsaysay and the Philippine Peasantry*. Berkeley and Los Angeles: University of California Press, 1961.

Steiner, M. L. *Philippine Ornamental Plants and Their Care*. 2d ed. Manila: Carmelo and Bauermann, 1960.

Taeuber, I. "The Bases of a Population Problem," *Population Index*, 26 (1960), 97–115.

Tamesis, Florencia and Luis Aguilar. *Important Commercial Timbers of the Philippines, Their Properties and Uses*. Popular Bulletin no. 32, Manila: Department of Agriculture and Natural Resources, 1953.

Tantuico, F. S., Jr. *Leyte, The Historic Islands.* Tacloban City: Leyte Publishing Corporation, 1964.

Taylor, G. E. *The Philippines and the U.S.: Problems of Partnership.* New York: Frederick A. Praeger, 1964.

Thorp, T. E. *High Velocity Winds in the Philippines.* Bloomington: Research Division, Indiana University Foundation.

Tiglao, T. V. *A Reevaluation of Health Practices in a Philippine Rural Community.* Quezon City: Community Development Research Council, University of the Philippines, 1964.

Ullman, E. L. "Trade Centers and Tributary Areas of the Philippines," *Geographical Review,* 50 (1960), 203–218.

Unesco. *Population Growth and Manpower in the Philippines.* Unesco Population Studies no. 32. New York: United Nations, 1960.

U.S. Department of Agriculture. Economic Research Service. *The Philippines: Long-Term Projection of Supply of and Demand for Selected Agricultural Products.* ERS-Foreign-34 (contract S-621-fa-984(AGRIC). Jerusalem: Israel Program for Scientific Translations, 1962.

Varona, A. P., and J. V. Castillo. "Consumption of Basic Food Items in the Philippines," *Philippine Geographical Journal,* 2 (1958), 67–74.

Vaughan, J. B. *The Land and People of the Philippines.* Philadelphia: Lippincott, 1956.

Villanueva, P. S. *Some Socio-Economic Effects of Rural Roads.* Quezon City: Community Development Research Council, University of the Philippines, 1959.

Warren, C. P. *The Batak of Palawan: A Culture in Transition.* University of Chicago. Philippine Studies Program. Chicago: University of Chicago Press, 1961.

Wernstedt, F. L. *The Role and Importance of Philippine Shipping and Trade.* Cornell University. Southeast Asia Program. Data Paper no. 26. Ithaca: Cornell University, 1957.

――――, and P. D. Simkins. "Migrations and the Settlement of Mindanao," *Journal of Asian Studies,* 25 (1965), 83–103.

Wickberg, E. *"The Chinese in Philippine Life, 1850–1898.* New Haven: Yale University Press, 1965.

Worcester, D.C. *The Philippines, Past and Present.* New York: Macmillan, 1914; 2d ed. (1930) contains biographical sketch of Worcester by Ralston Hayden.

Zaide, G. F. *Philippine Political and Cultural History.* Manila: Philippine Education Company, 1957.

Indexes

(Entries in italic are physical features)

A. Bonifacio Street (Manila), 388
Aborlan (Palawan), 339, 340, 341
Abra de Ilog (Occidental Mindoro), 434
Abra Province, 81, 328, 332, 333, 339, 341, 350, 352
Abra River, 18, 236, 311, 328, 330, 332, 333, 338, 340, 341, 344, 352
Abucay (Bataan), 367
Abulug River, 321, 344
Abuyog (Leyte), 459, 462
Adgoan River, 525, 539
Aduana Calle (Manila), 388
Aggunetan (Cagayan), 46, 55
Agno River, 18, 20, 311, 344, 371
Agoo (La Union), 341
Aguang River, 425
Agusan Lowland, 33, 77, 108, 301, 524–528, 537–542
Agusan Province, 33, 81, 208, 237, 242, 244, 303, 304, 461, 506, 513, 517, 523–526, 528, 538–541, 558
Agusan River, 12, 33, 34, 76, 104, 236, 266, 525, 527, 528, 537–541
Agus River, 35, 82, 514, 531, 560, 569
Agutaya Island, 440
Aklan Province, 490, 495, 501

Alabat Island, 148, 424
Alaminos (Pangasinan), 367, 368
Albay Gulf, 22, 410, 411, 412
Albay Province, 222, 409–418, 510
Alip Range, 546
Alip River, 36
Alip Valley, 545, 547
Allah (Cotabato), 548, 550
Allah River, 36, 546
Allah Valley, 35, 36, 471, 545–548, 550, 552, 554, 555, 556
Allen (Samar), 463
Almagro Island, 455
Aloneros (Quezon), 421
Aloran (Misamis Occidental), 512
Alubijid (Misamis Oriental), 515
Alutaya (Palawan), 439
Ambil Island, 23, 430
Ambuklao-Binga Project, 348
Ambuklao River, 348, 359
Amburayan River, 335, 344
Anda (Pangasinan), 367–368
Anda Peninsula, 27, 477
Angat River, 20, 371
Angeles (Pampanga), 381
Antipolo (Rizal), 407–408

Antique Province, 485, 490, 495–496, 499, 501
Apalit (Pampanga), 379
Aparri (Cagayan), 18, 40, 45, 61, 308, 310, 316, 318, 319, 320, 321, 324–326
Apayao District, 344–345, 360
Araceli (Palawan), 440, 442
Argao (Cebu), 255, 264, 477, 480
Aringay (La Union), 337
Aritao (Nueva Vizcaya), 318
Aroroy (Masbate), 449, 451–452, 454
Asia Bay, 499
Asid Gulf, 31, 449, 452, 454
Asid River, 31
Astorga (Davao), 529
Asuncion (Davao), 537
Atimonan (Quezon), 425–426
Aurora (Quezon), 425
Aurora (Zamboanga del Sur), 511, 581
Aviles Boulevard (Manila), 387
Azagra (Romblon), 454

Babuyan Channel, 16, 18, 308, 310, 314, 319, 344
Babuyan Group, 16, 201, 304, 307–311
Babuyan Island, 16, 308–309
Bacarra River, 335
Bacnotan (La Union), 255, 264, 339, 341
Bacolod (Negros Occidental), 172–173, 233, 235, 267, 269, 445, 496–497, 499–500
Bacuag (Surigao Del Norte), 519, 523
Bacuit (Palawan), 231
Bacuit Channel, 442
Bagabag (Nueva Vizcaya), 320
Bagacay (Samar), 252, 459
Baganga (Davao), 519, 523, 534
Baganian Peninsula, 36, 569, 571, 573, 575, 578, 579
Bago (Davao), 529
Bago (Ilocos Norte), 340
Bago River, 30
Baguio (Mountain Province), 41, 50, 170, 203, 252–253, 269, 312, 339, 345, 346, 348, 351, 358–359, 360–361
Bais (Negros Oriental), 29, 474, 478, 480, 484, 499
Balabac Group, 436
Balabac Island, 11, 22, 24, 78, 143, 436, 438, 439, 440
Balabac Strait, 436
Balanacan (Marinduque), 454
Balanga (Bataan), 368
Balayan (Batangas), 395
Balayan Bay, 395

Baler (Quezon), 425, 426
Baler Bay, 19, 381, 423, 425
Balete (Occidental Mindoro), 432
Baliangao (Misamis Occidental), 512
Balindong (Lanao del Sur), 565
Balingasag (Misamis Oriental), 515
Balintang Channel, 16, 308
Ballesteros (Cagayan), 327
Baloi (Lanao del Norte), 563, 565
Balud (Masbate), 235, 452–453
Balut Island, 535
Bamban (Tarlac), 381
Banago (Negros Occidental), 499
Banate (Iloilo), 496
Banaue (Mountain Province), 83, 347, 350, 354
Bangar (La Union), 341
Banga River, 546
Bangued (Abra), 339, 341
Bansalan (Davao), 532–533, 536
Bansud (Oriental Mindoro), 433
Bantay (Ilocos Sur), 341
Bantayan (Cebu), 484
Bantayan Island, 233, 480, 484
Banton Island, 449
Bao River, 457
Baras (Catanduanes), 46, 412
Barbacan (Palawan), 439
Barbacan River, 24, 439
Barili (Cebu), 469
Barotac Viejo (Iloilo), 496
Basco (Batanes), 40, 42, 308–309, 311
Basey (Samar), 462, 467
Bashi Channel, 16, 308
Basilan Group, 586
Basilan Island, 37, 88, 171, 210, 247, 570, 572, 574–575, 577–579, 581–582, 584–586, 590
Basilan Peak, 37, 572
Basilan Strait, 577
Basud (Camarines Norte), 420
Basud River, 412
Bataan Peninsula, 362, 364–365, 367, 383
Bataan Province, 75, 236, 246, 362, 364–368
Bataan-Zambales Area, 313
Batanes Province, 81, 141, 142, 308–309, 311
Batangas (Batangas), 397–399, 402, 405–407, 409, 433
Batangas Bay, 397
Batangas Peninsula, 190, 199, 205–206, 398
Batangas Province, 11, 64, 74, 81, 167, 193, 205, 213, 217, 236, 248, 393, 395, 398–400, 402–409, 425, 428, 433

Batan Group, 306–311
Batan Island (Northern Luzon), 16, 306–311
Batan Island (Southern Luzon), 22, 410
Bauen (Batangas), 405
Bay (Laguna), 399
Bayag (Mountain Province), 350
Bayang (Lanao del Sur), 565
Bayawan (Negros Oriental), 476, 499
Baybay (Leyte), 459, 462–463, 467
Bayombong (Nueva Vizcaya), 264, 319, 324, 326–327
Benguet District, 241, 316, 330, 360, 371
Bicol Lowland, 22, 312, 320–321, 411–412, 414–418
Bicol Peninsula, 13, 17, 21–22, 167, 195, 205, 222, 303, 313, 406, 409–412, 414–421
Bicol River, 12, 22, 311, 412, 414–416
Bilanbilan (Surigao Del Norte), 523
Bilatan Island, 37
Biliran Island, 26, 455, 457
Binalbagan (Negros Occidental), 498, 501
Binalbagan River, 30
Biñan (Laguna), 405–406, 408
Binangonan (Rizal), 396, 405, 408
Binondo (Manila), 384, 386–387
Bislig (Surigao del Sur), 519, 522
Bislig Bay, 33, 517–518, 523–524
Boac (Marinduque), 433, 452, 454
Boac River, 25, 452
Bobon (Samar), 467
Bogo (Cebu), 474, 484–485
Bohol Island, 11, 25, 27–28, 61, 70–71, 131, 142, 146–148, 195, 201, 205, 208, 237, 246, 254, 293, 444–446, 462, 468–485, 504, 510, 531, 540, 563, 566, 574, 575
Bohol Province, 81, 483
Bolinao (Pangasinan), 368
Bondoc Peninsula, 12, 19, 22, 31, 421, 423–426, 448
Bongabong (Occidental Mindoro), 433
Bongao (Sulu), 231
Bongao Island, 585, 595
Bongcanaway (Masbate), 453
Bonifacio (Misamis Occidental), 512
Bontoc (Mountain Province), 241, 320, 339, 350
Bontoc District, 353, 360–361
Borneo Island, 9, 11, 23, 24, 37, 106, 428, 431, 435–436, 439, 445, 539, 582, 588–590, 597
Borongan (Samar), 458–459, 463
Botolan (Zambales), 366

Brookes Point (Palawan), 24, 438, 440–441
Buayan River, 545–546
Buayan Valley, 546–547
Buaya River, 335
Bucas Grande Island, 33, 518
Buenavista (Agusan), 542
Bugo (Misamis Oriental), 513, 565, 567
Bugsanga River, 433
Bugsuk Island, 24, 71, 436, 439–440
Bukidnon-Lanao Plateau, 32, 34–35, 302, 506–507, 524, 557–569
Bukidnon Province, 35, 74, 102, 104, 147–148, 191, 210, 303, 511–513, 515, 545, 555, 558, 559–562, 566–568
Bulacacao (Oriental Mindoro), 431
Bulacan Province, 149, 235, 247, 250, 253, 369, 372, 377–379, 381
Bulan (Sorsogon), 415–416, 421
Buluan River, 545
Bunawan (Agusan), 538, 540, 542
Bunawan (Davao), 537
Burias Island, 12, 19, 409, 444, 447, 449–451
Burias Strait, 445
Busuanga (Palawan), 437, 439, 441
Busuanga Island, 24, 254, 436
Butig (Lanao Del Sur), 566
Butuan (Agusan), 250, 280, 515, 523, 535, 537, 539, 541–542
Butuan Bay, 33, 34, 518, 524–526, 537, 541

Cabadbaran (Agusan), 541–542
Cabalian (Southern Leyte), 463
Caballo Island, 384
Cabanatuan (Nueva Ecija), 378, 380–381, 426
Cabra Island, 23
Cabugao Bay, 410
Cabusao (Camarines Sur), 420
Cadiz (Negros Occidental), 235, 496, 501
Cagayancillo Island, 440
Cagayan de Oro (Misamis Oriental), 261, 482, 503, 510, 512–515, 517, 563, 565, 567, 580
Cagayan Province, 308, 314, 318, 321, 325, 326, 327, 335, 353, 423
Cagayan River (Luzon), 17–18, 88, 236, 311, 314, 316, 319–320, 325–327
Cagayan River (Mindanao), 507, 512, 560
Cagayan Sulu Group, 586
Cagayan Sulu Island, 581, 585

Cagayan Valley, 13, 17–19, 20, 42, 46, 55, 57, 61, 70, 102, 149, 167, 195, 199, 206, 224–225, 240, 293–294, 301–303, 312–313, 314–328, 332, 335, 336, 339, 342, 344, 353, 354, 357, 359, 373, 378, 381

Cagraray Island, 410

Cainta (Rizal), 407

Calabanga (Camarines Sur), 420

Calamba (Laguna), 402, 405–406, 408

Calambayangan Island, 419

Calamianes Group, 10, 22–24, 76, 428, 430, 436, 437, 438, 439, 440, 441, 443

Calapan (Oriental Mindoro), 432–433

Calape (Bohol), 484

Calasiao (Pangasinan), 379

Calatrava (Negros Occidental), 468, 484, 488

Calatrava (Romblon), 454

Calauag (Quezon), 425–426

Calauag Bay, 410

Calayan (Cagayan), 311

Calayan Island, 16, 143, 308–309, 311

Calbayog (Samar), 457, 462–463, 466–467

Calicoan Island, 26–27

Calinan (Davao), 537

Caliraya Project, 396

Caloocan (Rizal), 142, 168, 276, 389–391

Calumpang (Masbate), 453

Calumpan Peninsula, 395, 402

Camalaniugan (Cagayan), 318, 320, 324, 326–327

Camalig (Albay), 412

Camarines Norte Province, 88, 409–410, 413–414, 416–421

Camarines Peninsula, 12, 22, 400, 410, 412, 420–421, 424

Camarines Sur Province, 164, 222, 409, 414–421

Camiguin Island (Mindanao Sea), 35, 506–507, 509, 511–512, 515

Camiguin Island (North Luzon), 16, 143, 308

Caminawit Point, 434

Camotes Group, 28, 468, 480

Camotes Sea, 27

Camp Keithley (Lanao del Sur), 563–564

Campomanes Bay, 499

Candaba Swamp, 20, 104–105, 371, 526

Candon (Ilocos Sur), 341

Canlubang (Laguna), 402, 404, 408

Cantilan (Surigao del Sur), 519, 522

Caoayan (Ilocos Sur), 341

Cape Bojeador, 311, 327

Cape Bolinao, 362

Cape Engaño, 314, 320, 421, 423

Cape San Agustin, 32, 528, 535

Capiz (Capiz), 445

Capiz Province, 90, 236, 490, 495–496, **500**

Capul Island, 26

Caraballo Mountains, 12, 17–18, 264, 318–319, 342, 351, 371, 377

Carabao Island, 449

Caraga (Davao), 503, 519, 529, 539

Caramay River, 24

Caramoan Peninsula, 22, 410, 412–413, 420

Carcar (Cebu), 484–485

Carigara (Leyte), 400, 468

Carigara Bay, 457, 466

Carmen (Agusan), 542

Carmen (Bohol), 27, 468, 479

Carmen (Cebu), 469

Carmen (Cotabato), 550, 557

Carmen (Misamis Oriental), 513

Carmen (Pampanga), 378

Carmen Basin, 545, 547–548, 554

Carrascal (Surigao del Sur), 523

Casiguran (Quezon), 425

Casiguran Bay, 423, 425

Catabangan Bay, 410

Cataingan (Masbate), 31, 452, 454

Catanauan (Quezon), 425, 427

Catanduanes Island, 11–12, 22, 46, 148, 154, 222, 246, 409–420

Catanduanes Province, 409, 412

Catarman (Samar), 462–463, 467

Catarman River, 457, 461, 463

Catbalogan (Samar), 235–236, 452, 460, 462, 466–467

Catbalogan River, 467

Cateel (Davao), 523

Cateel Bay, 517–518

Cateel River, 33

Catisan Point, 462

Catisan River, 545

Catubig River, 26, 457, 461, 463, 467

Cauayan (Isabela), 327

Cavite (Cavite), 69, 270, 399, 403–408

Cavite Province, 41, 74, 81, 149, 154, 393, 395, 397–400, 402–408

Cebu (Cebu), 29, 55, 57–58, 171–172, 263, 269–270, 276, 280, 283–284, 289–290, 292–293, 382, 445–446, 451–454, 462, 465, 467, 469–471, 474, 476, 478–480, 482–483, 506, 513–514, 517, 537, 541, 579–580, 582–583

Cebu Island, 11, 25, 27–29, 41, 55, 70–72, 74, 78–82, 131, 133, 139,

142, 146–148, 154, 166–171, 184,
205, 208–209, 214, 217, 220, 233,
246, 250–252, 255, 259, 261, 264,
267, 292–293, 296, 303, 444–447,
450, 460, 462–463, 466, 468–485,
504, 508, 510, 516–517, 531–532,
540, 563, 566–568, 575

Cebu Province, 141, 236, 483–484, 548

Celebes Island, 11, 32–33, 588–589

Celebes Sea, 9, 32–33, 36, 546, 571,
582, 586, 588, 595

Central Cordillera (Leyte), 12, 19, 26,
301, 377, 457, 459

Central Mindanao Highlands, 32–34,
524–526, 546, 548, 551, 557–558,
560, 571

Central Plain, 13, 17, 20–21, 40, 42,
55, 57, 61, 133, 139, 142, 146–149,
154, 164, 167, 190, 192, 195, 216–
217, 263–264, 266, 293–294, 301,
303, 312–314, 317, 319, 326, 335,
339, 342, 351, 359, 362, 364, 368–
380, 382–383, 387, 393, 398, 400,
421, 423–424, 426, 485, 526

Central Range, 18, 342, 351, 353

Chico Pampanga River, 371

Chico River (Cagayan Valley), 17–18,
320, 327, 344, 353

Chico River (Ilocos Coast), 18, 316,
335

Clarin (Misamis Occidental), 509, 512,
516

Clark Airforce Base (Pampanga), 378,
381

Claver (Surigao del Norte), 523

Claveria (Cagayan), 318, 324, 326–327

Claveria (Misamis Oriental), 512

Cleopatra Needle, 24, 436

Columbio (Cotabato), 550

Compostela (Davao), 528, 531, 535

Compostela Basin, 525, 528, 537

Conical Peak, 449

Cordillera Central, 11, 17–18, 61, 240,
246, 248, 314, 316, 328, 330, 339,
342

Coron (Palawan), 441

Coron Bay, 442

Coron Island, 24, 440

Corregidor Island, 384

Cotabato (Cotabato), 269, 515, 535,
554–556, 565

Cotabato Cordillera, 542, 546, 571

Cotabato Hills, 545

Cotabato Peninsula, 32

Cotabato Province, 71, 74, 104, 141,
205, 208–210, 237, 303–304, 445,
461, 471–472, 511, 516, 524, 528,

533–535, 542–557, 565, 567–568,
574, 577

Cotabato River, 34–36, 76, 104–105,
236, 506, 524, 545, 547, 549, 551,
553–554, 556–557

Cotabato Valley, 12, 32, 35–36, 55, 77,
108, 301, 495, 515, 542–557

Crocker Range, 436

Cuernos de Negros, 29, 483

Cugmen River, 507

Culion Island, 24, 436, 439–441

Culion Reservation, 439–440

Cuyo (Palawan), 439, 441

Cuyo Channel, 442

Cuyo Group, 24, 25, 436, 439–440

Cuyo Island, 11, 22, 24, 440

Daanbantayan Island, 28–29, 475

Daet (Camarines Norte), 412–413, 415–
416, 420–421

Daguma (Cotabato), 550

Daguma Range, 545–547

Dagupan (Pangasinan), 378, 381

Dagupan River, 381

Daijagon Island, 29

Dalapuan River, 36

Daliao (Davao), 529

Dalton Pass, 319, 381

Dalupiri Island (North Luzon), 308

Dalupiri Island (Samar Sea), 26

Damortis (La Union), 339

Danao (Cebu), 255, 264, 477, 480

Dapitan (Zamboanga del Norte), 503,
515, 572, 574–575, 578

Dapitan Bay, 578

Dapitan River, 575

Daraga (Albay), 415

Darvel Bay, 37

Dasol (Pangasinan), 367–368

Datu Piang (Cotabato), 550–552, 554–
555, 557

Davao (Davao), 34, 172, 261, 263,
267, 269, 276, 289, 293, 512, 514,
523, 525–526, 528–530, 532–537, 554,
557, 580

Davao-Agusan Trough 32–33, 505, 517,
523–542

Davao Gulf Area, 32–34, 76, 199,
221–222, 266, 471, 524–537, 540,
549

Davao Penal Colony (Davao), 245

Davao Province, 32–34, 208, 210, 461,
472, 511, 516–517, 519, 525–537,
555, 565

Davao River, 526, 536

Del Gallego (Camarines Sur), 420

Del Monte (Bukidnon), 560, 566

Del Pilar (Palawan), 442

Dequey Island, 16, 308
Digos (Davao), 526, 528–529, 536
Digos River, 531–532, 536
Dimasalang (Masbate), 31, 452–54
Dimataling (Zamboanga del Sur), 578, 580
Dinagat Island, 12, 27, 32, 33, 253, 518, 522
Dinalupihan (Bataan), 368
Dingalan (Quezon), 423, 426
Dingalan Bay, 12, 19, 381, 423, 425
Diogo Island, 16, 308
Dipolog (Zamboanga del Norte), 515, 571, 574–575, 578, 580–581
Dipolog River, 575
Diuata Mountains, 33, 505, 524
Diuata Point, 34
Dolores (Samar), 459
Dolores River, 457
Dulag (Leyte), 467
Dulawan (Cotabato). *See* Datu Piang
Dumaguete (Negros Oriental), 28, 58, 61, 261, 445, 471, 473–474, 476, 479–480, 482–483
Dumanlinao (Zamboanga del Sur), 578
Dumanquilas Bay, 571, 575, 580
Dumaran (Palawan), 439
Dumaran Channel, 432
Dumaran Island, 143, 436
Dumingag (Zamboanga del Sur), 571, 573, 578, 581

Eastern Cordillera (Luzon), 12, 17, 19–22, 26, 31, 301, 314, 369, 371, 382, 394, 396, 421, 423, 426
Eastern Cordillera (Mindanao), 26, 32
Echague (Isabela), 326–327
Enrile (Cagayan), 320, 325
Epifanio de los Santos (Manila), 391
Ermita (Manila), 387, 392
Escalante (Negros Occidental), 497, 501
Escolta Avenue (Manila), 386–387
España (Manila), 387
Esperanza (Agusan), 538–539, 542
Estancia (Iloilo), 235, 496, 501

Fabrica (Negros Occidental), 498, 500–501
Floridablanca (Pampanga), 381
Fort Pilar (Zamboanga), 574
Fort San Pedro (Cebu), 483
Fuga Island, 16, 308

Gaang Bay, 339
Gallego (Cotabato), 554
Gandara River, 26, 457, 461
Gasan (Romblon), 454

Gattaran (Cagayan), 312
General Santos (Cotabato), 55, 547, 554–555
Genio (Cotabato), 554
Gibong River, 542
Gigaquit (Surigao del Norte), 522
Gingoog (Misamis Oriental), 512, 516
Gingoog Bay, 507, 509, 515
Golo Island, 23
Gonzaga (Cagayan), 326–327
Governor Generoso (Davao), 534
Green Island Bay, 71, 442
Guagua (Pampanga), 377, 381
Guagua River, 378
Guihulngan (Negros Oriental), 471, 484
Guimaras Island, 30, 172, 255, 486, 488, 496
Guimaras Strait, 30, 31, 233, 486, 488, 491, 497, 499
Guinayangan (Masbate), 453
Guinayangan (Quezon), 425
Guindulman (Bohol), 477, 484
Guinsorongan (Samar), 466
Guiuan (Samar), 462–463, 467
Guiuan Lowlands, 26
Guiuan Peninsula, 461
Gumaca (Quezon), 425–426

Hagonoy (Bulacan), 372, 381
Hagonoy (Davao), 533, 535
Hagonoy Isthmus, 21
Hagonoy River, 378
Hawaii, 52, 332
Hermosa (Zambales), 366–368
Hibuson Island, 27
Hijo (Davao), 528, 535
Hijo River, 525
Hilongos (Leyte), 463
Himamaylan (Negros Occidental), 499
Himugaan River, 488, 501
Hinatuan (Surigao del Sur), 519
Hinatuan River, 33
Hinigaran (Negros Occidental), 499, 501
Hinobaan River, 488
Homonhon Island, 27, 254, 455, 460, 522
Honda Bay, 24, 436, 441
Hondagua (Quezon), 425–427
Hope (Davao), 535
Hungtung Island, 308

Iba (Zambales), 58, 365, 367–368
Ibajay (Aklan), 499
Ibod River, 23
Ibuhos Island, 16, 308
Ifugao District, 360–361

Ilagan (Isabela), 18, 316, 324, 326
Ilagan River, 17, 18, 316, 326
Ilian River, 24
Iligan (Lanao del Norte), 252, 276, 503, 510–512, 514–516, 563, 565, 568, 574, 580
Iligan Bay, 32, 558, 563
Iligan River, 514
Illana Bay, 35, 36, 555, 557, 560, 563, 565, 568–569, 580
Ilocos Coast, 11, 18, 57, 126, 164, 167, 180, 190, 209, 225–226, 256, 303, 312–313, 327, 328–342, 359, 365, 373, 378, 550
Ilocos Norte Province, 147, 314, 316, 328, 330–333, 335, 337–341, 353
Ilocos Range, 330
Ilocos Sur Province, 81, 147, 311, 316, 328, 331, 333, 335, 337–341, 352, 510
Ilog (Negros Occidental), 494
Ilog River, 30
Iloilo (Iloilo), 172–173, 233, 235–236, 259, 261, 263, 269–271, 280, 283–284, 290, 292, 445, 490, 495–496, 498–500
Iloilo Basin, 30, 31, 74, 444, 448, 486, 488–489, 491–492, 495, 499
Iloilo Province, 74–75, 81, 193, 236, 490, 495–496, 499
Iloilo Strait, 30, 31, 486, 499, 500
Indonesia (East Indies), 9, 11, 13, 33, 52, 57, 435
Infanta (Quezon), 425–426
Inopacan (Leyte), 458, 466
Intramuros (Manila), 168, 276–278, 384, 388, 392
Ipil (Zamboanga del Sur), 573, 581
Iponon River, 507, 560
Iriga (Camarines Sur), 415–416
Isabela (Zamboanga del Sur), 578
Isabela Province, 314, 321, 323, 325–327, 423, 425
Itbayat (Batanes), 309
Itbayat Island, 16, 306–309
Itogon (Mountain Province), 360
Ivaña (Batanes), 309
Iwahig (Palawan), 245

Jagna (Bohol), 474
Jalaojalao (Misamis Oriental), 513
Jalaud River, 31, 486
Jaro River, 31, 172, 486, 499, 500
Java Island, 11, 49, 52
Java Sea, 11
Jia-an (Samar), 459
Jolo (Sulu), 40, 261, 263, 574, 591, 597

Jolo Island, 37, 201, 583–586, 590–596
Jomalig Island, 22, 423–424
Jones (Isabela), 327
Jose Panganiban (Camarines Norte), 416, 419–421
Juan Luna Street, 387

Kaataon (Bukidnon), 247
Kabacan (Cotabato), 545, 551, 555
Kabacan River, 545
Kabalokan Hills, 545
Kabankalan (Negros Occidental), 480, 499
Kabasalan (Zamboanga del Sur), 575, 579–581
Kabugao (Mountain Province), 339
Kalayan (Laguna), 405
Kalibo (Aklan), 501
Kankanai District, 360
Kapalong (Davao), 534
Kapatagan (Lanao del Norte), 506, 512, 515–516
Karomatan (Lanao del Norte), 512
Katilisan River, 546
Katipunan (Zamboanga del Norte), 578
Kiamba (Cotabato), 552, 557
Kibawe (Cotabato), 564
Kidapawan (Cotabato), 551, 554, 557
Kolambugan (Lanao del Norte), 515–**516**
Koronadal (Cotabato), 550, 554, 557
Koronadal Valley, 35, 36, 471, 545–548, 550–552, 554–556
Kudarangan Hills, 545
Kulaman Plateau, 547
Kulassein Island, 583

Labason (Zamboanga del Norte), 573
Labo River, 412
La Carlota (Negros Occidental), 501
La Castellaña (Negros Occidental), 480, 499
Lagao (Cotabato), 550
Lagonoy (Camarines Sur), 419
Lagonoy Gulf, 22, 253, 311, 410, 412, 418–419
Lagonoy Plain, 412
Laguna de Bay, 20–21, 112, 139, 167, 180, 236, 382, 384, 393, 395–399, 402–406
Laguna Province, 74–75, 149, 164, 213, 217, 393, 396–400, 402–408, 414, 425
Lake Adgoan, 539
Lake Baao, 412
Lake Balinsasayan, 29
Lake Bato, 236, 412
Lake Buluan, 35, 545–546, 551

Lake Dagan, 539
Lake Danao, 29
Lake Lanao, 35, 41, 236, 514–515, 527, 539, 555, 558–560, 562–564, 566, 568–569, 596
Lake Linao, 539
Lake Mainit, 33, 236, 517–518, 523, 541
Lake Mantood, 539
Lake Naujan, 23, 236
Lake Taal, 21, 395, 397, 399
Lala (Lanao del Norte), 506, 516
La Libertad (Negros Oriental), 476, 578
Lallo (Cagayan), 319–320, 326
Lambangan River, 378
Lamitan (Zamboanga del Sur), 578
Lamon Bay, 22, 89, 311, 423, 425
Lanao del Norte Province, 194, 208, 471, 506–507, 509–516, 558–560, 562–569, 574, 577, 581
Lanao del Sur Province, 74, 194, 208, 303, 444, 505, 510–511, 514, 558–560, 562–570, 574, 577
Lanao Province, 510
Lanuza (Surigao del Sur), 519
Lanuza Bay, 517, 518, 522–523
Laoag (Ilocos Norte), 337, 338–340
Laoag River, 328, 330–331, 335, 340, 344
Laoang (Samar), 463, 467
Lapac (Sulu), 40
Lapac Island, 585, 595
Laparan Island, 585, 595
La Paz (Davao), 535
Larap (Camarines Norte), 254, 263, 419
Larap-Calabayungan, 253–254
Las Piñas (Rizal), 391, 405
Latuan Island, 37
La Union Province, 81, 328, 331–333, 335–337, 340–341, 352
Laur (Nueva Ecija), 379
Laylay (Marinduque), 452
Lebak (Cotabato), 552, 557
Legaspi (Albay), 263–264, 283, 410, 412, 418, 420–421, 452
Lemery (Batangas), 395, 397, 405–406, 409
Lepanto District, 348
Lesser Sundas, 49
Leyte Gulf, 12, 27, 254, 455, 457, 460, 465–466, 518
Leyte Island, 11–13, 19, 25–27, 32, 52, 55, 61, 70, 94, 118, 132, 146–148, 193, 195, 199, 217, 220–222, 303, 424, 444, 446–447, 454–468, 479, 519, 534, 563

Leyte Province, 141, 455, 548
Leyte Valley, 26–27, 74, 444, 457–460, 463, 466
Lianga (Surigao del Sur) 522–523, 542
Lianga Bay, 33, 517–518, 524, 542
Liangan River, 507
Liargao (Zamboanga del Sur), 575
Libon (Albay), 414
Libona (Bukidnon), 562, 565, 568
Libuganon River, 525–526
Libungan Marsh, 36, 104, 545
Ligao (Albay), 414–415, 416
Liguasan Marsh, 36, 104, 545
Liloan (Southern Leyte), 463
Liloy (Zamboanga del Norte), 573, 578, 581
Limasawa Island, 460
Limay (Bataan), 244
Limbuhan (Masbate), 454
Linapacan (Palawan), 439
Linapacan Island, 24
Lingayen (Pangasinan), 371
Lingayen Gulf, 19–20, 205, 216, 224, 237–238, 256, 311, 328, 333, 344, 364–365, 368–369, 371–372, 374, 378, 380–381, 393
Lingig (Surigao del Sur), 519
Lipa (Batangas), 402, 405, 407, 409
Llorente (Samar), 467
Looc (Tablas-Romblon), 454
Lopez (Quezon), 425–426
Los Baños (Laguna), 64
Lourdes (Misamis Oriental), 253
Lower Pampanga Province, 372
Lubang (Occidental Mindoro), 434
Lubang Island, 11, 23, 430, 432, 434
Lubao River, 371
Lubuagan (Mountain Province), 320, 339
Lubungan River, 575
Lucena (Quezon), 397–398, 404, 406–407, 423, 425
Lugbon (Romblon), 452
Lumba-a-Bayabao (Lanao del Sur), 566
Luna (La Union), 335
Lupon (Davao), 526, 535, 537
Lutopan (Cebu), 477
Luzon Arc, 11–12, 24
Luzon Island, 11–13, 16–23, 25–26, 32, 38, 40–42, 45, 49; 52, 55, 57, 61, 71, 74–75, 77–78, 83, 87–88, 94–96, 99, 102, 104, 106–107, 112, 116–120, 123, 126, 129, 131, 133, 138–139, 141–142, 146–152, 154, 164, 167, 176, 180, 182–185, 187–188, 190, 192, 195, 198, 201, 203, 205–206, 209, 214, 216–217, 220–222, 224–225, 236–237, 240–242, 244–246,

248, 250–256, 261, 264, 266, 274,
275, 280, 292–294, 296, 301–304,
306, 308–309, 311–313, 428, 434–
435, 440, 444, 446–450, 468, 473,
482, 485, 496, 503–505, 510, 526,
530, 539, 548, 550, 575, 577, 582

Maao (Negros Occidental), 498
Maasin (Southern Leyte), 460, 463,
467–468
Mabini (Davao), 526, 535–537
Mabudis Island, 16, 306
Macabebe (Pampanga), 372
Macajalar Bay, 507, 512–513
Macassar Strait, 11
Mactan Island, 28–29, 171, 267, 474,
480, 482–483
Madaum (Davao), 534
Magallanes (Agusan), 541
Magat River, 17, 319, 321, 326, 344
Magat Valley, 319, 327
Magpayang (Surigao del Norte), 251
Mahatao (Batanes), 309
Mainit (Surigao del Norte), 523
Mainit River, 531, 536
Makati (Manila), 276, 389–391
Malabang (Lanao del Sur), 563, 568
Malabon (Rizal), 235, 276, 391
Malabul River, 36, 545
Malag (Davao), 529
Malalag (Davao), 526, 528, 535–536
Malampaya Sound, 442
Malangas (Zamboanga del Sur), 255,
263, 578, 580–581
Malate (Manila), 387–388, 392
Malayan Range, 18, 342, 351–352
Malay Peninsula, 11
Malaybalay (Bukidnon), 560, 562, 565,
568
Malbug River, 31
Malcampo (Palawan), 440
Malilipot (Albay), 416
Malita (Davao), 528, 534, 537
Malitbog (Southern Leyte), 463
Mallig River, 321
Malolos (Bulacan), 381
Maluso (Zamboanga del Sur), 578
Mambaguid (Negros Occidental), 499
Mambajao (Misamis Oriental), 515
Mamburao (Occidental Mindoro), 432,
434
Manay (Davao), 523
Mandaluyong (Rizal), 276, 389–391
Mandawe (Cebu), 483
Manicani Island, 27, 254, 460, 522
Manila (Manila), 19, 21, 42–45, 55–57,
71, 82, 99, 126–127, 133, 141–142,
146, 149, 154, 156, 162, 164, 166–

171, 183, 185, 187, 190, 199, 205,
209, 214, 221, 233, 235–236, 242,
244–247, 255, 257–259, 261, 263–
264, 266–267, 269–271, 274, 276–
280, 283–284, 289–294, 296–297,
303–304, 309–310, 312–313, 318–
319, 323–326, 337–340, 348, 359,
364, 366–367, 369, 373–375, 377–
380, 382–383, 385–389, 391–393,
396–400, 402–408, 413–415, 424–
425, 428–429, 433–435, 442, 447,
450–454, 461–462, 465, 471, 476,
480, 482–483, 496, 514, 517, 531,
534, 537, 541, 566, 568, 577–579
Manila Bay, 20–21, 90, 112, 119–120,
126–127, 133, 139, 180, 216, 231,
236–237, 256, 311, 364–365, 368–
369, 371–372, 374, 378–379, 381–
385, 393, 395, 397, 405
Manjuyod (Negros Oriental), 55, 477–
478
Mankayan (Mountain Province), 252,
359
Manolo Fortich (Bukidnon), 562, 565,
568
Mansalay (Oriental Mindoro), 432–433
Mantaban Island, 37
Mantalongan (Cebu), 41
Manukan (Zamboanga del Norte), 578
Maqueda Bay, 466
Maqueda Channel, 22, 410
Maramag (Bukidnon), 562, 565, 568
Marawi (Lanao del Sur), 563–565, 569
Marbel (Cotabato), 550
Marbel River, 546
Margosatubig (Zamboanga del Sur),
578
Maria Cristina Falls, 82, 276, 419, 511,
514–515
Marianas Islands, 50
Maridagao River, 34, 36, 560
Marihatag (Surigao del Sur), 523
Marikina (Rizal), 276, 391
Marinduque Island, 25, 154, 254, 425,
447–448, 450–454
Marinduque Province, 253, 447, 452
Maripipi Island, 455, 457
Mariveles (Bataan), 365, 368
Masara (Davao), 251–252, 535, 537
Masbate (Masbate), 451–454
Masbate Bay, 449, 452
Masbate Island, 11–12, 25, 31, 40, 70,
102, 148, 235, 248, 250, 409, 414,
444–451, 454
Masbate Pass, 449
Masbate Province, 81, 447, 452
Masinloc (Zambales), 253, 263, 365,
367–369

Mataling River, 565
Matanao (Davao), 532
Mati (Davao), 254, 518–519, 523, 534, 536
Matiao (Davao), 528
Matulas Range, 545–546
Matungao (Lanao del Norte), 563
Mauban (Quezon), 425–427
Mayo (Davao), 528
Mercedes (Camarines Norte), 416, 420
Merida (Leyte), 465
Mestizo River, 340
Miaryan Plain, 560
Midsayap (Cotabato), 554, 557
Milagros (Masbate), 449, 452–454
Mindanao Island, 9, 11–13, 25–27, 32–36, 40–42, 45, 48, 50, 52, 55, 57–58, 61, 70–71, 74–77, 82, 88, 94–95, 97, 99, 102, 104–108, 118, 120–121, 129, 132, 138–139, 141–142, 147–148, 150–154, 157, 164–165, 182, 191, 195, 198–199, 205, 208, 210, 221, 226, 233, 236–237, 240–242, 244, 246–248, 250–252, 254, 261, 263, 266–267, 269, 276, 279, 289–290, 292–293, 296, 298, 301–304, 311, 332, 419, 429, 438–439, 444–446, 455, 461, 463, 468, 471, 473–474, 476, 479–480, 482–484, 495, 502–581, 589–590, 597
Mindanao Sea, 12, 32–35, 38, 445, 507, 509, 517–518, 541, 580
Mindoro Island, 11, 23–24, 71, 75, 87–88, 95–96, 99, 102, 104, 107–108, 118, 132, 143, 148, 151, 154, 220, 236, 240–241, 246, 248, 257, 280, 292–293, 296, 303–304, 364, 428–435, 436, 446–448
Mindoro Strait, 23, 436
Misamis Occidental Province, 506–507, 509–513, 515–516, 571, 575, 578, 581
Misamis Oriental Province, 471, 506, 509–513, 516, 562, 565–569
M'lang (Cotabato), 551
Molave (Zamboanga del Sur), 511, 571, 575, 580
Molundo (Lanao del Sur), 565
Mompog Pass, 25
Monkayo (Davao), 528, 531, 537
Moro Gulf, 32, 36, 557, 569, 571–574, 577, 580
Moron (Bataan), 367
Mount Abra de Ilog, 23, 429
Mount Agudo, 30
Mountain Province, 77, 99, 117, 129, 148, 151–153, 183, 201, 204, 302–

303, 314, 316, 321, 327, 330, 339–340, 342–361, 371, 378, 419
Mount Amorong, 371
Mount Ampiro, 571–573
Mount Angelo, 19
Mount Apo, 32, 34, 503, 525, 527, 554
Mount Arayat, 20, 369
Mount Baco, 23, 429
Mount Bahu, 37
Mount Baloy, 30, 486
Mount Balungao, 371
Mount Banahao, 21, 394
Mount Banahao de Lucban, 21, 394
Mount Banay, 19
Mount Bangcay, 20, 371
Mount Bataan, 364
Mount Batulao, 395
Mount Blik, 546–547
Mount Bombon, 24
Mount Bontoc, 30
Mount Bulusan, 22, 74, 410, 418
Mount Butig, 559
Mount Caladang, 19
Mount Calavite, 23, 429
Mount Camiguin, 309
Mount Canlaon, 29, 30, 488
Mount Capotan, 26
Mount Carilao, 395
Mount Conico, 32
Mount Cresta, 19
Mount Data, 18
Mount Dome, 364
Mount Guitinguitan, 32, 449
Mount Halcon, 23, 429
Mount Hibokhibok, 35, 507
Mount Hilonghilong, 518
Mount Iraya, 16, 308, 311
Mount Iriga, 22
Mount Isarog, 22, 412, 418
Mount Kalatungan, 35, 559–560
Mount Kangagan, 37
Mount Katanglad, 35, 559–60, 565, 567
Mount Labo, 22, 410, 418
Mount Lanat, 364
Mount Macolod, 21, 394
Mount Madiac, 30, 486
Mount Magsanga, 26, 457
Mount Makaturing, 35, 559
Mount Malabahoc, 28
Mount Malepunyo, 21, 394
Mount Malinao, 22, 410
Mount Malindang, 36, 571, 572, 573
Mount Mandalagan, 29
Mount Maquiling, 21, 394
Mount Marlanga, 25
Mount Masarga, 22
Mount Matagob, 457

Mount Matalingajan, 24, 436
Mount Matungkup, 37
Mount Matutum, 34, 36, 525, 527, 546, 556
Mount Mayon, 22, 410, 415–416, 418
Mount Nailog, 32
Mount Nangtud, 30, 486
Mount Nasugbu, 21, 395
Mount Natib, 364
Mount Panay, 395
Mount Piagayanga, 559
Mount Pinatubo, 364
Mount Pulog, 18, 342, 503
Mount Ragang, 35, 559–560
Mount San Cristobal, 21, 394
Mount San Pedrino, 21, 395
Mount Silay, 29
Mount Tagdalit, 33, 518
Mount Three Peaks, 28
Mount Tumantangas, 37, 584
Mulita River, 545
Munai (Lanao del Norte), 563
Muntinlupa Penitentiary, 245, 405

Nabua (Camarines Sur), 415–416
Nabunturan (Davao), 537
Naga (Camarines Sur), 414–415, 420–421
Naga (Cebu), 255, 477, 484
Naga (Zamboanga del Sur), 580
Nagcarlan (Laguna), 408
Naic (Cavite), 408
Narvacan (Ilocos Sur), 338–339, 341
Nasipit (Agusan), 244, 541–552
Nasugbu (Batangas), 402, 408
Navotas (Rizal), 235, 276, 391
Negros Island, 11, 13, 25, 28–30, 38, 55, 61, 70–71, 74, 93, 95, 102, 142, 146, 148, 150, 154, 172, 173, 183, 190, 193, 199, 201, 217, 220–222, 235, 237, 240, 242, 248, 252, 255, 257, 267, 278, 293, 302–303, 444–447, 450, 468–501, 504, 508, 510, 541, 563, 575
Negros Occidental Province, 75, 141, 173, 242, 468, 480, 486, 488, 492, 495, 497–501, 548
Negros Oriental Province, 468, 473, 476, 483, 498
New Guinea Island, 11
New Washington (Aklan), 499, 501
Nonoc (Surigao del Norte), 522
Northeastern Highlands (Leyte), 457
North Harbor (Manila), 261, 277, 387, 389
North Island, 16, 306
North Luzon Highlands, 17, 293, 313, 342–361

North Ubian Island, 589
Northwestern Highlands, (Leyte), 457
Nueva Ecija Province, 99, 313, 369, 371–373, 375, 377, 379–381, 424
Nueva Vizcaya Province, 314, 319, 321, 323, 326–327
Nuling (Cotabato), 557
Nunungan (Lanao del Norte), 563

Oas (Albay), 416
Obando (Rizal), 391
Occidental Mindoro Province, 303, 433–434
Odiongan (Romblon), 454
Ogton (Iloilo), 490
Olagusan Uplands, 525
Olongapo (Zambales), 58, 364, 366, 368
Olutanga Island, 36
Opol (Misamis Oriental), 253
Opon (Cebu), 483
Oquendo (Samar), 467
Orani (Bataan), 367–368
Oras (Samar), 459
Oras River, 26, 457
Oriental Mindoro Province, 433
Orion (Bataan), 368
Ormoc (Leyte), 458, 463, 465, 467
Ormoc Bay, 457, 465, 467
Ormoc Plain, 27, 457, 461, 463, 465
Oroquieta (Misamis Occidental), 515–516
Ozamiz (Misamis Occidental), 510, 515–516

Pacific Cordillera, 32, 33, 505, 517–518, 524–525, 571
Paco (Manila), 388
Padada (Davao), 55, 526–528, 536
Padada River, 531–532, 535
Padada Valley, 529, 536
Padre Burgos Street (Manila), 388
Paete (Laguna), 405
Pagadian (Zamboanga del Sur), 511, 515, 565, 577–578, 580–581
Pagadian Bay, 36, 509, 571, 575, 577
Pagijan Island, 28
Pakil (Laguna), 405
Pakiputan Strait, 536
Palanan (Isabela), 425
Palanan Bay, 19
Palanan Point, 311
Palapag River, 26, 457
Palawan Bridge, 9
Palawan Island, 11, 22–24, 52, 71, 76, 85, 95–96, 106, 118–119, 132, 141, 143, 148, 150–152, 154, 157, 164, 231, 240–241, 246, 253, 255, 257,

292, 296, 303–304, 364, 431, 435–443
Palawan Province, 81, 247
Palimbang (Cotabato), 552
Palo (Leyte), 460
Palompon (Leyte), 463, 467
Paluan (Occidental Mindoro), 434
Pambuyan Sur (Samar), 459
Pamintayan Point, 580
Pampanga Province, 147, 167, 190, 362, 364–365, 368–369, 371–372, 375, 377–379, 381, 398
Pampanga River, 20, 104, 311, 371, 375, 377–378, 383
Pamplona (Camarines Sur), 421
Panabo (Davao), 533, 535, 537
Panacan (Palawan), 24
Panalian Point, 465
Panaon Island, 26, 455, 457
Panay Island, 11, 25, 30–31, 38, 61, 70, 73, 102, 133, 142, 146–148, 150, 154, 172–173, 180, 205, 210, 217, 235, 237, 248, 250, 264, 293, 303, 433–434, 444, 446–448, 450, 473, 485–501
Panay River, 486, 500
Pancho (Davao), 534
Pandacan (Manila), 388
Pandan (Catanduanes), 416
Pandan (Icocos Sur), 340
Pandan River, 23
Pangasinan Province, 88, 99, 141, 205, 224, 327, 332, 335, 362, 364–366, 368–369, 372, 375, 377, 381, 424, 548
Pangatukan (Bukidnon), 564
Panglao Island, 28
Panguil (Laguna), 399
Panguil Bay, 36, 506–509, 515, 558, 560, 563, 569, 571
Pangutaran Group, 37, 582–583, 588
Pangutaran Island, 581, 585–586, 595
Panigui (Tarlac), 381
Pansipit River, 236, 395, 397, 409
Pantao Bayabao (Lanao del Sur), 566
Pantao Ragat (Lanao del Norte), 563
Pantukan (Davao), 526, 536
Paoay (Ilocos Norte), 341
Paracale (Camarines Norte), 250–251, 416, 418–419
Parañaque (Rizal), 276, 389–391
Parang (Cotabato), 554–555, 557, 565
Parker Volcano, 36, 546
Pasay City (Rizal), 142, 168, 276–278, 389–391
Pasay River, 378
Pasig (Rizal), 276, 391, 405, 407

Pasig River, 21, 168, 276–277, 382–389, 393, 397
Pasuquin (Ilocos Norte), 338
Pasuquin River, 335
Pata Island, 585
Pateros (Rizal), 276, 391, 405, 407
Patnanongan Island, 22, 423–424
Peñablanca (Cagayan), 325
Piapi (Davao), 529
Pico de Loro, 21, 395
Piddig (Ilocos Norte), 253
Pilar River, 495
Pinamalayan (Oriental Mindoro), 432–434
Piñan (Zamboanga del Norte), 578
Placer (Masbate), 452–453
Placer (Surigao del Norte), 523
Pola (Oriental Mindoro), 435
Polanco (Zamboanga del Norte), 578
Polillo Group, 424
Polillo Island, 22, 32, 148, 280, 423–425
Polillo Strait, 12
Polis Range, 18, 342, 344, 353
Polloc Harbor, 554
Polo (Rizal), 391
Polomolok (Cotabato), 550
Pondaguitan (Davao), 529
Ponson Island, 28
Pontevedra (Negros Occidental), 499
Poro (La Union), 252, 339–340
Poro Island, 28
Port Area, 385, 388–389, 392
Port Aurora (Quezon), 425
Port Barrera (Masbate), 449
Port Capiz (Capiz), 499–500
Port Currimao (Ilocos Norte), 340
Port Lebak (Cotabato), 557
Port Linao (Cotabato), 557
Port Olongapo, 368
Port Surigao Bay, 523
Port Tilik (Occidental Mindoro), 434
Port Vicente (Cagayan), 319–320
President Roxas (Capiz), 501
Prosperidad (Agusan), 542
Puerto Galera (Oriental Mindoro), 433
Puerto Princesa (Palawan), 24, 255, 436, 438, 440–442
Puerto Real (Quezon), 426
Pujada Bay, 33, 517–518, 523
Pulanan (Zamboanga del Norte), 581
Pulanduta (Masbate), 453–454
Pulangi River, 34, 36, 104, 545, 559–560
Pulupandan (Negros Occidental), 173, 499

Quezon Boulevard (Manila), 387, 391

Quezon City (Rizal), 142, 168–169, 276, 278, 312, 385, 389–392
Quezon Province, 71, 88–90, 242, 247, 393, 399, 402–404, 406–407, 414, 423, 425–427
Quezon Range, 546
Quiapo (Manila), 386–387
Quiniluban Island, 24, 25

Ragay (Camarines Sur), 420
Ragay Gulf, 12, 22, 311, 410, 412, 419, 420–421, 426, 453
Ragay Hills, 22, 410, 412
Rapu Rapu Island, 22, 252, 410–411, 418–419
Rawan River, 507
Rio Grande de Mindanao. See Cotabato River
Rio Grande de Pampanga. See Pampanga River
Rizal (Isabela), 327
Rizal (Zamboanga del Norte), 578
Rizal Avenue, 387
Rizal Province, 74, 141, 149, 213, 235–236, 245, 276, 303, 310, 369, 371, 379, 382, 389, 392–393, 398–400, 403, 405, 408, 461, 471, 492, 548
Romblon (Romblon), 433, 452–454
Romblon Group, 31, 434, 447–451
Romblon Island, 25, 31–32, 40, 257, 444–446, 448–449, 451–454
Romblon Province, 447, 452
Rosario (Cavite), 405
Roxas (Dewey) Boulevard, 387–388
Roxas City (Capiz), 486, 499–500
Roxas Range, 545–546

Sabtang (Batanes), 309
Sabtang Island, 16, 306
Sagada (Mountain Province), 350
Sagay (Negros Occidental), 496, 498–500
Salomague Bay, 339–340
Salug River, 572
Samal (Davao), 367, 528, 535
Samales Island, 586, 595
Samal Island, 529, 536
Samar Arc, 12, 409–410
Samar Island, 11, 12, 25–27, 52, 70–71, 95, 132, 142, 221–222, 233, 235–236, 240, 248, 250, 252–253, 311, 409, 424, 444, 446–447, 454–468, 519, 534
Samar Province, 236, 455
Samar Sea, 26, 231, 233, 455, 457, 466
Sampaloc (Manila), 387
San Agustin (Isabela), 318

San Agustin Peninsula, 529
San Andreas Fault, 12
San Antonio (Zambales), 368
San Bernardino Strait, 26, 311, 409, 414, 420, 445, 455
San Carlos (Negros Occidental), 29, 468–469, 471, 474, 480, 484, 488
San Carlos (Pangasinan), 379
San Felipe (Zambales), 367
San Fernando (La Union), 41, 339–340
San Fernando (Pampanga), 20, 378, 381
San Francisco (Agusan), 540, 542
Sanga-Sanga Island, 581, 585
Sangi (Cebu), 82, 252, 263, 477
San Jose (Davao), 529
San Jose (Nueva Ecija), 264, 378
San Jose (Occidental Mindoro), 23, 432–435
San Jose de Buenavista (Antique), 499, 501
San Juan del Monte (Rizal), 276, 389–391
San Juanico Strait, 26, 455, 457, 466
San Luis River, 425
San Miguel (Manila), 387, 392
San Miguel (Tarlac), 381
San Miguel Bay, 22, 233, 410–412, 419
San Miguel Island, 22, 410
San Narciso (Zambales), 425–426
San Nicolas (Ilocos Sur), 341
San Nicolas (Manila), 277, 384, 386–387
San Pablo (Laguna), 400, 402, 404–407
San Pablo (Zamboanga del Sur), 580
San Pedro Bay, 466
San Quintin (Pangasinan), 378
San Sebastian (Cebu), 480
Santa (Ilocos Sur), 341
Santa Ana (Davao), 534, 536
Santa Ana (Manila), 388
Santa Catalina (Ilocos Sur), 337, 341
Santa Cruz (Davao), 528, 531, 536
Santa Cruz (Laguna), 399, 406, 408
Santa Cruz (Manila), 387
Santa Cruz (Zambales), 253, 365–369
Santa Cruz River, 378
Santa Fe (Cebu), 484
Santa Maria River, 335
Santa Mesa Boulevard, 387
Santa Mesa District, 387
Santiago (Isabela), 264, 321, 324, 327
Santo Nino Island, 455
Santo Tomas (Davao), 531, 537
Santo Tomas (La Union), 338, 341

Sarangani Bay, 35–36, 505, 528, 545–547, 551, 556
Sarangani Island, 535
Sarangani Islands, 529
Sarangani Ridge, 9
Sarangani Strait, 34
Saravia (Negros Occidental), 494
Sasa (Davao), 534, 536
Saug River, 525–526
Sayre Highway, 515, 535, 555, 558, 565, 568
Secuban Island, 37, 585
Semporna Peninsula (Borneo), 582
Siain (Quezon), 425–427
Siargao Island, 32–33, 518–519
Siasi (Sulu), 591, 597
Siasi Channel, 591
Siasi Island, 37, 574, 585, 591, 594–595
Siay (Zamboanga del Sur), 580
Siayan Island, 16, 308
Sibalom River, 31, 488
Sibuco (Zamboanga del Norte), 575
Sibuguey (Zamboanga del Sur), 254–255
Sibuguey Gulf, 88–89, 571, 573, 575, 580
Sibuguey Peninsula, 36–37, 569, 571–572, 580
Sibuguey River, 572
Sibutu Island, 582, 585–586, 592–593, 595–596
Sibuyan Island, 12, 25, 30–32, 444–445, 448–449, 454
Sibuyan Sea, 19, 31, 40, 42, 409, 447–454, 496
Sierra Bullones (Bohol), 479, 484
Sierra Madre Mountains, 17, 19, 312–314, 421, 423
Silang (Cavite), 41
Silay (Negros Occidental), 496, 501
Simara Island, 449
Simunul Island, 37, 585
Sindangan (Zamboanga del Norte), 571–572, 578
Siocon (Zamboanga del Norte), 581
Sipalay (Negros Occidental), 497
Sipalay River, 488, 497
Sipocot (Camarines Sur), 416, 420
Sipocot River, 416
Siquijor Island, 25, 28, 254, 444, 468, 477, 480
Siruma (Camarines Sur), 420
Sitangkai (Sulu), 231, 591, 595
Sogod Bay, 460
Solano (Nueva Vizcaya), 324–327
Solvec (Ilocos Sur), 339
Sorsogon (Sorsogon), 414–415, 420

Sorsogon Bay, 22, 410, 412, 414
Sorsogon Peninsula, 22, 199, 201, 221, 409–410, 414
Sorsogon Plain, 412
Sorsogon Province, 74, 222, 412–413, 416–417, 420
South China Sea, 9, 12, 18–19, 24, 49, 52, 116, 330–331, 338, 344, 362, 371, 436
Southeastern Peninsulas, 409
Southern Leyte Province, 455, 460, 468
South Harbor, 261, 277, 388–389
South Ubian Island, 585
Southwest Coast Range, 546
Sual (Pangasinan), 381
Subic (Zambales), 364–365, 368
Subic Bay, 365
Sudipen (La Union), 335
Sulop (Davao), 532
Sultan Sa Barongis (Cotabato), 550, 553–555
Suluan Island, 27
Sulu Archipelago, 11–12, 40, 48, 106, 126, 142, 152–154, 157, 159, 164, 166, 201, 214, 231, 232, 236, 247, 280–281, 283, 296, 304, 438–439, 445, 502–506, 536, 570–571, 577, 579, 581–597
Sulu Island Bridge, 9
Sulu Province, 194, 303, 502, 581–597
Sulu Sea, 10, 11, 24, 32, 37, 231, 233, 436, 439, 442, 445, 468, 571, 574, 580–597
Sumatra, 11
Sumilao River, 525
Sundaland, 11, 23, 116, 428, 436
Surigao (Surigao), 261, 515, 519, 523
Surigao del Norte Province, 517, 523
Surigao del Sur Province, 517, 523, 542
Surigao Peninsula, 32, 518–519
Surigao Province, 32, 81, 90, 253–254, 461, 517–518, 522
Surigao River, 523
Surigao Strait, 27, 445, 455, 518

Taal (Batangas), 397, 409
Taal Volcano, 21, 74, 395, 402, 408–409
Tabaco (Albay), 415, 416, 418
Tabaco Bay, 22, 410
Tabaco-Legaspi Plain, 412, 414
Tablas Island, 25, 31, 444, 448–449, 452, 454
Tablas Plateau, 29, 488–489, 491, 498–499
Tablas Strait, 31, 445
Tacloban (Leyte), 261, 283, 452, 454, 460, 462, 465–467

Tacurong (Cotabato), 557
Taft (Samar), 459, 462
Taft Avenue (Manila), 388
Tagabuli (Davao), 535
Taganaan (Surigao del Norte), 519, 523
Tagaytay (Cavite), 41, 408
Tagaytay Ridge, 395, 397
Tagbilaran (Bohol), 28, 469, 473, 480, 482–484
Tagburos (Palawan), 442
Tago (Surigao del Sur), 33, 519, 522
Tagoloan River, 34, 560
Tagudin (Ilocos Sur), 339
Taguig (Rizal), 276, 405, 407
Tagum (Davao), 527, 528, 534, 537
Tagum River, 33, 525
Taiwan, 9, 16, 49, 106, 306
Talacogon (Agusan), 538, 542
Talakag (Bukidnon), 565, 568
Talaud Ridge, 9, 33
Talim Island, 408
Talipaw (Sulu), 591–592
Talisay (Cebu), 469
Talisay (Negros Occidental), 501
Talomo River, 526
Taluntunan (Marinduque), 254, 454
Tambulig (Zamboanga del Sur), 571, 575
Tambungon (Davao), 535
Tamentaka River, 545
Tampi (Negros Oriental), 480
Tanauan (Batangas), 409
Tanauan (Leyte), 460, 466, 468
Tanay (Rizal), 408
Tandag (Surigao del Sur), 523, 579
Tandoc (Camarines Sur), 420
Tangkal (Lanao del Norte), 563
Tangub (Misamis Occidental), 512
Tanjay (Negros Oriental), 471, 476
Tanjay River, 29
Tañon Strait, 28, 29, 484
Taoma (Davao), 529
Tapul Island, 583, 584–586, 594
Tapul Island Group, 591
Taraka (Lanao del Sur), 565–566
Tarlac (Tarlac), 20, 378, 380–381
Tarlac Province, 310, 313, 340, 362, 369, 371–372, 375, 377, 380
Tarlac River, 20
Tawi-Tawi Group, 37, 388, 590
Tawi-Tawi Island, 37, 143, 247, 574, 581, 584, 586, 592–593, 595–596
Tawi-Tawi Lagoon, 37
Tayabas Bay, 25, 233, 393, 395, 397–398, 453
Tayabas Isthmus, 19, 21, 70, 311, 410, 420–421, 423–427

Taytay (Palawan), 439, 441–442
Taytay (Rizal), 407
Taytay Bay, 436, 442
Tibal-og (Davao). *See* Santo Tomas
Ticao Island, 12, 19, 31, 409, 414, 444, 447, 449–451
Ticao Strait, 445
Tigaon (Camarines Sur), 419
Tinaca Point, 34, 535
Tinaco Hills, 545
Tinambac (Camarines Sur), 420
Tinambacan (Samar), 467
Tineg River, 330
Tiruray Highlands, 32, 36, 506, 542, 546, 548, 551–552, 556, 557
Tiwi (Albay), 416
Toboso (Negros Occidental), 501
Toledo (Cebu), 252, 477, 480, 484
Tolong River, 29
Tondo (Manila), 277, 387–388, 392
Tongquil Island (Sulu), 584
Toril (Davao), 537
Trece Matires (Cavite), 408
Trinidad (Mountain Province), 360
Trinidad Valley, 45, 203, 345, 358, 360
Tuao (Cagayan), 327
Tubay (Agusan), 541
Tubay River, 518
Tubod (Lanao del Norte), 516
Tubigon (Bohol), 480
Tuganay River, 526
Tugbok (Davao), 537
Tuguegarao (Cagayan), 18, 45, 264, 320, 324–325
Tukuran (Zamboanga del Sur), 511, 578
Tulunan (Cotabato), 550
Tumindao Reef, 582, 591
Tupi (Cotabato), 550
Tutuban Station (Manila), 387

Ubay (Bohol), 484
Uling (Cebu), 255, 477
Ulugan Bay, 24
Ulut River, 26, 457
Umayan River, 525
Ungus Island, 37
Upi (Cotabato), 543, 556
Uyugan (Batanes), 309

Valencia (Bukidnon), 565
Vallehermoso (Negros Oriental), 471, 480, 499
Verde Island Passage, 23, 428
Vergara (Davao), 529
Victoria Peaks, 24
Victorias (Negros Occidental), 499, 501

Vigan (Ilocos Sur), 61, 330, 333, 339, 340–341
Villaba (Leyte), 257, 459
Viñas River, 410
Vintar River, 331, 335
Vira (Isabela), 327
Virac (Catanduanes), 22, 411, 416, 421
Visayan Islands (Visayas), 11, 12, 21, 25–32, 45, 52, 55, 57, 61, 70, 78–80, 106, 129, 138–139, 142, 146, 148, 152–154, 164, 167, 171–173, 176, 182, 187, 198–199, 205, 212, 217, 221, 231, 237–238, 240, 263, 266, 280–281, 290, 292, 296, 303–304, 306, 311, 317, 323, 336, 373, 384, 393, 409, 415, 428, 440, 444–501, 504, 506, 510, 514, 516, 521, 531, 535, 548, 550, 556, 558, 562–563, 566, 574–575, 577–579
Visayan Sea, 31, 233, 444, 445, 446, 488, 491, 496, 588

Wao (Lanao del Sur), 562, 563, 565, 568
Wawa River, 525
Western Cordillera (Panay), 30, 31, 362, 486

Wright (Samar), 459, 462, 467

Y'ami Island, 16, 306, 308
Ypolete (Palawan), 439

Zambales Mountains, 11, 17, 19, 20, 61, 99, 150, 240, 253, 301, 364, 368, 369, 371
Zambales Province, 11, 75, 148, 248, 332, 362, 364–365, 366–367, 368
Zamboanga (Zamboanga del Sur), 40, 42, 171, 235, 261, 263, 269, 283, 293, 503, 511, 512, 517, 535, 554, 557, 571, 572, 573, 574, 575, 576, 577, 578, 579, 580, 581, 594, 597
Zamboanga del Norte Province, 502, 506, 511, 570–581
Zamboanga del Sur Province, 37, 210, 237, 241, 242, 255, 303, 304, 461, 502, 505, 570–581
Zamboanga Peninsula, 12, 32, 36–37, 61, 214, 247, 502, 505–507, 511, 515, 569–581
Zamboanga Province, 194, 210, 246
Zamboanquita (Negros Oriental), 484
Zigzag Pass, 368
Zumarraga (Samar), 466

Abaca, 119, 179, 180, 183, 184, 192, 227, 282, 285, 293, 540, 556, 567–568, 579, 594; acreage of, table, 639; American stimulation of, 221; comparative financial return per acre of, 228; decortication and stripping of, 222; environmental requirements of, 220; fiber, uses of, 207, 221; handicrafts, decline of, 684 n.8; Japanese production of, Davao area, 530; producing areas, 220–222, 223; production in Davao Gulf subregion, 533–534; production in Leyte and Samar, 465; production in southeast Luzon, 417, 418

Abra River: description of, 330

Aglipayans: distribution of, map, 161; table of, by provinces, 626–627

Agricultural landscape: growth of, 181

Agriculture: change in, 179; comparative, domestic-commercial, 178; experiment stations, 129; historical growth of, 179–180; problems of modernization of, 193–194; productivity of, 179, 192, 227; Spanish stimulation of, 126; summary discussion of, 226–227; table of indices of, 659; technological level of, 227

Agusan River: description of, 525–526

Airfields: number of, 267

Air masses: and temperatures, 42; maps of, 47; seasonal system of, 46–49; types of, 46

Air traffic: pattern of, 267–269

Air transport, 266–269; and government airline, 267; and passenger traffic, 267; as revenue source, 267; scheduled routes of, map, 268; suitability of, for island world, 267

Allah Valley: description of, 546

Alluvium: as soil-forming materials, 72–74

Americanization: and commodity preferences, 133–134; cultural limit to, 134; discussion of, 128–134; of government, 129

Animal keeping: American influence on, 211; by shifting cultivators, 211

Animals: common species of, 106–107; discussion of, 105–108; zonal grouping of, 106

Architecture: domestic, 159–162; public, 162–163

Areas: of islands, table of, 600–604; of provinces, table of, 605–606

Asphalt, rock: produced on Layte, 257, 459

Automobiles: buses, 266; numbers of, 266; truck ratio, 266

Bacolod, 172–173
Badjao language: speakers, number of, 695 n.40
Bagoong: as fish preparation, 231, 236
Baguio: as summer resort and capital, 41, 170, 351; as trade center, 360; chartering of, 170, 360–361; population of, 361; temperatures of, 41
Baguios. See Typhoons
Balut: consumption of, 212–213
Bamboo: as minor forest product, 246; as secondary vegetation cover, 97; as source of fiber, 207; in forests, 97
Bananas, 71, 174, 179, 180, 183, 184, 192, 193, 204, 310, 355, 366, 473, 522, 533, 594; as crop staple, 182
Banaue: map of land-use and terracing in, 347
Bangos, 237
Barangay: as basic organizational unit, 118; as local political district, 122; as settlement focus, 158; as social unit, 158; in locating village site, 163
Barrio: as chief settlement form, 165; as local political district, 122; composition of, 165; growth of, 166; number of, 133, 164; population of, 166
Basement-complex: rocks of, 13
Basic themes: identification of, 5
Basilan City: area and population of, 171
Basilan Island: description of, 572
Batan-Babuyan Islands region, 306–311; agriculture in, 310; area of, 308; fishing industry in, 310; house types in, 310; islands in, 308; isolation of, 309; language of, 309; map of, 307; physiography of, 16, 308; population density of, 309; static population of, 309; towns of, 311; typhoon frequency in, 310–311
Beach sands: as soil-forming materials, 70
Beach vegetation: description of, 88
Beans: as minor crop, 209
Betel palm: as minor crop, 209
Beverage crops: discussion of, 206–207; table of, 644
Bicolandia. See Southeast Luzon region
Bikol: linguistic area of, 409, 413
Bikol language: speakers of, table, 620–624
Biota: discussion of, 106–107
Birds: discussion of, 105–108; limited use of, 106; total species of, 106
Birthrates: discussion of, 175–176
Boar hunts, 108

Bohol Island: description of, 27; 1960 population map of, 137
Bontoc: language speakers, 354
Branch assembly plants: impact of, on import trade, 287
Bukidnon-Lanao Plateau: description of, 35, 560
Bukidnon-Lanao region, 557–569; agriculture in, 566; Bukidnon tribal peoples of, 562; cattle ranching in, 568; Christian population of, 563–564; climate of, 561; description of, 35, 557–561; government settlements in, 562, 564; grasslands of, 561; industrial potential of, 569; in-migration to, 562; Lake Lanao and, 559; minor towns of, 565–566; Moslem population of, 563; physiography of, 558–561; pineapple plantation in, 562, 566–567; political structure of, 563; population densities in, 564; roads in, 568–569; soils of, 561; transport in, 568–569; urbanism in, 564–565
Burias Island: description of, 449
Buri palm: as beverage crop, 206
Burning: causes of, 101; impact of, on forests, 97; in dry forests, 97; of grasslands, 101, 680 n.14
Bus companies: transport routes of, 266–267

Cabeceras: definition of, 675–676 n.20; Spanish founding of, 164
Cacao: acreage of, 206; as beverage crop, 206; comparative financial return of, per acre, 228; planting distribution of, 206–207
Cadang-cadang disease: in coconut plantings, 214
Cagayan River: length of, 316; navigation of, 320, 325
Cagayan Valley: as large lowland, 17
Cagayan Valley region, 314–328; Aparri as single port for, 326; area of, 314; as pioneer region, 324; climate of, 316; corn production of, 320, 321, 322; description of, 314–317; drainage of, 314; in-migration to, 324, 327–328; map of, 315; mining in, 318; minor trade centers of, 327; population of, 1960, 317; pre-Spanish population of, 319; resource base of, 318; rice production of, 321–322; river navigation in, 320; roads of, 318–319; soils of, 317; Spanish influence on, 317; Spanish settlements in, 324; timber supply in, 318; tobacco production of, 322,

323, 324; towns of, 324–327; urban centers of, 324–327

Caingin. *See* Shifting cultivation

Caliraya power project: in southwest Luzon, 396

Caloocan: chartering of, 169

Camote, 201. *See* Sweet potatoes

Candaba Swamp: description of, 105

Capital resources: slow growth of, 273–274

Caraballo Mountains: description of, 17

Carabao: as chief draft animal, 210–211; distinction between water buffalo and, 680 n.15

Cassava. *See* Manioc

Catanduanes Island: description of, 22, 411

Catholic church: as landowner, 188–190

Catholic clergy: role of, 121–122

Cattle: as auxiliary draft animals, 211; role of, in economy, 210–211

Cattle ranching: in Bukidnon-Lanao region, 568; in southwest Luzon, 402–403; modern role of, 211–212; on Masbate Island, 451, 453; Spanish attempts at, 211

Cavan: definition of, 694 n.30

Cavite: Spanish naval base at, 407

Cebuano language: speakers, table of, 620–624

Cebuanos: as migrants, 147

Cebu City: area and population of, 171; as copra capital of Philippines, 474, 478–479; as first Spanish center, 482; as interisland shipping center, 261; as interisland trade center, 171, 292, 482; as Spanish city, 171; as urban center, 482; chartering of, 171; trade region of, 292

Cebu Island: area and population of, 600; description of, 28; soil erosion on, 78–81; village settlement patterns of, 482

Cement: production centers of, 255

Census: 1960, inadequacy of, 678–679 n.1

Central Cordillera of Mindanao. *See* Central Mindanao Highlands

Central Luzon: 1960 population map of, 139

Central Mindanao Highlands: description of, 34

Central places: Spanish towns as, 166–167

Central Plain of Luzon: annual precipitation on, 55; as largest lowland, 17; description of, 20; rice-growing in, 192

Central Plain of Luzon region, 369–382; agriculture of, 374–375; area of, 369; as cultural center, 369; chartered cities of, 381; chief cities of, 381; Clark Air Force Base in, 381; climate of, 371–372, 374; description of, 370–372; drainage system of, 371; fishponds in, 378–379; influence of Manila on, 380; irrigation in, 374–377; manufacturing in, 379–380; mining in, 379; minor towns of, 381; physiography of, map, 370; population distribution in, 374; population of, 369; ports of, 381; railway in, 378; rainfall seasons in, 374; rice production of, 374–375; roads in, 373, 378; settlement pattern of, 373, 380; Spanish influence on, 372; sugarcane in, 377–378; tenancy in, 373–374; transport in, 378, 381; unemployment in, 380

Central Visayan region, 468–485; agricultural processing in, 477–479; agriculture in, 472–475; and Cebu City, 470, 480, 482; climate of, 469; copra production in, 474; corn in, 472–473; description of, 468; emigration in, 471; fishing in, 475–476; interisland shipping routes from, 481; linguistic patterns of, 470; market towns in, 484; mining in, 476–477; physiography of, 468, 469; population density of, 470–471; roads in, 479; rural-settlement character of, 471; small-forest resource of, 476; subregionalisms in, 484; sugarcane production in, 474; sugar district narrow-gauge rail net in, 480; sugar quota production in, 478; ties of, to northern Mindanao, 471; towns of, 483–484; transport of, 479; urbanism in, 380–381, 482–484; water transport in, 480–482

Charcoal: production and use of, 246

Chartered cities: government services provided to, 677–678 n.34; special status of, 170–171; table of, 635–636

Chartering of cities: legislative controls over, 677 n.33

Chickens: role of, in economy, 210–212

Chili pepper: production of, 210

Chinese: Manila as early center of, 127; merchants Filipino reaction to, 687 n.35; racial intermixture of, 153; tenth-century contact with, 119; traders, spread of, 127

Christian-Moslem conflict: in Zamboanga Peninsula region, 574

Chromite: producing areas of, 253; rank

of, in mining industry, 252; reserves of, 253

Cigarette tobacco: in Ilocos coast region, 337

Cinchona: as minor forest product, 247

Cities: chartered, as statistical areas, 170; chartered, table of, 635–636; chartering of, 170; discussion of, 168–173; enlarged areas of, 171; growth of, 142, 146; number of, chartered in 1963, 170; presidential control of, 170; rank of, by tax base, 170–171; smaller, characteristics of, 173. *See also* under each region

Class structure: perpetuation of, 125

Climate: classification of, 58–62; general discussion of, 39; humid tropical, 40; Köppen map of, 59; maps of, 59–60; regionalism and, 156; special conditions of, for Philippines, 40; Thornthwaite map of, 60; tropical nature of, 3

Cloudiness: effect of, on temperature, 43

Coal production, 255; in Zamboanga Peninsula region, 580; on Cebu Island, 476–477

Coastal settlement: as early system, 117

Coconut, 71, 73, 74, 75, 119, 174, 179, 180, 182, 183, 184, 192, 204, 211, 227, 282, 285, 310, 312, 516, 522, 532, 540, 556, 579, 594, 595; acreage of, 214, 639; as beverage crop, 206; as crop staple, 182; as foreign exchange source, 216; as primary commercial crop, 214; comparative financial return of, per acre, 228; diseases of, 214; domestic consumption of, 214; environmental requirements of, 213–214; in Central Visayan region, 474; in eastern Luzon, 426; in southeast Luzon, 418; in southwest Luzon, 402; in traditional economy, 213; in Zamboanga Peninsula region, 579; production area of, 214, 215; tariffs on products of, 686 n.26; traditional planting system for, 214; tree, yield of, 213

Coffee: acreage of, 207; as beverage crop, 206; comparative financial return of, per acre, 228; consumption of, 207; in southwest Luzon, 402

Cogonales: discussion of, 84; uses of, 102–103, 104

Cogon grass: nature of, 99

Cold waves: seasonal occurrence of, 41

Commandancia, 122

Commandeering of soldiery: early Spanish, 128

Commerce: American dominance of, 284; and American free-trade policy, 282; and changing commodity pattern, 285–286; and early commodity pattern, 280–281; directions of, 284; discussion of, 280–288; effect of World War II on, 282; exports and, 285; foreign, tables of, 661–663; historical pattern of, 280; in nineteenth century, 282; late Spanish liberalization of, 282; long-term trend of, 287–288; progressive U.S. tariffs and, 283; rising consumer demand and, 286; role of American mining in, 282; role of Chinese in, 281; share of native product in, 282; Spanish monopoly over, 281; status of, on arrival of Spanish, 281; values of, 284

Commercial crops: discussion of, 213–226; tables of, 639, 646

Commercial fish: varieties of, 231

Commercial fishing: grounds, 232; methods, 233

Commercial forests: dipterocarp, 240; mangrove, 241; molave, 240; pine, 241; variety and extent of, 240

Consumer goods: spread of, 133–134

Copal: as minor forest product, 246

Copper: mining of, 251, 477; producing areas for, 252; reserves of, 252

Copra: tariffs on, 686 n.26

Coral reefs: building of, 111–112; locations of, 16

Cordillera Central: description of, 18; elevations in, 18; rocks of, 19

Core fleet: service routes of, 261; vessels in, 261

Corn, 71, 73, 78, 174, 178, 180, 181, 183, 184, 193, 194, 211, 292, 293, 294, 310, 312, 355, 522, 540, 566, 594; acreage of, table, 639; as crop staple, 182; comparative financial return of, per acre, 228; dietary preference for, on Cebu, 472–473; discussion of, 198–199; environmental requirements for, 198; growing consumption of, in Visayas, 678 n.38; in Cagayan Valley, 320–321, 322; in Cebu, 472, 473; in Central Visayan region, 472; increase in acreage of, 694 n.23; in Davao Gulf, 531–532; in Ilocos coast region, 336; in northern Mindanao, 516; in Samar and Leyte, 463, 464; in southeast Luzon, 417; in southwest Mindanao, 556; in Zamboanga Peninsula, 579; popularity of, increase in, 680 n.8; primary producing regions of, 199, 200; yields of, per acre, 199

"Corn rice": definition of, 680 n.9

Cotabato Basin: description of, 35

Cotton: acreage and producing area of, 208; as fiber source, 208

Crafts: and Manila, 127

Crocodiles: decrease in, 108; earlier distribution of, 107; hunting of, 108; in Mindanao swamps, 105

Crop areas: table of, 639

Crop breeding: advances by, 193–194

Crop combinations: patterns of, 183–184

Crop decline: on new lands in southwestern Mindanao region, 556–557

Crop frequencies: table of, 640–641

Crop introductions: American, 126; Asian, 180; early, 180; Spanish, 180–181

Cropping systems: details of, 192–193; discussion of, 182; Philippine patterns of, 183–184

Crop plants: domestication of, 118

Crops: comparative, tables of, 639–646; discussions of, 192–228; domestic, 194–213; primary, 182

Cultivated land: table of, by provinces, 633–634

Cultural continuity: under Spanish rule, 121

Cultural development: summary discussion of, 295–298

Cultural regionalisms, 156

Cultural unification: forces for, 157

Culture processes: summary notes on, 135

Customs offices: opening of, 283–284

Cutch: as minor forest product, 247

Cuyo Islands: description of, 24

Daeng: as dried-fish product, 236

Dairying: increasing role of, 213

Davao: area and population of, 172; growth of, 172; trade region of, 293

Davao-Agusan Trough: description of, 33–34

Davao-Agusan Trough region, 532–542; abaca production in, 533, 534; agriculture of, 531–532, 540; Agusan Valley subregion of, 537–542; American reorganization of, 529; area of, 524; as population vacuum, 524; climate of, 526–527; coconut production of, 534; corn production in Davao Gulf zone of, 531–533; corn surplus in, 533; Davao Gulf subregion of, 528–537; description of, 524; division of, into two units, 528; fishing in, 535, 541; floating houses in, 539; forests in, 527; industrial growth of, 535;

in-migration to, 531, 540; Japanese settlement of, 530; lumbering in, 534–535, 541; map of fields and crops in Davao Gulf subregion of, 532; market towns of, 536–537; mining in, 535; minor crops of, 533; minor towns of, 542; Mount Apo and, 525; NARRA settlement in, 531, 537; physiography of, 524; population density of, 531, 540; pre-Spanish occupance of, 528; rice deficit in, 533; roads in, 535–536, 540; settlement of, 530; soils in, 527; Spanish influence in, 529, 539–540; town plan in, 538; tribal peoples of, 528–529; tribal population total of, 529; urbanism in, 536, 541–542; volcanoes of, 525

Death rate: discussion of, 176

Density of population: of Agusan and Bukidnon, 303; of Rizal Province, 303; table of, by provinces, 633–634

Dietary: American impact on, 174, 211; changes in, 675; discussion of, 174–175; fish in, 229; Spanish additions to, 211; wheat in, 174; yams and taro in, 677

Dipterocarp forests: areas and stand of, 240; discussion of, 91–97; rattan in, 92–94

Directions of trade: comparative percentages, table of, 663; comparative values, table of, 662–663

Diversity: and regionalism, 301–304; kinds of, 302–304

Domestic architecture: changes in, 159–162; materials used in, 159

Domestic crops: discussion of, 194–213; tables of, 639, 646

Domestic trade: barter background of, 290–291; basic patterns of, 288; Cebu as interisland center of, 171, 289, 292, 482; Chinese role in, 291; coast-to-interior pattern of, 288; discussion of, 280–294; effect of incomplete land-transport network on, 294; financing of, 289; growth of Filipino influence in, 291; historical growth in, 290; insular flow of, 289; interisland pattern of, 288; Manila as focal center of, 289, 292; new regions of, 292; nineteenth-century structuring of, 290; regional centers of, 292–293; speculative alternatives to present pattern of, 289; twentieth-century developments in, 290

Drought: regional areas of, 57; seasonal pattern of, 57

Dry forests: climatic environment of, 95;

composition of, 95–96; discussion of, 95

Dry season: discomfort during, 45; months of, 53; timing of, 42, 53

Duck eggs: use of, around Manila, 212–213

Ducks: role of, in economy, 210–212

Eastern Cordillera: description of, 19; elevations in, 19

Eastern Luzon region, 421–427; agriculture in, 426; area of, 423; climate in, 424; coconut production in, 426–427; linguistic pattern of, 423; physiography of, 422, 423; population of, 424; railway in, 426; roads of, 426; towns of, 425–426; transport in, 426

Eastern Mindanao region, 517–523; agriculture of, 521–522; area of, 517; climate of, 520; description of, 517–520; forests of, 520; linguistic patterns of, 521; lumbering in, 522–523; mining in, 522; minor towns of, 523; offshore islands of, 521; physiography of, 517–520; population of, 517; population variation in, 521; ports of, 523; roads of, 523; settlement pattern in, 521; Spanish contact with, 520–521; towns of, 523

Economic policy: aim of, 287

Economy: early self-subsistence of, 126; Spanish influence on, 126

Educational system: American influence on, 132; failure of, to develop craft skills, 132; in Spanish period, 127

Emigration: discussion of, 146–148; from central Visayan region, 471–472; from Ilocos coast, 334, 341; maps of, 144–145

Encomiendas: decline of, 123; granting of, 123; nature of, 123–124; private landownership resulting from, 125; tenancy and, 188–189, 679 n.3

English language: speakers, number of, 153; table of speakers, by ages, 625; usage of, 135

Erosion: of soils, 78, 618–619; on Cebu Island, map of, 80

Ethnic stock: mixing of, 135; variations in, 149

Export crops: discussion of, 213–226

Export quotas: set by U.S., 686 n.23

Exports: list of ranking, 285; quotas on, for American market, 285; table of, 661, 662

Export trade: encouragement of, by American control, 181

Farms: table of, growing particular crops, 640–641

Faulting: role of, in physiography, 12

Fencing: against wild pigs, 108

Fertilizers, 82

Fiber crops, 207–209

Filipino: as term, 149

Filipinos: acceptance of Spanish culture by, 120–121; Americanization of, 128–129, 130; as farmers, 187; consumer preferences of, 133–134; ethnic stocks of, 116; littoral preference of, 143; mobility of, 146; modernization of, 128–129; orientation of, to Christian ways, 153; professions and, 132; spices in diet of, 210

Firewood: production of, 246

Fish: annual catch of, table, 650; markets, 235; species caught, table of, 612–613; varieties of commercial, 231

Fish consumption: fresh vs. preserved, 235

Fisheries: discussion of, 228–238

Fishery products: export of, 238; import of, 230, 238

Fishing: equipment, types of, 233; freshwater, discussion of, 236; in central Visayan region, 475–476; in Leyte and Samar region, 465; in Palawan waters, 442–443; in southwest Luzon, 403–404; in Sulu waters, 590, 593, 595–596; population engaging in, 230; subsistence patterns of, 235; traditional role of, 230; vessels, numbers of commercial, 234

Fishing grounds: commercial, map of, 232; distribution of, 233

Fishing industry: annual catch of, table, 650; types of, 230, 231

Fishing methods: types of commercial, 233

Fishponds: acreage of, 237; discussion of, 237–238; importance of, 230; in Central Plain of Luzon, 378–379; in western Negroes and Panay region, 496–497; in Zambales-Bataan hill country region, 367; potential expansion of, 237; production of, table, 650; share of, in fishery yield, 237

Fish preservation, 235–236

Fish raising: discussion of, 237–238

Flax: as source of fiber, 208

Floating houses: in Agusan Valley, 539

Floral community: species composition of, 105

Food consumption: American influence on, 211; Spanish additions to, 211

Forage grass: as minor crop, 209; production of, 210

Foreign trade: American dominance of, 284; commodity pattern of, changes in, 285–286; directions of, 284; discussion of, 280–288; early commodity pattern of, 280–281; effect of World War II on, 282; exports in, range of, 285; historical pattern of, 280; imports in, range of, 286; long-term trend of, 287–288; nineteenth-century changes in, 282; progressive U.S. tariffs and, 283; quotas on, for American market, 285; role of Chinese in, 281; Spanish and, 281; tables of, comparative, 661–663; tariff effects on, 283; values of, 284, 661–663

Forest industries: annual yield of, 238–239; discussion of, 238–247; employment in, 85, 244–245; importance of, 238–239; minor products of, 245

Forest resources: early pattern of, 239; exploitation of, in Spanish period, 239; present area covered by, 239

Forests: dipterocarp types, 91–97, 240; discussion of, 83–99; map of, 86; Molave, 240; regeneration of, 102; types and stands of, table, 87

Forests, commercial: area of, 240; types of, 87, 240, 241

Forest types: discussion of, 85–87

Free trade: and U.S. maxima on import quotas, 686 n.28; under American control, 129–130

Freshwater swamp: in Luzon, 104–105; in Mindanao, 104

Fruit crops: as complementary, 205–206; comparative financial return of, per acre, 228; discussion of, 204–206; production center of, 205

Fruits: acreage of, table, 639; role of, 182–183

Fruits and nuts: table of, 643

Furniture industry: establishments and products of, 245

Ganta: definition of, 694 n.30

Geese: role of, in economy, 210–211

Geologic structure: arcuate form of, 11–12; map of, 9; summary of, 9–11

Ginger: as minor crop, 209–210

Glass sands: mining of, 257

Goats: role of, in economy, 210–212

Gold: as leading mineral, 250; mining of, 250–251; production of, 251

Government: Americanization of, 129; modernization of, 129, 131; traditional system of, continued, 131

Government land settlement: inadequacy of, 130

Grass, forage: as minor crop, 209–210

Grasses: species of, in forest margins, 97

Grasslands: area of, 85; burning in, 101, 680 n.14; 84–85; composition of, 99–100; conversion of, to pineapple plantation, 104; extent of, 99; map of, 100; origins of, 101; table of, 103; utility of, 103

Grazing land: need for, 103–104

Greater Manila: areas included in, 685 n.19

Guimaras Island: description of, 488

Gutta-percha: as minor forest product, 247

Hamlet: nature of, 163

Headman: role of, 158

Hemp: as source of fiber, 208

Highland resorts, 41

Highways: as important carriers, 264; densities of, table, 653–654; map of, 265; mileage of, 266; regional variation in network of, 266; table of, 652

Hill stations, 41

Hispanization: as culture process, 120

Horses, 210–212

Hospitality: sense of, 676 n.24

Housing patterns: discussion of, 159–162; modern, 162; Spanish elements in, 159; traditional, 159

Hukbalahap: rise of, 131

Hurricanes. *See* Typhoons

Ifugao: language speakers, 353; map of land use by, 347

Iglesia ni Kristo: table of, by provinces, 626–627

Igorot: meaning of, 349

Iligan: as industrial center, 279

Iloco language: speakers, table of, 620–624

Ilocos coast region, 328–342; area of, 328; climate of, 331; corn in, 336; description of, 328; food deficit in, 333–334; forest remains in, 331; irrigation in, 335–336; Laoag, as largest city of, 340; manufacturing in, 338; map of, 329; minor towns of, 341; nonfarm occupations in, 337–338; out-migration from, map, 334; physiologic population densities of, 333; population of, 332; pre-Spanish population of, 333; resource base of, 332; rice deficiency in, 333–334; rice production in, 335–336; road system of, 338–339; salt production in, 338; sea-

sonal migration of labor from, 335; small towns of, 339–340; Spanish contact with, 333; tobacco production in, 336, 337; urbanism in, 339–341
Iloilo, 172, 292
Immigration: small volume of, 674 n.3
Imperata grasses: as cattle browse, 103; as forest invaders, 97; description of, 99; in grasslands, 99; mowing of, 104
Imports: list of ranking, 287; nature of, 286; table of, comparative, 661–662
Income: national, table of, 660
Indonesians: as migrants, 119
Industrial employees: table of, 657
Industrial establishments: table of, 656
Industry: centers of, map, 275; contribution of, to national income, 279; growing complexity of, 279; historical growth of, 269; immaturity of, 278; locational patterns of, 278; shift of, to suburbs, 277–278; status of, 1960's, 274; tables on, 656–658; zones, within Manila area, 277–278
Inhabited islands: number of, 142
Inibaloi: language speakers, 352; people, region of, 351
In-migration: table of, 637–638
Interisland shipping routes: map of, from Cebu City, 481; map of, from Manila, 262
Interisland trade: basic patterns of, 288; deficit regions of, 288; discussion of, 288–294; incomplete land-transport network and, 294; regions of surplus, 288
Intermarriage: among ethnic stocks, 153
Internal trade, 280–288; barter background of, 290–291; basic patterns of, 288; Chinese role in, 291; deficit regions of, 288; Filipino retailers and, 291; historical growth in, 290; incomplete land-transport network and, 294; Manila region and, 292; regional centers of, 292, 293; surplus regions of, 288
Intertropical front: as weather mechanism, 49; mean position of, 55; movement of, 49
Intramuros: as historical walled city 168; as section of Manila, 384; destruction of, 388; early settlement of, 676 n.27; World War II development and repopulation of, 677 n.31
Iron ore: distribution of, 253–254, 522; lateritic, reserves of, 522
Irrigated land: map of, 186
Irrigation: changes in acreage after, 679 n.2; early use of, 180; effect of, on

rice yields, 679–680 n.7; for rice fields, 185; in Cagayan Valley, 321; in Central Plain of Luzon, 374–377; in Ilocos coast region, 330–331, 335–336; in southwest Luzon, 401; lack of, in early times, 126; map of, for Philippines, 186; Spanish influence on, 126, 181; table of, 647, 648
Islam: distribution of, map, 160; expansion of, into Philippines, 119–120; in far south, 121; northward spread of, 120; Spanish and, 121, 157–158
Island forms: general discussion of, 13–37; map of, 14–15
Islands: and regionalism, 304; as compound structures, 110; as regions, 301; having names, 301; inhabited, 142; number of, in Philippines, 1, 142, 692; seasonal habitation of, 143; table of, 600–604; table of selected small, 607; uninhabited, 143
Islands of the Sunda Shelf: regions in, 428
Isneg: language speakers, 353

Japanese: abaca plantations started by, 530; fifteenth-century contact with, 119
Jolo Island: description of, 584
Jute: as fiber source, 208

Kalinga: language speakers, 353
Kankanai: language speakers, 352
Kapok: acreage and producing area of, 208; as minor export crop, 226; as source of fiber, 207
Karst topography: on Cebu and Bohol, 27, 468
Kenaf: as source of fiber, 208
Kingdom of Tondo: pre-Spanish settlement of, 384
Korondal Valley: description of, 545–546

Laguna de Bay: description of, 21, 393
Lakes: Baao, southeast Luzon, 412; Bato, southeast Luzon, 236, 412; Buluan, southwest Mindanao, 545; Laguna de Bay, southwest Luzon, 21, 393; Lanao, northern Mindanao, 35, 236, 559; Mainit, northeast Mindanao, 236; Naujan, Mindoro, 23; small, of Agusan Valley, 539; Taal, southwest Luzon, 21, 395
Land: acquisition of, 125; American system of, 181; early systems of, 180; encomienda rights to, 123–124; reforms, 130–131; Spanish system of, 181; subject to erosion, table of,

618–619; tenancy, growth of, 130; Torrens title system and, 130

Land area: of Philippines, 1

Land biota: discussion of, 105–108

Landforms: discussion of, 13–37; map of, 14–15

Landownership: native system of, 123; Spanish influence on, 123

Land reform: church lands and, 131; failure of, 131

Land survey: introduction of, 190; lack of, in Spanish times, 125; recent advances in, 190–191

Land system: American, introduction of, 189–190; discussion of, 184–192; pre-Spanish, 125; Spanish, 184–185, 188; traditional Filipino, 188

Land tenure: discussion of, 187–192

Land title: importance of, 673 n.12

Land transport: discussion of, 262–267

Languages: discussion of, 153–156; Indonesian family of, 154; map of, 155; number of, 153–154; regional patterns of, 154; table of, by speakers, 620–624

Lauan forests: description of, 93

Lead: mining of, 255

Lemon: in Bicol area, 205

Leyte and Samar region, 454–468: agriculture in, 463; area of, 455; climate of, 458–459; commercial crops in, 465; description of, 455–458; early population in, 460; fishing in, 465; forest resources of, 459; islands of, 455; lumbering in, 459; mining in, 459–460; minor towns of, 467–468; physiography of, 455–458; population of, 461; population contrasts in, 461–462; ports of, 462–463; rice and corn in, map, 464; roads of, 462; settlement patterns in, 461; Spanish contact with, 460; towns of, 466–467; typhoons in, 458–459; urbanism in, 466–467; water transport in, 462–463

Leyte Gulf: description of, 27

Leyte Island: description of, 26, 455–456

Limestones: as soil-forming rocks, 71–72

Linguistic patterns: discussion of, 153–156

Literacy: table of, by provinces, 628–629

Littoral: Filipino preference for, 143

Livestock: discussion of, 210, 213; Spanish introduction of, 126; table of, 649

Livestock farming: modern role of, 211–212; Spanish effort at, 211

Living systems: elaboration of, 118

Logging: annual yield of, 238–239; discussion of, 238–247; procedures employed in, 242; technology of, 241–242

Libungan-Liguasan marshes, 104

Luzon: as center of Spanish influence, 312; as largest island, 311; as most diversified island, 312; as most highly developed island, 312; description of, 17–22; highest elevation in, 18; percent of total population in, 138–139; physiography of, 17–22; political subdivisions of, 312; population maps of, 138–139; regions of, 17, 313; share of road network in, 266; structure of, 11; summary on, 310–313

Luzon Arc: trend of, 11

Madjapahit: relations to, 119

Magotes: on Bohol Island, 27

Maguey: acreage and producing area of, 208; as minor export crop, 226; as source of fiber, 207

Mahogany: as misnomer, 85

Mais. See Corn

Maize. See Corn

Malay: as ethnic stock, 149–150

Malays: as possible early migrants, 116; Christianity and, 152; culture of, 152; proto-Malay and, 152; sources of, 152

Manganese: mining of, 254

Mango: as crop complement, 183; production area of, 204–205

Mangosteen: farms growing, 194–195

Mangrove forest: areas and stand of, 241; description of, 88–90; species involved in, 89; uses of, 89

Manila: area of, 169; as chief entrepôt, 261, 276–277; as Chinese center, 127; as early trade center, 126; Asiatic quarter of, 168; as political capital, 169; as port, 168; chartering of, 168, 170; description of, 382; distributing trade in, 292; districts of, 385–386; early fortifications of, 676 n.25; early settlement of, 676 n.25; foreign shipping and, 385; foreign trade and, 284; government of, 169; growth of, 142; hourly air temperatures of, 44; in-migration and, 149; languages spoken in, 154; manufacturing in, 170, 277–278; map of, 383; metropolitan region of, 169, 276; population of, 168, 169, 677 n.28; population shifts in, 677 n.32; port area, development of, 677 n.29; residence in, of upper classes, 126; shift of manufacturing to suburbs of, 277–278; Spanish influence on, 126, 168; trade region of,

292; urbanism and, 142, 169; World War II development and repopulation of, 674; zoning of, 168. *See also* Manila metropolitan region; Metropolitan Manila region

Manila Bay: as harbor and port, 384; strategic location of, 384

Manila galleons, 414

Manila Galleon Trade: with Mexico and Spain, 281–282

Manila hemp. *See* Abaca

Manila metropolitan region: area defined, 276. *See also* Manila; Metropolitan Manila region

Manioc, 174, 180, 193, 366, 473, 522, 533, 595; as complementary crop, 201; as minor crop, 182; in Sulu Archipelago region, 594; production areas, map of, 202

Manufacturing: American influence on, 271, 273; and national income, 279; Chinese role in, 270–271, 273; Filipino role in, 270–271; government and, 272, 273; growth of, during commonwealth period, 272; historical growth of, 269–270; immaturity of, 278; in Central Plain of Luzon, 379–380; in Manila region, 274–276; in provincial towns, 276; in southwest Luzon, 404; map of centers of, 275; percentage of control of, by nationalities, 272–273; regional scattering of, 276; Spanish era and, 270; statistical compilation and, 684 n.9; table of, by establishments, 656; table of, by geographical regions, 657; table of, indexes, 659; table of, selected data, 658; variety of, 276; zones, within Manila area, 277–278

Marble: quarrying of, 257; quarrying on Romblon, 452

Maria Cristina Falls: hydroelectric development of, 82; industrial development of, 514

Marinduque Island: description of, 25, 450

Marine ecology: nature of, 229

Market gardening: status of, 183

Marshes, 104–105

Masbate Island: description of, 31, 449

Meat consumption, 212

Mercury: mining of, 255

Mestizo class: lack of, 127

Metal technologies: of pre-Spanish era, 248–250

Metropolitan Manila region, 382–392; Americans in, 392; area of, 382, 389; as educational center, 387, 392; central business district of, 387; Chinese in, 392; destruction of, in World War II, 385, 388; districts of, 385–386; foreign population of, 392; growth rate, table of, 390; industries of, 391; map of, 386; North Harbor of, 389; Pasay City in, 391; Pasig River wharfage in, 389; political status of, under Spanish, 385; population of, 382, 389–390; port area of, 388–389; Quezon City in, 390; site of, 382–384; South Harbor of, 388; strategic location of, 384; suburbs of, 389–390; universities in, 387

Mid-mountain forests, 97–98

Migration: causes for, 190; from central Visayan region, 471–472; from Ilocos coast, 334; increases in, 191; into North Luzon Highlands, 350–351; process of, 147; regional variation in, 147; sources of, map, 145; table of, by provinces, 637–638; targets of, map, 144; timing of, 148–149; to Cagayan Valley, 319, 327–328; to Masbate Island, 451; to Mindanao, 504, 510–512, 530–531, 537, 540, 548–553, 562–564, 574–578; to Mindoro Island, 433; to Mountain Province, 349–351

Milkfish: as pond-raised, 237

Mindanao Island: description of, 32–37; industry in, 279; lack of highways in, 266; population map of, 141; population percentage of, 138–139; regions of, 32; structure of, 12

Mindoro Island: description of, 23

Mindoro region, 428–435; aboriginal population of, 433; agriculture in, 433–434; climate of, 431; description of, 23, 429; early population of, 432; early population vacuum in, 429; forests of, 431; in-migration to, 433; lumbering in, 435; mining in, 435; physiography of, 429, 430; population, 432; rocks of, 430; towns of, 433–434

Mineral industries: discussion of, 248–257; employment in, 248; regional centering of, 248

Mineral production: table of, 651

Minerals: distribution of, map, 249; list of, in production, 248

Mining: development of, in American period, 250; discussion of, 248–257; employment in, 248; importance of, 248; recent Filipino participation in, 250; regional centering of, 248; table of indexes of, 659

Minor crops: discussion of, 209; table of, 645

Minor export crops: discussion of, 226

Minor forest products: bamboo, 246; charcoal, 245–246; firewood, 245–246; gums, resins, rubber, 246; matting, 246; rattan, 246

Mobility: increase in, 133; of early settlements, 164

Modernization: discussion of, 128–134; in public health, 129

Molave forests, 95, 240

Molybdenum: mining of, 255

Moro. *See* Moslems

Mortality rate, 176

Moslem-Christian conflict: in Zamboanga Peninsula region, 574

Moslem population: in Zamboanga Peninsula region, 570–571

Moslem raiding: cessation of, 129; in Zamboanga Peninsula region, 574

Moslems: as immigrants, 118; in Sulu Archipelago region, 588; map of, in Zamboanga Peninsula region, 576; political stratification of, 118; raids of, upon Spanish regions, 574; table of, by provinces, 626–627

Moslem settlement history: in Lake Lanao region, 563

Moss forests, 98

Mother tongues: table of, by speakers, 620–624

Motor vehicles, 266

Mountain Province. *See* North Luzon Highlands region

Mount Apo: as highest elevation in Philippines, 32

Mount Mayon: elevation of, 410

Mount Pulog: as highest point on Luzon Island, 342

Mung bean, 209

Municipality: as political unit, 122; definition of, 676 n.21

Municipal ports: facilities of, 263

Municipios: as political unit, 122; in 1900, number of, 122

Muscovado sugar: decline in production of, 219

Mustard, 210

National income: table of, comparative sectors, 660

National language: Pilipino as new, 135

National ports, 262, 664–665

Negrito, 116, 149–150

Negros Island: description of, 29, 488

Nets, fishing: types used, 234

Nipa palm: as beverage crop, 206; chief areas of, 90

Northern Mindanao region, 506–517; area of, 506; climate of, 507; description of, 506–509; fishing in, 517; forests of, 509; industrial development of, 514; in-migration and, 511–512; linguistic pattern, of, 510; lumbering, in, 516; migration patterns of, 511–512; minor towns of, 515; out-migration and, 511; physiography of, 506–509; population of, 506, 510–512, 513; relations of, with Cebu-Bohol, 510; religious mixture in, 510; roads in, 515; settlement pattern of, 510–511; soils of, 508–509; transport in, 513–514; urbanism in, 512–515; volcano in, 507

North Luzon Highlands region, 342–361; agriculture in, 356–358; American influence on, 351; area of, 342; Baguio as summer resort in, 360; basement-complex rocks in, 344; bases for regionalisms in, 354; Bontoc language in, 353–354; climate of, 346; cultural change in, 349–351; description of, 342–346; elevations in, 342; ethnic stocks of, 349; forest cover in, 345; forest resource of, 358; hydroelectric power in, 348; Ifugao language in, 353; Inibaloi language in, 352; in-migration and, 361; Isneg language in, 352–353; Kalinga language in, 353; Kankanai language in, 352; land-use data for, 347, 355; languages spoken in, 349–350, 354, 361; lumbering in, 358; mining in, 348, 358–359; physiography of, 342–345; political structure of, 360; population of, 361; precipitation in, 346; regions of, 351–354; religious affiliation in, 349–350; roads in, 359; sawmills in, 358; soils in, 345; Spanish impact on, 350; terracing in, map of, 347; Tinguian language in, 352; towns in, 360–361; trade systems of, 360; transport system in, 359; vegetable growing in, 348; vegetation in, 345

Nut crops, 204–205

Oceanic deeps, 9–10

Oranges, 205

Out-migration: table of, by provinces, 637–638

Ownership of land: discussion of, 181, 187–192

Pacific Cordillera: description of, 32–33
Paganism, 150–151, 156
Palawan Island: description of, 24, 436; population map of, 141
Palawan region, 435–443; agriculture of, 441; area, of, 436; biogeographic bridge of, 435; climate of, 438; cultivable landscape in, 436; description of, 436; early Moslem control of, 439; early Spanish contact with, 438–439; economy of, 440; fishing in, 442–443; forests of, 438; lumbering in, 441–442; map of, 437; mining in, 441–442; number of islands in, 435–436; physiography of, 436; political control acquired by, 439; population density of, 439; population total of, 440; roads in, 441; settlement pattern of, 440; soils in, 437–438; Spanish cabecera towns in, 439; towns in, 440–441
Palay. See Rice
Pampango language: speakers, table of, 620–624
Panay-Hiligaynon language: speakers, table of, 620–624
Panay Island: description of, 29–30, 486
Pangasinan language: speakers, table of, 620–624
Papaya, 183
Parangs, 97
Pasig River, 21, 382–383
Pasture crops: lack of, 210–212
Pasturelands: burning of, 680 n.14
Peace Corps, 135
Peanuts, 201
Peas, 209
Pepper: as minor crop, 209–210
Peso: devaluation of, 682 n.24
Petroleum: lack of commercial resources of, 255
Petroleum refining: in southwest Luzon, 405
Philippine Air Line, 267
Philippine Archipelago: origin of, 10
Philippine Fault Zone, 12
Philippine Rift, 12
Philippines: and Asian mainland, 1, 3; as island mountaintops, 10, 109–110; as trade center, 120; as youthful landscape, 111; blend of cultures in, 115; cultural worlds shared by, 1; culture pattern of, 132; early population of, 120; economic ties of, to U.S., 130; English language in, 115; environmental diversity of, 112; ethnic stocks of, 116; first inhabitants of, 116; geographic spread of, 1; land area of, 1;

location map of, 1; mixed cultures at early date in, 116; oriental influence on, 2, 115; percentage of upland in, 38; population density of, in sixteenth century, 146; predominance of Christianity in, 115; relationships of, to major wind systems, 110–111; soils of, 67–77; Southeast Asia and, 2; structural alignment of, 109
Philippinization: growth of, 132
Physiography: discussion of, 13–37; maps of, 14–15
Pig: as wild biotic form, 107–108; role of, in economy, 210–211
Pigeon pea, 210
Pigeons, 210–211
Pilipino: as national language, 135
Piña: as pineapple fiber, 207–208
Pineapple, 227, 285, 366, 556, 560; as fruit, 205; as minor export crop, 226; as source of fiber, 207; fiber production from, 205, 680 n.13; plantation at Del Monte, Bukidnon, 566–567; plantation an old grasslands, 104
Pine forests: areas and stand of, 241; discussion of, 98–99; distribution of, 99; in North Luzon Highlands, 345–346; species involved in, 99
Piracy, 281, 283, 590
Plant domestication, 118
Plywood industry: annual volume of, 239; products of, 244; recency of, 244
Poblacion: as town settlement, 122
Polillo Islands: description of, 424
Political capital: Manila as, 169; Quezon City as, 170
Political provinces: table of, areas and populations, 605–606
Political structure: growth of, 122; map of, 3; modernization of, 131; of 1900, units in, 122; Spanish development of, 158
Political system: evolution of, under Spanish, 122
Population: arithmetic densities of, 147–148; concentration of, 141; discussion of, 136–149; 1899 total, 128; growth of, 133, 136, 176–177; leading province in, 141; littoral concentration of, 143; map of, central and southern Luzon, 139; map of, central Visayas, 140; map of, northern Luzon, 1960, 138; map of, northern Mindanao, 513; map of, western Bohol Island, 137; map of, southern Philippines, 141; maps of, Cotabato Province, 552–553; 1960 total, 136; percentage distribution of, 138–139;

physiologic densities of, 147–148; projected total of, 177; smallest provincial total of, 141; Spanish period and, 127–128; table of, by islands and areas, 600–604; table of comparative, by provinces, 631–632

Population growth: discussion of, 133, 176, 177

Port development: American program of, 131

Ports: table of, by categories, 664–665

Ports of entry: increasing number of, 284; operations of, 263; roles of, 263; serving foreign trade, 261; table of, 664

Poultry: discussion of, 210–213; role of, in economy, 210–211; table of, 649

Precipitation: causes of, 46; discussion of, 46–53; distribution of, 53; elevation of maximum, 52; in Cebu, 55–56; in Manila, 55–56; map of, 54; maximum and minimum station levels of, 46; mechanisms producing, 49; orographic, 52–53; regional zoning of, 53–55; requirements, for rice, 53; seasonal patterns of, 53–55; table of, for selected stations, 610–611; variation in, 46, 53, 55

Principalia: role of, 122

Private landownership: Spanish introduction of, 123–124

Production index: table of, 659

Protestant religion, 158

Proto-Malay: as pagans, 150; continued identity of, 150; economy of, 150–151; ethnic stock of, 149–150; locations of, 150; share of, in modern Filipino bloodstream, 150

Provinces: areas and populations of, table, 605–606; comparative populations of, table, 631–632; irrigation in, table, 646–647; language speakers in, table, 620–624; road densities of, table, 653–654

Provincia: as major territorial unit, 122

Public architecture: American influences in, 162–163; modern trends in, 163; Philippinization of, 163; Spanish introduction of, 162

Public health: program of, 129, 175

Pueblo: as settlement, 164, 166–167; definition of, 675–676 n.20

Racial stock: Spanish classification of, 149

Railroads: construction of, 264; Manila system of, 264; mileage of, 263; Panay line, 264; pattern of, 263–264;

private, sugarcane and lumber lines, 492, 494–495, 681; Spanish beginning of, 673 n.10

Rainfall: table of, for selected stations, 610–611. *See also* Precipitation

Rainy season: discomfort during, 45; timing of, 42

Ramie, 208

Rattan: as minor forest product, 246; in dipterocarp forests, 93–94

Regeneration of vegetation, 102

Regionalisms: bases for, 304; Christian versus Moslem, 156; climatic, 156; cultural, 156; diversity of, 301; early patterns of, 119; in North Luzon Highlands, 351; insularity factor in, 301; littoral effect on, 156–157; numbers of, 304

Regionality: variety of, 3–4

Regions: map of, 305; number of, 304; of North Luzon Highlands, 351; table of, 306

Relief: discussion of, 11–12, 13–37, map of, 14–15. *See also* each specific region

Religions: discussion of, 157–158; table of, by provinces, 626–627

Remittance of funds: by migrants, to home areas, 147

Resettlement: government programs of, 531, 550–551, 562–563; sources of, map, 145; Spanish role in, 164; targets of, map, 144

Rice, 70, 71, 73, 74, 75, 77, 83, 117, 174, 175, 178, 179, 180, 181, 183, 192, 193, 194, 210, 211, 286, 287, 292, 294, 310, 312, 346, 351, 352, 353, 366, 381, 522, 532, 533, 540, 579, 594; acreage of, 639, 679 n.2, 694 n.23; as crop staple, 182; comparative financial return of, per acre, 228; effect of irrigation on, 679–680 n.7; environmental requirements of, 195; growing of, 195–196; in Bukidnon-Lanao region, 566; in Cagayan Valley, 321–322; in Central Plan of Luzon, 374–375; in Ilocos coast region, 335, 336; in North Luzon Highlands, 358; in Samar and Leyte, 463–464; in southeast Luzon, 416–417; in southwest Mindanao region, 556; map of lowland distribution of, 196; map of upland distribution of, 197; precipitation requirement of, 53, 55; production system of, 184–185, 195–196; reserve land for, 198; surplus of, Central Plain of

Luzon, 369; water need of, 195; yields per acre, 198

Rio Grande de Mindanao: description of, 36, 545

Rizal Province: population density of, 141, 303

Roads: classification of, 684 n.5; importance of, 264; influence of, on settlement patterns, 159; map of, 265; mileage of, 266; regional variation in network of, 266; table of, by classes and regions, 652; table of densities, by provinces, 653–654

Rock asphalt: produced on Leyte, 257, 459

Rocks: in soil formation, 66–67

Rock types: covering land areas, 13

Rock weathering: rapidity and depth of, 16

Roman Catholics: table of, by provinces, 626–627

Romblon Island, 449

Root crops: acreage of, 201, 639; comparative financial return of, per acre, 228; discussion of, 199–203; in Batan Islands, 184; in Samar and Leyte, 463–464; staple in Batan-Babuyan Islands, 310

Royal Company of the Philippines, 281

Rubber: acreage and production area of, 210; as agricultural product, 247; as minor crop, 209–210; as minor export crop, 226; as minor forest product, 247; production in Zamboanga Peninsula region, 579; recent increase in, 210

Saccharum grasses: as cattle browse, 103; as forest invaders, 97; description of, 99; in grasslands, 99

Sago palm, 105

Salt: beds, map of Manila, 256; production of, 256–257, 338, 341, 477, 534

Samal language, 587–588; speakers, number of, 695 n.40

Samar Arc: trend of, 12

Samar Island: description of, 25–26, 457

Samar-Leyte language: speakers, table of, 620–624

Sandstones: as soil-forming rocks, 70

Santo Tomas, Davao: town plan of, 538

Sawale matting, 246

Sawmills: capital investment in, 242–244; discussion of, 239–244; distribution of, map, 243; locations of, 242; nationalities owning, 244; number of, 239; technology of, 241–242

School attendance: by age groups, table of, 629; by class of school, table of, 630; by provinces, table of, 628–629

Schoolteacher: as agent of cultural change, 128–129

Sea gypsy: Samal Laut of Sulu Archipelago, 587–588

Seaports: table of, by categories, 664–665

Seasonal air masses: maps of, 47

Sea trading: in early culture of Sulu Islands, 117

Secondary forests, 96–97

Sedimentation: in Central Plain of Luzon, 20; Quaternary, 13; repeated history of, 111; Tertiary history of, 11

Sensible temperatures: humidity factor in, 45

Separation of Church and state: American influence on, 129

Settlement: barrio village, 165; coastal, 143; dispersal of, 132–133; failure of government program for, 130–132; formalized system of, 122; morphology of, 159, 166; Spanish founding of, 143, 166

Shales: as soil-forming rocks, 69–70

Sheep, 210–212

Shifting cultivation: agricultural system of, 117; as early economy, 117; as related to land system, 188; continuance of, 164, 182; impact of, on vegetation cover, 84, 101, 239; in Banaue, map of land use, 347; in North Luzon Highlands, 346, 352–353; on Palawan, 441; practice of, 117, 187

Shipping: role of small boats in, 683–684 n.2

Shipping routes: maps of, 262, 481

Sibuyan Island, 449

Sibuyan Sea region, 447–454; agriculture of, 452–453; area of, 447; Burias Island in, 449; cattle ranching in, 453; climate of, 450; description of, 447–450; fishing industry of, 453; in-migration to, 451; languages spoken in, 450; livestock farming in, 453; Manila hinterland and, 454; Marinduque Island in, 450; Masbate Island in, 448; mining in, 453–454; physiography of, 447–450; population of, 447; port towns of, 452; roads of, 454; Romblon Islands in, 449; settlement patterns of, 451; Sibuyan Island in, 449; Sibuyan Sea in, 448; Spanish contact with, 450–451; Tablas Island in, 449; Ticao Island in, 449; towns of, 452; transitional character of, 450;

transport in, 454; water transport in, 454

Sierra Madre. *See* Eastern Cordillera

Sitio: as local hamlet, 122; as part of barrio, 165; growth of, into town, 133; nature of, 163

Slave trade: pre-Spanish, 281

Small islands: table of selected, by area and population, 607

Social structure, 672 n.1; family system and, 675 n.14; growth of, 122; native system of, 125; pattern of, 158

Sociopolitical systems: earliest variety of, 118; structuring of, 118–119

Soil erosion: discussion of, 78–83; map of, 79; on Cebu, 78–81; table of, by province, 618–619

Soils: alluvial, 72–74; beach sand, 70–71; bog and marsh, 76; climatic impact on, 67; erosion of, 78; fertilization problems and, 82; genesis of tropical, 65–67; leaching of, 66; limestone, 71–72; map of erosion of, on Cebu, 80; metamorphic rock and 76; mineral deficiencies in, 81–82; on burned-over lands, 103; parent materials of, 68, 69–77; quality of Philippine, 67; Rendzina, 71–72; sandstone, 70; shale, 69–70; terracing and, 77; Terra Rossa 66, 72; tropical nature of, 63–67; volcanic, 74–75

Southeast Luzon region, 409–421; abaca production in, 413, 417, 418; agriculture in, 416; arable land in, 412; area of, 409; Bikol language in, 413; climate of, 412–413; coconut production in, 418; corn production in, 417; description of, 409–412; fishing in, 419–420; forest cover in, 413; lumbering, in, 420; mineral production in, 418–419; physiography of, 409–412; population of, 414; ports of, 415–416; railway in, 421; rice cultivation in, 412, 417; roads in, 420–421; Spanish development of, 414; towns of, 415–416; transport in, 420–421; typhoons in, 412–413; urbanism in, 415–416; volcanic landforms of, 410

Southern Philippines: area of, 502; historical background of, 503–506; introduction to, 502–506; islands of, 502; population of, 141, 502; regional character of, 503, 505–506

Southwestern Mindanao region, 542–557; agriculture in, 556; American political control of, 549; area of, 543; climate in, 547; crop declines on new lands in, 556–557; description of, 544–547; fishing in, 557; government settlement programs in, 550–551; in-migration to, 544, 548, 551; Koronodal Valley in, 545–546; Libungan Marsh-Liguasan Swamp area in, 545; lumbering in, 557; manufacturing in, 557; mining in, 557; minor towns of, 554–555; Moslem settlement of, 549; new towns in, morphology of, 555; physiography of, 553, 544–547; political restructuring of, 555; population of, 543, 549, 551 552, 553; religious mixture in, 548; Rio Grande de Mindanao in, 545; roads in, 555–556; settlement of, 548; soils in, 547–548; Tirrurai tribal peoples of, 551–552; transport in, 555–556; urbanism in, 553; water transport in, 556

Southwest Luzon region, 392–409; agricultural processing in, 404; agriculture of, 400–403; area of, 392; as Tagalog heartland, 392; climate of, 396–397; clothing manufacture in, 404; coconut landscape of, 402; commercial flower-growing in, 403; cropping systems in, 402–403; description of, 393; dormitory towns in, 400; early population of, 399; economic regions of, map, 401; farms of, 400; fishing in, 403; forest cover of, 396; fruit-growing in, 403; furniture industry in, 405; industrial labor force in, 404; irrigation in, 401; lack of migration from, 400; Laguna de Bay in, 393; livestock farming in, 402–403; Manila and, 392; manufacturing in, 404–406; minerals of, 396; minor towns of, 407–409; petroleum refining in, 405; physiography of, 393, 394; population of, 393, 399; poultry-raising in, 403; power resources of, 396; rice farms in, 401; roads in, 406–407; salt production in, 405; shoe manufacture in, 405; soils of, 396; Spanish cabeceras in, 400, 407; Spanish political structure in, 398–399; Spanish settlement of, 397–399; textile manufacturing in, 404; towns of, 399–400, 407–409; transport in, 401, 406–407; urbanism in, 399–400, 407–409; volcanic landscape of, 395

Spanish: as town dwellers, 127; Christianizing of Filipinos by, 121; colonial system in Philippines, 121; commandeering of soldiery by, 128; cultural systems introduced by, 121–122; role of, 120

Spanish clergy: early cabecera centers of, maps, 124; early numbers of, 123

Spanish government: financial deficit of, 125

Spanish influence: in various highlands, 688 n.20; on agriculture, 83

Spanish language: and early Spanish period, 127; as modern foreign language, 153; speakers, by ages, table of, 625; speakers, number of, 153

Spanish monopoly of trade: repeated effort at, 281

Spanish population: small numbers of, 123

Spanish religious centers: in early times, map of, 124

Species of fish caught: table of, 612–613

Species of trees: commonly logged, table of, 614–617

Sport hunting, 108

Sri Vijaya, 119

Standing timber: per-acre yield from, 240; volume of, 240

Strawberries, 209

Subic Bay, 368

Sugar: export quota agreements on, 681 n.18; export quota on, to U.S., 220; milling, in Western Negros and Panay region, 492

Sugarcane, 178, 179, 184, 192, 193, 227, 282, 285, 312, 366; acreage of, 219, 220, 639; American influence on production of, 217–218; areas of production of, 217; as labor-intensive crop, 217; change in crop status of, 183; comparative financial return of, per acre, 228; contracts regulating production of, 681 n.17; environmental requirements of, 216; government control over production of, 219; growing and milling of, 216–220; in Central Plain of Luzon, 377–378; in Leyte and Samar, 465; in Mindoro, 433–434; in southwest Luzon region, 402; in western Negros and Panay region, 492; labor requirements of, western Negros and Panay, 495; planting systems of, 681 n.17; production areas, map of, 217, 218; production districts, map of, 493; role of, in traditional economy, 216; Spanish encouragement of, 216–217

Sugar central: as cane-milling center, 219

Sugar district: map of, Western Negros and Panay region, 494; quasi-legal status of, 219

Sulu Archipelago: description of, 37

Sulu Archipelago region; 581–597; agriculture in, 595; area of, 582; climate of, 585–586; description of, 37, 582–583; economies of, 590; ethnic culture patterns in, 590; families enumerated in, 593–594; farms in, 594; fishery industry in, 593, 595–596; forests of, 586; interregional trade and, 597; "island" in, definition of, 583; islands in, number of, 694–695 n.21; Jolo Island of, 584; land environment of, 585; language patterns in, 588; littoral environment of, 585; manufacturing in, 596; map of, 583; marine products of, 595–596; minerals in, 586, 596; minor towns of, 591; mobility in, 589–590; Moslems in, 588–589; peoples of, map, 589; physiography of, 582–583; political separatism in, 597; political structuring of, 695 n.42; population of, 582; ports of, 592; roads in, 592; Samal Laut peoples of, 587–588; sea environment of, 585; seasonal local environments of, 586–587; selective lumbering in, 593; settlement systems in, 591; Tausog peoples of, 587; Tawi-Tawi Island in, 584; transport in, 592; urbanism in, 591

Sulu Islands: early living system of, 117

Summer: timing of, 42

Summer resorts, 41

Sundaland: Philippine sector of, 11

Suppression of Chinese trade: in Spanish era, 281

Swamps: composition of, 104; discussion of, 104–105; extent of, 104; Libungan-Liguasan, 545; settlement in, early, 117

Sweet potatoes, 73, 174, 179, 180, 184, 192, 193, 194, 351, 366, 473, 522, 533, 556, 579, 594; as crop staple, 182; in North Luzon Highlands, 357; primary production areas of, 201, 202

Taal Volcano, 395; eruptions of, 689 n.7

Tablas Island, 449

Tagalog: as national language, 135; language speakers, table of, 620–624; persons speaking, by ages, table of, 625; speakers, number of, 153

Tagalogs: as migrants, 147

Tagaytay Ridge: as summer resort, 397

Talahib grass, 99

Tamarau, 107

Taro, 201

Tausog language: speakers, number of, 695 n.40

Tawi-Tawi Island, 584

Tectonic activity: repeated history of, 111

Tectonic provinces: grouping of, 11; map of, 10

Temperatures: air mass effect on, 42; charts of, at Manila, 44; diurnal change in, 43; highland modification of, 41; island interiors, effect on, 45; map for May, 43; seasonal contrasts in, 41–42; table of, for selected stations, 608–609; variation in; effect of, 45

Tenancy: and landownership, 679 n.6; costs of, 679 n.4; encomienda and growth of, 679 n.3; growth of, 188–192; origins of, 125; percentage figure on, 191; population density and, 146. *See also* Land tenure; Title to land

Terracing: early use of, 117, 180; effect of, on soils, 77; in North Luzon Highlands, 83, 185–186, 351–356; slight use of, by Filipinos, 82

Ticao Island, 449

Tilapia: as pond-raised fish, 238

Timber production: annual yield of, 238–239; discussion of, 238–247; importance of, 238–239

Tinapa: as fish separation, 231

Tinguian: language speakers, 352

Tirur y Highlands: description of, 546–547

Title to land: importance of, 673 n.12; Torrens system of, 130. *See also* Land tenure; Tenancy

Tobacco, 73, 227, 282, 285, 294; as cash crop, 225–226; as garden crop, 224; changes in consumer demand for, 225; crop status of, 183; early producing centers of, 224; environmental requirements of, 224; government stimulation of, 224; in Cagayan Valley, 321–324; in Ilocos coast region, 336; map of, Cagayan Valley region, 322; 1960 acreage of, 226; present producing regions of, 225; production and trade of, 222–226; Spanish monopoly over, 224–225, 681 n.21; table of, 639

Towns: as seats of administration, 167; discussion of, 166–167; distribution of, in Spanish era, 167; founding of, 121; lack of, in pre-Spanish times, 166; morphology of Spanish, 121–122; number of, 133, 167; pull of, for residence, 146; services provided by, 167; size of, 166, 167

Trade: American policy of free, 282; early patterns of, 119, 280–281; encouragement of, by American control, 181; growth of native-product share in, 282; late Spanish liberalization of, 282; nationality participation in, 281; World War II effects on, 282

Trade policy: aim of Philippine, 287

Trade sites: pre-Spanish, 166

Trails: table of, by classes and regions, **652**

Transportation: American road building and, 131–132; bus companies and, 267; growth of, 133; historical development of, 258–259; land, 262–267, 652; large passenger movement and, 260; map of Cebu interisland routes of, 481; map of core fleet routes of, 262; need for, in island world, 259; table of seaports, by classification, 664–665; table of selected data on, 655; water, 260–263

Trees: commonly logged, table of, by species, 614–617

Tropical typhoon. *See* Typhoons

Tuba: as fresh or alcoholic drink, 206

Typhoons: areas affected by, 50; as element in regional climate, 52; description and frequency of, 50–51; in eastern Philippines, 458–459; seasonal occurrence, of, 50–51; tracks, map of, 51

Uplands: area of, 38

Urbanism: differences between Philippine and American, 677–678 n.34; growth of, 142; in southeast Luzon, 407–409, 415–416; Manila as center of, 142; peculiarity of, in Philippines, 170. *See also* Cities; Manila; Metropolitan Manila region; Towns

Urban populations: of chartered cities, 635–636

U.S. naval station: on Subic Bay, 368

Variables in precipitation: list of, 53

Vegetables: comparative financial return of, per acre, 228; in North Luzon Highlands, 183, 203–204, 348; introductions of, to Philippines, 203; kinds grown, 204; tables of, by farms, and acreages, 639, 642

Vegetation: discussion of, 83–105; map of, 86; nature of wild, 85–86; types of, table of, 84

Victorias sugar district: map of, 494

Villages: as chief settlement form, 165; growth of, 166; Moslem raids on, 164; nature of, 163; permanently sited, 164; population of average, 166; size of, 165; Spanish siting of, 163; splintering-off process of, 165; traditional, 163

Visayan Islands: definition of, 690–691 n.1; description of, 25–32; highest elevations in, 29; homogeneity of, 446; introductory discussion of, 444–447; islands included in, 444; languages of, 446; population densities in, 446; population map of, 140; population percentage of, 138–139; regions of, 447; structure of, 11

Volcanic landforms: discussion of, 13, 21–22, 29–30, 34–37; in southeast Luzon, 410; in southwest Luzon, 21, 395; in Sulu Archipelago, 582, 584–585; in western Negros and Panay region, 488

Volcanic rocks: and soil formation, 74; covering land areas, 13

Volcanoes: activity of, 21–22; Apo, 525; Canlaon, 29–30, 488; Hibokhibok, 507; Makaturing, 35; Matutum, 525; Mayon, 22; Ragang, 35; Taal, 21, 689 n.7

Vulcanism: in building Philippines, 109; map of, 9; nature of, 13

Water buffalo: distinction between carabao and, 677; economic role of, 210–211. See also Carabao

Water control, 184–187

Water transport: Cebu interisland routes of, map, 481; core fleet routes of, map, 262; discussion of, 260–263; island network of, 260; ports of, 261; vessels engaged in, 260–261

Weather: mechanisms producing, 49

Weathering: rapidity and depth of, 13

Western Negros and Panay region, 485–501; agriculture in, 492–496; area of, 486; climate of, 489; description of, 486; early Spanish contact with, 490; export sugar quota from, 494; fishing in, 496–497; fishponds in, 496; forests in, 489; industry in, 497–498; labor in, 495; languages in, 489–490; lumbering in, 498; mining in, 497; minor towns of, 500–501; Negros Island in, 488; nineteenth-century population of, 490–491;

Panay Island in, 486; physiography of, 486, 487; political structuring of, 490; population of, 491; ports of, 499–501; rice-growing in, 495; roads in, 498–499; soils in, 488; sugarcane production in, 492–495; textile manufacturing in, 498; transport in, 498–499; urbanism in, 499–501; Victorias Milling District of, map, 494; vulcanism in, 488

Wet-field rice: growing system of, 184–185

Wet-field system: early use of, 180

Wet season, 53

Wheat products: increasing use of, 134

Wild pig: as cropland raider, 107–108

Wind movements: maps of, 47

Winter: nonseasonal nature of, 42–43; weather changes during, 50

Yams: replacing taro, 201

Zambales-Bataan hill country region, 362–368; agriculture in, 365–366; area of, 362; climate of, 364–365; description of, 364; fishing in, 367; forest resources of, 366–367; mining in, 367; physiography, map of, 363; population densities of, 364; population of, 362; roads in, 367–368; settlement of, 365; shipyards in, 368; Spanish contact with, 365; towns in, 368

Zambales Mountains: description of, 19–20

Zamboanga City: area and population of, 171; trade region of, 293

Zamboanga Peninsula: description of, 36

Zamboanga Peninsula region, 569–581; agriculture in, 578–579; area of, 569–570; Basilan Island in, 572; Chavacano dialect in, 575; Christians and Moslems in, map, 576; climate of, 572; coconut production in, 579; corn production in, 579; description of, 571–572; fishing in, 579–580; forests in, 573; lumbering in, 580–581; mining in, 580; minor towns of, 578; physiography of, 570, 571–572; political structuring of, 576; population in, 575; roads in, 577; rubber production in, 579; soils in, 573; Spanish cabecera foundings in, 574; trade hinterland of, 577; transport in, 577; urbanism in, 576–578; water transport in, 581

Zinc: mining of, 255